GOLD COINS of the WORLD

"All passes. Art alone
Enduring, stays with us.
The bust outlasts the throne,
The coin, Tiberius."

GOLD COINS of the WORLD

COMPLETE FROM 600 A.D. TO 1958

An Illustrated Standard Catalogue with Valuations

by ROBERT FRIEDBERG

THE COIN AND CURRENCY INSTITUTE, INC.

Book Publishers

134 WEST 32nd STREET • NEW YORK 1, N. Y.

GOLD COINS OF THE WORLD
Complete from 600 A.D. to 1958
An Illustrated Standard Catalogue with Valuations

Published by **THE COIN AND CURRENCY INSTITUTE, INC., NEW YORK**

© 1958, by Robert Friedberg
Library of Congress catalog card no: 58-59687

Manufactured in the United States of America
by Hallmark Lithographers
First Edition

CONTENTS

CONTRIBUTORS

The author expresses his thanks and his gratitude to the contributors named below for reading and correcting various portions of the original manuscript or for other valuable assistance

These internationally known numismatists have given graciously and generously of their precious time, their numismatic knowledge and their accumulated experience, and without their cooperation, this book would hardly have been possible.

MR. EMILE BOURGEY *Paris*

MESSRS. ERICH and HERBERT A. CAHN *Basel*

MR. GIUSEPPE DE FALCO *Naples*

MR. LEONARD FORRER *Amsterdam*

MR. JACK FRIEDBERG *New York*

MR. KARL-LUDWIG GRABOW *Berlin*

MR. MAURICE GRENIER-LAFOREX *Paris*

MR. HENRY GRUNTHAL *New York*

MR. MORTIMER HAMMEL *New York*

MR. MARK M. SALTON-SCHLESSINGER *New York*

MR. HANS M. F. SCHULMAN *New York*

MR. JACQUES SCHULMAN *Amsterdam*

MESSRS. HERBERT A. and PETER SEABY *London*

MR. DAVID SPINK *London*

MESSRS. HARVEY and NORMAN STACK *New York*

and to

THE AMERICAN NUMISMATIC SOCIETY OF NEW YORK
for use of their library

THE BRITISH MUSEUM *for furnishing certain illustrations*

PREFACE

BRIEFLY ABOUT GOLD COINS

The collecting of gold coins seems to have become a part of mankind almost since the first gold coins were struck by the ancient Greeks about 700 B.C.

Since then, gold coins have been struck by almost every government that has come into existence. The term government as used here, is an extension of any coining authority—permanent or provisional, secular or ecclesiastical, national or local, republican or royal.

Formidable quantities of gold coins have thus been struck over the centuries, and fortunately many have survived to enrich the culture of our times and provide the numismatist with a lifetime of pleasure and study.

That so many gold coins have survived since ancient times—generally in a choice state of preservation—is no accident, and can be attributed to the nature of gold itself as a metal and then to the love of mankind for the metal.

The chemical and physical properties of gold are too well known to require elaboration here. For the numismatist, however, it is important to remember that gold was selected as the supreme coinage because its rarity made it precious, because its color is unique and because its lustre will last forever. Gold coins which have been buried or otherwise secreted for hundreds or even for 2000 years, when finally discovered, were found to be in the same brilliant and untarnished condition as when they were first hidden.

It is this age-old tendency for gold to go underground that continually results in the unexpected discovery of new, unpublished coins, some of which may cast important light on a personage or place otherwise unknown or beclouded in history.

Mankind has learned to love the metal for good reason. His bitter experience has shown that in the face of war, invasion, revolution, panic, inflation, or other economic disaster, the gold coin, small as it is in size, has alone survived as the symbol of security when all other familiar standards of value have fallen in the general ruin.

Knowing this, the peoples of the world have developed an especial reverence for the gold coin, always preserving it, never melting it and in the face of any danger, hiding it. Sometimes, the original owners did not or could not reclaim their treasure and the coins have been lost to the world until accidentally exposed many years later, by a plough share, or a surging tide or by dynamite.

Even today, the wealth of nations is measured in terms of gold, and since this is so, and to demonstrate how little the long history of gold has really changed, it will be noted that the governments of the world, as in the past, have hidden their monetary gold underground, where it is carefully kept in the safe control of their Central Banks, under permanent armed guard and protected by the latest devices against theft, burglary or assault, and by heavy construction against all forms of disaster.

Although the literature of numismatics is extensive, there are no books in existence devoted to gold coins of the world as a class by themselves. Considering the passionate interest in gold coins, the author has found this condition remarkable. Having been a professional numismatist for most of his adult life, the author, as well as many thousands of other numismatists the world over, has sorely regretted the lack of such a book in the literature of numismatics.

In order to get a reference on any gold coin struck before the 20th century, it was necessary to hunt out the standard work (if it existed) on the country involved, which work, of course, was devoted also to silver and minor coins. Obviously, there are many hundreds of such books; most of them are printed in a foreign language and are out of print; many of them are rare and valuable and simply unobtainable.

It was thus a formidable undertaking looking up, or looking for, earlier issues of gold coins of the world, requiring special facilities or outside research assistance or many hours of tedious, and sometimes fruitless labors in the library.

The author had long dreamed of improving this condition by creating a single volume to encompass the entire gold coinage of the world, excluding ancient coins. It seemed grandiose at first and impossible of ever bringing about, because of the colossal amount of coins to be found in 1300 years of coinage.

However, some preliminary calculations showed that with a certain economy of format, it would be possible to create a single, moderate size volume without sacrificing any vital information or the all-important illustrations.

Therefore, drawing on his own experience, and that of the valued contributors, the author has spent the last five years in gathering and collecting the information now at last published.

THE SCOPE OF "GOLD COINS OF THE WORLD"

This book concerns itself with the gold coinage of the world that began when the coinage of antiquity ended and following the age of nomadic invasion, when new governments with recognizable names came into existence. The aim has been to start the coin issues of each place with the first distinctive coins that positively identify the place as we know its name today, thus making the coinage truly national in character; having determined the starting point for each place, the coinage has been treated chronologically until it comes to its natural end by the suspension of gold coinage of the particular place. Some of the issues continue up to 1958.

The book has been divided into three numismatic categories. Part I is called America, and the earliest coins are the Spanish Colonial issues of Colombia, about 1621. Part II is called Europe, and the earliest coins here are from the Italian city of Beneventum of about 600 A.D. Part III is called Africa and the Orient, with the earliest coins listed being the Axumite issues of Ethiopia of about 300 A.D.

THE GEOGRAPHY OF THIS BOOK

The proper national placement of certain place-names, which sometimes posed a dilemma, has been solved by arbitrarily focusing on a period of time best known to the present generation. The period between the two World Wars has thus been selected, (and 1937 as a normal year of that period), as a point of reference for the geo-political boundaries of the world. Therefore, the coins of a country in existence in 1937 have been listed under the name of that country, even though the coins may have been struck much earlier under foreign suzerainty.

Certain innovations have thus been made, as under this rule, the coinage of countries like Estonia or Latvia are listed under their own names, rather than as a Swedish coinage, which is consistent, for example, with the traditional listing of Spanish-American coins under their American names, rather than under Spain. The geographical index in the book will be helpful in locating any coinage.

THE DESCRIPTIONS AND DATES

Every type of coin that falls within the scope of this book, and which the author could find, has been listed and described. The obverse of the coin is always described first. The description is followed by the various denominations and dates of that particular type. The use of a name only in the description indicates a standing figure. Otherwise, head, bust, etc. are used.

Coins without dates are followed by ND. In general, when a coin has from one to about four dates, all the dates have been listed; otherwise the first and last dates only have been used, but all years may not necessarily exist between these ultimate dates.

In a work of this magnitude and complexity, and considering that this is a first edition, it is inevitable that some types or denominations of coins will have escaped the author's attention and that they are not listed, despite the claim to completeness.

The author will be grateful for all such omissions which are called to his attention, so that the coins can be included in future editions of this book.

THE ILLUSTRATIONS

About one half of the space in this book is devoted to the illustrations of the coins which are shown in actual size. At great additional expense, they have been incorporated within the text, where they belong, rather than at the end of the book as a separate section of plates. The description of the illustration is immediately below it.

An asterisk (*) alongside the denomination and date indicates that this is the coin illustrated above the description. In case there is only one denomination for the type of coin being illustrated, no asterisk has been used.

A variety of sizes of illustrations has purposely been used, as this will help to identify the denominations of those coins which are without the mark of value.

Most types from the very beginning have been illustrated—certainly since about 1700, the illustrations are virtually complete for all types. There are more than 2700 illustrations of gold coins in this book—more than have ever been illustrated in any one coin book of comparable size, and the author believes that almost all coins of general familiarity to numismatists have been shown.

THE VALUATIONS AND STATE OF PRESERVATION

The author publishes the valuations as a general guide to the value of the coins on the numismatic market. No one by himself can profess to know the numismatic value of every gold coin that has ever been struck. Hence, voluminous sales record have been consulted. These have been used in conjunction with the author's twenty years of experience in professional numismatics combined with the accumulated experience of the contributors, and it is believed that the present valuations reflect the true rarity, condition, demand and availability of the coins as of the summer of 1958.

These valuations represent an approximate figure at which the coins would change hands as between a well informed buyer and a well informed professional numismatist. They are based on recent sales records or are an extension into the present time of old sales records.

The valuation of rarities has been especially difficult because the coins have appeared so seldom. In some cases, they have not been valued at all and have been merely marked "rare." In other cases, the valuation has been determined by comparison of the coin with the known value of another coin of equal rarity or other similar attributes.

In any case, the valuation of a great rarity must be considered as purely nominal and at best can be an indication only that the coin is of extraordinary value. The author's experience in modern times has shown that when a great rarity has been put on the numismatic market, it has always tended to exceed its last known price because of an ever increasing demand for such coins.

In general, the numismatic value of a coin is determined partly by condition, partly by rarity and almost always by the inexorable law of supply and demand, which might sometimes cause a great divergence from the valuations in this book.

These valuations are for the average condition in which the coin is most frequently encountered, **and for the commonest date or variety of the type.** Coins in a superior condition or with rarer dates would command a higher price. In general, experience has shown that these average conditions are as follows:

For coins up to about 1800, the valuations are for fine specimens.

For coins from about 1800 to 1914, the valuations are for very fine specimens.

For coins from about 1914 to date, the valuations are for uncirculated (mint state) specimens or for choice specimens showing hardly any wear.

For coins marked "not placed in circulation," the valuations are for uncirculated or proof specimens.

Overseas readers would do well to consult the Foreign

Exchange Table in the appendix, in relation to the valuations which are quoted in U. S. dollars.

PATTERNS, PROOFS, UNOFFICIAL ISSUES AND OFF-STRIKES

The author has attempted to include in the book, all manner of gold coins which from time to time appear among numismatists. Among such coins, are the fascinating series of patterns, proofs and essais. These have been designated by the general term "not placed in circulation." They are legitimate Government Mint issues and are among the rarest and most prized of gold coins, almost always appearing in proof condition.

Other coins have been plainly labelled as unofficially or privately made. These are not the official coins of any government and such coins have been manufactured exclusively for collectors, or for use in the gold markets of the world.

The question of including off-strikes in this book has posed a seemingly insoluble problem. (An off-strike is regarded as a coin struck in gold from the same die used to strike a non-gold coin). Off-strikes are generally the larger pieces of ducat coinage—from 3 Ducats up. Depending on what series was involved, they have sometimes been included, other times not, in keeping with traditional usage.

There is still no unanimity of opinion among numismatists whether to regard as legitimate, a gold coin weighing exactly what a 10 Ducat piece should weigh, but not bearing a mark of value and struck from the same die used to strike a silver Taler, similarly without the mark of value. Since most early gold coins are without the mark of value in any case (their true face value being their weight and purity), the question seems academic.

THE INTRODUCTION AND THE APPENDIX

An explanation of the mint marks (mm.) which appear in the text, will be found under the respective country in the General Introduction which follows.

Reference to the Introduction and Appendix will sometimes answer many questions which might arise when referring to the catalogue section of the book.

ABBREVIATIONS

ND for no date; mm for mint mark; Obv. for obverse; Rev. for reverse.

R. F.

Pour Le Lecteur Français.

PREFACE

BREVES NOTES SUR LES PIECES D'OR

Il semble que la collection des pièces d'or soit devenue une partie de l'humanité presque aussitôt que les premières pièces d'or aient été frappées par les Anciens Grecs, aux environs de l'an 700 Av. J.C.

Depuis lors, des pièces d'or ont été frappées par presque tous les gouvernements qui virent le jour. Le terme de gouvernement tel que nous l'utilisons ici, est une extension de toute authorité frappant de la monnaie, fût-elle permanente ou provisoire, séculaire ou ecclésiastique, nationale ou locale, républicaine ou monarchique.

Des quantités énormes de pièces d'or ont ainsi été frappées au cours des siècles, et, heureusement, beaucoup ont survécu pour enrichir la culture de notre époque et fournir au numismate une vie entière de plaisir et d'étude.

Le fait que tant de pièces d'or aient survécu depuis les temps anciens, généralement dans un état de conservation excellent, n'est pas un accident, et peut être attribué à la nature de l'or lui-même en tant que métal et aussi à l'amour de l'humanité pour ce métal.

Les propriétés physico-chimiques de l'or sont trop bien connues pour demander ici un approfondissement. Pour le numismate, toutefois, il est important de se souvenir que l'or a été choisi comme monnaie suprême parce qua sa rareté le rendait précieux, parce que sa couleur est unique et parce que son lustre dure éternellement. Les pièces d'or qui furent enterrées ou cachées d'une autre manière pendant des siècles et même jusqu'à 2000 ans, se révélèrent lorsqu'on les découvrit enfin dans leur condition inaltérée, brillantes et non ternies, telles qu'on les avait cachées.

C'est cette vieille tendance de l'or a s'enfouir sous terre qui a continuellement pour résultat la découverte inespérée de pièces nouvelles, inédites, dont certaines peuvent faire une importante lumière sur un personnage ou un endroit par ailleurs inconnu ou embrumé dans le cours de l'histoire.

L'humanité a appris à aimer ce métal pour une bonne raison. Son expérience amère lui a montré qu'en face de la guerre, de l'invasion, de la révolution, de la panique, de l'inflation ou d'autres désastres économiques, la pièce d'or, toute petite qu'elle n'en est soit pas moins restée, seule, le symbole de la sécurité alors que tous les autres standards de valeur familiers se sont effondrés dans la ruine générale.

Sachant cela, les peuples du monde ont développé une vénération spéciale pour la pièce d'or, la conservant toujours sans jamais la fondre et, devant tout danger, prompt à la cacher. Parfois, les propriétaires originaux ne réclamèrent pas ou ne purent pas réclamer leur trésor et les pièces furent perdues pour le monde jusqu'à ce qu'elles soient mises à jour par accident, de nombreuses années plus tard, par le soc d'une charrue, le flot de la marée ou de la dynamite.

Même aujourd'hui, la richesse des nations se mesure à la quantité d'or, et, puisqu'il en est ainsi et pour montrer combien la longue histoire de l'or a réellement peu changé, on notera que les gouvernements du monde, comme dans le passé, ont enfoui leur réserve d'or sous le sol où il est consciencieusement conservé sous le contrôle sûr de leurs Banques Centrales, par une garde permanente armée et protégée par les dispositifs les plus récents contre le vol, le cambriolage ou l'attaque, et par des constructions massives contre toute forme de désastre.

Bien que la littérature de la numismatique soit abondante, il n'existe aucun livre qui soit consacré aux pièces d'or mondiales et qui les considère comme une classe à part. Etant donné l'intérêt passionné pour les pièces d'or, l'auteur a trouvé cette situation pour le moins remarquable. Numismate professionnel pendant la plupart de sa vie adulte, l'auteur, ainsi que des milliers d'autres numismates de par le monde, a cruellement regretté l'absence d'un tel livre dans la littérature de la numismatique.

A seule fin d'obtenir une référence sur toute pièce d'or frappée avant le 20ème siècle, il était nécessaire de partir en chasse à travers les travaux standards (s'ils existaient) du pays en question, lesquels travaux, bien entendu, s'occupaient aussi des pièces d'argent et de moindre importance. De toute évidence, il y a des centaines de ces livres; la plupart sont imprimés en une langue étrangère et leur édition est épuisée; beaucoup sont rares et de grande valeur et on ne peut se les procurer.

C'était ainsi une entreprise formidable que de se lancer à l'étude, ou à la recherche d'émissions anciennes de pièces d'or mondiales, cela demandait des privilèges spéciaux ou bien des assistants faisant des recherches au dehors, ou encore de longues heures de travail fastidieux et des efforts parfois sans résultat à la bibliothèque.

Il y a longtemps que l'auteur rêvait d'améliorer cette situation en créant un seul volume qui comprendrait toute la monnaie d'or du monde, à l'exception des pièces antiques. Cela semblait prétentieux à première vue et impossible à mener jamais à bonne fin, du fait de la quantité colossale de pièces que l'on peut trouver au cours de 1300 ans de frappe de monnaie.

Néanmoins, quelques calculs préliminaires montrèrent qu'avec une certaine économie de format il serait possible de présenter un seul volume, de dimension modérée sans sacrifier aucun renseignement vital ni les très importantes illustrations.

Donc, puisant dans sa propre expérience et dans celle de ses estimables collaborateurs, l'auteur a passé les cinq années écoulées à réunir et rassembler les renseignements enfin publiés aujourd'hui.

CADRE ET OBJET DE "PIECES D'OR DU MONDE"

Ce livre s'intéresse à l'étude des monnaies d'or mondiales à partir de la fin des monnaies de l'Antiquité, à la suite de la période des invasions nomades, lorsque de nouveaux gouvernements avec des noms reconnus vinrent au monde. Le but du livre est de commencer avec les émissions de pièces qui en chaque endroit, étaient les premières pièces distinctives qui identifient avec certitude chaque lieu tel que nous le connaissons aujourd'hui, ce qui donne à la monnaie un caractère vraiment national; après avoir déterminé le point de départ pour chaque endroit, la monnaie a été traitée chronologiquement jusqu'à sa disparition naturelle par suspension de la monnaie en or en cet endroit particulier. Certaines émissions se poursuivent jusqu'en 1958.

Le livre a été divisé en 3 catégories numismatiques. La Partie I s'intitule Amérique où les pièces les plus anciennes sont les émissions Coloniales Espagnoles de Colombie, autour de 1621. La Partie II s'intitule Europe, là les premières pièces datent de la cité Italienne de Bénévent aux alentours de l'an 600 Après J.C. La Partie III s'intitule Afrique et Orient avec les premières pièces connues qui sont les émissions Axumites d'Ethiopie, autour de 300 Après J.C.

LA GEOGRAPHIE DE CE LIVRE

L'emplacement national correct de certains noms de lieux, qui posèrent parfois un dilemme, a été résolu en se concentrant arbitrairement sur une période mieux connue de la génération actuelle. C'est ainsi que la période entre les Deux Guerres Mondiales a été choisie. (1937 étant considérée comme une année normale de cette période), comme point de référence des frontières géo-politiques du monde. En conséquence, les pièces d'un pays existant en 1937 ont été classées sous le nom de ce pays, bien que ces pièces aient pu être frappées bien avant sous une suzeraineté étrangère.

On a ainsi fait quelques innovations, en suivant ce principe, c'est ainsi que les monnaies de pays comme l'Esthonie ou la Lettonie sont classées sous leurs propres noms, et non dans les monnaies Suédoises, ce qui est cohérent, par exemple, avec le classement traditionnel des pièces Hispano-Américaines sous leurs noms Américains et non sous la rubrique de l'Espagne. L'index géographique de ce livre aidera à situer n'importe quelle monnaie.

LES DESCRIPTIONS ET LES DATES

Chaque type de pièce qui entre dans le cadre de ce livre, et que l'auteur a pu trouver, a été classé et décrit. Le côté face (Obv.) est toujours décrit en premier. La description est suivie des diverses dénominations et dates de ce type en particulier. L'utilisation d'un nom seulement dans la description indique un personnage debout. Autrement, on se servira des mots tête, buste, etc. . . .

Les pièces sans date sont suivies de ND. En général, lorsqu'une pièce porte de une à quatre dates environ, on a énuméré toutes les dates; autrement on s'est servi seulement de la première et de la dernière, mais toutes les années n'existent pas forcément entre ces dates ultimes.

Dans un travail de cette envergure et de cette complexité, étant donné que ceci est une première édition, il est inévitable que certains types ou dénominations de pièces auront échappé à l'attention de l'auteur et qu'ils ne seront pas classés en dépit de notre prétention à être complets.

L'auteur sera reconnaissant de toute omission qui sera portée à son attention, de manière à ce que les pièces en question puissent figurer dans les éditions à venir de ce livre.

LES ILLUSTRATIONS

A peu près la moitié de l'espace de ce livre est consacrée aux illustrations des pièces qui sont présentées en grandeur réelle. A grands suppléments de frais, on les a incorporées dans le texte, là où elles doivent être, au lieu de les placer à la fin du livre sous forme d'une section de planches séparées. La description de l'illustration est immédiatement au-dessous.

Une astérisque (*) à côté de la dénomination et de la date indique qu'il s'agit de la pièce illustrée au-dessus de la description. Dans le cas où il y a seulement une dénomination pour le type de pièce illustré, on ne s'est pas servi d'astérisque.

Des illustrations de tailles différentes ont été utilisées à dessein, car cela aidera à identifier les dénominations des pièces sans marque de valeur.

La plupart des types — du tout début ont été illustrés — il est certain que depuis 1700 environ, les illustrations sont virtuellement complètes pour tous les types. Il y a plus de 2700 illustrations de pièces d'or dans ce livre — plus qu'on en a jamais représentées dans un seul livre de numismatique de dimensions comparables, et l'auteur pense bien que presque toutes les pièces avec lesquelles les numismates sont généralement familiers ont été montrées.

LES EVALUATIONS ET L'ETAT DE CONSERVATION

L'auteur publie les évaluations comme guide général de la valeur des pièces sur le marché numismatique. Personne ne peut se targuer de reconnaître tout seul la valeur numismatique de toutes les pièces d'or qui ont été frappées. Par conséquent, des livres de ventes volumineux ont été consultés. On les a utilisés conjointement aux 20 années d'expérience de l'auteur dans le domaine de la numismatique professionnelle et à l'expérience des collaborateurs, et l'on pense que ces évaluations font état de la véritable rareté, de la condition, de la demande et des disponibilités des pièces à la date de l'été 1958.

Ces évaluations représentent des chiffres approximatifs et l'on suppose que les pièces sont échangées entre un acheteur et un numismate professionnel tous deux bien informés. Elles sont basées sur des actes de ventes récents ou sont une mise à jour de vieux compte-rendus de vente.

L'évaluation de pièces rares a été particulièrement difficile car ces pièces n'ont fait que de rares apparitions. Dans certains cas elles n'ont pas été évaluées du tout et ont simplement été étiquetées "rares". Dans d'autres cas, l'évaluation a été déterminée par comparaison de la pièce avec la valeur connue d'une autre pièce de rareté égale ou qui représente des attributs similaires.

De toute manière, l'évaluation d'une pièce de grande rareté doit être considérée comme purement nominale et ne saurait être qu'une indication que la pièce est d'une valeur extraordinaire. L'expérience de l'auteur à l'époque actuelle a montré que lorsqu'une pièce d'une grande rareté a été mise sur le marché numismatique, elle a toujours tendance à excéder son dernier prix connu car il y a une demande toujours croissante pour de telles pièces.

En général, la valeur numismatique d'une pièce est déterminée en partie par la condition, en partie par la rareté et presque toujours par la loi inexorable de l'offre et de la demande, ce qui peut causer parfois de larges divergences avec les évaluations de ce livre.

Ces évaluations s'entendent pour la condition moyenne dans laquelle on trouve la pièce le plus fréquemment, **et pour l'époque ou la variété les plus communes de ce type.** Des pièces en meilleure condition ou avec des dates plus rares demanderaient un prix plus élevé. En général, l'usage a montré que ces conditions moyennes sont les suivantes:

Pour des pièces plus ou moins jusqu'à l'an 1800, les évaluations s'entendent pour des spécimens en bel état.

Pour des pièces allant jusqu'à 1800 et 1914 environ, les évaluations s'entendent pour des spécimens en très bel état.

Pour des pièces allant de 1914 environ à ce jour, les évaluations s'entendent pour des spécimens qui n'ont pas circulés (fleur de coin) ou pour des spécimens de choix qui n'ont guère circulés.

Pour des pièces marquées "non mises en circulation", les évaluations s'entendent pour des spécimens n'ayant pas circulé ou des spécimens d'épreuve. (Flan bruni.)

Les lecteurs situés outre-mer se trouveront bien de consulter la Foreign Exchange Table située dans l'appendice, eu égard aux évaluations qui sont marquées en dollars US.

ESSAIS, EPREUVES, EMISSIONS NON-OFFICIELLES, FRAPPES HORS-SERIES

L'auteur a essayé de placer dans le livre toutes sortes de pièces d'or qui apparaissent de temps en temps chez les numismates. Parmi ces pièces sont les fascinantes séries des épreuves et essais. On les a désignées du terme général de "non mises en circulation". Ce sont des émissions légitimes de la Monnaie du Gouvernement et elles comptent parmi les plus rares et les plus prisées des pièces d'or, apparaissant presque toujours dans la condition flan bruni.

D'autres pièces ont été nettement étiquetées non-officielles ou de facture privée. Ce ne sont les pièces officielles d'aucun gouvernement et de telles pièces ont été manufacturées exclusivement à l'usage des collectionneurs, ou à l'usage des marchés mondiaux de l'or.

La question d'inclure les frappes hors-séries dans ce livre a posé un problème qui semblait insoluble. (Une pièce hors-série est une pièce en or frappée de la matrice qui servait pour frapper de pièces d'autres métaux.) Ces frappes sont généralement des multiples d'un ducat — 3 Ducats et plus. D'après les séries intéressées, elles ont été parfois incluses, parfois exclues de la classification, suivant l'usage et la tradition.

L'opinion n'est toujours pas unanime parmi les numismates pour savoir s'il faut considérer comme légitime une pièce d'or qui pèse exactement ce que pèserait une pièce de 10 ducats, mais qui ne porte pas de marque de valeur et qui est frappée au même coin qui sert à frapper le Taler d'argent, lui aussi sans marque de valeur. Etant donné que la plupart des pièces d'or ne portaient pas de marque de valeur de toute manière, (leur valeur réelle étant leur poids et leur pureté) la question semble purement académique.

L'INTRODUCTION ET L'APPENDICE

Une explication des marques de matrice (mm.) qui apparaissent dans le texte, se trouvera sous la rubrique de chaque pays respectivement dans l'Introduction Générale qui suit.

Une référence à l'Introduction et à l'Appendice répondra souvent aux nombreuses questions qui pourront être soulevées quand on consultera la section Catalogue du livre.

ABREVIATIONS   ND pour Non Daté; mm. pour Marque monetaire; Obv. pour Côté Face ou avers; Rev. pour Revers.

R.F.

Fuer den deutschen Leser.

EINLEITUNG

ETWAS UEBER GOLDMUENZEN

Das Sammeln von Goldmuenzen gehoert zu der Geschichte der Menschheit beinahe seit die ersten Goldmuenzen von den alten Griechen um ungefaehr 700 v.C. gepraegt wurden.

Seit damals wurden Goldmuenzen von fast jeder Regierung, welche in Erscheinung trat, gepraegt. Der Begriff "Regierung", wie er hier gebraucht wird, ist eine Ausdehnung jeder Muenzen schlagenden Behoerde-sei sie dauernd oder voruebergehend, weltlich oder geistlich, national oder oertlich, republikanisch oder koeniglich. Beachtliche Mengen an Goldmuenzen wurden so durch die Jahrhunderte gepraegt und gluecklicherweise sind viele erhalten geblieben, um die Kultur unserer Zeit zu bereichern und dem Numismatiker ein Leben der Freude und des Studiums zu gewaehren.

Es ist kein Zufall, dass so viele Goldmuenzen seit aeltesten Zeiten erhalten geblieben sind — im allgemeinen in gut erhaltenem Zustand — und dies kann der Natur des Goldes selbst als Metall wie auch der Liebe der Menschheit fuer das Metall zugeschrieben werden.

Die chemischen und physikalischen Eigenschaften des Goldes sind zu gut bekannt, um deren Auseinandersetzung hier erforderlich zu machen. Es ist jedoch fuer den Numismatiker wichtig, sich daran zu erinnern, dass Gold als hoechstes Muenzmaterial gewaehlt wurde, weil seine Seltenheit es wertvoll machte, seine Farbe einzigartig ist und weil sein Glanz fuer immer bestehen wird. Goldmuenzen, welche begraben oder auf andere Weise hunderte oder sogar 2000 Jahre lang verborgen wurden, sind, als sie endlich entdeckt wurden, in derselben glaenzenden und unbefleckten Verfassung aufgefunden worden, als ob sie erst versteckt worden seien.

Es ist diese uralte Tendenz des Goldes, unterirdisch zu verschwinden, welche fortgesetzt die unerwartete Entdeckung neuer, unveroeffentlicher Muenzen zur Folge hat, von denen einige ein wichtiges Licht auf eine Persoenlichkeit, oder einen Ort, der sonst von der Geschichte ins Dunkel gehuellt wurde, werfen moegen.

Die Menschheit hat gelernt, das Metall aus gutem Grunde zu lieben. Ihre bittere Erfahrung hat gezeigt, dass die Goldmuenze, klein wie sie ist, angesichts des Krieges, der Invasion, Revolution, Panik, Inflation, oder anderer wirtschaftlicher Katastrophen, alleine als Symbol der Sicherheit erhalten geblieben ist, wenn alle anderen bekannten Wertbegriffe im allgemeinen Ruin zerfallen sind.

Indem sie dies erkannten, haben die Voelker der Welt eine besondere Ehrerbietung fuer die Goldmuenze entwickelt, indem sie sie immer bewahrten, niemals zusammenschmolzen und angesichts irgend einer Gefahr, verborgen hielten. Manchmal haben die urspruenglichen Besitzer ihren Schatz nicht wieder eingeholt oder konnten ihn nicht in Besitz nehmen. Die Muenzen waren dann fuer die Welt verloren, bis sie zufaellig nach vielen Jahren von der Pflugschar, einer Flutwelle oder durch Dynamit zum Vorschein gebracht wurden.

Selbst heute wird der Wohlstand von Nationen nach dem Goldstandard gemessen und nachdem dies so ist und um darzulegen, wie wenig sich die lange Geschichte des Goldes wirklich geaendert hat, kann man feststellen, dass die Regierungen der Welt, wie in der Vergangenheit, ihr Muenzgold unterirdisch verborgen halten, wo es sorgfaeltig unter der sicheren Kontrolle ihrer Zentralbanken bewahrt wird: es befindet sich unter dauernder Bewachung einer bewaffneten Wache, geschuetzt durch die letzten Vorrichtungen gegen Diebstahl, Einbruch oder Ueberfall und durch solide Bauweise gegen alle Ungluecksarten.

Obwohl die numismatische Literatur ausgedehnt ist, sind keine Buecher, die den Goldmuenzen der Welt als Klasse fuer sich gewidmet sind, vorhanden. Der Verfasser hat, in Anbetracht des leidenschaftlichen Interesses an Goldmuenzen, diesen Zustand bemerkenswert gefunden. Der Verfasser, der fast sein ganzes erwachsenes Leben ein berufsmaessiger Numismatiker war, als auch viele tausend anderer Numismatiker in der ganzen Welt, haben den Mangel eines solchen Buches in der numismatischen Literatur ausserordentlich bedauert.

Um eine Bezugnahme auf irgend eine Goldmuenze, welche vor dem zwanzigsten Jahrhundert geschlagen worden war, zu erhalten, war es notwendig, das massgebende Werk (falls ein solches vorhanden war) fuer das in Frage kommende Land, ausfindig zu machen, welches natuerlich auch den Silber — und

unbedeutenderen Muenzen gewidmet war. Es ist offensichtlich, dass es mehrere hunderte solcher Buecher gibt; die meisten von ihnen sind in einer Fremdsprache gedruckt und vergriffen; viele sind selten, wertvoll und nicht erhaeltlich.

Es war also eine betraechtliche Aufgabe, fruehere Ausgaben von Goldmuenzen der Welt nachzuschlagen oder nach ihnen zu suchen, welche besondere Einrichtungen oder aeussere Forschungsbeihilfe erforderlich machte oder viele Stunden ermuedender und manchmal erfolgloser Arbeit in der Bibliothek noetig machte.

Der Verfasser hatte lange davon getraeumt, diesen Zustand durch Ausgabe eines einzigen Bandes zu verbessern, welcher die gesamte Goldmuenzen der Welt, einschliesslich der alten Muenzen umfassen sollte. Dies erschien auf den ersten Blick grossartig und die Verwirklichung wegen der riesigen Menge an Muenzen, die in 1300 Jahren der Muenzpraegung in Umlauf waren, unmoeglich.

Einige vorgereitende Berechnungen zeigten jedoch, dass es mit einer gewissen Sparsamkeit an Format moeglich sein wuerde, einen einzigen Band maessigen Ausmasses zu schaffen, ohne lebenswichtige Auskunft oder die gaenzlich unentbehrlichen Abbildungen zu opfern.

Der Verfasser hat deshalb die letzten fuenf Jahre damit zugebracht, das Material, welches jetzt endlich veroeffentlicht wurde, zu erschliessen und zu sammeln, indem er seine eigene Erfahrung sowie diejenige geschaetzter Mitarbeiter verwertete.

DAS AUSMASS DER "GOLDMUENZEN DER WELT"

Dieses Buch befasst sich mit der Goldmuenzenpraegung der Welt, welche begann, als die Muenzenpraegung des Altertums endete und folgt dem Zeitalter des Einbruchs der Nomaden, als neue Regierungen mit erkennbaren Namen erstanden. Das Ziel bestand darin, die an jedem Ort ausgegebenen Muenzen mit den ersten deutlich erkennbaren Namen, die den Ort unter dem Namen, wie wir ihn heute kennen, eindeutig festlegen, zu beginnen und dadurch der Praegung einen wahrhaft nationalen Charakter zu verleihen; nachdem der Ausgangspunkt fuer jeden Ort bestimmt worden war, wurde die Muenzausgabe in chronologischer Reihenfolge gehandhabt, bis sie ihr natuerliches Ende durch Einstellung der Goldmuenzenpraegung an dem betreffenden Ort gefunden hatte. Einige der Ausgaben halten bis 1958 an.

Das Buch wurde in drei numismatische Kategorien eingeteilt. Teil I ist mit Amerika betitelt und die fruehesten Muenzen sind die spanischen Kolonialausgaben von Kolumbien, ungefaehr um 1621. Teil II ist mit Europa betitelt und die fruehesten Muenzen stammen hier aus der italienischen Stadt Beneventum, ungefaehr aus dem Jahre 600 A.D. Teil III ist betitelt Afrika und der Orient, dessen frueheste aufgefuehrte Muenzen die Axumitischen Praegungen Abbessiniens von ungefaehr 300 A.D. sind.

DIE GEOGRAPHIE DIESES BUCHES

Die genaue nationale Festlegung gewisser Ortsnamen, welche manchmal ein Dilemna darstellte, wurde dadurch geloest, dass eine Zeitspanne, welche der Heutigen Generation am Besten bekannt ist, willkuerlich in den Brennpunkt gestellt wurde. So wurde die Zeitspanne zwischen den zwei Weltkriegen gewaehlt (und 1937 als ein Normaljahr dieser Periode), als Bezugsnahmepunkt fuer die geo-politischen Grenzen der Welt. Deshalb wurden die Muenzen eines im Jahre 1937 bestehenden Landes unter dem Namen des Landes aufgefuehrt, selbst wenn sie viel frueher und unter fremder Souveraenitaet gepraegt worden sein sollten.

Es wurden also gewisse Veraenderungen vorgenommen, da

nach dieser Regel die Muenzen von Laendern wie Estland und Lettland unter ihren eigenen Namen aufgefuehrt wurden und nicht als schwedische Muenzen, was, zum Beispiel mit der ueberlieferten Auffuehrung der Spanisch-Amerikanischen Muenzen unter ihren amerikanischen Namen eher, als unter Spanien, uebereinstimmt. Das geographische Verzeichnis im Buch wird zum Auffinden aller Muenzer nuetzlich sein.

DIE BESCHREIBUNGEN UND DATEN

Jede Muenzentype, welche in den Rahmen dieses Buches faellt und welche der Verfasser finden konnte, wurde aufgefuehrt und beschrieben. Die Vorderseite der Muenze ist immer zuerst beschrieben. Der Beschreibung folgen die verschiedenen Wertangaben und Daten der betreffenden Type. Wenn in der Beschreibung nur der Name gebraucht wird, zeigt dies eine stehende Figur an. Andernfalls wird Kopf, Bueste, usw. gebraucht.

ND. folgt Muenzen ohne Zeitbestimmungen. Wenn eine Muenze ein bis etwa vier Daten aufweist, wurden im allgemeinen alle Daten angefuehrt; andernfalls wurden nur die ersten und letzten Daten benuetzt, doch sind nicht alle zwischen den Anfangs — und Enddaten liegenden Jahre notwendigerweise vorhanden.

In einem Werk dieser Groesse und Verwicklung ist es, wenn man hierbei auch beruecksichtigt, dass es sich um eine Erstausgabe handelt, unvermeidlich, dass einige Typen oder Wertangaben von Muenzen der Aufmerksamkeit des Verfassers entgangen sein werden und dass sie, trotz des Anspruchs auf Vollstaendigkeit, nicht aufgefuehrt sind.

Der Verfasser wird deshalb fuer alle solche Unterlassungen, auf welche er hingewiesen wird, dankbar sein, damit diese Muenzen in zukuenftigen Ausgaben dieses Buches mit eingeschlossen sind.

DIE ABBILDUNGEN

Ungefaehr die Haelfte des Raumes in diesem Werk ist Abbildungen der Muenzen in ihrer wirklichen Groesse gewidmet. Unter weiteren grossen Kosten wurden sie innerhalb des Textes, wohin sie gehoeren, eingefuegt und nicht als Stiche·in getrennter Abteilung am Ende des Buches. Die Beschreibung der Abbildung befindet sich unmittelbar darunter.

Ein Sternchen (*) neben dem Nennwert und Datum zeigt an, dass dies die ueber der Beschreibung abgebildete Muenze ist. Falls es nur einen Nennwert fuer die Art der abgebildeten Muenze gibt, wurde kein Sternchen gebraucht.

Verschiedene Groessen von Abbildungen wurden absichtlich verwendet, da dies bei der Kennzeichnung der Nennwerte jener Muenzen, die ohne Wertangabe sind, eine Hilfe ist.

Es wurden die meisten Typen von Anfang an abgebildet, bestimmt aber seit ungefaehr 1700 und sind die Abbildungen tatsaechlich fuer alle Typen vollstaendig. In diesem Buche befinden sich mehr als 2700 Abbildungen von Goldmuenzen, mehr als je in irgend einem Muenzebuch von vergleichbarer Groesse abgebildet wurden und glaubt der Verfasser, dass fast alle Muenzen, mit welchen Numismatiker im allgemeinen vertraut sind, dargestellt worden sind.

DIE BEWERTUNGEN UND DER ZUSTAND DER ERHALTUNG

Der Verfasser veroeffentlicht die Wertbestimmungen als allgemeine Anleitung fuer den Wert der Muenzen auf dem numismatischen Markt. Niemand kann von sich behaupten, den numismatischen Wert jeder Muenze, die gepraegt wurde, zu kennen. Aus diesem Grunde wurden umfangreiche Verkaufs-

aufzeichnungen einer Untersuchung unterzogen. Diese wurden in Verbindung mit der zwanzigjaehrigen Erfahrung des Verfassers in berufsmaessiger Numismatik sowie in der angehaeuften Erfahrung der Mitarbeiter verwertet und man glaubt, dass die gegenwaertigen Wertbestimmungen die wahre Seltenheit, die Verfassung, Nachfrage und Verfuegbarkeit der Muenzen nach dem Stand vom Sommer 1958 wiederspiegeln.

Diese Bewertungen stellen die annaehernde Zahl da, zu welcher die Muenzen den Besitz aus den Haenden eines gut unterrichteten Kaeufers in die eines gut informierten berufsmaessigen Numismatikers wechseln wuerden. Sie sind auf neuere Verkaufsverzeichnisse gegruendet oder basieren auf einer Ausweitung alter Verkaufsergebnisse in die gegenwaertige Zeit.

Die Bewertung von Seltenheiten war besonders schwierig, weil die Muenzen so selten aufgetaucht sind. In einigen Faellen wurden sie ueberhaupt nicht bewertet und wurden nur mit "selten" bezeichnet. In anderen Faellen wurde die Wertbestimmung durch den Vergleich der Muenze mit dem bekannten Wert einer anderen Muenze gleicher Seltenheit oder anderer aehnlicher Eigenschaften vorgenommen.

Auf jeden Fall muss die Bewertung einer grossen Seltenheit als rein nominell angesehen werden und kann bestenfalls nur ein Anzeichen dafuer sein, dass die Muenze ausserordentlichen Wert besitzt. Die Erfahrung des Verfassers in modernen Zeiten hat gezeigt, dass, wenn eine grosse Seltenheit auf dem numismatischen Markt angeboten wurde, dieselbe immer dazu neigte, den letzten bekannten Preis, wegen der sich fuer derartige Muenzen immer vermehrenden Nachfrage zu uebersteigen.

Allgemein gesehn, wird der numismatische Wert einer Muenze teilweise durch den Zustand, teilweise von der Seltenheit und fast immer durch das unerbittliche Gesetz von Angebot und Nachfrage bestimmt, ein Gesetz, welches manchmal eine grosse Abweichung von den Wertbestimmungen dieses Buches verursachen koennte.

Diese Wertbestimmungen beziehen sich auf den Durchschnittszustand, welchem man bei der Muenze am Haeufigsten begegnet und **fuer das gewoehnlichste Datum und Typenart.** Muenzen in erstklassigem Zustand oder mit selteneren Daten wuerden einen hoeheren Preis fordern. Im Allgemeinen hat die Erfahrung gezeigt, dass diese Durchschnittszustaende folgende sind:

Fuer Muenzen bis ungefaehr 1800 sind die Wertbezeichnungen fuer schoene Exemplare.

Fuer Muenzen von etwa 1800 bis 1914 bezieht sich die Bewertung auf sehr schoene Stuecke.

Bei Muenzen von ungefaehr 1914 bis heute sind die Werte fuer nicht kursierende (ungebrauchte) Stuecke oder fuer ausgesuchte Exemplare, welche kaum Abnuetzung aufweisen.

Die Bewertungen fuer Muenzen, die gekennzeichnet sind unter "nicht im Umlauf befindlich", beziehen sich auf nicht im Umlauf befindliche Stuecke oder Stuecke mit polierte Platte.

Auslaendische Leser sollten die im Anhang befindliche Tabelle fuer auslaendische Wechselkurse befragen, welche das Verhaeltnis der Waehrungen zu den in U.S. Dollars notierten Werten angibt.

PROBESTUECKE, STUECKE MIT POLIERTE PLATTE, UNOFFIZIELLE PRAEGUNGEN UND ABSCHLAEGE

Der Verfasser hat versucht, im Buch alle Arten von Goldmuenzen miteinzubeziehen, welche von Zeit zu Zeit bei numismatikern erscheinen. Zu solchen Muenzen gehoeren die bezaubernden Serien der Proben und Stuecke mit polierte Platte.

Diese sind unter dem allgemeinen Begriff "nicht in Umlauf gesetzt" gekennzeichnet worden. Sie sind gesetzliche, ungebrauchte Regierungsausgaben und sie gehoeren zu den seltensten und am Meisten geschaetzten Goldmuenzen. Sie treten fast immer im polierte Platte-Zustand auf.

Andere Muenzen sind einfach als nichtdienstliche oder privat hergestellte Stuecke bezeichnet worden. Dieselben sind keine Dienstmuenzen irgend einer Regierung und solche Muenzen sind ausschliesslich fuer Sammler oder zum Gebrauch auf den Weltgoldmaerkten hergestellt worden.

Die Frage, ob Abschlaege in diesem Buch einbezogen werden sollten, hat ein anscheinend unloesbares Problem hervorgerufen. (Als Abschlag wird eine Muenze angesehen, die in Gold auf derselben Praegeplatte geschlagen wurde, welche zur Herstellung einer nicht goldenen Muenze verwendet wurde.) Abschlaege sind im allgemeinen die groesseren Stuecke der Dukaten-Muenzpraegung-von 3 Dukaten aufwaerts. Dem ueberlieferten Gebrauch entsprechend, wurden sie manchmal mit Inbegriffen und manchmal nicht, je nachdem, welche Serien in Frage kamen.

Unter Numismatikern herrscht noch immer keine uebereinstimmende Meinung vor, ob eine Goldmuenze, die genau das Gewicht hat, das ein 10 Dukaten-Stueck wiegen sollte, aber keine Wertkennzeichnung enthaelt und von derselben Platte, die zur Praegung eines Silber-Talers, aehnlich ohne Wertkennzeichnung, geschlagen wurde, als gesetzlich anzusehen ist. Da die meisten fruehen Goldmuenzen sowieso ohne Wertbezeichnung sind (ihr wirklicher Nominalwert ist ihr Gewicht und ihre Feinheit), erscheint diese Frage akademisch.

DIE EINLEITUNG UND DER ANHANG

Eine Erklaerung der Muenzkennzeichen (mm.), welche im Text auftreten, findet man unter dem betreffenden Land in der allgemeinen Einfuehrung, welche folgt.

Viele Fragen, welche bei Bezugnahme auf den Katalogsteil des Buches entstehen koennten, werden manchmal durch Einblick in die Einleitung und den Anhang beantwortet werden koennen.

ABKUERZUNGEN

ND fuer ohne Jahr; mm fuer Muenzkennzeichen; Obv. fuer Vorderseite; Rev. fuer Rueckseite.

R.F.

Per il lettore Italiano.

PREFAZIONE

BREVI CENNI RIGUARDANTI LE MONETE D'ORO

Il collezionare monete d'oro sembra sia stata una passione dell'uomo sin da quando le prime monete d'oro furono coniate dagli antichi Greci, circa il 700 A.C.

Da allora, le monete d'oro son state coniate da quasi tutti i governi esistiti. Il termine governo, nel significato qui' datogli, si intende esteso ad ogni autorita' battente moneta, — permanente o provvisoria, secolare od ecclesiastica, nazionale o locale, repubblicana o monarchica.

Immense quantita' di monete d'oro sono state cosi' coniate attraverso i secoli, e per fortuna molte sono a noi pervenute, arrichendo cosi' la cultura del nostro tempo e fornendo al numismatico infinite possibilita' di piacere e di studio.

Non e' certo per caso, che tante monete d'oro ci siano pervenute dai tempi antichi — generalmente in ottimo stato di conservazione — e cio' puo' essere attribuito all natura dell'oro stesso come metallo ed inoltre all'amore dell'umanita' per detto metallo.

Le proprieta' chimiche e fisiche dell'oro son troppo ben conosciute per richiedere ulteriore specificazione qui'. Per quanto riguarda il numismatico e' tuttavia importante ricordare che l'oro e' stato scelto come il sommo mezzo di monetazione, perche' prezioso per la sua rarita', perche' il suo colore e' unico e perche' il suo lustro e' eterno. Monete d'oro che son state sotterrate od altrimenti nascoste per centinaia o persino per 2000 anni, quando infine scoperte, sono state trovate nelle stesse condizioni, brillanti e non offuscate, di quando furono nascoste.

E' questa vecchia tendenza dell'oro di scomparire sottoterra che continuamente risulta in scoperte inattese di nuove, sconosciute monete, alcune delle quali possono fornire importanti ragguagli su personaggi o luoghi altrimenti sconosciuti od avvolti nelle nebbie della storia.

L'uomo ha appreso ad amare detto metallo per buone ragioni. La propria amara esperienza gli ha dimostrato che, di fronte alla guerra, rivoluzione, invasione, panico, inflazione od altro disastro economico, la moneta d'oro, per quanto piccola come dimensioni, e' sola sopravvissuta come simbolo di sicurezza, quando tutti gli altri usuali valori sono stati trascinati nella generale rovina.

Sapendo cio', i popoli del mondo hanno tenuto in speciale reverenza le monete d'oro, sempre conservandole, giammai fondendole e, di fronte ad ogni pericolo, nascondendole. A volte, i possessori originali non vollero o non potettero reclamare il proprio tesoro, e dette monete sono state perdute per il mondo, finche accidentalmente venute alla luce, dopo molti anni, e cio' dovuto all'aratro, ad una marea montante od alla dinamite.

Anche oggi, la ricchezza delle nazioni si misura in termini di oro, e dato che e' cosi', e per dimostrare quanto poco la lunga storia dell'oro sia realmente cambiata, sara' bene notare che i governi del mondo, come nel passato, hanno nascosto il loro oro monetato nel sottosuolo, dove e' accuratamente tenuto sotto la salvaguardia delle Banche Centrali, sotto permanente guardia armata e con la protezione degli ultimi ritrovati contro il furto, lo scasso o la rapina, e, data la pesante struttura, puo' resistere a tutti i possibili disastri.

Sebbene la letteratura numismatica sia estesa, non ci sono attualmente libri che si occupino delle monete d'oro nel mondo, come di una categoria a se' stante. Tenendo in considerazione l'interesse profondo nelle monete d'oro, l'autore ha trovato cio' alquanto sorprendente. Essendo stato un numismatico professionale per quasi tutto il periodo della sua vita, l'autore, come pure migliaia di altri numismatici attraverso il mondo, ha dolorosamente sentito la mancanza di tale libro nella letteratura numismatica.

Per cercare un riferimento su una moneta d'oro coniata prima del 20mo secolo, era necessario pescare il lavoro standard (sempre che esistesse), riguardante la nazione considerata, il quale lavoro, naturalmente, era dedicato anche all'argento ed ad altre monete di minore importanza. Come e' ovvio, ci sono centinaia di tali libri; la maggior parte di essi sono pubblicati in lingue straniere e le loro edizioni sono esaurite; molti di essi sono rari e di valore e semplicemente non ottenibili.

L'intraprendere cosi' la ricerca delle emissioni piu' antiche delle monete d'oro nel mondo, si presentava come qualcosa di formidabile, richiedente speciali mezzi di ricerca o assistenza esterna o molte ore di tedioso, ed a volte improduttivo, lavoro in biblioteca.

L'autore ha a lungo contemplato di migliorare tale condizione, col creare un solo volume che includa la totalita' delle monete d'oro coniate nel mondo intero, con esclusione delle monete antiche. Cio' e' sembrato dapprima un grandioso progetto, impossibile a realizzare, dato il colossale ammontare di monete coniate in 1300 anni.

Tuttavia, alcuni calcoli preliminari hanno mostrato che con una certa economia di formato, sarebbe possibile creare un solo volume, di formato moderato, senza sacrificare alcuna vitale informazione o le importantissime illustrazioni.

Percio', attingendo alla propria esperienza, nonche' a quella di collaboratori di valore, l'autore ha impiegato gli ultimi cinque anni nell'accumulare e raccogliere le informazioni ora infine pubblicate.

LA FINALITA' DI "LE MONETE D'ORO NEL MUNDO"

Questo libro si occupa del monetaggio in oro nel mondo, che e' cominciato quando il monetaggio dell'epoca antica e' terminato e susseguentemente alle invasioni dei popoli nomadi, quando nuovi Stati, dai nomi ben definiti, vennero alla ribalta della scena mondiale. Lo scopo del libro consiste nel prendere in considerazione le monete, nei vari luoghi, che identificano con sicurezza il luogo con il nome con cui lo conosciamo oggi, cosi' rendendole incontestabilmente nazionali, nelle loro caratteristiche; dopo aver determinato il punto d'inizio per ogni luogo, il monetaggio e' stato preso in considerazione cronologicamente, sino a quando giunga a terminazione per la sospensione nell'emissione di monete d'oro, in un particolar luogo. Alcune emissioni continuano sino al 1958.

Il libro e' stato diviso in tre categorie numismatiche. La prima parte e' intitolata America, e le monete piu' antiche le emissioni Coloniali Spagnole della Colombia, risalenti circa al 1621. La seconda parte e' intitolata Europa, ed in essa le monete piu' antiche provengono dalla citta' Italiana di Benevento, circa l'anno 600 D.C. La terza parte e' intitolata Africa, ed Oriente, e le monete piu' antiche elencate sono le emissioni Axumite di Etiopia, risalenti al 300 D.C. circa.

CONSIDERAZIONI GEOGRAFICHE DEL PRESENTE VOLUME

L'appropriata posizione di certi luoghi, nel quadro di alcune nazioni, che a volte pone un dilemma, e' stata risolta con il fissarsi arbitrariamente in un periodo di tempo meglio conosciuto dalla presente generazione. E' stato scelto il periodo tra le due Guerre Mondiali, (ed il 1937 come anno normale per detto periodo), come punto di riferimento per i confini geografico-politici del mondo. Percio', le monete di una nazione esistente nel 1937 sono state elencate sotto il nome di detta nazione, anche se tali monete possano essere state coniate molto prima, sotto differente sovranita'.

Si notano cosi' certe innovazioni; per esempio, secondo questa regola, le monete di nazioni come l'Estonia o la Lituania sono elencate sotto i rispettivi nomi, anzice' come monete Svedesi, il che e' consistente, caso pratico, con l'elen-cazione tradizionale delle monete Ispano-Americane sotto i propri nomi Americani, anzice' sotto la Spagna. L'indice geografico nel volume aiutera' nel localizzare ogni moneta.

DESCRIZIONI E DATE

Ogni tipo di moneta che rientri nelle finalita' di questo libro, e che l'autore ha potuto trovare, e' stato elencato e descritto. La diritto della moneta e' sempre descritta per prima. La descrizione e' seguita dalle varie denominazioni e dalle date riguardanti quel tipo particolare. L'uso del nome soltanto nella descrizione indica una figura eretta. In caso contrario, testa, busto, ecc. vengono usati.

Monete senza data sono seguite da ND. In generale, quando una moneta ha da una a circa quattro date, tutte tali date sono state elencate; altrimenti sono state usate solamente la prima e l'ultima data, ma cio' non indica necessariamente decorso del tempo tra tali date basilari.

In un'opera di tale importanza e complessita', ed in considerazione del fatto che questa e' la prima edizione, e' inevitabile che alcuni tipi o denominazioni di monete siano sfuggiti all'attenzione dell'autore, e che non siano elencati, nonostante la pretesa di un'elencazione completa.

L'autore sara' grato per ognuna di tali omissioni che venga richiamata alla sua attenzione, in modo che tutti i tipi di moneta possano essere inclusi nelle future edizione del presente libro.

LE ILLUSTRAZIONI

Circa la meta' dello spazio di questo volume e' dedicata alle illustrazioni delle monete che sono mostrate nella grandezza originale. Nonostante una notevole spesa supplementare, esse sono state incorporate nel testo, nei punti cui si riferiscono, anzice' alla fine del libro, si' da formare una sezione separata. La spiegazione delle illustrazioni e' immediatamente al disotto di esse.

Un asterisco (*) accanto alla denominazione e data indica che la moneta e' quella cui si riferisce l'illustrazione che trovasi sopra la spiegazione. In caso ci sia solamente una denominazione riguardante il tipo di moneta illustrato, non e' stato usato alcun asterisco.

Illustrazioni di differenti grandezze sono state scientemente usate, dato che cio' aiutera' ad identificare le denominazioni di quelle monete che siano senza indicazione del loro valore.

La maggior parte dei tipi sin dall'inizio presentano la corrispondente illustrazione — e certamente dopo il 1700 circa, le illustrazioni sono virtualmente complete per ogni tipo. In questo libro ci sono oltre 2700 illustrazioni di monete d'oro, — piu' di quante non se ne trovino in un libro di tale carattere e di formato corrispondente, e l'autore ha fiducia che quasi tutte le monete, familiari ai numismatici, siano state mostrate.

VALUTAZIONI E STATO DI PRESERVAZIONE

L'autore pubblica il prezzo stimato, come guida generale del valore delle monete sul mercato numismatico. Nessuno puo' da se' pretendere di conoscere il valore numismatico di tutte le monete d'oro che siano state coniate in ogni epoca. Percio', voluminose registrazioni di vendite sono state consultate. Esse sono servite, congiutamente ai venti anni di esperienza dell'autore come numismatico professionale ed insieme all'-accumulata esperienza dei collaboratori, a dare un'idea sufficientemente esatta, si spera, del fatto che le valutazioni in parola riflettono esattamente rarita', condizioni, richiesta e disponibilita' delle monete sino all'estate del 1958.

Queste valutazioni rappresentano il valore approssimato a cui le monete sarebbero scambiate tra un compratore ben informato ed un numismatico professionale, anche ben informato. Sono basate su recenti registrazioni di vendite, o rappresentano una trasposizione nel presente di vecchie registrazioni di vendite.

La stima riguardante rarita' e' stata particolarmente difficile perche' tali monete sono apparse talmente raramente. In alcuni casi, esse non sono state affatto stimate, e sono state semplicemente contrassegnate "rare". In altri casi, la stima e' stata determinata comparando la moneta in questione con altra di noto valore, di uguale rarita' o avente simili attributi.

In ogni caso, la stima di una grande rarita' deve essere considerata puramente nominale, ed al piu' puo' essere considerata indicazione che la moneta e' di straordinario valore. L'esperienza dell'autore in tempi moderni, suggerisce che, quando una grande rarita' sia stata immessa nel mercato numismatico, ha avuto sempre tendenza ad eccedere l'ultimo prezzo conosciuto, data la continua, crescente domanda per tali monete.

In generale, il valore numismatico di una moneta e' determinato in parte dalle condizione in cui si trova, in parte dalla rarita' e quasi sempre dalla inesorabile legge di domanda ed offerta, che a volte puo' portare a sensibili differenze con le valutazioni di questo libro.

Tali valutazioni si riferiscono alle condizioni medie in cui la moneta si trovi piu' frequentemente, **e per la piu' comune data o varieta' di tale tipo.** Monete in condizioni superiori, o con date piu' rare, richiederebbero un piu' alto prezzo. In generale, l'esperienza ha dimostrato che tali condizioni medie sono le seguenti:

Per monete fino al 1800 circa, le valutazioni si riferiscono a belli esemplari.

Per monefe dal 1800 circa al 1914, le valutazioni si riferiscono a molto belli esemplari.

Per monete dal 1914 ad oggi, le valutazioni si riferiscono ad esemplari che non siano stati mai immessi in circolazione (zecca dello Stato) o ad esemplari scelti, che non presentino quasi alcuna traccia di uso.

Per monete contraddistinte "non immesse in circolazione", le valutazioni si riferiscono ad esemplari che non abbiano circolato o che siano fondo specchio.

I lettori di oltre mare e' consigliabile che consultino la Tavola di Divise Straniere in appendice, in relazione alle valutazioni, che sono quotate in Dollari americani.

PROVE, FONDO SPECCHIO, EMISSIONI NON UFFICIALI ED A PRODUZIONE ANORMALE

L'autore ha cercato di includere nel libro, ogni sorta di monete d'oro che, di tanto in tanto, appaiono tra i numismatici. Tra tali monete, e' la affascinante serie di prove e fondo specchio. Tutti questi sono stati designati col termine generale "non immessi in circolazione". Sono legittimi esemplari emessi dalla Zecca Governativa e sono tra le monete d'oro piu' rare e piu' pregiate, e quasi sempre appaiono nelle condizioni originali di fondo specchio.

Altre monete sono state semplicemente definite come emesse non ufficialmente o privatamente. Esse non sono monete ufficiali di alcun governo, e sono state fabbricate esclusivamente per collezionisti, o per uso nei mercati mondiali nell'oro.

La questione di includere i modelli a produzione anormale in questo libro ha costituito un problema pressoche' insolubile. (Un esemplare a produzione anormale e' inteso come un esemplare coniato in oro per mezzo dello stesso conio usato per monete non d'oro). Gli esemplari a produzione anormale sono generalmente i pezzi piu' grandi del tipo ducato — da 3 Ducati in su. In dipendenza della serie considerato, alcune volte essi sono stati inclusi, altre volte no, secondo l'uso tradizionale.

Non c'e' unanimita' di opinione tra i numismatici circa il riguardare come legittima una moneta d'oro che pesi esattamente cio' che un pezzo da 10 Ducati normale possa pesare, ma che non porti indicazione del proprio valore, e sia coniata con lo stesso conio usato per Talleri d'argento, similmente senza indicazione di valore. Dato che la maggior parte delle antiche monete d'oro non presentano indicazione di valore in alcun caso (il loro reale valore facciale essendo dato dal loro peso e purezza), la questione sembra accademica.

INTRODUZIONE ED APPENDICE

Una spiegazione dei contrassegni della zecca (mm.) che appaiono nel testo, puo' trovarsi sotto la nazione rispettiva nella Introduzione Generale che segue.

Riferimento all'Introduzione ed all'Appendice puo' a volte fornire risposta a varie domande che possano sorgere con riferimento alla sezione catalogo del libro.

ABBREVIAZIONI

ND sta per nessuna data; mm. per contrassegno della zecca; Obv. per diritto; Rev. per rovescio.

R.F.

Para el Lector de Habla Hispana.

PROLOGO

BREVE RESENA SOBRE MONEDAS DE ORO

El coleccionar monedas de oro pareciera haber interesado a la humanidad prácticamente desde que las primeras monedas fueron acuñadas por los griegos cerca de 700 años antes de Jesucristo. Desde entonces, casi todos los gobiernos que han existido, han acuñado monedas de oro. El término gobierno según se emplea aquí, se refiere a toda autoridad permanente o provisional, secular o eclesiástica, nacional o local, real o republicana encargada del cuño.

Cantidades formidables de monedas de oro han sido acuñadas a través de los siglos y afortunadamente muchas de ellas han sobrevivido enriqueciendo la cultura de nuestra época y proporcionando al numismático una fuente de estudio y placer permanentes.

No es en forma accidental que tantas monedas de oro han sobrevivido y llegado a nuestros días desde el fondo de los tiempos antiguos — generalmente en excelente estado de conservación — y esto puede atribuirse a la naturaleza del oro propiamente y al amor de la humanidad por este metal.

Las propiedades físicas y químicas del oro son bien conocidas y no vale la pena entrar en detalles sobre ellas en este artículo. Para el numismático sin embargo, es importante recordar que el oro fue seleccionado como el mejor material de cuño porque su escasez lo hacía precioso, porque su color es típico y porque su lustre y brillo son permanentes. Las monedas de oro que han sido enterradas u ocultadas por siglos y hasta por milenios, cuando son finalmente descubiertas se encuentran en la misma condición de brillo y lustre que tenían al ser escondidas.

Es esta vieja tendencia a enterrar el oro lo que resulta en inesperados descubrimientos de monedas nuevas y desconocidas, algunas de las cuales arrojan luz sobre algún sitio o personaje que de otra manera sería desconocido o permanecería envuelto en las nubes de la historia.

La humanidad ha aprendido a amar este metal por una buena razón: su amarga experiencia le ha demostrado que frente a guerras, invasiones, revoluciones, pánicos, inflación o cualquier otro desastre económico, la moneda de oro, pequeña como es en tamaño, ha sido única en sobrevivir como símbolo de seguridad cuando todos los otros estandards familiares de valores han sucumbido dentro de la ruina general.

Sabiendo ésto, los pueblos del mundo han desarrollado una especial reverencia por la moneda de oro, conservándola siempre, no fundiéndola y escondiéndola frente al peligro. Algunas veces, los dueños originales no pudieron reclamar o no reclamaron su tesoro y las monedas estuvieron perdidas para el mundo hasta que fueron accidentalmente expuestas muchos años después por un golpe de arado, una marea embravecida o una explosión de dinamita.

Aún hoy, la riqueza de las naciones se mide en términos de su oro, y ya que este es el caso y para demostrar lo poco que ha cambiado la larga historia del oro, llamamos la atención sobre el hecho de que los gobiernos del mundo en el pasado, han ocultado sus reservas de oro acuñado, bajo tierra, donde es cuidadosamente mantenido bajo el seguro control de sus Bancos Centrales, bajo permanente custodia armada y protegidos por las últimas novedades en aparatos preventores de robo o asalto así como por construcciones capaces de hacer frente a cualquier forma de desastre.

A pesar de que la literatura sobre numismática es extensa, no existen libros especiales sobre las monedas de oro en el mundo. Considerando el interés apasionado que existe sobre la materia, al autor le ha llamado mucho la atención este hecho. Habiendo sido un numismático profesional durante la mayor parte de su vida adulta, el autor, al igual que miles de otros numismáticos en el mundo entero, ha resentido, echando mucho de menos, la falta de un libro semejante en la literatura numismática.

Para poder obtener una referencia sobre cualquier moneda de oro acuñada antes del siglo veinte, era necesario ponerse a la búsqueda del material impreso estandard en el país de que se trataba, material que como es de suponer se refería también a monedas de plata y a otras monedas menores. Es obvio que existen cientos de estos libros, la mayor parte impresos en lenguas extranjeras y en ediciones agotadas; muchos constituyen ejemplares raros y valiosos y son inobtenibles.

Era por lo tanto una empresa formidable ponerse a buscar o consultar material de referencia sobre las monedas de oro en el mundo ya que ello requería facilidades especiales, asistencia de otros en las investigaciones o muchas horas de trabajo tedioso y muchas veces estéril, en las bibliotecas.

El autor había acariciado por mucho tiempo la idea de mejorar este estado de cosas con la creación de un solo volumen que abarcara en forma total la acuñación de moneda en el mundo, con excepción de lo referente a monedas antiguas. Esto parecía enorme al principio y de imposible realización a causa de la cantidad colosal de monedas encontradas en 1300 años de acuñación.

Sin embargo, algunos cálculos preliminares demostraron que con una cierta economía de formato sería posible crear un solo volumen de tamaño moderado sin sacrificar ninguna información vital ni las ilustraciones que son tan importantes.

Por lo tanto, usando la fuente de su propia experiencia y la de sus valiosos colaboradores, el autor ha dedicado los últimos cinco años a la recolección y reunión de la información que al fin ahora se publica.

LO QUE ABARCA "LAS MONEDAS DE ORO DEL MUNDO"

Este libro se refiere a la acuñación de oro en el mundo que comienza al terminar la acuñación de la antigüedad e inmediatamente después de la era de las invasiones nómadas, cuando comenzaron a existir nuevos gobiernos con nombres determinados. El propósito ha sido comenzar a catalogar las emisiones de moneda de cada lugar, con las primeras monedas distintivas que identifican positivamente el lugar al que damos hoy día un determinado nombre, haciendo la acuñación verdaderamente nacional en carácter. Habiendo establecido el punto de partida en el caso de cada sitio, la acuñación ha sido tratada cronológicamente hasta llegar a su fin natural por la suspensión de acuñamiento de oro en cada lugar en particular. Algunas de las emisiones llegan hasta 1958.

El libro ha sido dividido en tres categorías numismáticas. La Parte I se ha llamado América y las primeras monedas son las emisiones hispano-coloniales de Colombia cerca de 1621. La Parte II se ha llamado Europa y en ella las más antiguas monedas datan del sexto siglo de la Era Cristiana y corresponden a la ciudad italiana de Beneventum. La Parte III se ha llamado Africa y el Oriente, dentro de la cual las monedas más antiguas corresponden al siglo tercero de nuestra era y a la ciudad de Axumit en Etiopía.

LA GEOGRAFIA DE ESTE LIBRO

La apropiada ubicación nacional de ciertos nombres de lugares que muchas veces significaba un dilema, ha sido resuelta por medio del enfoque arbitrario sobre la época mejor conocida de la generación actual. El período entre las dos guerras ha sido seleccionado (y el año de 1937 como un año normal de ese paríodo), como punto de referencia en lo que se refiere a los límites geopolíticos del mundo. Por lo tanto las monedas de un país en existencia en 1937 han sido incluídas bajo el nombre de ese país a pesar de que hayan sido acuñadas en épocas anteriores y bajo soberanía extranjera.

Algunas innovaciones han sido así llevadas a cabo ya que bajo este sistema la acuñación de moneda de países como Estonia o Latvia aparece bajo su propio nombre en vez de aparecer como acuñación de Suecia, lo que es consistente por ejemplo con la forma tradicional de incluir las monedas hispanoamericanas bajo sus nombres americanos, en vez de incluirlas como acuñación de España. El índice geográfico en el libro ayudará a localizar cualquier acuñación.

DESCRIPCIONES Y FECHAS

Cada tipo de moneda que cae dentro de las categorías contempladas por este libro, y que el autor pudo encontrar, ha sido anotado y descrito. El anverso de la moneda siempre está descrito en primer lugar. Su descripción es seguida por las varias denominaciones y fechas de ese tipo en particular. El uso de un nombre solamente en la descripción, indica una figura de pie. De otra manera, son usadas las palabras cabeza, busto, etc.

Las monedas sin fecha van seguidas de las letras SF. Por lo general, cuando una moneda tiene de una a cuatro fechas, todas las fechas han sido anotadas; de lo contrario se habrán anotado solamente la primera y última fechas y ésto no querrá decir que existan todos los años comprendidos entre ambas.

En un trabajo de esta magnitud y complejidad y considerando que se trata de una primera edición, es inevitable que algunos tipos o denominaciones de monedas hayan escapado a la atención del autor y que no hayan sido anotados a pesar de lo dicho acerca de la total integridad del trabajo.

El autor agradecerá cada una de las omisiones que sea llevada a su atención de manera que las monedas en cuestión puedan ser incluídas en ediciones futuras de este libro.

LAS ILUSTRACIONES

Cerca de la mitad del espacio de este libro está dedicado a ilustraciones de las monedas, que son presentadas en tamaño natural. Con gasto adicional considerable han sido incorporadas dentro del texto, donde pertenecen, en vez de al final del libro como un conjunto de láminas adicionales. La descripción de las ilustraciones se encuentra al pie de las mismas.

Un asterisco (*) al lado de la denominación y la fecha indica que esta es la moneda ilustrada en el espacio anterior a la descripción. En el caso de que haya una sola denominación para el tipo de moneda que se ilustra, no se ha usado el asterisco.

Una variedad de tamaños ha sido usado a propósito para las ilustraciones ya que ésto ayudará a identificar la denominación de las monedas que carecen de la marca del valor.

La mayor parte de los tipos, aún los más antiguos, han sido ilustrados y ciertamente, después de 1700, las ilustraciones son virtualmente completas en todos los tipos. Este libro incluye más de 2700 ilustraciones de monedas de oro, más de las que han sido nunca ilustradas en ningún otro libro de tamaño comparable y el autor cree haber ilustrado casi todas las monedas con que está generalmente familiarizado el numismático.

LAS EVALUACIONES Y EL ESTADO DE CONSERVACION

El autor publica las evaluaciones como una guía general acerca del valor de las monedas en el mercado numismático. Nadie por sí mismo puede pretender conocer el valor numismático de cada moneda de oro que ha sido acuñada. Para presentar este trabajo se han consultado voluminosos registros de ventas. Estos han sido usados en conjunción con la experiencia de veinte años del autor, en numismática profesional, combinada con la experiencia acumulada de los colaboradores. El autor cree que las evaluaciones aquí presentadas reflejan la verdadera condición de curiosidad o rareza de la pieza, la condición, la demanda y la abundancia de las monedas hasta el verano de 1958.

Estas evaluaciones representan la cantidad aproximada en que las monedas cambiarían de mano entre un comprador bien informado y un numismático profesional. Están basadas en registros de ventas recientes o son una extensión dentro del tiempo presente de viejos registros de ventas.

La evaluación de piezas raras ha sido especialmente difícil porque las monedas han aparecido muy raras veces. En algunos casos no han sido evaluadas del todo y han sido marcadas simplemente "raras." En otros casos la evaluación ha sido determinada por comparación de la moneda con el valor conocido de otra moneda de igual rareza u otros atributos similares.

En todo caso, la evaluación de una verdadera rareza debe ser considerada como puramente nominal, y en el mejor de los casos puede ser solamente una indicación de que la moneda es de extraordinario valor. La experiencia del autor en los tiempos modernos le ha demostrado que cuando una verdadera rareza ha sido puesta en el mercado numismático, siempre ha tendido a exceder su último precio conocido a causa de la demanda siempre en aumento de esa clase de monedas.

En general el valor numismático de una moneda está determinado en parte por la condición, en parte por la rareza y casi siempre por la ley inexorable de la oferta y la demanda. Esta última puede a veces ser causa de gran divergencia entre los precios del momento y los anotados en este libro.

Estas evaluaciones se refieren a la condición corriente en que la moneda es más frecuentemente encontrada, y para la más corriente fecha y variedad del tipo. Las monedas en condición superior o con fechas más raras, exigirán un precio más elevado. En general la experiencia ha demostrado que estas condiciones corrientes son las siguientes:

Para monedas hasta cerca de 1800, las evaluaciones son para especímenes bien conservados.

Para monedas de cerca de 1800 a 1914, las evaluaciones son para especímenes muy bien conservados.

Para monedas de cerca de 1914, a esta fecha, las evaluaciones son para especímenes flor de cuño o para especímenes escogidos que casi no muestren señales de desgaste.

Para monedas marcadas "no puestas en circulación," las evaluaciones son para "no circulante" o cospel bruñido.

Los lectores en el extranjero harían bien en consultar la Tabla de Cambio Extranjero en el apéndice, en relación con las evaluaciones que están cotizadas en dólares americanos.

ENSAYOS, PRUEBAS, EMISIONES NO OFICIALES Y ACUNACIONES ESPECIALES

El autor ha intentado incluir en el libro toda clase de monedas de oro de las que de tiempo en tiempo aparecen entre los numismáticos. Entre esas monedas puede incluirse la fascinante serie de ensayos y pruebas. Estas han sido designadas con el término general de "no puestas en circulación." Son emisiones legítimas de las oficinas gubernamentales del cuño, y pueden contarse entre las más raras y más apreciadas monedas de oro. Aparecen casi siempre en la condición de cospel bruñido.

Otras monedas han sido simplemente marcadas como extraoficialmente o privadamente hechas. Estas no son monedas oficiales de ningún gobierno y han sido manufacturadas exclusivamente para coleccionistas o para uso en los mercados de oro del mundo.

La inclusión de acuñaciones especiales en este libro ha presentado un problema aparentemente insoluble. (Una acuñación especial es considerada como una moneda acuñada en oro de la misma matriz o cuño que se ha usado para acuñar una moneda de otro metal.) Las acuñaciones especiales son generalmente múltiplos de ducados, de 3 ducados en adelante. De acuerdo con el uso tradicional, unas veces han sido incluídas y otras no, según la serie de que se trate.

No hay unanimidad de opinión entre los numismáticos acerca de si debe considerarse como legítimo una moneda de oro que pese exactamente lo que debería pesar una moneda de 10 ducados pero que no lleve la marca del valor y acuñada con la misma matriz usada para un tálero de plata, igualmente sin la marca del valor. Dado que la mayor parte de las monedas de oro tempranas no llevan en ningún caso la marca del valor (siendo su valor facial el peso y la pureza), la cuestión resulta académica.

Una explicación de las marcas monetarias (mm) que aparecen en el texto, se encontrará en la sección correspondiente al respectivo país en la Introducción General que sigue.

Refiriéndose a la Introducción y al Apéndice muchas veces se encontrará la respuesta a algunas de las preguntas que podrían surgir al consultar el catálogo en el libro.

ABREVIACIONES

SF para sin fecha; mm para marca monetaria; Anv. para anverso; Rev. para reverso.

R.F.

General Introduction to the Coins

PART I.   AMERICA

GENERAL REFERENCES: The gold coins of North and South America by Raymond; Brazil Coinage by Santos Leitao; Standard Catalogue of U. S. Coins by Raymond; A Guide Book of U. S. Coins by Yeoman; Vidal Quadras and Tolra Collections of Spanish Gold Coins.

ARGENTINA. Mints and mint marks:—PTS monogram for Potosi; RA for Rioja. The 1 Escudo of 1813 remains unknown and its existence is in doubt. Many counterfeits exist of the large Rosas pieces. All gold coins of Argentina are considered rare except the 5 Peso piece, which is the equivalent of the 25 Franc piece of the Latin Monetary Union.

BOLIVIA. Mints and mint marks:—PTS monogram for Potosi. No. 6 has been included as it most likely was struck. The bust on No. 17 is the same type as Chile No. 28.

BRAZIL. Mints and mint marks:—P for Pernambuco; R for Rio de Janeiro; M for Minas; B for Bahia.

Brazilian gold coins were extensively counterstamped during the 18th and 19th centuries for use in other localities. Such coins may be found under British Guiana, Grenada, Guadeloupe, Martinique; Saint Martin, Saint Vincent and Portugal, (Mary II).

Under the Portuguese Kings, the coins on the colonial or decimal standard (4000 Reis and fractions) show the denominations, whereas the coins on the National or Escudo standard (12,800 Reis, 6400 Reis and fractions thereof) are without the marks of value.

The first gold coin under the Empire (No. 84) was not approved for circulation by the Emperor, and of the 64 originally struck, only about a dozen have survived.

The 10,000 Reis pieces dated 1833-1840 have the same intrinsic value as the 6400 Reis pieces of similar type dated 1832 and 1833, but are smaller and thicker.

It is interesting to note that of the two gold coins of the Republic, Nos. 98, 99, only the 10,000 Reis piece shows the mark of value.

BRITISH COLUMBIA. The only two coins are of extreme rarity. They were struck in British Columbia as trials for a proposed coinage, but the actual issuance of the coins was forbidden by England.

CHILE. Mints and mint marks:—S topped by small o for Santiago.

On the coins from 1846-1851, the Grecian helmet worn by Liberty on earlier years, is replaced by the Liberty Cap.

COLOMBIA. Mints and mint marks:—Under the Spanish Kings, NR for Bogota; P or PN for Popayan; under the Republic, the mints of Bogota, Popayan and Medellin used their names in full on the coins, with an occasional B or P for the first two.

All 5 Peso pieces of the 19th century are rare. During the 19th century, the coinage was based on that of the Latin Monetary Union, and in the 20th century, on that of the English Pound.

CUBA. The coinage was struck at the Philadelphia Mint, and is without a mint mark. The 20 Pesos of 1916 is extremely rare as proof specimens only were struck and only a few are known. Cuban coinage is based on the U. S. gold standard.

DOMINICAN REPUBLIC. It will be noted that there has been only one issue of gold coins. This 30 Peso is unique in that it is the only gold coin of the Americas, the face value of which is based on the present-day value of gold, viz, $35.00 per ounce. The coin was originally issued at a premium, the amount over 30 Pesos reverting to the Government.

ECUADOR. Mints:—Quito and Birmingham. The unique 50 Franc piece of 1862 was discovered in 1956.

GUATEMALA. Mints and mint marks:—G or NG (New Guatemala) for Guatemala. Almost every coin issued under the Spanish Kings is a rarity.

During the 19th century, the coinage was based on that of the Latin Monetary Union, and is unique in that so many denominations were struck—the equivalent of 100, 80, 50, 40, 25, 10, 5 and 2½ Franc pieces (20 Pesos to 4 Reales). Of all the countries in the Union, only Guatemala struck so tiny a coin as the 2½ Franc equivalent.

The only coins of the 20th century were struck in 1926 and are based on the U. S. gold Dollar.

MEXICO. Mints and mint marks:—

MO	mm for Mexico City
A or AS	mm for Alamos
C or CN	mm for Culican
CA or CH	mm for Chihuahua
DO	mm for Durango
EO MO	mm for Tlalpam
GA	mm for Guadalaxara
GC	mm for Guadelupe y Calvo
GO	mm for Guanaxuato
HO	mm for Hermosillo
O or OA	mm for Oaxaca
PI	mm for San Luis Potosi
ZS	mm for Zacatecas

The Escudo system, inherited from the Spanish Kings, was continued under the Republic as late as the 1870's. The Peso system was instituted in 1870 and until 1905 it varied little from that of U. S. gold coinage, the Peso almost being equal to the Dollar. In 1906, the Gold Peso was devalued about one half and the first coins on the new standard appeared in 1906.

The 50 Peso piece or Centennario was struck as a regular circulating medium until 1931. Since then and until 1947 it was struck mainly to satisfy the world wide demand for gold coins.

PERU. Mints and mint marks:—LM, ME or monogram for Lima; C or CO for Cuzco. Like the Mexican Centennario, the gold coinage of 1950-1956 was struck to satisfy the demand for gold coins. As in Colombia, the 19th century coinage was based on that of the Latin Monetary Union, and this century's coinage on that of the English Pound.

TIERRA DEL FUEGO. Julius Popper, who struck these coins, was a South American adventurer. This coinage may be considered as a territorial issue of Argentina.

UNITED STATES OF AMERICA. Mints and mint marks:—

Without mint mark	Philadelphia (Pennsylvania)
C	mm for Charlotte (North Carolina)
CC	mm for Carson City (Nevada)
D	mm for Dahlonega (Georgia, 19th century)
D	mm for Denver (Colorado, 20th century)
O	mm for New Orleans (Louisiana)
S	mm for San Francisco (California)

The initial gold coinage, 1795-1834, was of sterling purity, .916⅔ Fine. In 1834, the fineness was reduced to .899¼ and at the same time, the weight of the coins themselves was also reduced, the 5 Dollar piece, for example, going from 135 to 129 grains, and the 2½ Dollar piece in proportion. In 1837, the fineness was increased to .900, at which point it remained until the end of gold coinage in 1933. United States gold coins dated before 1808 do not show the mark of value. The Philadelphia Mint coined 20 Dollar gold pieces dated 1933, but this date is not listed in the catalogue since the coins were not released officially and possession of this one date is illegal.

There is also in existence, a large amount of so-called coins of ¼, ½ and 1 Dollar denominations. Most of these coins are octagonal and they are sometimes called California gold coins or charms. They were privately struck in California or other western areas until the early years of this century. They are not included in this book since they do not form a part of regular U. S. coinage.

VENEZUELA. Venezuelan coinage is based on that of the Latin Monetary Union. The 50 and 5 Bolivar pieces are of exceptional rarity, and of the two, only the 1888 date of the first coin was placed in circulation. The 1875 dates of both pieces are specimen proofs marked "ESSAI."

PART II. EUROPE

ALBANIA. Mints and mint marks:—R for Rome; V for Vienna. The 100 Franc pieces of 1928 and 1929 were unknown until about 1950. Albanian coinage is based on that of the Latin Monetary Union.

AUSTRIA. (For additional remarks, see under Holy Roman Empire). Reference: Miller-Aichholz, Vienna, 1948; Cejnek, Vienna, 1935; Horsky Collection, Frankfurt, 1910; Jaeckel, Basel, 1956; Bernhart and Roll (For Salzburg).

Mints and mint marks for period from about 1750-1916.

A	mm for Vienna
B	mm for Kremnitz
C	mm for Prague
D	mm for Salzburg
E	mm for Karlsburg
F	mm for Hall
G	mm for Nagybanya
H	mm for Gunzburg
M	mm for Milan
V	mm for Venice
W	mm for Vienna
Hand	mm for Antwerp
Small head	mm for Brussels
Lion	mm for Bruges

It will be seen that the series of coins struck under the Holy Roman Emperors is both long and extensive. It is regretted that lack of space did not permit a listing of the coinage of each mint, as has been done beginning with the reign of Joseph II. About 20 mints operated over a period of some 250 years, each with its own letter or symbol as a mint mark and a detailed listing of this formidable coinage would be beyond the scope of this book.

In many cases, some of the larger gold coins in the Austrian series are off-strikes. The denomination "Souverain" is traditionally applied to the coinage of the Austrian and Belgian Mints while its counterpart "Sovrano" is used for the coinage of the Milan and Venice Mints. The coins of Franz Joseph are especially noteworthy, since five different standards of gold coinage existed during his long reign, viz, Ducats, Sovranos, Krones, Florins and Corona. The unique specimen of No. 434 is in the Vienna Mint Cabinet.

The Republic issues of 1923, 1924 are extraordinary in that far more of the larger coins were struck than of the smaller. 17,325 specimens were struck of the 100 Kronen piece, and 3468 of the 20 Kronen piece.

BELGIUM. Reference: Dupriez, Gaillard, Nussbaum. Belgian coinage is based on that of the Latin Monetary Union. The coins listed as not being placed in circulation were all struck in proof condition and all are rare. Only 6 pieces were struck of the 100 Franc piece of 1912 with French legends and only 3 pieces of the same coin with Flemish legends.

BOHEMIA. This is the ancient Kingdom occupying the territory now known as Czechoslovakia.

BULGARIA. Reference: Ljubica, Zagreb, 1875. Bulgarian coinage is based on that of the Latin Monetary Union, excepting the Ducat coinage. The coins of 1894 are rare in perfect uncirculated condition; the coinage of that year is as follows: 100 Leva, 7500 pieces; 20 Leva, 175,000 pieces; 10 Leva, 75,000 pieces.

DANZIG. Reference: Hutten-Czapski, St. Petersburg, 1871. The 25 Gulden pieces of both 1923 and 1930 were struck in proof condition only. 1000 specimens were struck in 1923 and 4000 in 1930, but the later issue was not placed in circulation, and very few are known.

DENMARK. Reference: Schou, Copenhagen, 1926. It will be noted that some of the earlier coins are in imitation of English, German or Hungarian types.

FRANCE. Reference: Ciani, Paris, 1926; F. Poey d'Avant, Paris, 1838; LaFaurie, Paris, 1951, 1956; Monsieur V. G., Paris, 1943. Additional coins of the French Kings will be found under some of the Italian States over which France had suzerainty.

Mints and mint marks for the period 1806-1870:—(Later coinage was struck only at the Paris Mint).

A	mm for Paris
B	mm for Rouen
BB	mm for Strasbourg
CL	mm for Genoa (Italy)

D	mm for	Lyon
H	mm for	La Rochelle
I	mm for	Limoges
K	mm for	Bordeaux
L	mm for	Bayonne
M	mm for	Toulouse
MA	monogram for	Marseille
Q	mm for	Perpignan
R	Crowned mm for	Rome (Italy)
R	(1815 only) for	London (England)
T	mm for	Nantes
U	mm for	Turin (Italy)
W	mm for	Lille
Fish and Mast	mm for	Utrecht (Netherlands)

French coinage from 1803 to 1914 was based on that of the Latin Monetary Union. Actually, the French gold Franc was the mainstay of this coinage system which was adopted by many European and some South American countries. It was not until 1929 that the first coins appeared based on the revaluation of the gold Franc.

GERMANY. General reference works consulted:—Jaeger, Basel, 1956; Kohler, Hannover, 1759; Soothe, Hamburg, 1784; Reimmann, Frankfurt, 1892; Rudolph, Dresden, 1911.

Specialized reference works consulted:

City	Author	Place and Date
Aachen	Menadier	Berlin 1913
Anhalt	Mann	Hannover 1907
Augsburg	Forster	Leipzig 1910, 1914
Baden	Wielandt	Karlsruhe 1955
Bamberg	Heller	Bamberg 1839
Bavaria	Beierlein	Munich 1894, 1900, 03, 06
Bentheim	Kennepohl	Frankfurt 1927
Brandenburg-Franconia	Schroetter	Halle 1927, 29
Bremen	Jungk	Bremen 1875
Brunswick	Fiala	Prague 1910
Cologne	Noss	Cologne 1926
Dortmund	Meyer	Vienna 1883
Eichstadt	Gebhardt	Halle 1924
Einbeck	Buck	Leipzig 1939
Emden	Knyphausen	Hannover 1872
Erfurt	Leitzman	Weissensee 1864
Frankfurt	Joseph and Fellner	Frankfurt, 1896, 1903
Fulda	Schneider	Fulda 1826
Hamburg	Gaedechens	Hamburg 1850
Hanau	Suchler	Hanau 1897
Hesse	Hoffmeister	Hannover 1880 and Prince Alexander, Darmstadt, 1877-85
Hildesheim	Buck	Leipzig 1937
Julich Cleve Berg	Noss	Munich 1929
Lauenburg	Schmidt	Ratzeburg 1884 and Dorfmann, Ratzeburg, 1940
Lippe	Grote	1867
Lubeck	Behrens	Berlin 1905
Magdeburg	Schroetter	Magdeburg 1909
Mansfeld	Tornau	Prague 1937
Mayence	Prince Alexander	Darmstadt 1882
Mecklenburg	Evers	Schwerim 1799
Minden	Stange	Munster 1913
Moers	Noss	Munich 1927
Munster	Niessert	Coesfeld 1839, 1841

City	Author	Place and Date
Nassau	Isenbeck	Wiesbaden 1890
Nordhausen	Lejeune	Dresden 1910
Nuremberg	Kellner	Grunwald 1957
Oettingen	Loeffelholz	Oettingana 1883
Osnabruck	Kennepohl	Munich 1938
Paderborn	Weingartner	Munster 1882
Palatinate	Noss	Munich 1938 and Exter, Zweibrucken, 1759, 1775
Prussia	Schroetter	Berlin 1902-25 and Bahrfeldt, Halle, 1913
Quedlinburg	Duning	Quedlinburg 1886
Rantzau	Meyer	Vienna 1882
Ratzeburg	Bahrfeldt	Schwerin 1913
Regensburg	Plato	Regensburg 1779
Reuss	Schmidt and Knab	Dresden 1907
Rosenberg	Friedensburg and Seger	Breslau 1901
Rostock	Grimm	Berlin 1905
Salm	Joseph	Frankfurt 1914
Saxony	Tentzel	Dresden 1705, 1714 and Baumgarten, Dresden 1812
Schauenburg	Weinmeister	Berlin
Schleswig-Holstein	Lange	Berlin 1908, 1912
Schwarzburg	Fischer	Heidelberg 1904
Silesia	Friedensburg and Seger	Breslau 1901
Solms	Joseph	Frankfurt 1912
Speyer	Harster	Speyer 1882
Stolberg	Frederick	Dresden 1911
Stralsund	Bratring	Berlin 1907
Teutonic Order	Waschinski	Gottingen 1952
Treves	Noss	Bonn 1916
Ulm	Binder	Stuttgart 1846
Wallenstein	Meyer	Vienna 1886
Wismar	Grimm	Berlin 1897
Worms	Joseph	Darmstadt 1906
Wurttemberg	Ebner	Stuttgart 1910-1915

Mints and mint marks for the coinage of the German Empire from 1871 to 1915.

A	mm for	Berlin
B	mm for	Hannover
C	mm for	Frankfurt
D	mm for	Munich
E	mm for	Dresden
F	mm for	Stuttgart
G	mm for	Karlsruhe
H	mm for	Darmstadt
J	mm for	Hamburg

The colossal coinage of Germany is no way better evidenced than that it comprises about one third of this book. It must be remembered that Germany until 1871 was not a unified country and for hundreds of years consisted of a multitude of independent coin issuing localities, each one of which merits the same numismatic attention as a sovereign nation. This mingled secular coinage has been further enlarged by the extensive issues of many ecclesiastical rulers.

Even the issues of the German Empire from 1871-1914 were similar only in denominations for they still bore the heads and titles of the many different rulers whose states formed the Empire.

As a matter of fact, it can truly be said that there is no such thing as a "German" gold coin—only a Prussian coin or a Cologne coin, etc. Actually, it was not until the formation of the German Republic after World War I that a truly national German coinage came into existence, and under this coinage, there were unfortunately no gold coins.

GREAT BRITAIN. Reference: Brooke, London, 1932; Seaby, London, 1956; Spink, London, 1950. Additional English type gold coins will be found among the various parts of the British Empire, namely, Canada, Australia, India, and South Africa.

These coins were first struck in 1871 and are of the same types as the contemporary English coins, but they bear the distinguishing mint mark of the issuing country. The coinage of the London Mint is without a mint mark.

The English gold Pound enjoyed enormous popularity and prestige during its years of issue and was known and accepted throughout the world. In order to identify themselves more closely with this unit of currency, many other countries struck their own local coins in the same weight and fineness as the Pound. Such coins can be noted in the appendix under "the principal gold coins of the world."

GREECE. Greek coinage is based on that of the Latin Monetary Union. The coins of 1852 are of extraordinary rarity. Although 8 specimens were struck of the 40 Drachmae piece and 32 specimens of the 20 Drachmae piece, the author knows of only one 40 Drachmae coin and none of the 20 Drachmae.

Only 76 pieces were struck of the 100 Drachmae piece of 1876 and 182 pieces of the 50 Drachmae.

HOLY ROMAN EMPIRE. Reference: Same as Austria. For the sake of as much simplicity as could be gained, this most complicated and involute of all coinage systems has been divided among Austria, Bohemia and Hungary. Necessity has forced this arrangement, since the Holy Roman Empire was a political concept and not a geographical entity with clearly defined borders.

Under Austria will be found those coins of the Hapsburg Emperors which are of similar type, whether the coins were struck in Austria proper or in the various mints of Bohemia or Hungary (including Transylvania). These similar type coins differ from each other only in the minor aspect of mint marks, mint symbols or in variations of the armorial devices or legends.

Under Bohemia and Hungary will be found the coins of these same Hapsburg Emperors, but of types which are peculiar only to their own areas, and these coins differ markedly in design from those listed under Austria.

Other coins, with either the portraits or names of the Holy Roman Emperors will be found throughout the cities and states of Germany, as well as in several other European countries.

The coinage of the Holy Roman Empire as such ended in 1806, at which time the incumbent Emperor Francis II became Francis I of the newly created Austro-Hungarian Empire, which in turn lasted until the First World War.

HUNGARY. Reference: Same as Austria and for Transylvania, Resch, Hermannstadt, 1901. The Hungarian Goldgulden and Ducat of the standing Emperor type were among the most popular coins of Europe and were circulated and accepted throughout the Continent. Many cities and states imitated this type for their own local coinage.

The St. George coins of Kremnitz have always been carried on the person to bring good luck to the bearer and keep him from harm. The coins of Transylvania are notable for the striking portraits and costuming that appear on them.

ITALY. Reference: Corpus Nummorum Italicorum by King Victor Emanuele III. Mints and mint marks or symbols for the Italian and Sardinian Kingdoms during the period 1821-1878.

(Later coinage was struck only at the Rome Mint):—

R	mm	for Rome
Eagles head	mm	for Turin
Anchor	mm	for Genoa
T and BN	mm	for Turin
M and BN	mm	for Milan

National Italian coinage from 1806 to 1927 is based on that of the Latin Monetary Union. The Italian gold Lira was subsequently re-valued and the first coins on the new standard were struck by the Vatican in 1929 and by Italy in 1931.

The Italian series is second only to the German in its extent and variety, since there were no truly national coinage until 1861. Prior to that time, Italy had a multitude of autonomous local coinages dating back to about 600 A.D.

The Florentine Florin, the Genoese Genovino (and later Ducat) and the Venetian Ducat (and later Zecchino) were the principal gold coins of the late Middle Ages, 1200 and later. They were universally known and respected for the purity of their gold which was from about .990 to 1000 fine, and the size, weight and purity of these coins became the prototypes for the principal part of later Continental coinage.

The enduring nature of the Ducat can be seen from the fact that it was struck as an official government coin as recently as 1938. The country of issue was Czechoslovakia and it is interesting to note that the specifications of the Ducat of 1938 were about the same as the original Ducat which Venice introduced to the world about 1200.

LIECHTENSTEIN, LUXEMBOURG, MONACO, MONTENEGRO. The modern gold coinage of these countries is based on that of the Latin Monetary Union.

NETHERLANDS. Reference: Stephanik, Amsterdam, 1904; Schulman, Amsterdam, 1946. Mint and mint marks:—Torch or lis for Utrecht; B for Brussels.

Early Dutch coins were adaptations of types existing in Spain, England, France and the Holy Roman Empire.

The Guilder as a true Dutch denomination was first introduced about 1680 in Zeeland. The Guilder is sometimes also called a Florin.

POLAND. Reference: Hutten-Czapski, St. Petersburg, 1871. Other coins of the Kings of Poland will be found under Danzig, Latvia, Lithuania and Germany-Elbing.

PORTUGAL. Reference: Vaz, Lisbon, 1948; Batalha-Reis, Lisbon, 1956. Other coins of the Portuguese Kings will be found under Brazil, India-Diu, India-Goa and Mozambique. The only appearance of mint marks on Portuguese coins took place in the period 1712-1722 at which time L was used for Lisbon and P for Porto.

ROUMANIA. The entire gold coinage of Roumania is based on that of the Latin Monetary Union. The 12½ Lei piece of 1906 is the only example of this denomination in the Union's coinage. The 50, 25 and 12½ Lei pieces struck in 1906 and 1922 are broad and thin and are struck in imitation of Ducat coinage to represent the equivalent of 4, 2 and 1 Ducat pieces. The commemorative coins of 1939 and 1940 (numbers 13-20) are rare and seldom appear.

RUSSIA. Reference: Schubert, St. Petersburg, 1855. Most of the early gold coins (numbers 1-60) exist as later re-strikes.

Russia affords us the only example of platinum coins actually being struck for circulation, and the 12, 6 and 3 Rouble coins of this metal are highly prized.

At the time platinum was discovered in the Ural Mountains it was worth so much less than gold that a 3 Rouble platinum coin weighing 10.3600 grams was the equal of a 3 Rouble gold coin weighing only 3.4900 grams. As a matter of fact, gold coins began to be counterfeited in platinum or struck in platinum at government mints (unofficially) from original dies. The platinum coins were then gold plated, and since platinum is slightly denser than gold and passes the same chemical tests as gold does, the gilded coins became indistinguishable from all-gold coins. These platinum coins are also highly prized.

The 3 Rouble gold piece struck from 1869 to 1885 is the Russian equivalent of the 1 Ducat. The 10 and 5 Rouble pieces struck from 1886 to 1894 and then re-valued in 1897 to 15 and 7½ Roubles, were struck according to the Latin Monetary Union and are equal to 40 and 20 Franc pieces.

SCOTLAND. Reference: Stewart, London, 1955.

SERBIA. Reference: Ljubica, Zagreb, 1875. Serbian coinage is based on that of the Latin Monetary Union.

SPAIN. Reference: Vidal Quadras, Barcelona, 1892; Tolra, Barcelona, 1936. Mints and mint marks:—

S	mm	for Seville
M or MD	mm	for Madrid
B or BA	mm	for Burgos or Barcelona
C	mm	for Cadiz
G	mm	for Granada
T	mm	for Toledo
V	mm	for Valencia
Aqueduct	mm	for Segovia

Geographically, Spanish coinage is the most universal in the annals of world numismatics. At one time or another, Spain had control over much of the world and her coinage followed the course of empire.

The Spanish series is, therefore, the most far flung of all national coinages, extending beyond the borders of Continental Spain into the following areas:

Europe: Portugal; Belgium (see Brabant and Flanders); France (see Besancon, Dole, Navarre, Provence and Rousillon); Italy (see Cagliari, Messina, Milan and Naples); Netherlands (see Gelderland, Holland, and United Provinces).

America: Bolivia, Chile, Colombia, Guatemala, Mexico and Peru.

Orient: Philippine Islands.

The Spanish and Spanish-American gold Doubloon was the most popular coin of its day. Most of the coinage was struck from gold mined in the American colonies.

After the Escudo-Real standard was abandoned about 1850, Spain joined the Latin Monetary Union and the first coin on the new standard was struck in 1870.

SWEDEN. Reference: Levin, Stockholm, 1887; Brunn Collection, Frankfurt, 1914; Gluck-Hesselblad, Stockholm, 1953.

This section in the catalogue is devoted to the coinage struck in Sweden proper. Additional coins of the Swedish Kings will be found under Esthonia, Latvia, Livonia and in Germany under Augsburg, Bremen and Verden, Elbing, Erfurt, Furth, Hesse-Cassel, Mayence, Nuremberg, Osnabruck, Pomerania, Stettin and Wurzburg.

Sweden was on the Ducat standard as late as 1868. After that, a brief coinage was made on the Latin Monetary Union and a Carolin or 10 Franc piece was struck from 1868 to 1872. The modern coinage of Sweden is based on that of the Scandinavian Monetary Union, to which Denmark and Norway also subscribed.

SWITZERLAND. Modern Swiss coinage is based on that of the Latin Monetary Union. In 1955, a new standard was introduced, but the coins that were then struck have not yet been released.

Switzerland, though small in area, has produced a body of coinage that for historical interest, variety of type and numis-

matic value, rivals that of any major power of the world, past or present.

VATICAN. Reference: Corpus Nummorum Italicorum by King Victor Emanuele III. Papal coinage closely follows Italian issues insofar as coinage standards are concerned.

PART III. AFRICA AND THE ORIENT

AFGHANISTAN. Reference: Wilson, London, 1841. Prior to 1896, the type, style and workmanship of the coins were similar to those of Persia and the neighboring Indian states. The first modern style coins were the Dinars of 1896. This new denomination introduced for the first time the arms of Afghanistan, of which the dominant motif is the throne room.

ANNAM. Reference: Schroeder, Paris, 1905. The coins are dated in Annamese years. Most coins also exist in silver and are struck from the same dies. This series maintains a great popularity in France.

ARAB-ASIAN EMPIRES. Reference: Berlin Museum, 1898, and British Museum, 1941, 1956 for Arab-Byzantine and Arab-Sassanian issues. The designation "Arab-Asian Empires" has been created especially for this book. Although they range over a vast expanse of earth, the coinages are basically similar in type, consisting mainly of native legends on each side of the coin. It was therefore felt that a single designation should encompass all such issues, except for those of Afghanistan, India, Persia and Turkey, which are catalogued separately.

Although it would have been possible to make a complete catalogue of the coins struck under each ruler (as has been done throughout this book), it was decided not to do so because all the coins look alike to the average Western eye (except for those trained in Oriental studies), and because the monotony of type and appearance remains unbroken over centuries of issue.

AUSTRALIA. Reference: Deacon, Melbourne, 1952. Mints and mint marks:—M for Melbourne; P for Perth; S for Sydney.

CEYLON. Reference: Codrington, Colombo, 1924.

CHINA. The fourteen coins listed are the only ones which can be regarded as authentic Chinese gold coins, and of these fourteen, only numbers 4, 5, 10, 11 and 12 circulated to any extent. The many other Chinese "gold coins" which exist are either gold impressions from dies for silver coins or are outright fantasies.

CYPRUS. Reference: Schlumberger, Paris, 1877. The gold coinage of Cyprus belongs to the series of the Crusader Kings.

EGYPT. Only 600 pieces were reported struck of number 21. Coins 22-29 exist in either reddish or greenish gold.

ETHIOPIA. Reference: Anzani, Rome, 1926. The earliest coins that appear in this book are those of the Axumite Kings of Ethiopia of about 300 A.D. This historical but little known coinage has been listed here since these coins are not included in the standard reference works on ancient coins. The ancient Kingdom of Axum was under Pagan rule until the period of Ousanas I, who converted to Christianity about 350 A.D.

GERMAN NEW GUINEA. The two gold coins of this colony have always been popular and in demand. 1500 specimens were struck of the 20 Mark piece and 2000 of the 10 Mark piece.

INDIA. References: Calcutta Museum, 1906; Delhi Museum, 1936; British Museum, 1892; Marsden, London, 1823; Meili Collection of Schulman, Amsterdam, 1910.

The coinage of the Mogul Emperors of Hindustan is the most extensive and varied of Indian coinages. The largest gold coins of the entire world were struck by these Emperors. The whereabouts of most of these large coins is now unknown, but they are all reported as having been seen in contemporary literature. The largest coin of all is the 200 Mohur piece of Shah Jahan. The actual coin was last reported seen in India in the early part of the 19th century, and a cast of the coin is now in the British Museum (see the back page of the dust jacket).

The Mogul Emperors also issued the famous set of Zodiac Mohurs. There are many variations of the Zodiac figures and the illustrations in this book are of typical examples.

JAPAN. Reference: Jacobs and Vermuele, New York, 1953. The first modern gold coins of Japan were allied to the U. S. gold standard but in 1897 the gold Yen was devalued by 50% and a new coinage was issued to mark the change.

JERUSALEM. Reference: Schlumberger, Paris, 1877.

MALTA. Reference: Schembri, London, 1910. The coinage of both Malta and Rhodes was produced by the same order of Grand Masters; until 1530 at Rhodes and afterward at Malta.

NETHERLANDS EAST INDIES. Reference: Netcher, Batavia, 1863; Bucknill, London, 1931; Scholten-Schulman, Amsterdam, 1953.

PERSIA. Reference: British Museum, 1887. It will be noted that the Shahs did not picture themselves on their coinage until recent times, the first portrait piece appearing in 1854.

RHODES. Reference: Schlumberger, Paris, 1877. Most of the coinage is of Venetian style and type.

SIAM. Reference: Le May, Bangkok, 1932. The conventional or standard gold coins are of far greater scarcity than the earlier bullet money.

SOUTH AFRICA. Reference: Kaplan, Germiston, 1950. Only 837 specimens were struck of the Burgers Pound of 1874. The ½ Pound of 1893 is very rare, as are also the English type Pounds and ½ Pounds of 1923 and 1924.

TUNIS. Reference: Monsieur V. G., Paris, 1943. The only 10 Franc piece that it is normally possible to obtain is dated 1891. All other dates are very rare.

TURKEY. Reference: British Museum, 1883. As is typical of the Arab-Asian Empires (which see) the coinage of the Ottoman Sultans was of the same general type over a period of about 400 years. It was, therefore, not felt necessary to describe the coinage of each Sultan, since such a catalogue would be more a chronological list of names than of coin types.

ZANZIBAR. The two gold coins are of extraordinary rarity. The author knows of only four specimens of the 5 Rial piece and only one of the 2½ Rial piece which was last noted in 1938. The coins were struck at the Brussels Mint.

Part I

....

AMERICA

North, Central and South America and the West Indies

ARGENTINA	DANISH WEST INDIES	NEWFOUNDLAND
BOLIVIA	DOMINICAN REPUBLIC	PARAGUAY
BRAZIL	ECUADOR	PERU
BRITISH COLUMBIA	GRENADA	SAINT MARTIN
BRITISH GUIANA	GUADELOUPE	SAINT VINCENT
CANADA	GUATEMALA	SALVADOR
CHILE	HONDURAS	TIERRA DEL FUEGO
COLOMBIA	JAMAICA	UNITED STATES OF AMERICA
COSTA RICA	MARTINIQUE	URUGUAY
CUBA	MEXICO	VENEZUELA

Radiant sun with human features. Rev. Arms.

1. 8 Escudos 1813. PTS mm. 1000.00
2. 8 Escudos 1826-35. RA mm. 275.00
3. 2 Escudos 1824, 25, 26. RA mm. .... * 125.00
4. 1 Escudo 1813. PTS mm. .... Unknown

Mountain with crossed flags below and with legend "Repub. Argentina Confederada R." Rev. Arms.

5. 8 Escudos 1838 .... 275.00

Similar Obv. but with legend "Republica Argentina R." Rev. Arms.

6. 8 Escudos 1840 .... Rare

Uniformed bust of General Rosas. Rev. Mountain.

7. 8 Escudos 1836 .... Rare

Uniformed bust of General Rosas. Rev. Arms.

8. 8 Escudos 1842 .... Rare
9. 2 Escudos 1842 .... * 150.00

Sun over mountain. Rev. Arms.

10. 2 Escudos 1843 .... 100.00

Shield. Rev. Arms.

11. 8 Escudos 1845 .... 600.00

Liberty head. Rev. Arms.

12. 5 Pesos 1881-89, 96 .... * 25.00
13. 2½ Pesos 1881, 84 .... 200.00

A. Spanish Kings of —
CHARLES III, 1759-1788

Bust. Rev. Arms.

1. 8 Escudos 1779-88 .... 125.00
2. 4 Escudos 1779-87 .... * 125.00
3. 2 Escudos 1778-88 .... 40.00
4. 1 Escudo 1780-87 .... 40.00

CHARLES IV, 1788-1808
Bust of the previous King, Charles III. Rev. Arms.

5. 8 Escudos 1789, 90 .... 175.00
6. 4 Escudos .... Unknown
7. 2 Escudos 1789, 90 .... 75.00
8. 1 Escudo 1789, 90 .... 50.00

Laureate bust. Rev. Arms.

9. 8 Escudos 1791 .... * 200.00
10. 4 Escudos 1791 .... 200.00
11. 2 Escudos 1791 .... 250.00
12. 1 Escudo 1791 .... 75.00

Plain bust. Rev. Arms.

13. 8 Escudos 1791-1808 .... 100.00
14. 4 Escudos 1791-1808 .... 75.00
15. 2 Escudos 1791-1808 .... 35.00
16. 1 Escudo 1791-1808 .... 25.00

FERDINAND VII, 1808-1833
Uniformed bust. Rev. Arms.

17. 8 Escudos 1809 .... Rare

Laureate head. Rev. Arms.

18. 8 Escudos 1817, 1822, 23, 24 .... * 150.00
19. 1 Escudo 1822, 23 .... 50.00

B. Republic of —

Uniformed bust of Bolivar. Rev. Arms.

20.	8 Escudos 1831-40	..............................*	100.00
21.	4 Escudos 1834	....	500.00
22.	2 Escudos 1834	....	75.00
23.	1 Escudo 1831-39	....	35.00
24.	½ Escudo 1839, 40	....	30.00

Small laureate head of Bolivar to right, his name below. Rev. Arms.

25.	8 Escudos 1841-47	..........................*	100.00
26.	4 Escudos 1841	....	750.00
27.	2 Escudos 1841	....	350.00
28.	1 Escudo 1841. 42	....	50.00
29.	½ Escudo 1841-47	....	25.00

Plain head of Bolivar to left. Rev. Arms.

30.	8 Escudos 1851	....	350.00
31.	1 Escudo 1851	......................Unknown	

Laureate head of Bolivar to left, his name on neck. Rev. Arms.

32.	8 Escudos 1852	....	350.00

Laureate head of Bolivar to right, his name on neck. Rev. Arms.

33.	8 Escudos 1852-56	....	125.00
34.	1 Escudo 1852-56	..........................*	30.00
35.	½ Escudo 1852-56	....	22.50

Arms. Rev. Value, weight and fineness in wreath.

36.	1 Onza 1868	..........................*	Rare
37.	1 Escudo 1868	....	200.00
38.	½ Escudo 1868	....	75.00

Special Issue of 1952

These coins commemorate the revolution of October 31, 1952. The values are expressed by weight in grams. All coins are dated 1952. The reverses of all coins show the National arms. The obverses are as follows:

39.	35	Grams. Head of Villaroel	85.00
40.	14	Grams. Head of Busch	40.00
41.	7	Grams. Miner	25.00
42.	3½	Grams. Head of worker	15.00

BRAZIL

A. Dutch Colony of —

Monogram and value. Rev. Name and date. Square necessity coins struck by the Dutch West India Company.

1.	12 Guilders 1645, 46	....	1250.00
2.	6 Guilders 1645, 46	..........................*	1000.00
3.	3 Guilders 1645, 46	..........................*	750.00

B. Portuguese Kings of —

JOHN IV, 1640-1656 AND ALFONSO VI, 1656-1683

Crown bearing numeral of value counterstamped on Obv. of Portuguese coins or on contemporary Spanish coins.

4.	4 Cruzados 1640-83	..........................*	750.00
5.	2 Cruzados 1640-83	....	750.00
6.	1 Cruzado 1640-83	....	1000.00

Three counterstamps on the Cruzado coinage of Portugal; one being the value in Reis, the second being the value in Cruzados, and the third being a crowned globe.

7.	4 Cruzados—4400 Reis 1640-83	....	750.00
8.	2 Cruzados—2200 Reis 1640-83	..........................*	750.00
9.	1 Cruzado—1100 Reis 1640-83	....	1000.00

BRAZIL (cont'd)

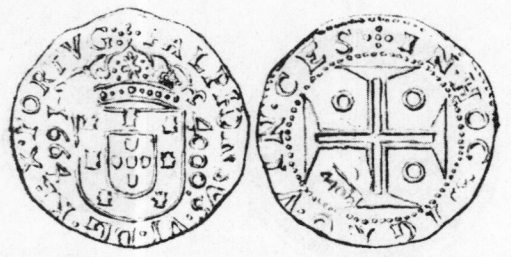

Crowned value counterstamped on the Cruzado coinage of Portugal.

10.	4400 Reis 1640-83	...............................*	750.00
11.	2200 Reis 1640-83	....	750.00
12.	1100 Reis 1640-83	....	1000.00

PETER II, 1683-1707

Arms. Rev. Plain cross in quadrilobe.

13.	4000 Reis 1695-1700. No mm.	.................*	65.00
14.	4000 Reis 1702. P mm.	....	250.00
15.	2000 Reis 1695-1700. No mm.	....	65.00
16.	1000 Reis. 1696-1700. No mm.	....	40.00

Arms. Rev. Cross of Jerusalem

17.	4000 Reis 1703-07. R mm.	.................*	150.00
18.	2000 Reis 1703. R mm.	....	350.00

JOHN V, 1707-1750

Arms. Rev. Cross of Jerusalem

19.	20,000 Reis 1724-27. M mm.	....	300.00
20.	10,000 Reis 1724-27. M mm.	....	150.00
21.	4000 Reis 1707-27. R mm.	....	65.00
22.	4000 Reis 1714-27. B mm.	....	65.00
23.	4000 Reis 1724-27. M mm.	....	150.00
24.	2000 Reis 1723, 25, 26. R mm.	....	75.00
25.	2000 Reis 1714, 15, 16. B mm.	.............*	40.00
26.	2000 Reis 1724-27. M mm.	....	150.00
27.	1000 Reis 1708, 26. R mm.	....	125.00
28.	1000 Reis 1714-25. B mm.	....	200.00
29.	1000 Reis 1724-27. M mm.	....	150.00

Crowned name and value. Rev. Cross of Jerusalem.

30.	400 Reis 1730. R mm.	....	300.00
31.	400 Reis 1725, 26. M mm.	.......................*	200.00

Arms. Rev. Plain cross in quadrilobe. Without mintmark but struck at Lisbon for the state of Maranhao.

32.	4000 Reis 1749	....	75.00
33.	2000 Reis 1749	....	40.00
34.	1000 Reis 1749	....	35.00

Laureate head. Rev. Arms. These coins do not show the value but they correspond to the Spanish Gold Escudos of the period. The 12,800 Reis piece is equivalent to the 8 Escudos or Doubloon.

35.	12,800 Reis 1727-33. R mm.	....	250.00
36.	12,800 Reis 1727-32. B mm.	....	250.00
37.	12,800 Reis 1727-33. M mm.	....	200.00
38.	6400 Reis 1727-50. R mm.	....	75.00
39.	6400 Reis 1727-50. B mm.	.................*	75.00
40.	6400 Reis 1732, 33, 34. M mm.	....	300.00
41.	3200 Reis 1727-49. R mm.	....	175.00
42.	3200 Reis 1727-50. B mm.	....	250.00
43.	3200 Reis 1729-33. M mm.	....	200.00
44.	1600 Reis 1727-36. R mm.	....	100.00
45.	1600 Reis 1727-50. B mm.	....	125.00
46.	1600 Reis 1727-33. M mm.	....	100.00
47.	800 Reis 1727-34. R mm.	....	40.00
48.	800 Reis 1727-51. B mm.	....	150.00
49.	800 Reis 1727-34. M mm.	....	50.00

Laureate head. Rev. Crown over date.

50.	400 Reis 1734. R mm.	.....................*	30.00
51.	400 Reis 1730-34. M mm.	....	30.00

JOSEPH I, 1750-1777

Laureate head. Rev. Arms.

52.	6400 Reis 1751-77. R mm.	....	60.00
53.	6400 Reis 1751-77. B mm.	....	60.00
54.	3200 Reis 1756-72. R mm.	.................*	125.00
55.	3200 Reis 1752-73. B mm.	....	200.00
56.	1600 Reis 1752, 63, 72. R mm.	....	100.00
57.	1600 Reis 1754-77. B mm.	....	175.00
58.	800 Reis 1752, 63. R mm.	....	100.00
59.	800 Reis 1752-77. B mm.	....	125.00

Arms. Rev. Cross in quadrilobe. Without mintmark but struck at Rio.

60.	4000 Reis 1751-77	.....................*	50.00
61.	2000 Reis 1752-73	....	35.00
62.	1000 Reis 1749-74	....	30.00

MARY I AND PETER III, 1777-1786

Conjoined busts. Rev. Arms.

63.	6400 Reis 1777-86. R mm. ....*		65.00
64.	6400 Reis 1777-86. B mm.		65.00
65.	3200 Reis 1780-86. B mm.		150.00
66.	1600 Reis 1780-84. B mm.		175.00
67.	800 Reis 1782, 86. B mm.		175.00

Arms. Rev. Cross in quadrilobe. Without mintmark but struck at both Rio and Lisbon.

68.	4000 Reis 1778-86	50.00
69.	2000 Reis 1778, 82	40.00
70.	1000 Reis 1778-82	30.00

MARY I, 1786-1805

Bust with widow's veil. Rev. Arms.

71.	6400 Reis 1786-89. R mm.	65.00
72.	6400 Reis 1787-90. B mm. ....*	65.00

Bust in decorative headdress. Rev. Arms.

73.	6400 Reis 1789-1805. R mm. ....*	65.00
74.	6400 Reis 1790-1804. B mm.	65.00

Arms. Rev. Cross in quadrilobe. Without mintmark but struck at both Rio and Bahia.

75.	4000 Reis 1787-1805	50.00
76.	2000 Reis 1787-92, 93 ....*	75.00
77.	1000 Reis 1787	30.00

JOHN, PRINCE REGENT. 1805-1818

Laureate bust. Rev. Arms.

78.	6400 Reis 1805-17. R mm.	65.00

Arms. Rev. Cross in quadrilobe. Without mintmark but struck at both Rio and Bahia.

79.	4000 Reis 1805-17	50.00

JOHN VI, 1818-1822

Laureate bust. Rev. Arms.

80.	6400 Reis 1818-22. R mm.	250.00

Arms in wreath. Rev. Crosss in quadrilobe. Pieces from the Rio Mint have the date between two small flowers; those from the Bahia Mint have the date between two small crosses.

81.	4000 Reis 1818-22. Rio Mint ....*	65.00
82.	4000 Reis 1819, 20. Bahia Mint	125.00

Crudely shaped rectangular gold bars, 1805-1822, issued at different assay offices in Brazil and punched with various stamps including arms on globe, date, weight and fineness.

83.	Gold Bar 1805-22	600.00

C. Emperors of —

PETER I, 1823-1831

Laureate head. Rev. Arms. This coin was not placed in circulation.

84.	6400 Reis 1822	2000.00

Bust in naval uniform. Rev. Arms.

85.	6400 Reis 1822-30. R mm.	250.00
86.	6400 Reis 1825-28. B mm.	250.00
87.	4000 Reis 1823-27. R mm. ....*	175.00
88.	4000 Reis 1825-28. B mm.	175.00

PETER II, 1831-1889

Child head. Rev. Arms. The 10,000 Reis piece is without the mark of value.

BRAZIL (cont'd)

89.　6400 Reis 1832, 33 .... 125.00
89a.　6400 Reis 1832. "Azevedo" below bust 200.00
90.　4000 Reis 1832, 33 .... 275.00
90a.　4000 Reis 1832. "Azevedo" below bust 1000.00
91.　10,000 Reis 1833-40 ....* 100.00

Bust in naval uniform. Rev. Arms. Without the mark of value.

92.　10,000 Reis 1841-48 .... 125.00

Bust in Coronation uniform. Rev. Arms. Without the mark of value.

93.　20,000 Reis 1849, 50, 51 ....* 125.00
94.　10,000 Reis 1849, 50, 51 .... 100.00

Bearded head. Rev. Arms. Without the mark of value.

95.　20,000 Reis 1851-89 .... 75.00
96.　10,000 Reis 1853-89 .... 50.00
97.　5000 Reis 1854-59 ....* 35.00

D. Republic of —

Liberty head. Rev. The Stars of the Southern Cross.

98.　20,000 Reis 1889-1922 .... 150.00

Liberty head. Rev. Large star.

99.　10,000 Reis 1889-1922 .... 150.00

BRITISH COLUMBIA

Crown. Rev. Value and date. These coins were not placed in circulation.

1.　20 Dollars 1862 .... 3500.00
2.　10 Dollars 1862 ....* 3000.00

BRITISH GUIANA

Brazilian gold coins of the period 1727-1804 counterstamped ED (Essequibo and Demerara) and with or without other counter-stamps.)

1.　6400 Reis 1727-1804 .... 150.00

CANADA

EDWARD VII, 1901-1910

Head. Rev. St. George. As the English Pound but with the distinguishing mintmark C on ground below horse.

1.　1 Pound 1908, 09, 10 .... 125.00

GEORGE V, 1910-1936

Head. Rev. St. George. As the English Pound but with the distinguishing mintmark C on ground below horse.

2.　1 Pound 1911-19 .... 75.00

Crowned head. Rev. Arms.

3.　10 Dollars 1912, 13, 14 .... 60.00
4.　5 Dollars 1912, 13, 14 .... 30.00

CHILE

A. Spanish Kings of —

PHILIP V, 1700-1746

Bust. Rev. Arms. This issue was not placed in circulation. The last two coins were struck during the reign of Ferdinand VI.

1.　8 Escudos 1744 .... Rare
2.　4 Escudos 1744 .... Rare
3.　2 Escudos 1758 .... Rare
4.　1 Escudo 1754 .... Rare

FERDINAND VI, 1746-1760

Small bust. Rev. Arms.

5.　8 Escudos 1750-60 ....* 150.00
6.　4 Escudos 1749-52 .... 175.00
7.　1 Escudo 1754, 58, 59 .... 200.00

Large bust. Rev. Arms.

8.　8 Escudos 1760 .... 175.00

CHARLES III, 1759-1788

Bust of the previous King, Ferdinand VI. Rev. Arms.

9.	8 Escudos 1760-63	.........................*	......	150.00
10.	1 Escudo 1761, 62	....		175.00

Bust. Rev. Arms without value.

11.	8 Escudos 1764-72	....		125.00
12.	4 Escudos 1763	.........................*	.....	200.00
13.	1 Escudo 1763, 64, 66	....		100.00

Bust. Rev. Arms with value.

14.	8 Escudos 1772-88	.........................*	......	100.00
15.	4 Escudos 1775-88	....		150.00
16.	2 Escudos 1783, 87	....		100.00
17.	1 Escudo 1772-87	....		40.00

CHARLES IV, 1788-1808

Bust of the previous King, Charles III with title as "Carol IV." Rev. Arms.

18.	8 Escudos 1789, 90	.........................*	......	125.00
19.	4 Escudos 1789, 90	....		150.00
20.	1 Escudo 1790	....		75.00

Bust of the previous King, Charles III with title as "Carol IIII."

21.	8 Escudos 1791-1808	.........................*	......	100.00
22.	4 Escudos 1791	....		250.00
23.	2 Escudos 1792-1808	....		40.00
24.	1 Escudo 1792-1808	....		30.00

Bust. Rev. Arms.

25.	4 Escudos 1795-1808	....	100.00
26.	2 Escudos 1792-1808	....	50.00
27.	1 Escudo 1792-1808	....	35.00

FERDINAND VII, 1808-1833

Large uniformed bust. Rev. Arms.

28.	8 Escudos 1808-11	....	125.00

Bust of the previous King, Charles IV. Rev. Arms.

29.	8 Escudos 1812-17	....		100.00
30.	4 Escudos 1810-17	.........................*	.....	75.00
31.	2 Escudos 1813-17	....		100.00
32.	1 Escudo 1811-17	....		30.00

B. Republic of —

Sun, mountains and volcanos. Rev. Crossed flags.

33.	8 Escudos 1818-34	....		100.00
34.	4 Escudos 1824-34	....		100.00
35.	2 Escudos 1824-34	.........................*	.....	60.00
36.	1 Escudo 1824-34	....		35.00

Hand on the book of the Constitution. Rev. Arms.

37.	8 Escudos 1835-38	.........................*	......	100.00
38.	4 Escudos 1836, 37	....		200.00
39.	2 Escudos 1837, 38	....		50.00
40.	1 Escudo 1838	....		40.00

Liberty as Pallas Athene standing at altar. Rev. Arms.

41. 8 Escudos 1839-51 ....*...... 100.00
42. 4 Escudos 1839, 41 .... 500.00
43. 2 Escudos 1839-51 .... 60.00
44. 1 Escudo 1839-51 .... 35.00

Liberty standing at altar. Rev. Arms.

45. 10 Pesos 1853-90 ....*...... 40.00
46. 5 Pesos 1858-73 .... 25.00
47. 2 Pesos 1857-75 .... 15.00

Liberty standing at altar. Rev. Value in wreath.

48. 1 Peso 1860-73 .... 12.50

Head of Liberty wearing cap. Rev. Arms.

49. 10 Pesos 1895 ....*...... 27.50
50. 5 Pesos 1895, 96 .... 17.50

Draped Liberty head with coiled hair. Rev. Arms.

51. 20 Pesos 1896-1917 ....*...... 40.00
52. 10 Pesos 1896, 98, 1901 ....*..... 25.00
53. 5 Pesos 1898, 1900 .... 22.50

Liberty head with coiled hair. Rev. Arms. Two values appear on these coins.

54. 100 Pesos—10 Condores 1926-55 ....*...... 47.50
55. 50 Pesos— 5 Condores 1926 .... 27.50
56. 20 Pesos— 2 Condores 1926 ....*...... 20.00

COLOMBIA

A. Spanish Kings of —

PHILIP IV, 1621-1665
Arms. Rev. Cross. Crude Cob type.

1. 2 Escudos ND. NR mm. 75.00

FERDINAND VI, 1746-1760

Bust. Rev. Arms.

2. 8 Escudos 1756-59. NR mm. 150.00
3. 8 Escudos 1758, 59. P or PN mm. 175.00
4. 4 Escudos 1757-59. NR mm. 150.00
5. 4 Escudos 1758-60. P or PN mm. 150.00
6. 2 Escudos 1756-59. NR mm. ....*.... 50.00
7. 2 Escudos 1758-61. P or PN mm. 50.00
8. 1 Escudo 1757-59. NR mm. 40.00
9. 1 Escudo 1758, 59. P or PN mm. 50.00

CHARLES III, 1759-1788

Bust of the previous King, Ferdinand VI. Rev. Arms.

10. 8 Escudos 1759-62. NR mm. 200.00
11. 8 Escudos 1760-71. P or PN mm. 150.00
12. 4 Escudos 1760. NR mm. 250.00
13. 4 Escudos 1760-69. P or PN mm. 125.00
14. 2 Escudos 1760-62. NR mm. 60.00
15. 2 Escudos 1760-71. P or PN mm. ....*.... 40.00
16. 1 Escudo. NR mm. ....Unknown
17. 1 Escudo 1760-69. P or PN mm. 35.00

Bust with name as "Carolus." Rev. Arms without value. This type was not struck at the Popayan Mint.

18. 8 Escudos 1763-71. NR mm. 125.00
19. 4 Escudos 1769-71. NR mm. 250.00
20. 2 Escudos 1762-71. NR mm. ....*.... 35.00
21. 1 Escudo 1767. NR mm. 125.00

Bust with name as "Carol." Rev. Arms with value.

22. 8 Escudos 1772-89. NR mm. 100.00
23. 8 Escudos 1772-89. P or PN mm. 100.00
24. 4 Escudos 1775-79. NR mm. 125.00
25. 4 Escudos 1771-86. P or PN mm. 85.00
26. 2 Escudos 1772-89. NR mm. 30.00
27. 2 Escudos 1771-89. P or PN mm. ....*.... 30.00
28. 1 Escudo 1772-89. NR mm. 25.00
29. 1 Escudo 1772-89. P or PN mm. 20.00

CHARLES IV, 1788-1808

Bust of the previous King, Charles III. Rev. Arms.

30.	8 Escudos 1789-91. NR mm.		125.00
31.	8 Escudos 1789-91. P or PN mm.		125.00
32.	4 Escudos 1789, 90. NR mm.		125.00
33.	4 Escudos 1789, 90. P or PN mm.		100.00
34.	2 Escudos 1789, 90. NR mm.		50.00
35.	2 Escudos 1789-91. P or PN mm.	*	40.00
36.	1 Escudo 1790. NR mm.		40.00
37.	1 Escudo 1789, 90. P or PN mm.		30.00

Bust. Rev. Arms.

38.	8 Escudos 1791-1808. NR mm.		100.00
39.	8 Escudos 1791-1808. P or PN mm.		100.00
40.	4 Escudos 1792-1807. NR mm.		75.00
41.	4 Escudos 1792-1801. P or PN mm.		100.00
42.	2 Escudos 1791-1804. NR mm.		35.00
43.	2 Escudos 1791-1805. P or PN mm.	*	35.00
44.	1 Escudo 1792-1808. NR mm.		20.00
45.	1 Escudo 1792-1808. P or PN mm.		20.00

FERDINAND VII, 1808-1833

Bust of the previous King, Charles IV. Rev. Arms.

46.	8 Escudos 1808-20. NR mm.		100.00
47.	8 Escudos 1808-20. P or PN mm.	*	100.00
48.	4 Escudos 1818, 19. NR mm.		100.00
49.	2 Escudos 1808-17. NR mm.		30.00
50.	2 Escudos 1817-19. P or PN mm.		35.00
51.	1 Escudo 1808-20. NR mm.		20.00
52.	1 Escudo 1808-19. P or PN mm.		20.00

B. Republic of —

I. Coinage of the Republic of Colombia

Liberty head. Rev. Fascses within a double cornucopia and above, "Bogota" or "Popayan," the place of minting.

53.	8 Escudos 1822-37. Bogota.		90.00
54.	8 Escudos 1822-36. Popayan.		90.00
55.	4 Escudos 1826. Bogota.		300.00
56.	2 Escudos 1822-37. Bogota.		25.00
57.	1 Escudo 1822-37. Bogota.		15.00
58.	1 Escudo 1823-36. Popayan.	*	15.00
59.	1 Peso 1825-36. Bogota.		12.50

II. Coinage of the Republic of New Granada

Draped Liberty head. Rev. Arms and "Bogota" or "Popayan"

60.	16 Pesos 1837-49. Bogotoa.		90.00
61.	16 Pesos 1837-46. Popayan.		90.00
62.	2 Pesos 1837-46. Popayan.	*	20.00
63.	1 Peso 1837-49. Bogota.	*	12.50

Plain Liberty head. Rev. Arms with the value of the coins expressed by their weight in grams.

64.	16 Pesos 1849-53. Bogotoa. 25.8064 grams.	*	200.00
65.	10 Pesos 1854-57. Bogota. 16.400 grams.		150.00
66.	10 Pesos 1853. Popayan. 16.400 grams.		150.00
67.	2 Pesos 1849, 51. Bogota. 3.2258 grams.		100.00

Liberty head and "Nueva Granada." Rev. Value in wreath with B or P as mint marks.

68.	5 Pesos 1856, 57, 58. B mm.	*	75.00
69.	2 Pesos 1856, 57, 58. P mm.		50.00
70.	1 Peso 1856, 58. B mm.		100.00

Liberty head and "Republica de la Nueva Granada." Rev. Arms with place of minting below.

71.	10 Pesos 1857, 58. Bogota.	*	250.00
72.	10 Pesos 1856, 57, 58. Popayan.		150.00

III. Coinage of the Granadine Confederation

Liberty head. Rev. Arms and place of minting.

73.	20 Pesos 1859. Bogota.		Rare
74.	10 Pesos 1859-61. Bogota.	*	100.00
75.	10 Pesos 1858-62. Popayan.		150.00
76.	5 Pesos 1859. Popayan.		450.00

Liberty head. Rev. Value in wreath.

77.	5 Pesos 1862. Medellin.		Rare
78.	2 Pesos 1859, 60. Popayan.	*	40.00
79.	1 Peso 1862. Medellin.		100.00

IV. Coinage of the United States of Colombia

Liberty head with "Colombia" only in legend. Rev. Value and date in wreath. Medellin Mint.

COLOMBIA (cont'd)

80. 5 Pesos 1862, 63, 64. . . . . * 250.00
81. 1 Peso 1863, 64. . . . . 50.00

Liberty head with "Estados Unidos de Colombia" in legend. Rev. Value in wreath. Medellin Mint.

82. 5 Pesos 1863. . . . . * . . . . . . Rare
83. 2 Pesos 1863. . . . . 50.00
84. 1 Peso 1863. . . . . 40.00

Liberty head. Rev. Arms and place of minting.

85. 20 Pesos 1862-77. Bogota. 150.00
86. 20 Pesos 1862-75. Popayan. 150.00
87. 20 Pesos 1868-72. Medellin. 150.00
88. 10 Pesos 1862, 63. Bogota. 50.00
89. 10 Pesos 1863-67. Popayan. 50.00
90. 10 Pesos 1863-76. Medellin. . . . . * 50.00
91. 5 Pesos 1885. Medellin . . . . Rare
92. 2 Pesos 1871-76. Medellin. 12.50
93. 1 Peso 1872, 73. Medellin. 12.50

Liberty head. Rev. Condor and place of minting.

94. 1 Peso 1872. Medellin. 17.50
95. 1 Peso 1871-78. Bogota. . . . . * 12.50

V. Coinage of the Republic of Colombia (again)

Workman chipping at rock. Rev. Arms.

96. 5 Pesos 1913-19. . . . . 22.50
97. 2½ Pesos 1913. . . . . 75.00

Large head of Bolivar. Rev. Arms.

98. 10 Pesos 1919-24. . . . . 50.00
99. 5 Pesos 1919-24. . . . . 22.50
100. 2½ Pesos 1919, 20. . . . . * 25.00

Small head of Bolivar. Rev. Arms.

101. 5 Pesos 1924-30. . . . . * 25.00
102. 2½ Pesos 1924-28. . . . . 25.00

COSTA RICA

Sun and five mountain peaks. Rev. Tree. The 2, 1 and ½ Escudo pieces come with or without a counterstamped lion.

1. 8 Escudos 1828, 33, 37. . . . . 250.00
2. 4 Escudos 1828-50. . . . . 100.00
3. 2 Escudos 1828-50. . . . . * 27.50
4. 1 Escudo 1825-49. . . . . 20.00
5. ½ Escudo 1825-49. . . . . 12.50

Small star on larger radiant star. Rev. Tree.

6. 1 Escudo 1842. . . . . 50.00

Indian leaning against column. Rev. Arms.

7. ½ Onza 1850. . . . . * 75.00
8. 2 Escudos 1850-63. . . . . 25.00
9. 1 Escudo 1850-55. . . . . 20.00
10. ½ Escudo 1850-64. . . . . 12.50

Arms. Rev. Value spelled out.

11. 10 Pesos 1870, 71, 72. Large size. 40.00
12. 10 Pesos 1876. Small size. 75.00
13. 5 Pesos 1867-70. Large size. 25.00
14. 5 Pesos 1873, 75. Small size. 35.00
15. 2 Pesos 1866-68. Large size. . . . . * 15.00
16. 2 Pesos 1876. Small size. 250.00
17. 1 Peso 1864-71. Large size. 12.50
18. 1 Peso 1871, 72. Small size. 15.00

Arms. Rev. Value expressed in numerals.

19. 20 Pesos 1873. . . . . 750.00
20. 5 Pesos 1873. . . . . * 150.00

Head of Columbus. Rev. Arms.

21. 20 Colones 1897-1900. . . . . 60.00
22. 10 Colones 1897-1900. . . . . * 27.50
23. 5 Colones 1899, 1900. . . . . 17.50
24. 2 Colones 1897-1928. . . . . 12.50

CUBA

Head of Marti. Rev. Arms.

1.	20 Pesos 1915, 16.	85.00
2.	10 Pesos 1915, 16.	40.00
3.	5 Pesos 1915, 16. ....*	22.50
4.	4 Pesos 1915, 16. ....*	22.50
5.	2 Pesos 1915, 16. ....*	15.00
6.	1 Peso 1915, 16.	22.50

DANISH WEST INDIES

(Now the U. S. Virgin Islands.)

Head of Christian IX of Denmark. Rev. Seated female. Two values appear on these coins.

1.	10 Daler—50 Francs 1904.	100.00
2.	4 Daler—20 Francs 1904, 05. ....*......	37.50

DOMINICAN REPUBLIC

Head of Trujillo. Rev. Arms. On the 25th year of his rule.

1.	30 Pesos 1955.	80.00

ECUADOR

Liberty head. Rev. Sun over two mountain peaks. Issued while Ecuador was part of Colombia.

1.	2 Escudos 1833-35.	60.00
2.	1 Escudo 1833-35.	35.00

Liberty head. Rev. Sun and Zodiac over three mountain peaks.

3.	8 Escudos 1838-43.	175.00
4.	4 Escudos 1836-41. ....*......	75.00

Head of Bolivar to right. Rev. Arms.

5.	8 Escudos 1844.	Rare

Larger head of Bolivar to left. Rev. Flag-draped arms, the poles showing below.

6.	8 Escudos 1845.	300.00

Type as above but the flagpoles do not show below the arms.

7.	8 Escudos 1845.	350.00

Head of Bolivar. Rev. Flag-draped oval arms.

8.	8 Escudos 1847-56.	175.00

Head of Bolivar. Rev. Arms.

9.	50 Francs 1862.	Unique

Head of General Sucre. Rev. Arms.

10.	10 Sucres 1899, 1900.	25.00

Head of Bolivar. Rev. Arms.

11.	1 Condor 1928.	50.00

GRENADA

Gold coins of Brazil counterstamped three times along the outer edge of the obverse with a G and with or without a plugged hole in the center.

1.	6400 Reis 1727-1804.	175.00

GUADELOUPE

Gold coins of Brazil or Portugal counterstamped with a "G"
(plain or crowned) and with or without a fleur-de-lis or "82.10."

1. 82 Livres, 10 Sous 1727-1804 . . . . 100.00

GUATEMALA

A. Spanish Kings of —

PHILIP V, 1700-1746
Bust. Rev. Arms.

1. 8 Escudos 1734 . . . . Rare

FERDINAND VI, 1746-1760

Crude bust of the previous King, Philip V. Rev. Arms.

2. 8 Escudos 1750 . . . . 500.00
3. 1 Escudo 1751 . . . . 250.00

Bust. Rev. Arms with star hanging at bottom.

4. 8 Escudos 1754, 55 . . . . * 500.00
5. 1 Escudo 1755 . . . . 250.00

Bust. Rev. Arms with the Golden Fleece hanging at bottom.

6. 8 Escudos 1756, 57 . . . . * 500.00
7. 1 Escudo 1757 . . . . 250.00

CHARLES III, 1759-1788
Crude small bust. Rev. Arms.

8. 8 Escudos 1761 . . . . Rare

Crude large bust. Rev. Arms without value.

9. 8 Escudos 1765, 68 . . . . 350.00

Normal style bust. Rev. Arms with value.

10. 8 Escudos 1778-87 . . . . * 250.00
11. 4 Escudos 1778, 83 . . . . 400.00
12. 2 Escudos 1783, 85 . . . . 150.00
13. 1 Escudo 1778 . . . . 150.00

CHARLES IV, 1788-1808

Bust of the previous King, Charles III. Rev. Arms.

14. 8 Escudos 1789, 90 . . . . * 250.00
15. 4 Escudos 1789 . . . . 500.00
16. 2 Escudos . . . . Unknown
17. 1 Escudo 1789, 90, 91 . . . . 100.00

Bust. Rev. Arms.

18. 8 Escudos 1794, 97, 1801 . . . . * 250.00
19. 4 Escudos 1794, 97, 1801 . . . . 350.00
20. 2 Escudos 1794 . . . . 200.00
21. 1 Escudo 1794, 97, 1801 . . . . 150.00

FERDINAND VII, 1808-1833

Laureate head. Rev. Arms.

22. 8 Escudos 1808, 11, 17 . . . . 150.00
23. 4 Escudos 1813, 17 . . . . * 125.00
24. 2 Escudos 1817 . . . . 75.00
25. 1 Escudo 1817 . . . . 65.00

B. Republic of —

Sun over five mountain peaks. Rev. Tree.

GUATEMALA (cont'd)

26.	8 Escudos 1824, 25.	1000.00
27.	4 Escudos 1824, 25.	750.00
28.	2 Escudos 1825-47. ....*	40.00
29.	1 Escudo 1824.	50.00
30.	½ Escudo 1824-43.	20.00

Head of Carrera with title as "PTE" (President). Rev. Arms.

31.	16 Pesos 1863. Size 31½ millimetres.	Rare
32.	16 Pesos 1865. Size 33 millimetres. ....*	Rare
33.	8 Pesos 1864.	200.00
34.	4 Pesos 1861, 62.	75.00
35.	2 Pesos 1859.	25.00

Obv. similar to above. Rev. Value in wreath.

36.	1 Peso 1859, 60.	12.50
37.	4 Reales 1859-64.	9.00

Head of Carrera with title as "Fundator" (Founder). Rev. Arms.

38.	20 Pesos 1869.	100.00
39.	16 Pesos 1867, 69.	150.00
40.	10 Pesos 1869.	60.00
41.	5 Pesos 1869. ....*	25.00
42.	4 Pesos 1866, 68, 69.	50.00

Liberty head with flowing hair. Rev. Arms.

43.	20 Pesos 1877, 78.	750.00
44.	5 Pesos 1872-78. ....*	50.00

Liberty head with coiled hair. Rev. Arms. These coins were not placed in circulation.

45.	10 Pesos 1894.	750.00
46.	5 Pesos 1894. ....*	750.00

Quetzal on column. Rev. Arms.

47.	20 Quetzals 1926.	125.00
48.	10 Quetzals 1926.	60.00
49.	5 Quetzals 1926. ....*	32.50

HONDURAS

Arms. Rev. Tree. With plain or reeded edges. These coins were not placed in circulation.

1.	10 Pesos 1871. ....*	1000.00
2.	5 Pesos 1871.	1000.00

Liberty head. Rev. Arms. Most coins have overstruck dates.

3.	20 Pesos 1888.	Rare
4.	10 Pesos 1889.	Rare
5.	5 Pesos 1883-1908. ....*	150.00
6.	1 Peso 1887-1922. ....*	50.00

JAMAICA

Gold coins of Spain or Spanish-American Mints counterstamped GR (George III of England) in a circular depression.

1.	8 Escudos 1732-1820.	500.00
2.	4 Escudos 1733-1820.	500.00
3.	2 Escudos 1733-1820. ....*	300.00
4.	1 Escudo 1733-1820.	250.00
5.	½ Escudo 1744-1820.	200.00

MARTINIQUE

Gold coins of Brazil or Portugal counterstamped with "22" or "20" (for karats) and a small eagle.

1.	6400 Reis 1727-1804. ....*	125.00
2.	3200 Reis 1727-1786.	200.00
3.	4000 Reis 1707-1817.	75.00
4.	1000 Reis 1752-1787.	50.00
5.	400 Reis 1725-1796.	50.00
6.	½ Escudo 1752-1796.	50.00

MEXICO

A. Spanish Kings of —

(All coins are from the Mexico City Mint, unless otherwise noted)

CHARLES II, 1665-1700
Arms. Rev. Cross. Cob type.

1.	8 Escudos ND (1665-1700)	275.00
2.	2 Escudos 1695	175.00

PHILIP V, 1700-1746

Arms. Rev. Cross.

3. 8 Escudos 1720-31. Cob type .... * 175.00
4. 8 Escudos 1712. Modern type 400.00

Bust. Rev. Arms.

5. 8 Escudos 1732-47 .... 175.00
6. 4 Escudos 1732-46 .... 175.00
7. 2 Escudos 1732-46 .... 60.00
8. 1 Escudo 1732-46 .... * 40.00

LOUIS I, 1724
Arms. Rev. Cross. Cob type.

9. 8 Escudos ND (1724) 750.00

FERDINAND VI, 1746-1760

Large bust. Rev. Arms.

10. 8 Escudos 1747 .... * 200.00
11. 4 Escudos 1747 .... 500.00
12. 2 Escudos 1747 .... 250.00
13. 1 Escudo 1747 .... 125.00

Small bust in high relief. Rev. Arms. The value does not appear on the coins dated from 1752-56.

14. 8 Escudos 1748-56 .... 150.00
15. 4 Escudos 1748-56 .... * 300.00
16. 2 Escudos 1748-56 .... 75.00
17. 1 Escudo 1748-56 .... 50.00

Re-designed bust in lower relief. Rev. Arms.

18. 8 Escudos 1757-59 .... 175.00
19. 4 Escudos 1757-59 .... * 300.00
20. 2 Escudos 1757-59 .... 75.00
21. 1 Escudo 1757-59 .... 50.00

CHARLES III, 1759-1788

Small bust. Rev. Arms.

22. 8 Escudos 1760, 61 .... * 175.00
23. 4 Escudos 1760, 61 .... 400.00
24. 2 Escudos 1760, 61 .... 100.00
25. 1 Escudo 1760, 61 .... 75.00

Large bust. Rev. Arms.

26. 8 Escudos 1762-71 .... 150.00
27. 4 Escudos 1764-71 .... 500.00
28. 2 Escudos 1763-71 .... * 100.00
29. 1 Escudo 1762-71 .... 50.00

Older bust of different style. Rev. Arms.

30. 8 Escudos 1772-88 .... 100.00
31. 4 Escudos 1772-88 .... * 100.00
32. 2 Escudos 1772-88 .... 30.00
33. 1 Escudo 1772-88 .... 20.00

CHARLES IV, 1788-1808

*Bust of the previous king, Charles III, with name as "Carol IV."
Rev. Arms.*

34. 8 Escudos 1789, 90 .... * 125.00
35. 4 Escudos 1789, 90 .... 300.00
36. 2 Escudos 1789 .... 200.00
37. 1 Escudo 1789, 90 .... 75.00

Similar to above type but with name as "Carol IIII."

38. 8 Escudos 1790 .... 175.00
39. 4 Escudos 1790 .... 300.00

Bust. Rev. Arms.

MEXICO (cont'd)

40.	8 Escudos 1791-1808	100.00
41.	4 Escudos 1792-1808	90.00
42.	2 Escudos 1791-1808 . . . .*	30.00
43.	1 Escudo 1792-1808	20.00

FERDINAND VII, 1808-1833

Large armored bust. Rev. Arms.

44.	8 Escudos 1808-12 . . . .*	125.00
45.	4 Escudos 1808-12	100.00
46.	1 Escudo 1809-12	30.00

Large uniformed bust. Rev. Arms.

47.	8 Escudos 1813. GA mm. . . . .*	500.00
48.	4 Escudos 1812. GA mm.	Rare

Laureate head. Rev. Arms.

49.	8 Escudos 1814-21. MO mm.	100.00
50.	8 Escudos 1821. GA mm. . . . .*	175.00
51.	4 Escudos 1814-20	90.00
52.	2 Escudos 1814-20	30.00
53.	1 Escudo 1814-20	20.00
54.	½ Escudo 1814-20	12.50

Draped bust. Rev. Arms.

55.	8 Escudos 1821. GA mm.	200.00

B. Emperors of —

AUGUSTIN ITURBIDE I, 1822-1823

Head. Rev. Eagle on cactus.

56.	8 Escudos 1822	200.00

Head. Rev. Arms.

57.	8 Escudos 1823	200.00
58.	4 Escudos 1823 . . . .*	125.00

MAXIMILIAN I, 1864-1867

Head. Rev. Arms.

59.	20 Pesos 1866	150.00

C. Republic of —

Hand with Liberty Cap over book. Rev. Eagle facing left. The so-called "Hooked neck" eagle.

60.	8 Escudos 1823	500.00

Hand with Liberty Cap over book. Rev. Eagle facing right.

8 ESCUDOS

61.	MO mm. 1824-70.	75.00
62.	A mm. 1870-72.	500.00
63.	C mm. 1846-70. . . . .*	100.00
64.	CA mm. 1841-71.	150.00
65.	DO mm. 1832-70.	125.00
66.	EO MO mm. 1828-30.	1000.00
67.	GA mm. 1825-70.	300.00
68.	GC mm. 1843-52.	250.00
69.	GO mm. 1828-70.	75.00
70.	HO mm. 1861-73.	300.00
71.	O mm. 1860-70.	175.00
72.	ZS mm. 1850-70.	125.00

MEXICO (cont'd)

4 ESCUDOS

73.	MO mm. 1825-70		100.00
74.	C mm. 1846-70		200.00
75.	DO mm. 1832-70		150.00
76.	EO MO mm. 1828-30		Unknown
77.	GA mm. 1823-70		350.00
78.	GC mm. 1843-52		500.00
79.	GO mm. 1828-70		100.00
80.	HO mm. 1861-73		250.00
81.	O mm. 1858-70		Unknown
82.	ZS mm. 1824-70		150.00

2 ESCUDOS

83.	MO mm. 1825-70		25.00
84.	C mm. 1846-70		50.00
85.	DO mm. 1824-70		100.00
86.	EO MO mm. 1828-30		500.00
87.	GA mm. 1825-70		50.00
88.	GC mm. 1843-52		150.00
89.	GO mm. 1828-70		25.00
90.	HO mm. 1861-73		150.00
91.	O mm. 1858-70		Unknown
92.	ZS mm. 1824-70		75.00

1 ESCUDO

93.	MO mm. 1825-70		15.00
94.	C mm. 1846-70		20.00
95.	DO mm. 1832-70		20.00
96.	EO MO mm. 1828-30		Unknown
97.	GA mm. 1833-70		25.00
98.	GC mm. 1843-52		75.00
99.	GO mm. 1825-70		15.00
100.	HO mm. 1861-73		Unknown
101.	O mm. 1858-70		Unknown
102.	ZS mm. 1824-70		30.00

½ ESCUDO

103.	MO mm. 1825-70		10.00
104.	A mm. 1864-72		75.00
105.	C mm. 1846-70		12.50
106.	CA mm. 1831-70		40.00
107.	DO mm. 1824-70		12.50
108.	EO MO mm. 1828-30		250.00
109.	GA mm. 1833-70		12.50
110.	GC mm. 1843-52		40.00
111.	GO mm. 1825-70		10.00
112.	HO mm. 1861-73		60.00
113.	O mm. 1858-70		40.00
114.	ZS mm. 1824-70		20.00

Scales and Liberty Cap. Rev. Eagle.

20 PESOS

115.	MO mm. 1870-1905	*	90.00
116.	AS mm. 1876-78		250.00
117.	CH mm. 1872-95		150.00
118.	CN mm. 1870-1905		100.00
119.	DO mm. 1870-95		125.00
120.	GO mm. 1870-1900		100.00
121.	HO mm. 1874-95		400.00
122.	OA mm. 1870-93		200.00
123.	ZS mm. 1870-1905		150.00

10 PESOS

124.	MO mm. 1870-1905		50.00
125.	AS mm. 1870-95		125.00
126.	CH mm. 1888, 89		Unknown
127.	CN mm. 1870-1905		75.00
128.	DO mm. 1870-95		75.00
129.	GA mm. 1870-95		250.00
130.	GO mm. 1870-1900		100.00
131.	HO mm. 1870-95		200.00
132.	OA mm. 1870-93		100.00
133.	PI mm. 1888		2,500.00
134.	ZS mm. 1870-1905		60.00

5 PESOS

135.	MO mm. 1870-1905		30.00
136.	AS mm. 1870-95		125.00
137.	CH mm. 1888, 89		150.00
138.	CN mm. 1870-1905		32.50
139.	DO mm. 1870-95		35.00
140.	GO mm. 1870-1900		35.00
141.	HO mm. 1870-95		100.00
142.	OA mm. 1870-93		Unknown
143.	ZS mm. 1870-1905		32.50

Eagle. Rev. Value.

2½ PESOS

144.	MO mm. 1870-1905		25.00
145.	AS mm. 1888		200.00
146.	CH mm. 1870-95		Unknown
147.	CN mm. 1870-1905		30.00
148.	DO mm. 1870-95		Unknown
149.	GO mm. 1870-1900		30.00
150.	HO mm. 1870-95		100.00
151.	OA mm. 1870-93		Unknown
152.	ZS mm. 1870-1905		27.50

1 PESO

153.	MO mm. 1870-1905	*	12.50
154.	AS mm. 1870-95		100.00
155.	CH mm. 1888		150.00
156.	CN mm. 1870-1905		12.50
157.	GO mm. 1870-1900		12.50
158.	HO mm. 1870-95		50.00
159.	OA mm. 1870-93		Unknown
160.	ZS mm. 1870-1905		15.00

Head of Hidalgo to right. Rev. Eagle.

161.	20 Pesos 1892		Rare
162.	10 Pesos 1892		Rare

Head of Hidalgo to left. Rev. Eagle.

163.	10 Pesos 1906-20		16.00
164.	5 Pesos 1906-20, 1955	*	9.00
165.	2½ Pesos 1918-45	*	5.00

Eagle. Rev. Value in wreath.

166.	2 Pesos 1919-45		4.50

Aztec Calendar stone. Rev. Eagle.

167.	20 Pesos 1916-21		35.00

Winged Victory. Rev. Eagle. The so-called Centenario. The denomination does not appear on the coins dated 1943.

MEXICO (cont'd)

168. 50 Pesos 1921-47 .... 65.00

Half length figure of Hidalgo with cathedral in background. Rev. Eagle. On the 200th year of his birth. Although the value does not appear on these coins, they are struck to the same specifications as the older coins of these values, 1906-1921.

169. (20 Pesos) 1953 .... 35.00
170. (10 Pesos) 1953 ....*...... 25.00

Bust of Juarez. Rev. Eagle. On the 100th year of the Constitution. The value does not appear on this coin. (See above.)

171. (10 Pesos) 1957 .... 25.00

D. Revolutionary Period, 1913 - 1916

OAXACA STATE

Head of Juarez. Rev. Liberty Cap over scales.

172. 60 Pesos 1916 .... **Rare**

Head of Juarez. Rev. Value in wreath. Struck in low grade gold.

173. 20 Pesos 1915 ....*...... 40.00
174. 10 Pesos 1915 .... 25.00
175.   5 Pesos 1915 .... 20.00

NEWFOUNDLAND

Head of Queen Victoria of Great Britain. Rev. Value and date.

1. 2 Dollars 1865-88 .... 35.00

PARAGUAY

Lion seated before pole bearing the Liberty Cap. Rev. Justice seated. This coin was not placed in circulation.

1. 4 Pesos 1867 .... **2500.00**

PERU

A. Spanish Kings of —

CHARLES II, 1665-1700

Pillars and date. Rev. Cross. Cob type.

1. 8 Escudos 1697-1701 ....*...... 300.00
2. 4 Escudos 1697-1701 .... 300.00
3. 2 Escudos 1697-1701. LM mm. 200.00
4. 2 Escudos 1698. C mm. 250.00

PHILIP V, 1700-1746

Pillars and date. Rev. Cross. Cob type.

5. 8 Escudos 1702-46 .... 175.00
6. 4 Escudos 1702, 39 .... 250.00
7. 2 Escudos 1704-20 ....*...... 125.00

Crude castle. Rev. Cross.

8. 1 Escudo 1704-42 .... 75.00

LOUIS I, 1724
Pillars and date. Rev. Cross. Cob type.

9. 8 Escudos 1724 .... 500.00

FERDINAND VI, 1746-1760
Pillars and date. Rev. Cross. Cob type.

10. 8 Escudos 1747-50 .... 175.00
11. 4 Escudos 1747-50 .... 300.00
12. 2 Escudos 1747-50 .... 150.00
13. 1 Escudo 1747-50 .... 75.00

Large bust with flowing wig. Rev. Arms with value.

14. 8 Escudos 1751, 52, 53 .... 150.00
15. 4 Escudos 1751, 52 .... 350.00
17. 2 Escudos 1751, 52, 53 ....*...... 125.00
18. 1 Escudo, 1751, 52 .... 75.00

Smaller bust. Rev. Arms without value.

19.	8 Escudos 1754-60	*	150.00
20.	4 Escudos 1757, 58		350.00
21.	2 Escudos 1758, 59		150.00
22.	1 Escudo 1754, 57, 59		75.00

CHARLES III, 1759-1788

Small armored bust. Rev. Arms.

23.	8 Escudos 1761, 62		200.00
24.	4 Escudos 1762		500.00
25.	2 Escudos 1761, 62	*	200.00
26.	1 Escudo 1762		150.00

Large bust. Rev. Arms without value.

27.	8 Escudos 1763-72		125.00
28.	4 Escudos 1769, 70		400.00
29.	2 Escudos 1765-72		50.00
30.	1 Escudo 1766-72	*	60.00

Bust. Rev. Arms with value.

31.	8 Escudos 1771-89	*	125.00
32.	4 Escudos 1777-88		125.00
33.	2 Escudos 1772-89		40.00
34.	1 Escudo 1772-89		30.00

CHARLES IV, 1788-1808

Bust of the previous King, Charles III. Rev. Arms.

35.	8 Escudos 1789, 90, 91		125.00
36.	4 Escudos 1789, 91	*	150.00
37.	2 Escudos 1791		100.00
38.	1 Escudo 1789, 90, 91		50.00

Bust. Rev. Arms.

39.	8 Escudos 1792-1807		100.00
40.	4 Escudos 1792-1807		100.00
41.	2 Escudos 1792-1808	*	40.00
42.	1 Escudo 1792-1808		25.00

FERDINAND VII, 1808-1833

Bust in uniform. Rev. Arms.

43.	8 Escudos 1808-12	*	150.00
44.	4 Escudos 1810, 11		500.00
45.	2 Escudos 1810, 11		250.00
46.	1 Escudo 1810, 12		125.00

Large bust. Rev. Arms.

47.	8 Escudos 1812		250.00

Small bust. Rev. Arms.

48.	8 Escudos 1812, 13	*	125.00
49.	4 Escudos 1812, 13		250.00
50.	2 Escudos 1812, 13		100.00
51.	1 Escudo 1812, 13		75.00

Laureate head. Rev. Arms.

52.	8 Escudos 1814-21. ME mm.	*	100.00
53.	8 Escudos 1824. CO mm.		300.00
54.	4 Escudos 1814-21		75.00
55.	2 Escudos 1814-21		50.00
56.	1 Escudo 1814-21		35.00
57.	½ Escudo 1815-21		15.00

B. Republic of —

Llama, tree and cornucopia. Rev. Wreath and place of minting.

58.	½ Escudo 1826. Cuzco		22.50
59.	½ Escudo 1827-56. Lima	*	15.00

Liberty standing holding shield and pole; the place of minting in the legend. Rev. Arms.

60.	8 Escudos 1826-55. Lima	100.00
61.	8 Escudos 1826-55. Cuzco	125.00
62.	4 Escudos 1828-55. Lima .... *	75.00
63.	2 Escudos 1828-55. Lima	25.00
64.	1 Escudo 1826-55. Lima	17.50
65.	1 Escudo 1830-46. Cuzco	22.50

Liberty seated facing left. Rev. Arms.

66.	8 Escudos 1862, 63	100.00
67.	4 Escudos 1863	Rare
68.	20 Soles 1863 .... *	100.00
69.	10 Soles 1863	60.00
70.	5 Soles 1863	27.50

Liberty seated facing right. Rev. Arms.

71.	100 Soles 1950-57	100.00
72.	50 Soles 1950-57	50.00
73.	20 Soles 1950-57 .... *	25.00
74.	10 Soles 1956, 57 .... *	15.00
75.	5 Soles 1956, 57	10.00

Indian head. Rev. Arms.

76.	1 Libra 1898-1929 .... *	25.00
77.	½ Libra 1902-13	17.50
78.	⅕ Libra 1906-55	12.50

Arms. Rev. Motto.

79.	5 Soles 1910	17.50

Head of the Inca Indian Chief, Manco Capoc. Rev. Inca emblems.

80.	50 Soles 1930, 31	325.00

C. Republican States of —

NORTH PERU

Liberty standing holding shield and pole. Rev. Arms and "Estado Nor Peruano".

81.	8 Escudos 1838 .... *	1000.00
82.	4 Escudos 1838	1500.00
83.	2 Escudos 1838	500.00
84.	1 Escudo 1838	200.00

SOUTH PERU

Sun over flags and "Estado Sud Peruano". Rev. Volcano and castle and below "Federacion".

85.	8 Escudos 1837	175.00

Obv. similar to above but with legend "Repub. Sud Peruano". Rev. similar to above but with "Confederacion".

86.	8 Escudos 1837, 38	150.00

Radiant sun. Rev. Value in wreath.

87.	1 Escudo 1838	50.00
88.	½ Escudo 1838	30.00

SAINT MARTIN

Gold coins of Brazil counterstamped on Obv. with "22" or "20" (for karats), a small H and a small negro head.

1. 6400 Reis 1727-1804 .... 125.00

SAINT VINCENT

Gold coins of Brazil counterstamped three times along the outer edge of the Obv. with an S and usually with a plugged hole in the center.

1. 6400 Reis 1787-1804 .... 175.00

SALVADOR

Liberty head. Rev. Arms.

1. 20 Pesos 1892 .... 350.00
2. 10 Pesos 1892 .... 175.00
3. 5 Pesos 1892 ....*...... 175.00
4. 2½ Pesos 1892 .... 75.00

Conjoined heads of Alvarada (1525) and Quinonez (1925). Rev. Arms. On the 400th year of Salvador.

5. 20 Colones 1925 .... 200.00

TIERRA DEL FUEGO

The name Popper centered over crossed hammers and pick axe. Rev. Value in circle.

1. 5 Gramos 1889 .... 250.00
2. 1 Gramo 1889 .... 75.00

UNITED STATES OF AMERICA

A. Coinage of the Official U. S. Government Mints

(The valuations are for the commonest date of the respective mint.)

1 DOLLAR

Liberty Head. Rev. Value. Small size.

1. No mm. 1849-54 .... 22.50
2. C mm. 1849-53 .... 75.00
3. D mm. 1849-54 ....*...... 85.00
4. O mm. 1849-53 .... 25.00
5. S mm. 1854. .... 60.00

Small Liberty Head with feather head-dress. Rev. Value. Large size.

6. No mm. 1854, 55 .... 30.00
7. C mm. 1855. .... 65.00
8. D mm. 1855 ....*...... 400.00
9. O mm. 1855 .... 50.00
10. S mm. 1856. .... 60.00

Large Liberty Head with feather head-dress. Rev. Value. Large size.

11. No mm. 1856-89 .... 22.50
12. C mm. 1857, 59 .... 85.00
13. D mm. 1856-61 .... 150.00
14. S mm. 1857-60, 1870 ....*...... 40.00

For the Louisiana Purchase Exposition.

15. 1903. Head of Jefferson 50.00
16. 1903. Head of McKinley 60.00

For the Lewis & Clark Exposition.

17. 1904, 05. Head on each side 175.00

For the Panama-Pacific Exposition.

18. 1915. Panama Canal Laborer 30.00

For the McKinley Memorial.

19. 1916, 17. Head of McKinley 40.00

For the Grant Memorial.

20. 1922. Head of Grant 125.00
21. 1922. Same but with star on Obv. 85.00

2½ DOLLARS (QUARTER EAGLES)

(The reverses bear various types of eagles)

Liberty Head without stars.

22. No mm. 1796. . . . . 1000.00

Liberty Head with stars.

23. No mm. 1796-98, 1802, 04-07 . . . . 200.00

Draped bust of Liberty with round cap.

24. No mm. 1808 . . . . 1000.00

Liberty Head with round cap.

25. No mm. 1821, 1824-27 . . . .* 200.00
26. No mm. 1829-34. Size reduced 150.00

Liberty Head with ribbon and without motto on Rev.

27. No mm. 1834-39 . . . .* 22.50
28. C mm. 1838, 39 . . . . 50.00
29. D mm. 1839 . . . . 60.00
30. O mm. 1839 . . . . 35.00

Liberty Head with Coronet.

31. No mm. 1840-1907 . . . .* 20.00
32. No mm. 1848-"Cal" over eagle 500.00
33. C mm. 1840-44, 46-52, 54-56, 58, 60 . . . . 35.00
34. D mm. 1840-57, 59 . . . . 40.00
35. O mm. 1840, 42, 43, 45-47, 50-52, 54, 56, 57 . . . . . 25.00
36. S mm. 1854, 56-63, 65-73, 75-79 . . . . 20.00

Indian Head with designs and legends incused.

37. No mm. 1908-15, 26-29 . . . . 15.00
38. D mm. 1911, 14, 25 . . . .* 15.00

For the Panama-Pacific Exposition.

39. 1915. Columbia on hippocamp 125.00

For the Philadelphia Sesquicentennial.

40. 1926. Liberty standing and Independence Hall 30.00

3 DOLLARS

Liberty Head with feather head-dress. Rev. Value and date.

41. No mm. 1854-89 . . . .* 75.00
42. D mm. 1854 . . . . 300.00
43. O mm. 1854 . . . . 90.00
44. S mm. 1855-57, 60, 70 . . . . 90.00

4 DOLLARS (STELLA)

Liberty Head with flowing hair. Rev. Star.

45. No mm. 1879, 80 . . . . 1500.00

Liberty Head with coiled hair. Rev. Star.

46. No mm. 1879, 80 . . . . 4000.00

5 DOLLARS (HALF EAGLES)

(The reverses bear various types of eagles.)

Liberty Head with small eagle.

47. No mm. 1795-98 . . . . 350.00

Liberty Head with large, heraldic eagle.

48. No mm. 1795, 1797-1807 . . . . 100.00

Draped bust of Liberty with round cap.

49. No mm. 1807-12 .... **100.00**

Liberty Head with round cap.

50. No mm. 1813-29 .... **125.00**
51. No mm. 1829-34. Size reduced **300.00**

Liberty Head with ribbon and without motto on Rev.

52. No mm. 1834-38 ....* **25.00**
53. C mm. 1838 .... **75.00**
54. D mm. 1838 .... **90.00**

Liberty Head with coronet and without motto on Rev.

55. No mm. 1838-65 ....* **22.50**
56. C mm. 1839-44, 46-61 .... **35.00**
57. D mm. 1839-61 .... **45.00**
58. O mm. 1840-47, 51, 54-57 .... **27.50**
59. S mm. 1854-66 .... **22.50**

Liberty Head with coronet and with motto on Rev.

60. No mm. 1866-1908 ....* **17.50**
61. O mm. 1892-94 .... **30.00**
62. S mm. 1866-88, 92-1906 .... **17.50**
63. CC mm. 1870-84, 90-93 .... **30.00**
64. D mm. 1906, 07 .... **17.50**

Indian Head with designs and legends incused.

65. No mm. 1908-15, 1929 ....* **17.50**
66. O mm. 1909. .... **150.00**
67. S mm. 1908-16 .... **17.50**
68. D mm. 1908-11, 1914 .... **17.50**

10 DOLLARS (EAGLES)

(The reverses bear various types of eagles.)

Liberty Head with small eagle.

69. No mm. 1795-97 .... **350.00**

Liberty Head with large heraldic eagle.

70. No mm. 1797-1801, 03, 04 .... **175.00**

Small Liberty Head without motto on Rev.

71. No mm. 1838, 39 .... **125.00**

Large Liberty Head without motto on Rev.

72. No mm. 1840-65 ....* **40.00**
73. O mm. 1841-60 .... **45.00**
74. S mm. 1854-66 .... **40.00**

Liberty Head with motto on Rev.

75. No mm. 1866-1907 ....* **35.00**
76. O mm. 1879-83, 88, 92-95, 97, 99, 1901, 03, 04, 06 **40.00**
77. S mm. 1866-74, 76-89, 92-1903, 05-07 ...... **35.00**
78. CC mm. 1870-84, 90-93 .... **50.00**
79. D mm. 1906, 07 .... **37.50**

Indian Head without motto on Rev.

U.S.A. (cont'd)

80. No mm. 1907. With period before and after the Rev. legend   250.00
81. No mm. 1907, 08. Without periods . . . .* 40.00
82. D mm. 1908 . . . . 40.00

Indian Head with motto on Rev.

83. No mm. 1908-15, 26, 32, 33 . . . .* 37.50
84. S mm. 1908-16, 20, 30 . . . . 37.50
85. D mm. 1908-11, 14 . . . . 37.50

20 DOLLARS (DOUBLE EAGLES)
(The reverses bear various types of eagles.)

Liberty Head without motto on Rev.

86. No mm. 1850-65 . . . .* 65.00
87. No mm. 1861. Rev. by Paquet . . . . Rare
88. O mm. 1850-61 . . . . 100.00
89. S mm. 1854-66 . . . . 65.00
90. S mm. 1861. Rev. by Paquet 4500.00

Liberty Head with motto on Rev., and "Twenty D."

91. No mm. 1866-76 . . . .* 60.00
92. S mm. 1866-76 . . . . 60.00
93. CC mm. 1870-76 . . . . 100.00

Liberty Head with motto on Rev., and "Twenty Dollars."

94. No mm. 1877-1907 . . . .* 60.00
95. S mm. 1877-85, 1887-1907 . . . . 60.00
96. CC mm. 1877-79, 82-85, 89-93 . . . . 100.00
97. D mm. 1906, 07 . . . . 60.00

Liberty standing (St. Gaudens type) with date in Roman Numerals.

98. No mm. 1907. Very high relief (concave) and very wide edge   Rare
99. No mm. 1907. Normal high relief with wire or
    flat edge . . . .* 200.00

Liberty standing with date in usual numerals and without motto on Rev.

100. No mm. 1907, 08 . . . .* 65.00
101. D mm. 1908 . . . . 65.00

Liberty standing with motto on Rev.

102. No mm. 1908-15, 20-29, 31, 32 . . . . 60.00
103. S mm. 1908-11, 13-16, 20, 22, 24-27, 30 . . . .* 60.00
104.- D mm. 1908-11, 13, 14, 23-27, 31 . . . . 60.00

50 DOLLARS

*For the Panama-Pacific Exposition.
Head of Minerva. Rev. Owl.*

105. 1915. Round coin 2750.00
106. 1915. Octagonal coin . . . .* 2000.00

GOLD COINAGE FOR FOREIGN COUNTRIES
*(Gold coins struck at the Philadelphia Mint in 1945 and 1946
for use in Saudi Arabia.)*

*Weight and fineness in three line rectangular tablet. Rev. Eagle
and "U.S. Mint, Philadelphia, U.S.A."*

U.S.A. (cont'd)
107. 4 Saudi Pounds ND ....* 250.00
108. 1 Saudi Pound ND 85.00

B. Coinage of the Territorial and Private Mints

(Pioneer Gold)

BALDWIN & CO.
San Francisco, California

Horseman with lariat. Rev. Eagle.

109. 10 Dollars 1850 .... 1750.00

"Baldwin & Co" on head band of Liberty. Rev. Eagle.

110. 5 Dollars 1850 .... 300.00
111. 10 Dollars 1851 .... 1500.00
112. 20 Dollars 1851 .... 5000.00

AUGUST BECHTLER
Rutherford, North Carolina

Value and legend. Rev. Weight and legend. The coins are undated but were struck from 1842 to 1852.

113. 1 Dollar ND. One variety ....* 50.00
114. 5 Dollars ND. Three varieties 250.00

CHRISTOPHER BECHTLER
Rutherford, North Carolina

Value and legend. Rev. Weight and legend. The coins are undated, but were struck from 1831 to 1842.

115. 1 Dollar ND. Four varieties 75.00
116. 2½ Dollars ND. Seven varieties ....* 250.00
117. 5 Dollars ND. Six varieties 250.00
118. 5 Dollars August 1, 1834. Two varieties ....* 275.00

BLAKE & CO.
Sacramento, California

Stamping machine. Rev. Value and legend.

119. 20 Dollars 1855 .... Rare

BLAKE & AGNELL
Sacramento, California

Square shaped ingot with name, weight, fineness and value stamped on both sides.

120. $23.30 1855 .... Rare

EPHRAIM BRASHER
New York

Radiant sun over mountains. Rev. Eagle with "EB" punched on either the wing or breast. The famous Brasher Doubloon.

121. Doubloon 1787 ....* 15,000.00
122. ½ Doubloon 1787 .... Unique

Cross of Jerusalem and "EB" punch mark. Rev. Pillars with "Brasher" below. An imitation of a Lima Mint 8 Escudos dated 1742.

123. 8 Escudos or Doubloon (1787) .... Rare

CALIFORNIA & SIERRA CO.
California

Rectangular ingot with various punch marks and lettered edges.

124. $36.57 1860 .... Rare

CINCINNATI MINING & TRADING CO.
San Francisco, California

Indian Head. Rev. Eagle.

125. 5 Dollars 1849 .... 3000.00
126. 10 Dollars 1849 .... 5000.00

CLARK, GRUBER & CO.
Denver, Colorado

View of Pikes Peak. Rev. Eagle

127. 10 Dollars 1860 ....* 400.00
128. 20 Dollars 1860 .... 1500.00

"Clark & Co." On head band of Liberty. Rev. Eagle.

129. 2½ Dollars 1860 .... 75.00
130. 5 Dollars 1860 .... 75.00

"Pikes Peak" on head band of Liberty. Rev. Eagle.

131. 2½ Dollars 1861 .... 75.00
132. 5 Dollars 1861 ....* 75.00
133. 10 Dollars 1861 .... 250.00
134. 20 Dollars 1861 .... 1000.00

J. J. CONWAY & CO.
Georgia Gulch, Colorado

Name of company. Rev. Value and "Pikes Peak". Undated but struck in 1861.

135.	2½	Dollars ND	4000.00
136.	5	Dollars ND	3500.00
137.	10	Dollars ND	Rare

DUBOSQ & CO.
San Francisco, California

"Dubosq & Co." on head band of Liberty. Rev. Eagle.

138.	5 Dollars 1850	2750.00
139.	10 Dollars 1850	3500.00

DUNBAR & CO.
San Francisco, California

"Dunbar & Co." on head band of Liberty. Rev. Eagle.

140. 5 Dollars 1851	2500.00

AUGUSTUS HUMBERT
U.S. Assayer of gold, San Francisco, California.

Eagle Rev. Four line legend in tablet.

141.	10 Dollars 1852 ....*	125.00
142.	20 Dollars 1852	1000.00

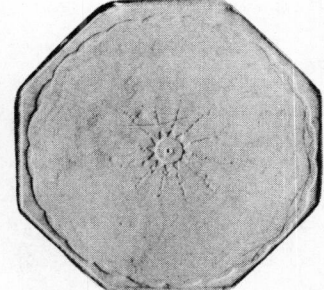

Eagle. Rev. Small 50, star or circle in center of otherwise blank Rev. Octagonal shaped with lettered edge.

143. 50 Dollars 1851. Five varieties	1500.00

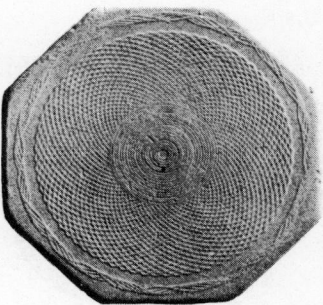

Eagle. Rev. Machine made criss-cross of circular lines. Octagonal shaped with reeded edge.

144. 50 Dollars 1851, 52. Three varieties	1000.00

KELLOGG & CO.
San Francisco, California

"Kellogg & Co." on head band of Liberty. Rev. Standard Eagle.

145. 20 Dollars 1854, 55	150.00

Obv. Similar to above. Rev. Eagle holding shield.

146. 50 Dollars 1855	6500.00

KELLOGG & HEWSTON
San Francisco, California

Rectangular ingot with various punch marks and name along edge.

147. $49.50 ND. (1860)	Rare

F. D. KOHLER
State Assayer, San Francisco and Sacramento, California

Rectangular gold ingots bearing name, weight, fineness and value.

148.	$36.55 1850	Rare
149.	$37.31 1850	Rare
150.	$40.07 1850	Rare
151.	$45.34 1850	Rare
152.	$50.00 1850	Rare
153.	$54.09 1850	Rare

MASSACHUSETTS & CALIFORNIA CO.
San Francisco, California

Arms supported by bear and stag. Rev. Value in wreath.

154. 5 Dollars 1849. Four varieties	3000.00

MINERS BANK
San Francisco, California

Name and value. Rev. Eagle.

155. 10 Dollars 1849 .... 1000.00

MOFFAT & CO.
San Francisco, California

"Moffat & Co." on head band of Liberty. Rev. Eagle.

156.	5 Dollars 1849, 50	....	60.00
157.	10 Dollars 1849, 52	....	200.00
158.	20 Dollars 1853	......................*......	250.00

Rectangular ingots bearing legends, values and weights.

159.	$ 9.43 ND (1849-1853)	....	Unique
160.	$14.25 ND (1849-1853)	....	Unique
161.	$16.00 ND (1849-1853)	....	Rare

THE MORMONS
Salt Lake City, Utah

Eye and Bishop's Mitre. Rev. Clasped hands.

162.	2½ Dollars 1849	....	200.00
163.	5 Dollars 1849, 50	...................*......	175.00
164.	10 Dollars 1849	...................*......	3000.00
165.	20 Dollars 1849	...................*......	2000.00

Lion. Rev. Beehive on breast of eagle.

166. 5 Dollars 1860 .... 500.00

NORRIS, GRIEG & NORRIS
San Francisco, California

Eagle. Rev. Legend.

167. 5 Dollars 1849. Plain or reeded edge 250.00

OREGON EXCHANGE CO.
Oregon City, Oregon

Beaver and initials. Rev. Legend.

168.	5 Dollars 1849	....	750.00
169.	10 Dollars 1849	....	5000.00

J. S. ORMSBY
San Francisco, California

"J.S.O." Rev. Value. Undated but struck in 1849.

170.	5 Dollars ND	....	Rare
171.	10 Dollars ND	...........................*......	Rare

PACIFIC CO.
San Francisco, California

Liberty Cap. Rev. Eagle.

172.	5 Dollars 1849	...........................*......	Rare
173.	10 Dollars 1849	....	Rare

JOHN PARSONS & CO.
Tarryall Mines, Colorado

Stamping machine. Rev. Eagle and "Pikes Peak Gold." Undated but struck in 1861.

174.	2½ Dollars ND	....	3000.00
175.	5 Dollars ND	....	4000.00

Rectangular ingot bearing name and various legends.

176. 20 Dollars 1860 .... Unique

SHULTS & CO.
San Francisco, California

"Shults & Co." on head band of Liberty. Rev. Eagle.

177. 5 Dollars 1851 .... 1250.00

TEMPLETON REID

Lumpkin County, Georgia

Legend on each side.

178.	2½ Dollars 1830	....	750.00
179.	5 Dollars 1830	....	3500.00
180.	10 Dollars 1830	....	Rare
181.	10 Dollars ND	....	Rare

TEMPLETON REID

San Francisco, California

Legend on each side.

182.	10 Dollars 1849	....	Rare
183.	25 Dollars 1849	....	Unknown

UNITED STATES ASSAY OFFICE OF GOLD

San Francisco, California

Eagle. Rev. Legend in tablet.

184.	10 Dollars 1852, 53. Two varieties	............*......	125.00
185.	20 Dollars 1853. Two varieties	....	175.00

 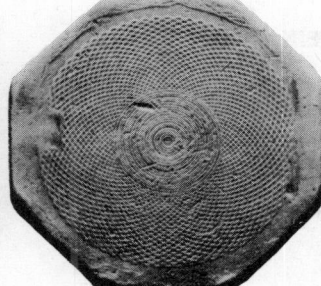

Eagle. Rev. Machine made criss-cross of circular lines. Octagonal shaped.

186.	50 Dollars 1852. Two varieties	....	1000.00

WASS, MOLITOR & CO.

San Francisco, California

"W.M. & Co." on head band of Liberty. Rev. Eagle.

187.	5 Dollars 1852	....	125.00
188.	10 Dollars 1852, 55. Two varieties	............*......	200.00
189.	20 Dollars 1855. Two varieties	....	650.00

Liberty head. Rev. Name and value.

190.	50 Dollars 1855	....	2500.00

URUGUAY

Arms. Rev. Value in wreath. These coins were not placed in circulation.

1.	40 Reales 1854	....	Rare
2.	1 Doblon 1870	.......................*.....	Rare
3.	5 Pesos 1870	....	Rare
4.	2 Pesos 1870	....	Rare
5.	1 Peso 1870	....	Rare

Head of Artigas. Rev. Value and dates 1830 and 1930. On the Centennial of the Republic.

6.	5 Pesos 1930	....	100.00

VENEZUELA

Head of Bolivar. Rev. Arms. The values are expressed on the Rev. by the weight of the coins in grams. The 5 Bolivar piece was not placed in circulation.

1.	100 Bolivares 1875, 86, 89 (32.2580 Grams)	......*......	200.00
2.	50 Bolivares 1875, 88 (16.1290 Grams)	....	Rare
3.	25 Bolivares 1875 (8.0645 Grams)	....	75.00
4.	20 Bolivares 1879-1912 (6.4516 Grams)	....	25.00
5.	10 Bolivares 1930 (3.2258 Grams)	............*......	25.00
6.	5 Bolivares 1875 (1.6129 Grams)	....	Rare

Part II

•••

EUROPE

The Continent and The British Isles

ALBANIA	**GREAT BRITAIN**	**POLAND**
AUSTRIA	**GREECE**	**PORTUGAL**
BELGIUM	**HUNGARY**	**ROUMANIA**
BOHEMIA	**ITALY**	**RUSSIA**
BULGARIA	**LATVIA**	**SAN MARINO**
COURLAND	**LIECHTENSTEIN**	**SCOTLAND**
CROATIA	**LITHUANIA**	**SERBIA**
CZECHOSLOVAKIA	**LIVONIA**	**SPAIN**
DANZIG	**LUXEMBOURG**	**SWEDEN**
DENMARK	**MOLDAVIA**	**SWITZERLAND**
ESTHONIA	**MONACO**	**VATICAN CITY**
FINLAND	**MONTENEGRO**	**WALLACHIA**
FRANCE	**NETHERLANDS**	**YUGOSLAVIA**
GERMANY	**NORWAY**	

ALBANIA

Presidents, and later, Kings of —

ZOG I, 1925-1939

Head with one, two or no stars below. Rev. Chariot.

1. 100 Francs 1926, 27 .... 100.00

Head. Rev. Eagle.

2. 20 Francs 1926, 27 .... 30.00
3. 10 Francs 1927 .... 30.00

Bust of Skanderbeg. Rev. Winged lion.

4. 20 Francs 1926. R mm. 40.00
5. 20 Francs 1926. Fasces mm. 65.00
6. 20 Francs 1927. V mm. ....*...... 25.00

Bare head to left. Rev. Eagle. Not placed in circulation.

7. 100 Francs 1928 .... 250.00

Uniformed bust to right. Rev. Eagle. Not placed in circulation.

8. 100 Francs 1928 .... 250.00

Bare head to left in wreath. Rev. Eagle. Not placed in circulation.

9. 100 Francs 1928 .... 250.00

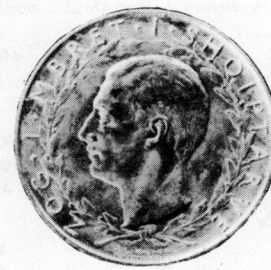 

*Bare head to left in wreath. Rev. Eagle with "Albania" added.
Not placed in circulation.*

10. 100 Francs 1929 .... 300.00

*Bare head. Rev. Arms and dates 1912-1937. On the 25th year
of Independence.*

11. 100 Francs 1937 .... 225.00
12. 20 Francs 1937 ....*...... 40.00

Bare head. Rev. Arms and date, "27. IV. 1938." On his wedding.

13. 100 Francs 1938 .... 200.00
14. 20 Francs 1938 ....*...... 35.00

*Bare head. Rev. Arms and dates 1928-1938. On the 10th year
of his rule.*

15. 100 Francs 1938 .... 200.00
16. 50 Francs 1938 .... 150.00
17. 20 Francs 1938 ....*...... 35.00

AUSTRIA

(See remarks under Holy Roman Empire.)

A. Dukes of —

ALBERT II, 1330-1358

St. John. Rev. Lily.

1. 1 Goldgulden ND 50.00

RUDOLPH IV, 1358-1365
St. John. Rev. Lily.

2. 1 Goldgulden ND 100.00

B. Holy Roman Emperors and Archdukes of —

ALBERT II, 1437-1439

Madonna. Rev. Orb in trilobe.

2a. 1 Goldgulden ND 300.00

FREDERICK III, 1439-1493
Ruler standing. Rev. Four shields and floriated cross.

3. 1 Goldgulden ND 125.00

ARCHDUKE SIGISMUND, 1439-1496
Ruler standing. Rev. Four shields and floriated cross.

4. 1 Goldgulden ND 40.00

MAXIMILIAN I, 1493-1519
St. Leopold. Rev. Arms.

5. 1 Goldgulden 1511 .... 400.00

St. Leopold. Rev. Cross and shield.

6. 1 Goldgulden 1514 .... 200.00

St. Leopold. Rev. Five shields.

7. 1 Goldgulden 1517, 19, 20 .... 200.00

Crowned bust. Rev. Carinthian shield.

8. 1 Goldgulden 1516, 19 .... 100.00

Bust with hat. Rev. Carinthian shield.

9.	4 Ducats 1518	600.00

FERDINAND I, 1521-1564
Bust. Rev. Legend.

10.	4 Ducats 1529. Square	500.00
11.	3 Ducats 1529. Square	300.00
12.	2 Ducats 1529. Square	200.00

Bust. Rev. Cross and four shields.

13.	1½ Ducats 1529. Square	150.00
14.	1 Ducat 1529. Square ....*	125.00
15.	½ Ducat 1529. Square	75.00

Austrian shield. Rev. Legend.

16.	½ Ducat 1529. Square	100.00

(The above seven coins were struck during the Siege of Vienna.)

Bust. Rev. Double eagle.

17.	12 Ducats 1532	600.00
18.	8 Ducats 1532	500.00
19.	6 Ducats 1526	400.00
20.	2 Ducats 1560	200.00

Bust. Rev. Arms.

21.	1 Ducat 1525, 32, 42	100.00

Middle aged bust. Rev. St. Ladislas.

22.	1 Goldgulden 1531-58	50.00

Ruler standing. Rev. Floriated cross and four shields.

23.	1 Goldgulden ND	250.00

Ruler standing. Rev. Arms.

24.	2 Ducats ND	100.00
25.	2 Ducats 1565. Posthumous	150.00
26.	1 Ducat ND	50.00
27.	1 Ducat 1565. Posthumous	75.00

Bust. Rev. Legend. On his burial.

28.	2 Ducats 1565	500.00
29.	1 Ducat 1565	350.00

ARCHDUKE CHARLES, 1564-1590

Ruler standing. Rev. Arms.

30.	12 Ducats 1579	Rare
31.	10 Ducats 1572, 76	Rare
32.	2 Ducats 1576-87	125.00
33.	1 Ducat 1565-90 ....*	40.00
34.	1 Ducat 1591, 92. Posthumous	50.00

Bust. Rev. Four shields.

35.	3 Ducats 1572	400.00

Fortuna standing. Rev. Five shields.

36.	3 Ducats 1573	300.00

ARCHDUKE FERDINAND, 1564-1595
Bust. Rev. Arms.

37.	3 Ducats ND	250.00

38.	1 Ducat 1564-95	50.00
39.	½ Ducat 1591	50.00

Bust. Rev. Eagle.

40.	20 Ducats 1590	Rare
41.	10 Ducats 1590	750.00
42.	5 Ducats 1590	350.00
43.	1 Ducat 1569-83	40.00
44.	⅛ Ducat ND	40.00
45.	1 Gold Crown (Gulden) ND	250.00

Busts of Maximilian I, Charles V and Ferdinand I. Rev. Double eagle.

46.	8 Ducats ND	Rare

RUDOLPH II, 1576-1612
Bust. Rev. Double eagle.

47.	10 Ducats 1589-1611	400.00
48.	5 Ducats 1587-1611	200.00
49.	4 Ducats 1589-1604	175.00
50.	3 Ducats 1580-1607	150.00
51.	2 Ducats 1598-1611	100.00
52.	1 Ducat 1577-1611	40.00

Ruler standing. Rev. Double eagle.

53.	10 Ducats 1599-1610 ....*	400.00
54.	5 Ducats 1587-1611	250.00
55.	4 Ducats 1589-1604	250.00
56.	3 Ducats 1598-1606	175.00
57.	2 Ducats 1598-1611	125.00
58.	1 Ducat 1577-1611	50.00

Ruler standing. Rev. Arms.

58a.	1 Ducat 1578-1608	50.00

Busts of Maximilian I, Charles V and Ferdinand I. Rev. Double eagle.

59.	10 Ducats ND	Rare
60.	5 Ducats ND	600.00

MATTHIAS II, 1612-1619
Bust. Rev. Arms. Struck as Archduke.

61.	6 Ducats 1608-11	250.00
62.	5 Ducats 1608, 09	200.00
63.	1 Ducat 1609-11	50.00

Bust. Rev. Double eagle.

64.	25 Ducats 1615. Square	Rare
65.	20 Ducats 1612	Rare
66.	15 Ducats 1612, 17	500.00
67.	10 Ducats 1611-19	300.00
68.	8 Ducats 1612	250.00
69.	5 Ducats 1612-19	175.00
70.	4 Ducats 1612	300.00
71.	3 Ducats 1613, 17	200.00
72.	2 Ducats 1613-19	100.00
73.	1 Ducat 1612-19	40.00

Armored bust. Rev. Busts of Maximilian I, Charles V and Ferdinand I.

74.	15 Ducats ND	Rare
75.	10 Ducats ND	Rare

ARCHDUKE MAXIMILIAN, 1612-1618
Ruler standing. Rev. Arms.

76.	1 Ducat ND	150.00

AUSTRIA (cont'd)

Armored bust. Rev. Cross.

77.	½ Ducat ND	....	100.00

ARCHDUKE FERDINAND, 1592-1618
Armored bust. Rev. Arms.

78.	8 Ducats 1618		500.00
79.	1 Ducat 1617	....	50.00

Bust. Rev. Double eagle.

80.	5 Ducats 1602		500.00
81.	1 Ducat 1598-1616	....	40.00

Ruler standing. Rev. Arms.

82.	1 Ducat 1598-1617	....	40.00

Initials. Rev. Legend.

83.	½ Ducat 1617	....	25.00

FERDINAND II, 1618-1637
Legend. Rev. Crown.

84.	2 Ducats 1618, 19	....	75.00
85.	1 Ducat 1618	....	40.00

Ruler on throne. Rev. Double eagle.

86.	1 Ducat 1620-37	....	40.00

Armored bust. Rev. Double eagle.

87.	20 Ducats 1622, 36		Rare
88.	15 Ducats 1636	....	850.00
89.	12 Ducats 1626	....	750.00
90.	10 Ducats 1621-37	....	300.00
91.	6 Ducats 1624, 27, 28	....	250.00
92.	5 Ducats 1621-37	....	150.00
93.	4 Ducats 1622-34	....	150.00
94.	3 Ducats 1637	....	200.00
95.	2 Ducats 1620-37	....	75.00
96.	1 Ducat 1620-37	....	40.00
97.	½ Ducat 1633, 36	....	40.00

Laureate bust. Rev. Silesian eagle.

98.	1 Ducat 1623	....	50.00

Armored bust. Rev. Arms.

99.	20 Ducats 1636	....	1250.00
100.	12 Ducats 1632	....	750.00
101.	10 Ducats 1621-37	....	300.00
102.	9 Ducats 1632	....	350.00
103.	8 Ducats 1632	....	300.00
104.	6 Ducats 1628, 32	....	250.00
105.	5 Ducats 1621-37	.... *	150.00
106.	4 Ducats 1627. Square	....	450.00
107.	3 Ducats 1634. Square	....	400.00
108.	2 Ducats 1620-37	....	75.00
109.	1 Ducat 1620-37	....	40.00

Ruler standing. Rev. Arms.

109a.	1 Ducat 1620-37	....	50.00

Bust facing. Rev. City view of Breslau, eagle above.

110.	10 Ducats 1626, 31	....	750.00

Double eagle. Rev. Arms.

111.	4 Ducats 1621, 22	....	200.00

INTERREGNUM IN TYROL, 1618-1619
Tyrolian eagle shield. Rev. Arms of Austria.

112.	1 Goldgulden 1618, 19	....	250.00

ARCHDUKE LEOPOLD, 1619-1632
Busts of Leopold and Claudia. Rev. Eagle. Struck in 1626 on their marriage.

113.	20 Ducats ND	....	Rare
114.	8 Ducats ND	....	500.00
115.	6 Ducats ND	....	400.00
116.	6 Ducats ND. Square	....	500.00
117.	5 Ducats ND	....	350.00

Ruler standing. Rev. St. Leopold.

118.	1 Ducat 1631	....	75.00

Tyrolian shield. Rev. Arms.

119.	½ Ducat ND	....	100.00

St. Leopold. Rev. Tyrolian shield.

120.	1 Ducat 1619, 20	....	60.00

FERDINAND III, 1627-1657

Youthful bust. Rev. Arms.

121.	12 Ducats 1629	....	750.00
122.	10 Ducats 1627-29	.... *	450.00
123.	9 Ducats 1629	....	400.00
124.	8 Ducats 1629	....	350.00
125.	2 Ducats 1629-31	....	100.00
126.	1 Ducat 1629-36	....	50.00

Armored bust. Rev. Arms.

130.	15 Ducats 1641	....	1000.00
131.	12 Ducats 1641	....	750.00
132.	10 Ducats 1638-57	.... *	350.00
133.	8 Ducats 1638	....	350.00
134.	7 Ducats 1638	....	350.00
135.	6 Ducats 1638	....	250.00
136.	5 Ducats 1638-57	....	150.00
137.	4 Ducats 1638	....	200.00
138.	2 Ducats 1637-57	....	100.00
139.	1 Ducat 1637-57	....	40.00

Armored bust. Rev. Double eagle.

140.	20 Ducats 1645	....	1250.00
141.	10 Ducats 1638-57	.... *	350.00
142.	10 Ducats 1658. Posthumous	....	450.00
143.	6 Ducats 1639-46	....	250.00
144.	5 Ducats 1636-57	....	150.00
145.	4 Ducats 1645	....	150.00
146.	3 Ducats 1643, 56	....	150.00
147.	2 Ducats 1637-57	....	100.00
148.	1 Ducat 1637-57	....	40.00
149.	½ Ducat 1637-49	....	30.00

AUSTRIA (cont'd)

Laureate bust. Rev. Three shields.

150.	1 Ducat 1637, 38	125.00
151.	1 Ducat 1637, 38. Square	175.00

Ruler standing. Rev. Double eagle.

152.	2 Ducats 1637-57 ....*	150.00
153.	1 Ducat 1637-57	75.00

PROTESTANT ASSEMBLY OF SILESIA, 1633-1635
Armored bust of Ferdinand III. Rev. Double eagle.

154.	3 Ducats 1634	300.00
155.	1 Ducat 1634, 35	150.00

ARCHDUKE FERDINAND CHARLES, 1632-1662

Bust. Rev. Eagle.

156.	6 Ducats 1632-37	750.00
157.	5 Ducats 1632-37, ND	500.00
158.	2 Ducats 1632-62, ND ....*	150.00

Bust. Rev. Arms.

159.	1 Ducat 1632-62 ....*	75.00
160.	½ Ducat 1632-62	125.00

Bust with hat. Rev. Eagle.

161.	20 Ducats 1632-62	Rare

Ruler on horseback. Rev. St. Leopold.

162.	3 Ducats 1642	150.00
163.	2 Ducats 1642 ....*	125.00

Ruler standing. Rev. St. Leopold.

164.	1 Ducat 1632-62, ND	50.00

FERDINAND IV, 1646-1654
Legend. Rev. Altar.

165.	1 Ducat 1646	60.00

ARCHDUKE SIGISMUND FRANCIS, 1662-1665
Bust with long hair. Rev. Eagle.

166.	20 Ducats ND	Rare
167.	1 Ducat ND	125.00

Bust with long hair. Rev. Crowned arms.

168.	1 Ducat ND	200.00

LEOPOLD I (THE HOGMOUTH), 1658-1705
Two angels with crown. Rev. Globe under two hands. On his Coronation.

169.	4 Ducats 1658	200.00

Laureate bust. Rev. Tyrolian eagle.

170.	30 Ducats ND	Rare
171.	20 Ducats ND	Rare
172.	12 Ducats ND	650.00
172a.	4 Ducats ND ....*	175.00

Laureate bust. Rev. Double eagle.

173.	12 Ducats 1674	650.00
174.	10 Ducats 1658-1703 ....*	300.00
175.	10 Ducats 1694. Square	500.00
176.	8 Ducats 1678	400.00
177.	6 Ducats 1669-1703	300.00
178.	5 Ducats 1659-1703	150.00
179.	5 Ducats 1694. Square	350.00
180.	4 Ducats 1692-1703	150.00
181.	4 Ducats 1696-98. Square	300.00
182.	3 Ducats 1694-1701	150.00
183.	2 Ducats 1659-1705	75.00
184.	2 Ducats 1660, 96. Square	150.00
185.	1 Ducat 1658-1705	35.00
186.	1 Ducat 1691, 95, 99. Square	75.00
187.	½ Ducat 1661-95	25.00
188.	⅓ Ducat 1675-98	20.00
189.	¼ Ducat 1669-1705	12.50
190.	⅙ Ducat 1669-99	12.50
191.	⅛ Ducat 1686-98	12.50
192.	$1/12$ Ducat 1675-99	12.50

Crowned bust. Rev. Double eagle.

193.	5 Ducats 1676-95	200.00
193a.	3 Ducats 1665 ....*	250.00

AUSTRIA (cont'd)

Laureate bust. Rev. Arms.

194.	30 Ducats 1678	....	Rare
195.	20 Ducats 1670	....	Rare
196.	10 Ducats 1658-1703	....	300.00
197.	6 Ducats 1662-1703	....	250.00
198.	5 Ducats 1659-1703	....	150.00
199.	4 Ducats 1658-95	....	150.00
200.	4 Ducats 1661. Square	....	200.00
201.	3 Ducats ND	....	150.00
202.	2 Ducats 1659-1705	....	75.00
203.	1 Ducat 1659-93	.... *	35.00
204.	¼ Ducat 1669, ND	....	15.00

Laureate bust. Rev. Bust of Empress Eleonora.

205.	1 Ducat 1689	....	75.00

Ruler on horseback. Rev. Double eagle.

205a.	1 Ducat 1661	....	300.00

JOSEPH I, 1705-1711
Bust. Rev. Tyrolean eagle.

206.	24 Ducats ND	....	Rare

Bust. Rev. Double eagle.

207.	10 Ducats 1705-09	....	400.00
208.	5 Ducats 1706-08	....	250.00
209.	4 Ducats 1708	....	200.00
210.	3 Ducats 1706-11	....	200.00
211.	2 Ducats 1796-09. Round or square	.... *	150.00
212.	1 Ducat 1705-11	....	35.00
213.	½ Ducat 1706-10	....	25.00
214.	⅓ Ducat 1706	....	25.00
215.	¼ Ducat 1706-11	....	20.00
216.	⅙ Ducat 1706-11	....	15.00
217.	⅛ Ducat 1706-09	....	15.00
218.	1/12 Ducat 1705-11	....	15.00

Bust. Rev. Arms.

219.	10 Ducats 1706	....	500.00
220.	3 Ducats 1710	....	200.00
221.	1 Ducat 1706, ND	....	50.00

Ruler standing. Rev. Double eagle.

222.	1 Ducat 1710, 11	....	60.00

Double Arms. Rev. Blank.

223.	⅛ Ducat 1710	....	20.00

CHARLES VI, 1711-1740

Armored bust. Rev. Double eagle.

224.	20 Ducats 1739	....	Rare
225.	12 Ducats 1740	....	600.00
226.	10 Ducats 1712-40	....	400.00
227.	6 Ducats 1714, 28	....	300.00
228.	5 Ducats 1713-39	....	200.00
229.	4 Ducats 1713-30	....	175.00
230.	3 Ducats 1717-38	....	150.00
231.	2 Ducats 1715-35	....	75.00
232.	2 Ducats 1734. Square	....	175.00
233.	1 Ducat 1712-40	.... *	30.00
234.	½ Ducat 1728-40	....	20.00
235.	¼ Ducat 1720-38	....	15.00
236.	⅙ Ducat 1731	....	12.50
237.	⅛ Ducat 1729	....	12.50
238.	1/16 Ducat 1729	....	12.50

Globe. Rev. Sceptre.

239.	1 Ducat 1716	....	35.00

Legend. Rev. Globe.

240.	1 Ducat 1723	....	35.00

Crowned bust with name and title as Charles III, King of Spain. Rev. Arms. With hand mint mark for Antwerp.

241.	2 Souverain d'or 1711	....	400.00

Lion standing with same title. Rev. Arms. Hand mint mark.

242.	1 Souverain (Lion) d'or 1710	....	300.00

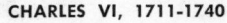

Crowned bust with name and title as Charles VI, Holy Roman Emperor. Rev. Eagle and shield. Hand mint mark.

243.	2 Souverain d'or 1719, 25	....	250.00

Laureate bust with titles as above. Rev. Arms. Hand mint mark.

244.	2 Souverain d'or 1724-26	....	150.00

(For additional coins of Charles VI, as well as of the rulers following, see under Italy-Milan.)

CHARLES VII, 1740-1745
(Elector of Bavaria with title of Holy Roman Emperor).
Eagle. Rev. Crown.

245.	1 Ducat 1742	....	50.00

MARIA THERESA, 1740-1780
Youthful bust. Rev. Elaborate arms.

246.	12 Ducats 1744	....	500.00
247.	10 Ducats 1742-45	....	400.00
248.	6 Ducats 1741-45	....	200.00
249.	5 Ducats 1742-46	....	150.00
250.	4 Ducats 1743	....	150.00
251.	1 Ducat 1741-46	....	30.00

Mature bust. Rev. Double eagle.

252.	10 Ducats 1748-61	.... *	400.00
253.	7 Ducats 1758	....	300.00
254.	6 Ducats 1745-68	....	200.00
255.	5 Ducats 1746-65	....	150.00
256.	4 Ducats 1759-65	....	125.00
257.	3 Ducats 1754-61	....	125.00
258.	2 Ducats 1746-65	....	65.00
259.	1 Ducat 1746-65	....	30.00
260.	½ Ducat 1748-65	.... *	25.00

AUSTRIA (cont'd)

261.	¼ Ducat 1749-65	15.00
262.	⅙ Ducat 1752	12.50
263.	⅛ Ducat 1749, 61	12.50

Head. Rev. Double eagle.

264.	¼ Ducat 1749, 51	15.00

Bust with widow's veil. Rev. Double eagle.

265.	5 Ducats 1777	200.00
266.	4 Ducats 1778-80	175.00
267.	2 Ducats 1767-80	75.00
268.	1 Ducat 1765-80	35.00
269.	½ Ducat 1765-80	25.00
270.	¼ Ducat 1768-80	15.00

Arms. Rev. Value and date.

271.	⅛ Ducat 1778	12.50

Ruler standing. Rev. Crowned arms.

272.	1 Ducat 1744-65	35.00

Bust. Rev. Bust of Francis.

273.	1 Ducat ND	40.00

Busts of the Imperial Couple. Rev. Crossed hammers.

274.	1 Mining Ducat 1751	100.00

Bust with or without crown or veil. Rev. Arms.

275.	2 Souverain d'or 1756-80. W mm or without W	125.00
276.	2 Souverain d'or 1749-58. Hand mm. ....*	100.00
277.	2 Souverain d'or 1749-52. Lion mm.	150.00
278.	2 Souverain d'or 1758-80. Head mm.	100.00
279.	1 Souverain d'or 1749-57. Hand mm.	60.00
280.	1 Souverain d'or 1750-54. Lion mm.	75.00
281.	1 Souverain d'or 1757-77. Head mm. ....*	60.00

FRANCIS I, 1745-1765

Bust with long hair. Rev. Double eagle.

282.	6 Ducats 1747	300.00
283.	5 Ducats 1745, 47	250.00
284.	2 Ducats 1745, 46	75.00
285.	1 Ducat 1745-65 ....*	30.00
286.	1 Ducat 1766-80. Posthumous	35.00
287.	¼ Ducat 1755-65	15.00

JOSEPH II, 1765-1790

Youthful bust. Rev. Double eagle. Struck as co-regent with Maria Theresa, 1765-80.

288.	3 Ducats 1773, 76, 78	150.00
289.	2 Ducats 1768-80	75.00
290.	1 Ducat 1764-80 ....*	30.00
291.	¼ Ducat 1765, 77	15.00

Draped laureate bust. Rev. Double eagle.

292.	4 Ducats 1786. A mm.	200.00
293.	1 Ducat 1781-84. C mm.	40.00
294.	1 Ducat 1781-86. F mm. ....*	30.00
295.	1 Ducat 1780, 82. A mm.	30.00
296.	1 Ducat 1781, 82. E mm.	30.00
297.	1 Ducat 1781, 82. G mm.	30.00

Laureate head. Rev. Double eagle.

298.	2 Ducats 1784, 86, 87. A mm.	40.00
299.	2 Ducats 1786, 87. B mm.	40.00
300.	2 Ducats 1781-87. E mm.	37.50
301.	2 Ducats 1786. M mm. ....*	150.00
302.	1 Ducat 1782-90. A mm.	25.00
303.	1 Ducat 1786-90. B mm.	27.50
304.	1 Ducat 1783-90. E mm.	27.50
305.	1 Ducat 1787-90. F mm.	27.50
306.	1 Ducat 1783-90. G mm.	27.50
307.	1 Ducat 1786, 87, 88. M mm.	35.00
308.	½ Ducat 1787. A mm. .... Unknown

Laureate head. Rev. Circular shield over cross.

309.	1 Souverain d'or 1783-90. A mm.	125.00
310.	1 Souverain d'or 1786. F mm.	125.00
311.	1 Souverain d'or 1781-89. Head mm.	100.00
312.	½ Souverain d'or 1786-90. A mm. ....*	35.00
313.	½ Souverain d'or 1786-90. F mm.	35.00
314.	½ Souverain d'or 1786, 88. Head mm.	50.00
315.	1 Sovrano 1786-90. M mm. ....*	75.00
316.	½ Sovrano 1787-90. M mm.	40.00

LEOPOLD II, 1790-1792
Laureate head. Rev. Arms.

317.	1 Ducat 1790	100.00

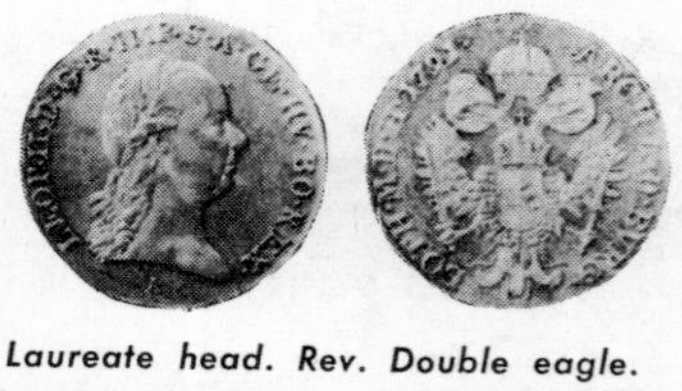

Laureate head. Rev. Double eagle.

318.	4 Ducats 1790. A mm.	200.00
319.	2 Ducats 1790. A mm. .... Unknown
320.	1 Ducat 1790, 91. A mm. ....*	30.00
321.	1 Ducat 1791. B mm.	35.00
322.	1 Ducat 1791, 92. E mm.	30.00
323.	1 Ducat 1791, 92. F mm.	30.00
324.	1 Ducat 1791, 92. G mm.	30.00

AUSTRIA (cont'd)

Laureate head. Rev. Arms.

325.	1 Souverain d'or 1791. Head mm.	Unknown
326.	1 Souverain d'or 1790, 91. A mm.	125.00
327.	1 Souverain d'or 1792. B mm.	150.00
328.	1 Souverain d'or 1792. E mm.	150.00
329.	1 Souverain d'or 1792. F mm.	150.00
330.	1 Sovrano 1790, 91, 92. M mm. .... *	150.00
331.	½ Souverain d'or 1791, 92. A mm.	75.00
332.	½ Souverain d'or 1792. B mm.	100.00
333.	½ Souverain d'or 1792. E mm.	100.00
334.	½ Sovrano 1790, 91, 92. M mm. .... *	75.00
335.	¼ Sovrano 1791. M mm.	75.00

FRANCIS (II, 1792-1806; I, 1806-1835)

Laureate head. Rev. Arms.

336.	1 Ducat 1792. A mm.	125.00

Laureate bust. Rev. Double eagle.

337.	4 Ducats 1793-1830. A mm.	100.00

Laureate head. Rev. Double eagle.

338.	2 Ducats 1799-1804. A mm.	60.00
339.	1 Ducat 1792-1831. A mm.	20.00
340.	1 Ducat 1792-1830. B mm.	20.00
341.	1 Ducat 1797-1807. C mm.	75.00
342.	1 Ducat 1806, 08, 09. D mm.	75.00
343.	1 Ducat 1792-1830. E mm.	20.00
344.	1 Ducat 1793-1826. G mm. .... *	22.50
345.	1 Ducat 1819, 24. V mm.	50.00
346.	½ Ducat 1796. E mm.	150.00

Older laureate head. Rev. Double eagle.

347.	1 Ducat 1832-35. A mm.	20.00
348.	1 Ducat 1832-35. B mm.	20.00
349.	1 Ducat 1833, 34, 35. E mm.	22.50

Laureate head. Rev. Arms.

350.	1 Souverain d'or 1793. Head mm.	175.00
351.	1 Souverain d'or 1792-98. A mm.	60.00
352.	1 Souverain d'or 1794, 95, 96. B mm.	75.00
353.	1 Souverain d'or 1796. F mm.	125.00
354.	1 Souverain d'or 1793. H mm.	75.00

355.	1 Sovrano 1793-1800. M mm. .... *	65.00
356.	1 Sovrano 1793. V mm.	100.00
357.	1 Sovrano 1796. MM monogram mm. (Mantua)	250.00
358.	½ Souverain d'or 1792-98. A mm.	50.00
359.	½ Souverain d'or 1794, 95. B mm.	50.00
360.	½ Souverain d'or 1795. E mm.	125.00
361.	½ Souverain d'or 1793-96. F mm.	75.00
362.	½ Souverain d'or 1793, 98. H mm.	125.00
363.	½ Sovrano 1800. M mm.	100.00
364.	½ Sovrano 1793. V mm.	75.00

Older laureate head. Rev. Double eagle.

365.	1 Sovrano 1822, 23, 31. A mm.	75.00
366.	1 Sovrano 1820-35. M mm. .... *	65.00
367.	1 Sovrano 1822. V mm.	75.00
368.	½ Sovrano 1822, 23, 31. A mm.	50.00
369.	½ Sovrano 1820, 22, 31, 35. M mm.	40.00
370.	½ Sovrano 1822. V mm.	60.00

Ruler kneeling before St. Mark. Rev. Christ. Struck at Venice in the style of the old Venetian Ducats.

371.	1 Zecchino ND	60.00

FERDINAND I, 1835-1848

Laureate bust. Rev. Double eagle.

372.	4 Ducats 1835-48. A mm. .... *	125.00
373.	4 Ducats 1848. E mm.	175.00

Laureate head. Rev. Double eagle.

374.	1 Ducat 1835-48. A mm.	20.00
375.	1 Ducat 1837-48. B mm.	22.50
376.	1 Ducat 1835-48. E mm.	22.50
377.	1 Ducat 1840-48. V mm.	35.00

Laureate head. Rev. Double eagle. The 1849-M ½ Sovrano is Posthumous.

378.	1 Sovrano 1837-47. A mm.	75.00
379.	1 Sovrano 1837-48. M mm.	100.00
380.	1 Sovrano 1837-47. V mm. .... *	75.00
381.	½ Sovrano 1837. A mm.	Unknown
382.	½ Sovrano 1837-49. M mm. .... *	75.00
383.	½ Sovrano 1837-47. V mm.	65.00

AUSTRIA (cont'd)

FRANZ JOSEPH, 1848-1916

Young laureate bust. Rev. Double eagle.

384.	4 Ducats 1854-59. A mm.	....................*	75.00
385.	4 Ducats 1857. V mm.	....	200.00

Laureate bust with small side whiskers. Rev. Double eagle.

386.	4 Ducats 1860-65. A mm.	....	65.00
387.	4 Ducats 1864, 65. V mm.	....	100.00

Older bust with heavier whiskers. Rev. Double eagle.

388.	4 Ducats 1866-72	....	60.00

Oldest bust with thick whiskers. Rev. Double eagle.

389.	4 Ducats 1872-1914	....	50.00
390.	4 Ducats 1915. Proof restrike	.................*	35.00

Young laureate head to left. Rev. Double eagle. With large date in legend and additional small date 1898. Struck in 1898 on the 50th year of his reign.

391.	1 Ducat 1848, 49, 50, 51	....	35.00

Young laureate head to right. Rev. Double eagle.

392.	1 Ducat 1852-59. A mm.	....	25.00
393.	1 Ducat 1853-59. B mm.	....	30.00
394.	1 Ducat 1853-59. E mm.	....	30.00
395.	1 Ducat 1855, 58. M mm.	....	75.00
396.	1 Ducat 1854-59. V mm.	...............*	40.00

Laureate head with small side whiskers. Rev. Double eagle.

397.	1 Ducat 1860-65. A mm.	....	25.00
398.	1 Ducat 1860-65 B mm.	....	30.00
399.	1 Ducat 1860-65. E mm.	....	30.00
400.	1 Ducat 1860-65. V mm.	...............*	35.00

Older head with heavier whiskers. Rev. Double eagle.

401.	1 Ducat 1866-72. A mm.	....	20.00
402.	1 Ducat 1866, 67. B mm.	....	35.00
403.	1 Ducat 1866, 67. E mm.	....	35.00
404.	1 Ducat 1866. V mm.	....	50.00

Oldest head with thick whiskers. Rev. Double eagle.

405.	1 Ducat 1872-1914	....	15.00
406.	1 Ducat 1915. Proof restrike	.................*	10.00
407.	1 Ducat 1951. Unofficial Mint error for 1915	....	50.00

Laureate head. Rev. Double eagle.

408.	1 Sovrano 1853, 55, 56. M mm.	.............*	125.00
409.	1 Sovrano 1854, 55, 56. V mm.	....	125.00
410.	½ Sovrano 1854, 55, 56. M mm.	....	100.00
411.	½ Sovrano 1854, 55, 56. V mm.	.............*	100.00

Laureate head. Rev. Value and date in wreath.

412.	1 Krone 1858-66. A mm.	...............*	60.00
413.	1 Krone 1859. B mm.	....	Unique
414.	1 Krone 1858. E mm.	....	125.00
415.	1 Krone 1859. M mm.	....	300.00
416.	1 Krone 1858, 59. V mm.	....	300.00
417.	½ Krone 1858-66. A mm.	....	50.00
418.	½ Krone 1859, 60, 61. B mm.	....	125.00
419.	½ Krone 1858, 59, 61. E mm.	....	125.00
420.	½ Krone 1858. V mm.	....	250.00

Head in circle of shields. Rev. Double eagle. On the Vienna Shooting Match.

421.	4 Ducats 1873	....	200.00

Uniformed bust. Rev. Tourist Inn. On the building of the Charles Louis Inn on Mt. Raxalpe.

422.	6 Ducats 1877. (Same die as for the silver coin)	....	3000.00

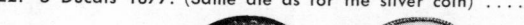

Head. Rev. Double eagle and values.

423.	8 Florins-20 Francs 1870-92	.................*	22.50
424.	4 Florins-10 Francs 1870-92	....	15.00

Old laureate head. Rev. Double eagle.

425. 20 Corona 1892-1909 ....*...... 17.50
426. 10 Corona 1892-1909 .... 12.50

Plain head. Rev. Double eagle.

427. 100 Corona 1909-15 .... 90.00
428. 20 Corona 1909-16 ....*...... 20.00
429. 20 Corona 1916. Change in arms ....- 30.00
430. 10 Corona 1909-12 .... 12.50

Plain head. Rev. Female reclining on clouds. On the 60th year of reign.

431. 100 Corona 1908 .... 100.00

Plain head. Rev. Double eagle. On the 60th year of reign.

432. 20 Corona 1908 .... 27.50
433. 10 Corona 1908 ....*...... 17.50

KARL I, 1916-1918
Head. Rev. Eagle.

434. 20 Corona 1918 .... Unique

C. Republic of —

Large eagle. Rev. Value in circular wreath.

435. 100 Kronen 1923, 24 ....*...... 175.00
436. 20 Kronen 1923, 24 .... 35.00

Eagle. Rev. Value between branches.

437. 100 Schillings 1926-34 .... 65.00
438. 25 Schillings 1926-34 ....*...... 17.50

Standing figure of the Maria Zell Madonna. Rev. Eagle.

439. 100 Schillings 1935-38 .... 90.00

St. Leopold holding model of Church. Rev. Eagle.

440. 25 Schillings 1935-38 .... 30.00

D. Cities of —

BRIXEN

Bishops of —

CHARLES OF AUSTRIA, 1613-1624
Bust. Rev. Arms.

1. 7 Ducats 1614 .... 500.00
2. 3 Ducats 1614 .... 200.00

Bust. Rev. Three shields and two hooks.

3. 1 Ducat 1614, 18 .... 150.00
4. ½ Ducat 1618 .... 100.00

CASPAR IGNATZ OF KUENIGL, 1702-1747

Bust. Rev. Two shields.

5. 1 Ducat 1717, 45 .... 125.00

LEOPOLD MARIA JOSEPH OF SPAUR, 1747-1778
Bust. Rev. Arms.

6. 1 Ducat 1768 .... 150.00

KEVENHULLER

Counts of —

JOHN JOSEPH, 1742-1776

Bust. Rev. Arms.

1. 1 Ducat 1761 .... 150.00

KLOSTERNEUBURG

Priors of —

THOMAS
St. Leopold. Rev. Castle.

1. 1 Ducat ND (1750) 150.00

MONTFORT

Counts of —

ANTON III THE YOUNGER, 1693-1734

Crown over draped shield. Rev. Orb on eagle.

1. 1 Ducat 1715 .... **300.00**

Bust. Rev. Crown over draped shield.

2. 1 Ducat 1718 ....* **200.00**
3. ½ Ducat 1722 .... **100.00**
4. ¼ Ducat 1722, 28, 30 ....* **65.00**

ERNST MAX JOSEPH, 1734-1758

Bust. Rev. Arms.

5. 1 Carolin 1735, 36 .... **125.00**
6. ½ Carolin 1734, 35 .... **100.00**
7. 1 Ducat 1745 ....* **200.00**

Bust. Rev. Cross of four crossed monograms around central "X".

8. 1 Carolin 1735 ....* **250.00**
9. ¼ Carolin 1736 .... **75.00**

FRANCIS XAVIER, 1758-1780

Bust. Rev. Arms.

10. 1 Ducat 1758 .... **175.00**

ORTENBURG

Counts of —

CHRISTOPHER WIDMAN, 1640-1660

Bust. Rev. Arms.

1. 2 Ducats 1657 .... **350.00**
2. 1 Ducat 1658 .... **200.00**

SALZBURG

Archbishops of —

PILGRIM II OF PUCHEIM, 1365-1396

Shield. Rev. St. John.

A. 1 Goldgulden ND **400.00**

LEONARD OF KEUTSCHACH, 1495-1519

Bust. Rev. Two shields, date below.

1. 4 Ducats 1513. Square **400.00**
2. 3 Ducats 1513. Square ....* **300.00**
3. 2 Ducats 1513. Square **200.00**

Bust. Rev. Arms between divided date.

4. 6 Ducats 1513.   a. Square ....500.00   b. Round **400.00**
5. 5 Ducats 1513.   a. Square ....400.00   b. Round **300.00**
6. 4 Ducats 1513.   a. Square ....350.00   b. Round **250.00**
7. 3 Ducats 1513, 19. a. Square ....250.00   b. Round **175.00**

St. Rupert. Rev. Arms in enclosure.

8. 1 Ducat 1500-19 .... **60.00**

St. Rupert. Rev. Shield.

9. 1 Goldgulden 1500-10 .... **60.00**

MATTHEW LANG OF WELLENBURG, 1519-1540

Bust. Rev. Two shields.

10. 3 Ducats 1521 .... **150.00**
11. 2 Ducats 1521 ....* **125.00**

Bust. Rev. Saint standing.

12. 3 Ducats 1521 .... **150.00**
13. 2 Ducats 1521 ....* **125.00**

Bust. Rev. Arms.

14.	10 Ducats 1522, 39	750.00
15.	8 Ducats 1522, 39	650.00
16.	8 Ducats 1522. Square	750.00
17.	6 Ducats 1522, 39	350.00
18.	5 Ducats 1522	300.00
19.	5 Ducats 1522. Square	375.00
20.	4 Ducats 1521, 22	300.00
21.	4 Ducats 1522. Square	350.00
22.	3 Ducats 1522	175.00

Bust. Rev. Two saints seated.

23.	8 Ducats 1522	650.00
24.	6 Ducats 1522	350.00

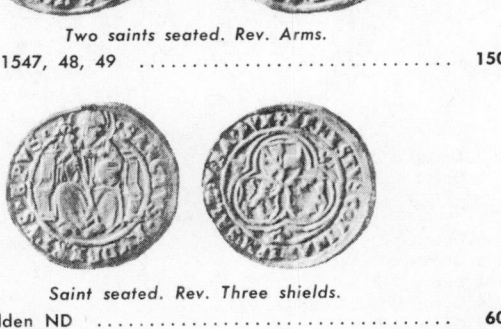

Bust. Rev. Legend. On the end of rebellion.

25.	2 Ducats 1523. Square or round		200.00
26.	1 Ducat 1523. Square or round	*	150.00

Two saints seated. Rev. Arms.

27.	10 Ducats 1539	750.00
28.	6 Ducats 1539	400.00

Saint standing. Rev. Arms.

29.	1 Ducat 1519-40	75.00

ERNST, DUKE OF BAVARIA, 1540-1554
Saint seated. Rev. Arms.

30.	10 Ducats 1540, 46	700.00

Saint standing. Rev. Arms.

31.	8 Ducats 1540		500.00
32.	4 Ducats 1540, 50		300.00
33.	1 Ducat 1541-54	*	75.00

Two saints seated. Rev. Arms.

34.	2 Ducats 1547, 48, 49	150.00

Saint seated. Rev. Three shields.

35.	1 Goldgulden ND	60.00

MICHAEL OF KUENBURG, 1554-1560
Saint seated. Rev. Two shields.

36.	8 Ducats 1554, 59	600.00
37.	6 Ducats 1555	450.00
38.	4 Ducats 1559	250.00

Two saints seated. Rev. Arms.

39.	4 Ducats 1555		250.00
40.	3 Ducats 1555	*	175.00

Saint standing. Rev. Arms.

41.	3 Ducats 1555		175.00
42.	2 Ducats 1555, 59		125.00
43.	1 Ducat 1555-59	*	65.00

JOHN JACOB KHUEN OF BELASI-LICHTENBERG, 1560-1586

Saint standing. Rev. Arms.

44.	4 Ducats 1561, 63		300.00
45.	3 Ducats 1561		200.00
46.	2 Ducats 1561-67	*	125.00
47.	2 Ducats 1561. Thick flan.		175.00
48.	1 Ducat 1561-65		60.00

Two saints seated. Rev. Arms.

49.	20 Ducats 1565	Rare
50.	12 Ducats 1565	Rare
51.	10 Ducats 1565	650.00
52.	6 Ducats 1565	350.00
53.	4 Ducats 1565	250.00

Saint seated with lions. Rev. Arms.

54.	20 Ducats 1572	Rare

Two saints seated. Rev. Two shields.

55.	8 Ducats ND	600.00

Saint seated. Rev. Two shields.

56.	8 Ducats 1571	450.00
57.	6 Ducats 1561, 63	350.00

Two saints seated. Rev. Three shields.

58.	5 Ducats ND	450.00
59.	4 Ducats ND	350.00

Saint seated. Rev. Three shields.

60.	3 Ducats 1565, 67	*	175.00
61.	1 Goldgulden 1566		200.00

AUSTRIA-SALZBURG (cont'd)

Saint seated with lions. Rev. St. Radiana with wolves.

62. 15 Ducats 1571 . . . .   **Rare**

Double eagle. Rev. Arms.

63.	2 Ducats 1568, 69	. . . .*	125.00
64.	1 Ducat 1568	. . . .	125.00

Saint with shield. Rev. Double eagle.

65.	2 Ducats 1569-85	. . . .	75.00
66.	1 Ducat 1569-82	. . . .*	75.00

GEORGE OF KUENBURG, 1586-1587

Two saints seated. Rev. Arms.

67.	6 Ducats 1586	. . . .	450.00
68.	5 Ducats 1586	. . . .	400.00
69.	4 Ducats 1586	. . . .	300.00
70.	4 Ducats 1586. Square	. . . .	350.00
71.	3 Ducats 1586, ND	. . . .	250.00
72.	2 Ducats, ND	. . . .	125.00

Saint standing. Rev. Double eagle.

72a.	2 Ducats 1586, 87	. . . .*	125.00
72b.	1 Ducat 1586	. . . .	75.00

Saint seated. Rev. Three shields.

73.	1 Goldgulden 1586	. . . .	75.00

WOLFGANG THEODORE OF RAITENAU-LANGENSTEIN, 1587-1612

Two saints seated. Rev. Arms.

74.	20 Ducats ND	. . . .	**Rare**
75.	12 Ducats ND	. . . .	**Rare**
76.	10 Ducats 1587	. . . .	700.00
77.	8 Ducats 1587, ND	. . . .	600.00
78.	7 Ducats ND	. . . .	500.00
79.	6 Ducats 1587, ND	. . . .	400.00
80.	5 Ducats ND	. . . .	350.00
81.	4 Ducats ND	. . . .	250.00
82.	4 Ducats ND. Square	. . . .	300.00
83.	3 Ducats ND	. . . .	200.00
84.	3 Ducats ND. Square	. . . .	250.00
85.	2 Ducats ND	. . . .	125.00
86.	2 Ducats ND. Square	. . . .*	200.00

Saint seated. Rev. Arms.

86a.	2 Ducats 1598-1611	. . . .*	100.00
87.	2 Ducats 1600. Square	. . . .	175.00
88.	1 Ducat 1600, 02	. . . .	60.00
89.	1 Ducat 1600, 02. Square	. . . .	100.00

Arms. Rev. Shield.

90.	1 Ducat ND. Square	. . . .	75.00
91.	½ Ducat 1603, ND. Square	. . . .*	60.00

Oval shield. Rev. Tower.

92.	14 Ducats 1590	. . . .	**Rare**
93.	12 Ducats 1594	. . . .	**Rare**
94.	12 Ducats 1594. Square	. . . .	**Rare**
95.	10 Ducats 1590, 94	. . . .	600.00
96.	9 Ducats 1594	. . . .	600.00
97.	8 Ducats 1594	. . . .	500.00

Saint with shield. Rev. Tower.

98.	16 Ducats 1593	. . . .	**Rare**
99.	12 Ducats 1593	. . . .	**Rare**
100.	10 Ducats 1593	. . . .	500.00
101.	10 Ducats 1593. Square	. . . .	650.00
102.	8 Ducats 1593	. . . .	450.00
103.	7 Ducats 1593	. . . .	400.00
104.	7 Ducats 1593. Square	. . . .	500.00
105.	6 Ducats 1593	. . . .	350.00
106.	5 Ducats 1593	. . . .	300.00
107.	5 Ducats 1593, ND. Square	. . . .	350.00
108.	4 Ducats 1593, ND	. . . .*	250.00
108.	4 Ducats ND. Square	. . . .	300.00
110.	3 Ducats ND	. . . .	200.00
111.	3 Ducats ND. Square	. . . .	250.00

Saint with shield. Rev. Double eagle.

112.	2 Ducats 1587-97	. . . .	125.00
113.	1 Ducat 1587-97	. . . .*	75.00

Saint seated. Rev. Tower.

114.	8 Ducats ND	. . . .	400.00
115.	5 Ducats ND	. . . .	250.00
116.	4 Ducats ND	. . . .	200.00
117.	4 Ducats 1587. Square	. . . .	300.00
118.	3 Ducats ND	. . . .	150.00

Four shields. Rev. Two shields.

119.	½ Ducat 1611. Square	....	75.00
120.	½ Ducat 1599/1611. Square hybrid	...........*	100.00
121.	¼ Ducat 1599/1559. Square hybrid	....	50.00

Four shields. Rev. Blank.

122.	¼ Ducat 1610. Square	....	50.00

MARCUS SITTICUS, COUNT OF HOHENEMS, 1612-1619

Bust. Rev. Two saints seated.

123.	14 Ducats 1612	....	Rare
124.	12 Ducats 1612	....	Rare
125.	8 Ducats 1613	....	450.00
126.	6 Ducats 1615	....	350.00
127.	5 Ducats 1615	....	300.00
128.	4 Ducats 1615, 16, 18	...................*	250.00

Saint seated. Rev. Tower.

129.	6 Ducats 1617	....	400.00

Saint seated. Rev. Arms.

130.	10 Ducats 1613. Square	....	750.00
131.	10 Ducats 1617	....	600.00
132.	8 Ducats 1613	....	450.00
133.	7 Ducats 1618. Square	....	450.00
134.	6 Ducats 1617, 18	....	375.00
135.	6 Ducats 1616, 17. Square	....	400.00
136.	5 Ducats 1612	....	250.00
137.	5 Ducats 1612, 17. Square	....	300.00
138.	4 Ducats 1612, 14, 15, 17	....	200.00
139.	3 Ducats 1617	....	175.00
140.	3 Ducats 1612. Square	....	200.00
141.	2 Ducats 1612-16	....	100.00
142.	2 Ducats 1612-16. Square	....	125.00
143.	1 Ducat 1612-18	....	50.00
144.	1 Ducat 1613-18. Square	....	60.00

Two saints seated. Rev. Arms.

145.	2 Ducats ND. Square	....	125.00

Saint standing. Rev. Arms.

146.	1 Goldgulden 1619	....	75.00

Arms on each side.

147.	1 Ducat 1614, 15, 18. Square	....	75.00
148.	½ Ducat 1612, 14, 18. Square	....	50.00

PARIS, COUNT LODRON, 1619-1653

Cathedral carried by two saints. Rev. Reliquary carried by eight Bishops.

149.	20 Ducats 1628	....	Rare
150.	16 Ducats 1628	....	Rare
151.	12 Ducats 1628	....	Rare
152.	10 Ducats 1628	....	500.00
153.	10 Ducats 1628. Square	....	650.00
154.	8 Ducats 1628	....	300.00
155.	8 Ducats 1628. Square	....	350.00
156.	6 Ducats 1628	....	250.00
157.	5 Ducats 1628	....	200.00
158.	5 Ducats 1628. Square	....	250.00
159.	4 Ducats 1628	...................*	250.00
160.	4 Ducats 1628. Square	....	250.00
161.	3 Ducats 1628	....	150.00

Saint standing. Rev. Madonna.

162.	10 Ducats 1628, 31	....	400.00
163.	8 Ducats 1625, 28	....	350.00
164.	6 Ducats 1628	....	250.00
165.	4 Ducats 1624. Square	....	200.00
166.	4 Ducats 1624, 25, 29, 38	....	175.00
167.	3 Ducats 1631, 38, 42	....	150.00
168.	3 Ducats 1624-42. Square	....	175.00
169.	2 Ducats 1626	....	100.00
170.	2 Ducats 1626. Square	....	125.00

Saint seated. Rev. Arms.

171.	8 Ducats 1620	....	400.00
172.	5 Ducats 1620	....	350.00
173.	4 Ducats 1620	....	250.00
174.	4 Ducats 1620. Square	....	300.00
175.	3 Ducats 1620	....	175.00
176.	2 Ducats 1624-48	....	100.00
177.	2 Ducats 1634-51. Square	....	150.00
178.	1 Ducat 1620-53	....	40.00
179.	1 Ducat 1627-51. Square	...................*	50.00
180.	½ Ducat 1643-52	....	30.00
181.	½ Ducat 1643-50. Square	....	35.00
182.	¼ Ducat 1652	....	20.00

Arms. Rev. Arms on cross.

183.	½ Ducat 1634-46	....	30.00
184.	¼ Ducat 1624	....	35.00

GUIDOBALD, COUNT OF THUN-HOHENSTEIN, 1654-1668

Arms. Rev. Cathedral carried by two saints.

185.	50 Ducats 1654. Square	Rare
186.	24 Ducats 1654	Rare
187.	20 Ducats 1654	Rare
188.	16 Ducats 1654	Rare
189.	12 Ducats 1654	Rare
190.	10 Ducats 1654	450.00
191.	8 Ducats 1654	375.00
192.	6 Ducats 1654, 55	250.00
193.	5 Ducats 1654, 55 ....*.....	200.00
194.	4 Ducats 1654, 55	175.00

Saint seated. Rev. Arms.

195.	2 Ducats 1654, 59, 62	100.00
196.	1 Ducat 1654-68 ....*......	40.00
197.	1 Ducat 1655, 57, 66. Square	65.00
198.	½ Ducat 1654-66	25.00
199.	¼ Ducat 1654-68	20.00

MAX GANDOLPH, COUNT KUENBURG, 1668-1687

Arms. Rev. Five saints standing. On the 1100th year of Salzburg.

200.	12 Ducats 1682. Square ....*......	Rare
201.	10 Ducats 1682	400.00
202.	10 Ducats 1682. Square	500.00
203.	8 Ducats 1682. Square	300.00
204.	7 Ducats 1682	250.00
205.	6 Ducats 1682	250.00
206.	5 Ducats 1682	200.00
207.	4 Ducats 1682	200.00
208.	3 Ducats 1682	150.00

Arms under triangle. Rev. Legend. On the 1100th year of Salzburg.

209.	3 Ducats 1682	150.00
210.	2 Ducats 1682 ....*......	100.00

Two saints seated with Church. Rev. Arms.

211.	44 Ducats 1668	Rare
212.	25 Ducats 1668	Rare
213.	25 Ducatas 1668. Square	Rare
214.	20 Ducats 1668	Rare
215.	20 Ducats 1668. Square	Rare
216.	15 Ducats 1668	Rare
217.	12 Ducats 1668	Rare
218.	12 Ducats 1668. Square ....*.....	Rare
219.	10 Ducats 1668	500.00
220.	10 Ducats 1668. Square	500.00
221.	9 Ducats 1668	400.00
222.	8 Ducats 1668	400.00
223.	6 Ducats 1668	350.00
224.	5 Ducats 1668	300.00
225.	4 Ducats 1668	200.00
226.	3 Ducats 1668	200.00

Saint standing. Rev. Arms.

227.	10 Ducats 1686	500.00

Saint seated. Rev. Arms.

228.	6 Ducats 1668	250.00
229.	5 Ducats 1668	200.00
230.	4 Ducats 1673. Square	200.00
231.	3 Ducats 1670, 73	150.00
232.	3 Ducats 1673. Square	200.00
233.	2 Ducats 1668, 73 ....*.....	100.00
234.	2 Ducats 1673. Square	125.00
235.	1 Ducat 1668-87	40.00
236.	1 Ducat 1668-74. Square	50.00
237.	½ Ducat 1668-86	30.00
238.	½ Ducat 1668. Square	40.00
239.	¼ Ducat 1668-86	25.00

JOHN ERNST, COUNT OF THUN-HOHENSTEIN, 1687-1709
Two saints seated with Church. Rev. Arms.

240.	50 Ducats 1687. Square	Rare
241.	20 Ducats 1687	Rare
242.	15 Ducats 1687	Rare
243.	12 Ducats 1687	Rare
244.	10 Ducats 1687	400.00
245.	8 Ducats 1687	300.00
246.	7 Ducats 1687	250.00
247.	6 Ducats 1687	200.00
248.	5 Ducats 1687	175.00
249.	4 Ducats 1687	150.00

Saint seated. Rev. Arms.

250.	10 Ducats 1687	400.00
251.	3 Ducats 1690	150.00
252.	2 Ducats 1688, 1707, 08	100.00

AUSTRIA-SALZBURG (cont'd)

253.	2 Ducats 1688. Square	....	125.00
254.	1 Ducat 1687-1708	....	40.00
255.	½ Ducat 1687-1707	..................*	25.00
256.	¼ Ducat 1687-1707	..................*	20.00

"WAS." Rev. "IRS." On the visit to Salzburg of Joseph I and Wilhelmina Amalia.

257.	1 Ducat 1699	..................*	60.00
258.	¼ Ducat 1699	....	30.00

FRANZ ANTON, PRINCE OF HARRACH, 1709-1727
Bust. Rev. Arms.

259.	25 Ducats 1709	....	Rare
260.	20 Ducats 1709	....	Rare
261.	10 Ducats 1709, 11	....	400.00
262.	5 Ducats 1709	....	250.00
263.	1 Ducat 1710-26	....	40.00

Bust. Rev. City view.

264.	25 Ducats 1711	....	Rare
265.	20 Ducats 1711	....	Rare

Bust. Rev. Horse in landscape.

266.	25 Ducats 1709	....	Rare
267.	20 Ducats 1709	....	Rare
268.	10 Ducats 1709	....	400.00
269.	5 Ducats 1718, ND	....	250.00

Saint seated. Rev. Arms.

270.	2 Ducats 1709. Square	....	150.00
271.	1 Ducat 1709-26	..................*	40.00
272.	½ Ducat 1709-27	....	25.00
273.	¼ Ducat 1709-25	....	20.00

LEOPOLD ANTON ELEUTHERIUS OF FIRMIAN, 1727-1744

Bust. Rev. Arms.

274.	1 Ducat 1728-44	....	40.00

Saint seated. Rev. Arms.

275.	2 Ducats 1734, 35	....	75.00
276.	1 Ducat 1727-40	....	35.00
277.	½ Ducat 1728	....	30.00
278.	¼ Ducat 1728-40	....	20.00

JACOB ERNST, COUNT OF LIECHTENSTEIN, 1745-1747
Bust. Rev. Arms.

279.	1 Ducat 1745, 46, 47	....	60.00

Saint seated. Rev. Arms.

280.	1 Ducat 1745, 46	....	40.00
281.	¼ Ducat 1745	....	25.00

ANDREW JACOB, COUNT OF DIETRICHSTEIN, 1747-1753

Bust. Rev. Arms.

282.	2 Ducats 1750	..................*	125.00
283.	1 Ducat 1748-51	....	80.00
284.	½ Ducat 1751	....	30.00
285.	¼ Ducat 1751	....	25.00

Saint seated. Rev. Arms.

286.	2 Ducats 1752	....	100.00
287.	1 Ducat 1747-52	....	35.00
288.	½ Ducat 1749	....	30.00
288a.	¼ Ducat 1749	....	25.00

SIGISMUND III, COUNT OF SCHRATTENBACH, 1753-1771
Bust. Rev. Arms.

289.	2 Ducats 1755	....	100.00
290.	1 Ducat 1754-63	....	40.00
291.	½ Ducat 1755, 61	....	30.00
292.	¼ Ducat 1755, 70	....	20.00

Bust. Rev. Saint seated.

293.	5 Ducats 1759	....	250.00

Bust. Rev. Two shields.

294.	2 Ducats 1764	..................*	100.00
295.	1 Ducat 1762-64	..................*	40.00

Bust. Rev. Draped arms.

296.	2 Ducats 1765-71	..................*	100.00
297.	1 Ducat 1763-71, ND	....	40.00

Bust. Rev. Saint seated with small Madonna.

298.	6 Ducats 1760	....	400.00

Bust. Rev. View of the Mint.

299.	3 Ducats 1766	....	175.00

Saint standing with small Madonna. Rev. Arms.

300.	1 Ducat 1763	....	75.00

Saint seated. Rev. Arms.

301.	1 Ducat 1753	....	50.00
302.	¼ Ducat 1753	....	20.00

AUSTRIA-SALZBURG (cont'd)

SEDE VACANTE, 1772

Saint seated. Rev. Arms.

303. 1 Ducat 1772 .... 40.00

JEROME, COUNT OF COLLOREDO-WALLSEE, 1772-1803

Bust. Rev. Arms.

304.	2 Ducats 1773	125.00
305.	1 Ducat 1772-1803 ....*	30.00
306.	½ Ducat 1776	25.00
307.	¼ Ducat 1776, 77, 82	20.00

Bust. Rev. Temple.

308.	2 Ducats 1782	75.00
309.	1 Ducat 1782	35.00

FERDINAND, PRINCE AND ELECTOR, 1803-1806

Bust. Rev. Draped arms.

310. 1 Ducat 1803, 04 .... 60.00

Bust. Rev. Crowned arms.

311. 1 Ducat 1805, 06 .... 60.00

FRANCIS II (I), HOLY ROMAN AND AUSTRIAN EMPEROR, 1806-1810

Head. Rev. Eagle.

312. 1 Ducat 1806, 09 .... 65.00

TRAUTSON-FALKENSTEIN

Counts, and later, Princes of —

PAUL SIXTUS I, 1589-1621
Arms. Rev. Double eagle.

1. 1 Ducat ND 75.00

Bust. Rev. Arms.

2. 5 Ducats 1620 .... 500.00

JOHN FRANCIS, 1620-1663
Bust. Rev. Arms.

3.	1 Ducat 1634, 38	100.00
4.	¼ Ducat 1635	30.00

FRANCIS EUSEBIUS, 1678-1728
Bust. Rev. Arms.

5. 1 Ducat 1708, 15 .... 75.00

JOHN LEOPOLD, 1663-1724
Bust. Rev. Arms.

6. 1 Ducat 1719 .... 125.00

VIENNA

Archbishops of —

CHRISTOPHER ANTON OF MIGAZZI, 1757-1803

Bust. Rev. Arms.

1. 1 Ducat 1781 .... 75.00

WINDISCHGRAETZ

Counts of —

LEOPOLD VICTOR JOHN, 1727-1746
Bust. Rev. Arms.

1.	10 Ducats 1732	Rare
2.	1 Ducat 1733	150.00

JOSEPH NICHOLAS, 1746-1802
Bust. Rev. Arms.

3.	5 Ducats 1777	200.00
4.	1 Ducat 1777	100.00

BELGIUM

A. United Provinces of —

Lion standing. Rev. Circle of eleven shields. Struck during the Insurrection against the Austrian Hapsburgs.

1. 1 Lion d'or 1790 .... 175.00

B. Kings of —

LEOPOLD I, 1831-1865

Laureate head. Rev. Value and date. This issue was not placed in circulation.

2.	40 Francs 1834-41	350.00
3.	20 Francs 1835-41 ....*	150.00

Plain head. Rev. Arms.

4.	25 Francs 1847-50	40.00
5.	10 Francs 1849, 50	30.00

Plain head. Rev. Conjoined heads of the Duke and Duchess of Brabant. On their marriage. Without the mark of value.

6. (100 Francs) 1853 .... 250.00

Plain head. Rev. Value.

7. 20 Francs 1865 .... 25.00

LEOPOLD II, 1865-1909

Head. Rev. Arms. The 10 Franc piece was not placed in circulation.

8. 20 Francs 1866-82 .... 16.00
9. 10 Francs 1867 .... 150.00

ALBERT, 1909-1934

Uniformed bust. Rev. Arms. Only the 20 Franc piece was placed in circulation. 100 Franc pieces dated 1911 were not officially struck.

10. 100 Francs 1912. French legends ....*...... 2500.00
11. 100 Francs 1912. Flemish legends 3000.00
12. 20 Francs 1914. French legends ....*...... 22.50
13. 20 Francs 1914. Flemish legends 22.50
14. 10 Francs 1911, 12. French legends 150.00
15. 10 Francs 1911, 12. Flemish legends 150.00

C. Cities of —

BORNE

Lords of —

WALRAM, 1356-1378
Bust of Emperor Charles IV. Rev. Lion.

. 1 Goldgulden ND 500.00

BRABANT

Dukes of —

JOHN II, 1294-1312
St. John. Rev. Lily.

1. 1 Florin ND 200.00

JOHN III, 1312-1355

Ruler on throne. Rev. Cross.

2. 1 Chaise d'or ND 125.00
3. 1 Chaise d'or ND. With name of Louis of Bavaria..*...... 100.00

St. John. Rev. Lily.

4. 1 Florin ND 75.00

JOAN AND WENCESLAS, 1355-1383
Bust of St. Peter. Rev. Cross.

5. 1 Peter d'or ND 100.00

Lamb. Rev. Cross.

6. 2 Mouton d'or ND 250.00
7. 1 Mouton d'or ND ....*...... 100.00

Cavalier on horse. Rev. Cross.

8. 1 Cavalier d'or ND 100.00

St. Servais seated under Gothic dais. Rev. Shield.

9. 1 Florin ND 500.00

St. John. Rev. Lily.

10. 1 Florin ND 75.00

JOAN AND PHILIP, 1384-1389
Two shields. Rev. Cross.

11. 1 Ecu d'or ND 500.00

JOAN, 1383-1406

Knight on horse. Rev. Cross.

12. 1 Franc a cheval ND 150.00

Angel holding shield. Rev. Cross.

13. 1 Angel ND 800.00

Church of St. Peter at Louvain. Rev. Cross.

14. 1 Tourelle d'or ND 750.00

ANTHONY OF BURGUNDY, 1406-1415
Shield supported by lions. Rev. Cross.

15. 1 Lion d'or ND 400.00
16. ½ Lion d'or ND 400.00

BELGIUM-BRABANT (cont'd)

JOHN IV, 1414-1427
Arms. Rev. Cross.

17. 1 Ecu d'or ND **75.00**

Ruler on throne. Rev. Cross.

18. 1 Chaise d'or ND **100.00**

St. John standing. Rev. Four shields.

19. 1 Florin ND **200.00**

Lamb. Rev. Cross.

20. ½ Mouton d'or ND **100.00**

PHILIP OF ST. POL, 1420-1430
Ruler on throne. Rev. Cross.

21. 1 Chaise d'or ND **125.00**

St. Peter standing. Rev. Five shields.

22. 1 Florin ND **100.00**

Bust of St. Peter over arms. Rev. Cross.

23. 1 Ecu d'or ND **150.00**

PHILIP THE GOOD, 1430-1467
Ruler on throne. Rev. Cross.

24. 1 Chaise d'or ND **100.00**

Bust of St. Peter over arms. Rev. Cross.

25. 1 Peter d'or ND **75.00**

Ruler on horse. Rev. Cross.

26. 1 Cavalier d'or ND **75.00**
27. ½ Cavalier d'or ND **150.00**

Lion seated under dais. Rev. Arms.

28. 1 Lion d'or ND ....* **75.00**
29. ⅓ Lion d'or ND **150.00**

St. Andrew standing with cross. Rev. Arms on cross.

30. 1 Florin ND **75.00**

CHARLES THE BOLD, 1467-1477

St. Andrew standing with cross. Rev. Arms.

31. 1 Florin ND ....* **75.00**
32. ½ Florin ND **125.00**

MARIE OF BURGUNDY, 1477-1482
St. Andrew standing with cross. Rev. Arms on cross.

33. 1 Florin ND **100.00**

St. Andrew standing with cross. Rev. Shield.

34. ½ Florin ND **500.00**

MAXIMILIAN AND PHILIP, 1482-1496
Christ on throne. Rev. Four shields.

35. 1 Florin 1492 .... **750.00**

Ruler standing in ship. Rev. Cross.

36. ½ Noble 1488 .... **175.00**

Maximilian standing. Rev. Arms on cross.

37. 2 Florins 1490 .... **1250.00**

St. Andrew standing with cross. Rev. Arms on cross.

38. 1 Florin 1482-89 .... **300.00**

St. Andrew standing with cross. Rev. Shield.

39. ½ Florin 1489, ND **300.00**

St. Andrew standing with open book. Rev. Arms on cross.

40. 1 Florin 1487 .... **750.00**

PHILIP III, 1494-1506
St. Philip with shield. Rev. Cross.

41. 1 Florin 1499-1502, ND **150.00**
42. ½ Florin 1500, ND **75.00**

St. Philip standing. Rev. Four shields in angles of cross.

43. 1 Florin ND **200.00**

Arms supported by lions. Rev. Cross.

44. 2 Souverain d'or 1500-09 .... **500.00**

CHARLES V OF SPAIN, 1506-1555
St. Philip with shield. Rev. Floriated cross.

45. 1 Florin (1506-55), ND **50.00**
46. ½ Florin (1506-55), ND **50.00**

Crowned bust. Rev. Arms on eagle.

47. 1 Real d'or ND ....* **100.00**
48. ½ Real d'or ND **75.00**

Crowned arms. Rev. Arms on floriated cross.

49. 1 Couronne d'or 1544-54 .... **60.00**

Arms supported by lions. Rev. Cross.

50. 2 Souverain d'or 1513 .... **750.00**

PHILIP II OF SPAIN, 1555-1598

Bust. Rev. Arms.

51. 1 Real d'or (1555-98), ND ....* **100.00**
52. ½ Real d'or (1555-98), ND **75.00**

Arms. Rev. Floriated cross.

BELGIUM-BRABANT (cont'd)

53. 2 Florins ND 350.00
54. 1 Couronne d'or 1580-86, ND ....*...... 50.00

St. Andrew standing with cross. Rev. Arms.

55. 1 Florin 1567-69 .... 125.00

FRANCIS OF ALENCON, 1582
Arms. Rev. Cross.

56. 1 Couronne d'or 1582 .... 750.00

INDEPENDENT STATES OF BRABANT, 1584-1585
Lion seated under Gothic dais. Rev. Arms on cross.

57. 1 Lion d'or 1585 .... 300.00
58. ½ Lion d'or 1585 .... 400.00

ALBERT AND ISABELLA OF SPAIN, 1598-1621
(Governors for the Crown).

Crowned busts facing each other. Rev. Arms.

59. 2 Ducats (1598-1621), ND ....*...... 100.00
60. 1 Ducat (1598-1621), ND 125.00

Arms. Rev. Cross.

61. 2 Albertins (⅔ Ducat) 1601-04 ....*...... 50.00
62. 1 Albertin (⅓ Ducat) 1601-04 .... 30.00
63. 1 Couronne d'or 1598-1621 .... 100.00

Albert and Isabella on thrones. Rev. Arms.

64. 2 Souverain d'or 1598-1621, ND 125.00

Conjoined busts. Rev. Arms.

65. 1 Souverain d'or ND 150.00

Crowned shield and crowned initials. Rev. Cross.

66. ½ Souverain d'or 1616, ND ....*...... 150.00
67. 1 Couronne d'or 1614, ND 150.00

Albert and Isabella walking to right. Rev. Arms.

68. ⅔ Souverain d'or ND 500.00

PHILIP IV OF SPAIN, 1621-1665

Crowned bust. Rev. Arms.

69. 2 Souverain d'or 1623-65 .... 85.00

Crowned lion standing. Rev. Arms.

70. 1 Lion d'or (1621-65) 75.00

Cross. Rev. Arms.

71. 1 Couronne d'or 1623-65 .... 50.00

CHARLES II OF SPAIN, 1665-1700
Crowned child bust. Rev. Arms.

72. 2 Souverain d'or 1667-97 .... 175.00

Older bust with long curls. Rev. Arms.

73. 2 Souverain d'or 1686-94 .... 200.00

Lion standing. Rev. Arms.

74. 1 Lion d'or (1665-1700) 100.00

PHILIP V OF SPAIN, 1700-1712
Bust. Rev. Arms.

75. 2 Souverain d'or 1700-12 .... 350.00

AUSTRIAN KINGS
(For Austrian type coins struck at the Belgian Mints, see under Austria beginning with the year 1711).

BRUSSELS

Legend and "84". Rev. Blank. Square coins struck at Brussels while under siege by Alexander Farnese.

1. 4 Florins 1584 ....*...... 600.00
2. 2 Florins 1584 .... 750.00

FAGNOLLE

Counts of —
CHARLES DE LIGNE, 1770-1803
Bust. Rev. Arms.

1. 1 Ducat ND 200.00

FLANDERS

Counts of —

LOUIS DE CRECY, 1322-1346
St. John. Rev. Lily.

1. 1 Florin ND 75.00

LOUIS DE MALE, 1346-1384

Ruler seated on throne. Rev. Cross.

2. 1 Chaise d'or ND ....* 150.00
3. ½ Chaise d'or ND 100.00
4. ¼ Chaise d'or ND 75.00

Ruler on horse. Rev. Cross.

5. 1 Franc a Cheval ND 125.00

Ruler standing. Rev. Initials and cross.

6. 1 Franc a Pied ND 100.00

Lion seated. Rev. Initials and cross.

7. 1 Lion d'or ND ....* 150.00
8. ½ Lion d'or ND 100.00

Lamb. Rev. Cross.

9. 1 Mouton d'or ND 100.00

Helmeted shield. Rev. Initials and cross.

10. 1 Heaume d'or ND ....* 150.00
10a. ⅓ Heaume d'or ND 500.00

PHILIP THE BOLD, 1384-1404
Ruler seated. Rev. Cross.

11. 1 Chaise d'or ND 100.00

Ruler in ship. Rev. Cross.

12. 1 Rosenoble ND 250.00
13. ½ Rosenoble ND 500.00

Angel with two shields. Rev. Cross.

14. 1 Angel ND 600.00

Two shields. Rev. Cross.

15. 2 Heaume d'or ND 500.00

JOHN, 1405-1419
Ruler in ship, Rev. Cross.

16. 1 Rosenoble ND 200.00

PHILIP THE GOOD, 1419-1467

Ruler in ship. Rev. Cross.

17. 1 Rosenoble ND ....* 150.00
18. ½ Rosenoble ND 300.00

Ruler on throne. Rev. Cross.

19. 1 Chaise d'or ND 100.00
20. ½ Chaise d'or ND 40.00

Ruler on horse. Rev. Arms on cross.

21. 1 Cavalier d'or ND 75.00
22. ½ Cavalier d'or ND 150.00

BELGIUM-FLANDERS (cont'd)

Lion seated. Rev. Arms on cross.

23.	1 Lion d'or ND	100.00
24.	½ Lion d'or ND	50.00
25.	⅔ Lion d'or ND ....*	100.00
26.	⅓ Lion d'or ND	50.00

St. Andrew. Rev. Arms on cross.

27.	1 Florin ND	75.00

CHARLES THE BOLD, 1467-1477
St. Andrew. Rev. Arms.

28.	1 Florin ND	75.00
29.	½ Florin ND	125.00

MARIE OF BURGUNDY, 1477-1482

St. Andrew. Rev. Arms.

30.	1 Florin ND	100.00

PHILIP THE HANDSOME, 1482-1506
St. John and lamb. Rev. Arms.

31.	1 Florin ND	125.00

St. Andrew and arms. Rev. Eagle shield.

32.	½ Florin ND	150.00

St. Philip and arms. Rev. Arms.

33.	1 Florin ND	75.00
34.	½ Florin ND ....*	100.00

Arms supported by lions. Rev. Cross.

35.	1 Toison d'or ND	850.00

CHARLES V OF SPAIN, 1515-1555

Bust with sword and sceptre. Rev. Arms on eagle.

36.	1 Real d'or ND ....*	100.00
37.	1 Florin ND	75.00

Eagle shield on cross. Rev. Arms.

38.	½ Real d'or ND	50.00

St. Philip and arms. Rev. Cross.

39.	1 Florin ND	75.00
40.	½ Florin ND	100.00

Arms between briquets. Rev. Cross.

41.	1 Couronne d'or 1545, 46	100.00

PHILIP II OF SPAIN, 1555-1598
Plain bust. Rev. Arms on floriated cross.

42.	2 Reales d'or 1586, ND	125.00

Crowned bust. Rev. Arms in golden fleece.

43.	1 Real d'or ND	75.00

Plain bust. Rev. Crowned arms.

44.	½ Real d'or ND	60.00

Arms. Rev. Floriated cross.

45.	1 Couronne d'or ND	50.00

ALBERT AND ISABELLA OF SPAIN, 1598-1621
Rulers on thrones. Rev. Arms.

46.	2 Souverain d'or 1613	150.00

Initials and cross. Rev. Arms.

47.	1 Couronne d'or 1620	500.00

PHILIP IV OF SPAIN, 1621-1665
Crowned bust. Rev. Arms.

48.	2 Souverain d'or 1646	150.00

Lion standing. Rev. Arms.

49.	1 Lion d'or 1648-62	75.00

CHARLES II OF SPAIN, 1665-1700
Bust. Rev. Arms supported by lions.

50.	8 Souverain d'or 1694	650.00
51.	4 Souverain d'or 1696	200.00

Lion standing. Rev. Arms.

52.	1 Lion d'or 1700	100.00

GHENT

Royal figure in ship. Rev. Cross.

1.	1 Rosenoble 1581, 82, 83	125.00
2.	½ Rosenoble 1581, 82, 83	75.00

GRONSFELD

Lords of —

WILLIAM, 1558-1663
St. George on horse. Rev. Arms on cross.

1.	1 Florin ND	175.00

St. Martin. Rev. Lion.

2.	1 Florin ND	175.00

JUSTUS MAXIMILIAN, 1617-1667

Arms. Rev. Legend.

3.	1 Ducat 1642, 57, 64	100.00

Horseman. Rev. Arms.

4.	1 Florin ND	125.00

HAINAUT

Counts of —

LOUIS OF BAVARIA, 1345-1347
Lamb. Rev. Cross.

1. 1 Mouton d'or ND 100.00

Ruler on throne. Rev. Cross.

2. 1 Chaise d'or ND 150.00

WILLIAM III, 1356-1389
Lamb. Rev. Cross.

3. 2 Mouton d'or ND 300.00
4. 1 Mouton d'or ND 100.00

Ruler on horse. Rev. Cross.

5. 1 Grand Chevalier ND 250.00
6. 1 Franc a Cheval ND 125.00

Ruler standing. Rev. Cross.

7. 1 Royal ND 350.00

ALBERT OF BAVARIA, 1389-1404

Arms. Rev. Cross.

8. 2 Couronne d'or ND 500.00
9. 1 Couronne d'or ND .... * 100.00

WILLIAM IV, 1404-1417
Angel with shield. Rev. Cross.

10. 1 Angel ND 500.00

Arms. Rev. Cross.

11. 1 Couronne d'or ND 75.00

JACQUELINE, 1417-1433
Round shield. Rev. Cross.

12. 2 Couronne d'or ND 300.00

JOHN IV, 1418-1427
Arms. Rev. Cross.

13. 1 Couronne d'or ND 75.00

PHILIP THE GOOD, 1433-1467

Ruler on horse. Rev. Arms on cross.

14. 1 Cavalier d'or ND 75.00

Lion. Rev. Arms on cross.

15. 1 Lion d'or ND .... * 100.00
16. ½ Lion d'or ND 75.00
17. ¼ Lion d'or ND 60.00

St. Andrew. Rev. Arms on cross.

18. 1 Florin ND 125.00

PHILIP II AND THE STATES GENERAL, 1577-1599
Arms. Rev. Cross.

19. 2 Florins 1577 .... 150.00
20. 1 Florin 1577 .... 75.00

HOORN

Counts of —

DIRK LOOF, 1358-1390
St. John. Rev. Lis.

1. 1 Ducat ND 100.00

WILLIAM VII, 1358-1415
Half length bust. Rev. Double eagle.

2. 1 Florin ND 200.00

PHILIP OF MONTMORENCY, 1550-1568
St. Martin. Rev. Arms.

3. 1 Florin ND 100.00

LIEGE

Bishops of —

ENGELBERT OF MARK, 1345-1364
St. John. Rev. Lily.

1. 1 Florin ND 65.00

JOHN D'ARCKEL, 1364-1378

Lamb. Rev. Cross.

2. 1 Mouton d'or ND 250.00

St. Peter and shield. Rev. Cross.

3. 1 Ecu d'or ND 150.00

ARNOLD, 1378-1389
Bishop under dais. Rev. St. John.

4. 1 Florin ND 150.00

St. Peter under dais. Rev. Two shields.

5. 1 Florin ND 150.00

JOHN OF BAVARIA, 1389-1418
Ruler on throne. Rev. Cross.

6. 1 Chaise d'or ND 150.00

Ruler standing. Rev. Arms.

7. 1 Florin ND 125.00

St. John. Rev. Three shields.

8. 1 Florin ND 100.00

St. John. Rev. Five shields.

9. 1 Florin ND 100.00

Griffin and arms. Rev. Cross.

10. 1 Ecu d'or ND ....* 150.00
11. ½ Ecu d'or ND 100.00

JOHN OF HEINSBERG, 1419-1455
Ruler on throne. Rev. Cross.

12. 1 Chaise d'or ND 150.00

Griffin and arms. Rev. Cross.

13. 1 Ecu d'or ND 100.00

St. Peter with shield. Rev. Cross.

14. 1 Ecu d'or ND 100.00

Angel with shield. Rev. Arms on cross.

15. 1 Ecu d'or ND ....* 150.00
16. ½ Ecu d'or ND 100.00

St. Lambert standing. Rev. Arms.

17. 1 Florin ND 125.00

LOUIS OF BOURBON, 1456-1482
Lion with arms. Rev. Arms on cross.

18. 1 Lion d'or ND 100.00

Two lions with shield. Rev. Cross.

19. 1 Ecu d'or ND 100.00

St. Lambert standing. Rev. Arms.

20. 1 Florin ND 125.00

Madonna. Rev. Arms on cross.

21. 1 Florin ND 100.00

JOHN OF HOORN, 1484-1505
St. Lambert standing. Rev. Arms.

22. 1 Florin ND 100.00

Christ standing. Rev. Cross of four shields.

23. 1 Florin ND 100.00

EBERHARD OF MARK, 1506-1538
Arms. Rev. Cross.

24. 2 Florins 1512, 13 .... 250.00
24a. 1 Florin 1512, 13 .... 150.00

St. Lambert standing. Rev. Arms.

25. 1 Florin ND 75.00

St. Lambert standing. Rev. Cross of four shields.

26. 1 Florin ND 75.00

CORNELIUS OF BERGHES, 1538-1544
St. Lambert standing. Rev. Arms.

27. 1 Florin ND 75.00

Christ on throne. Rev. Four shields.

28. 1 Florin ND 75.00

GEORGE OF AUSTRIA, 1544-1557
St. George and shield. Rev. Cross of four shields.

29. 1 Florin ND 125.00

GERHARD OF GROESBECK, 1564-1580
Arms. Rev. Double eagle.

30. 1 Florin 1568 .... 150.00

Saint seated. Rev. Initials and cross.

31. 1 Florin ND 75.00

ERNST OF BAVARIA, 1581-1612
Arms and three shields. Rev. Double eagle.

32. 1 Florin 1581, 85 .... 75.00

Bust. Rev. Arms.

33. 1 Ducat 1612, ND 150.00

FERDINAND OF BAVARIA, 1612-1650
Bust. Rev. Arms.

34. 1 Ducat 1613 .... 125.00

Arms. Rev. Legend on tablet.

35. 1 Ducat ND 75.00

Arms. Rev. Cross.

36. 2 Florins 1613 .... 125.00
37. 1 Florin 1613 .... 75.00

Arms. Rev. Initials and cross.

38. 1 Florin 1614, 35, 37 .... 65.00

Ruler seated. Rev. Arms.

39. 1 Florin ND 65.00

MAXIMILIAN HENRY OF BAVARIA, 1650-1688
Arms. Rev. Legend on tablet.

40. 1 Ducat 1658 .... 65.00

Bust. Rev. Arms.

41. 1 Ducat 1668, ND 100.00

JOHN LOUIS OF ELDERN, 1688-1694

Bust. Rev. Arms.

42. 2 Ducats 1690 ....* 200.00
43. 1 Ducat 1690 .... 150.00

JOSEPH CLEMENT OF BAVARIA, 1694-1723
Bust. Rev. Arms.

44. 3 Ducats 1700 .... 350.00

JOHN THEODORE OF BAVARIA, 1744-1763
Bust. Rev. Arms.

45. 1 Ducat 1749 .... 125.00

SEDE VACANTE ISSUES
(Coins struck in the period between the death of one bishop and the coronation of another).

Bust of St. Lambert. Rev. Arms.

46. 1 Ducat 1688, 94, 1724 .... 100.00
47. 1 Ducat 1744, 63, 71, 84, 92 ....* 75.00
48. ½ Ducat 1724 .... 75.00

LOOS

Counts of —

THEODORE III, 1336-1361
Lamb. Rev. Cross.

1. 1 Mouton d'or ND 300.00

St. John. Rev. Lily.

2. 1 Florin ND 150.00

MEGEN

Counts of —

MARIA, 1572-1580
Ruler on throne. Rev. Arms in rose.

1. 2 Souverain d'or ND 350.00

Ruler in ship. Rev. Rose.

2. 1 Noble ND 200.00

Ruler in ship. Rev. Cross.

3. 1 Noble ND 200.00

RECKHEIM

Counts of —

THE VLODORPS, 1562 AND LATER

St. Peter. Rev. Madonna.

1. 1 Florin ND 100.00

St. Victor. Rev. Madonna.

2. 1 Goldgulden ND 100.00

RUMMEN

Counts of —

JOHN II, 1294-1312
Ruler on horse. Rev. Cross.

1. 1 Franc a Cheval ND 150.00

ARNOLD OF OREY, 1331-1364
Lamb. Rev. Cross.

2. 1 Mouton d'or ND 350.00

HENRY AND JOANNA, 1464-1474

Lamb. Rev. Cross.

3. 1 Mouton d'or ND ....*...... 175.00
4. ½ Mouton d'or ND 150.00

STAVELOT

Abbots of —

CHRISTOPHER OF MANDERSCHEID, 1546-1576
Arms. Rev. Double eagle.

1. 1 Ducat 1567 .... 150.00

Ruler standing. Rev. Arms.

2. 1 Ducat ND 150.00

THOREN

Abbess Nuns of —

MARGUERITE IV OF BREDERODE, 1531-1579
Madonna seated. Rev. Arms.

1. 1 Ducat ND 75.00

Bust of Ferdinand II. Rev. Madonna.

2. 1 Ducat ND 100.00

Bust of Ferdinand II. Rev. Arms.

3. 1 Ducat ND 100.00

St. Michael. Rev. Ship.

4. 1 Angel ND ....*...... 100.00
5. ½ Angel ND 150.00

VALKENBERG (FALKENBERG)

Barons of —

REINHALD OF SCHONFORST, 1354-1355
St. John. Rev. Lily.

1. 1 Florin ND 250.00

BOHEMIA

A. Kings of —

WENCESLAS II, 1278-1305
W in shield. Rev. Lion.

1. 1 Florin ND 400.00

JOHN OF LUXEMBOURG, 1310-1346
St. John. Rev. Lily.

2. 1 Florin ND 75.00

CHARLES IV, 1355-1378

Bust facing. Rev. Lion.

3. 1 Goldgulden ND 100.00

LOUIS I, 1343-1382
St. John. Rev. Lily.

4. 1 Florin ND 40.00

BOHEMIA (cont'd)

JODOCUS OF MORAVIA, 1374-1411
Ruler standing. Rev. Shield.

5. 1 Florin ND 750.00

WENCESLAS III, 1378-1419
Facing bust of St. Wenceslas. Rev. Lion.

6. 1 Ducat ND 350.00

Shield. Rev. Lion.

7. 1 Ducat ND 350.00

LADISLAS II, 1471-1516
St. Wenceslas. Rev. Lion in shield.

8. 1 Goldgulden ND 125.00

LOUIS II, 1510-1526
St. Wenceslas. Rev. Lion in shield.

9. 1 Ducat 1518, 21, ND 75.00

St. Wenceslas. Rev. Lion.

10. 1 Ducat ND 100.00

FERDINAND I, 1526-1564
St. Wenceslas. Rev. Lion.

11. 1 Goldgulden 1536-45, ND 60.00

MAXIMILIAN II, 1548-1576
Ruler standing. Rev. Arms.

12. 1 Ducat 1566, 73 .... 60.00

MATTHIAS II, 1612-1619
Bust. Rev. Legend.

13. 2 Ducats 1611 .... 75.00
14. 1 Ducat 1611 .... 40.00

Ruler standing. Rev. Double eagle.

15. 10 Ducats 1611-19 .... 400.00
16.   5 Ducats 1611-19 .... 200.00
17.   2 Ducats 1611-19 .... 100.00
18.   1 Ducat 1611-19 .... 50.00

Ruler standing. Rev. St. Wenceslas.

19. 1 Ducat 1612-19 .... 40.00

Stork. Rev. Legend.

20. 2 Ducats 1611 .... 100.00

FREDERICK V OF PALATINATE, 1619-1621

Ruler standing. Rev. Arms.

21. 10 Ducats 1620 .... * ...... Rare
22.   5 Ducats 1620 .... Rare
23.   1 Ducat 1620 .... 250.00

Bust. Rev. Lion.

24. 1 Ducat 1620 .... 125.00

Crowned bust. Rev. Arms on lion.

25. 2 Ducats 1620 .... 275.00
26. 1 Ducat 1620, ND .... * 250.00

Lion. Rev. Three shields under hat.

27. 1 Goldgulden 1621 .... 100.00

Legend. Rev. Crown. On the Coronation.

28. 2 Ducats 1619 .... 150.00

Crowned initial. Rev. Legend. On the Coronation.

29.   1 Ducat 1619 .... * 50.00
29a. ½ Ducat 1619 .... 40.00

NATIONAL ASSEMBLY OF BOHEMIA AND MORAVIA, 1619-1620
Crowned Moravian Eagle. Rev. Obelisk.

30. 25 Ducats 1620 .... Rare
31. 10 Ducats 1620 .... Rare
32.   5 Ducats 1620 .... Rare

NATIONAL ASSEMBLY OF MORAVIA AND SILESIA, 1621
Silesian Eagle. Rev. Blank.

33. 25   Taler 1621 .... Rare
34. 12½ Taler 1621. Round .... Rare
35. 12½ Taler 1621. Square .... Rare

FERDINAND II, 1618-1637

Ruler standing. Rev. Double eagle.

36. 12 Ducats 1632 .... Rare
37. 10 Ducats 1621-37 .... * 300.00
38.   5 Ducats 1621-37 .... 150.00
39.   2 Ducats 1620-37 .... 75.00
40.   1 Ducat 1620-37 .... 40.00

FERDINAND III, 1627-1657
Bust in ruff collar. Rev. Bohemian Lion in shield.

40a. 100 Ducats 1629 .... 6000.00
40b. 50 Ducats 1629 .... 2500.00
40c. 40 Ducats 1629 .... 2000.00

CHARLES VI, 1711-1740

Ruler standing. Rev. Globe and owl. From gold of the Eule Mines.

41. 2 Ducats 1715-22 .... * 200.00
42. 1 Ducat 1713-22 .... 125.00

BOHEMIA (cont'd)

Ruler standing. Rev. St. John on clouds. From gold of the Eule Mines.

43.	5 Ducats 1722. City view below St. John	.........*	300.00
44.	2 Ducats 1722-27		175.00
45.	1 Ducat 1719-29		75.00

MARIA THERESA, 1740-1780
Legend. Rev. Bohemian Lion. On the Coronation.

46.	1 Ducat 1743		40.00

B. Cities of —

LOBKOWITZ

Princes of —

FERDINAND AUGUST LEOPOLD, 1677-1715
Armored bust. Rev. Arms.

1.	1 Ducat ND		200.00

OLMUTZ

Archbishops of —

FRANCIS OF DIETRICHSTEIN, 1599-1636

Madonna seated, Rev. Arms.

1.	1 Ducat 1626, 28, ND		125.00

Shield of Dietrichstein. Rev. Arms.

2.	½ Ducat 1636		50.00

LEOPOLD WILLIAM OF AUSTRIA, 1637-1662
Bust. Rev. Arms.

3.	10 Ducats 1656, 58		750.00
4.	4 Ducats 1656		300.00

Bust. Rev. Two shields.

5.	1 Ducat 1658		75.00

CHARLES II OF LIECHTENSTEIN-CASTELCORN, 1664-1695

Bust. Rev. Arms.

6.	10 Ducats 1678		500.00
7.	8 Ducats 1678		400.00
8.	6 Ducats ND		300.00
9.	5 Ducats 1672, 76, 78		250.00
10.	2 Ducats 1680, 84, 91	.........*	175.00
11.	1 Ducat 1684, ND		75.00
12.	⅛ Ducat 1671, ND		25.00

CHARLES III, JOSEPH OF LORRAINE, 1695-1711
Bust. Rev. Arms.

13.	8 Ducats 1707		400.00
14.	5 Ducats 1703, 04, 05, 07, ND		350.00
15.	3 Ducats 1707		200.00
16.	2 Ducats 1703, ND		125.00
17.	1 Ducat ND		75.00
18.	⅛ Ducat ND		40.00

WOLFGANG OF SCHRATTENBACH, 1711-1738

Bust. Rev. Arms.

19.	5 Ducats 1722	.........*	200.00
20.	4 Ducats 1713		175.00
21.	3 Ducats 1717		150.00
22.	1 Ducat 1725, 26, 28, ND		65.00

Bust with hat. Rev. Two shields.

23.	1 Ducat 1736, 37		125.00

Bust and value. Rev. Three shields.

24.	¼ Ducat ND		25.00

JAMES ERNST OF LIECHTENSTEIN-CASTELCORN, 1738-1745
Bust. Rev. Arms.

25.	1 Ducat 1739, 40		40.00
26.	¼ Ducat ND		25.00

ANTON THEODORE OF COLLOREDO-WALLSEE, 1777-1811
Bust. Rev. Arms.

27.	1 Ducat 1779		40.00

RUDOLPH JOHN OF AUSTRIA, 1819-1831
Bust. Rev. Arms.

28.	1 Ducat 1820		100.00

SCHLICK

Counts of —

HENRY IV, 1612-1650

St. Anne and Virgin with shield. Rev. Eagle.

1.	10 Ducats 1627-46	.........*	450.00
2.	5 Ducats 1634, 46, 49		350.00
3.	1 Ducat 1628-38		125.00

FRANCIS ERNST, 1652-1675
St. Anne above arms and Madonna. Rev. Eagle.

4.	5 Ducats 1661, 62		300.00

FRANCIS JOSEPH, 1675-1740
St. Anne. Rev. Eagle.

5.	1 Ducat 1716		60.00

BOHEMIA-SCHLICK (cont'd)

FRANCIS HENRY, 1740-1766
Madonna over arms. Rev. Eagle.

6. 1 Ducat 1759 .... 150.00

LEOPOLD HENRY, 1766-1770
Arms. Rev. Eagle.

7. 1 Ducat 1767 .... 75.00

SCHWARZENBERG

Princes of —
JOHN ADAM, 1641-1683

Bust. Rev. Arms.

1. 1 Ducat 1682 .... 150.00

FERDINAND WILLIAM EUSEBIUS, 1683-1703

Bust. Rev. Arms.

2. 5 Ducats ND ....*...... 350.00
3. 1 Ducat 1693, 95 .... 100.00

ADAM FRANCIS, 1703-1732
Bust. Rev. Arms.

4. 1 Ducat 1710. Mint: Cologne 150.00
5. 1 Ducat 1721-32. Mint: Vienna 75.00

JOSEPH ADAM, 1732-1782

Bust. Rev. Arms.

6. 1 Ducat 1768 .... 100.00

JOHN, 1782-1789

Bust. Rev. Arms.

7. 1 Ducat 1783 .... 75.00

TESCHEN

Dukes of —

(See under GERMANY (SILESIA-TESCHEN))

VISHEHRAD

Abbots of —
CHARLES JOSEPH MARTINITZ
Two shields. Rev. Legend.

1. 1 Ducat 1734 .... 125.00

FERDINAND KINDERMANN OF SCHULSTEIN, 1782-1801
Arms. Rev. Legend.

2. 1 Ducat 1782 .... 125.00

PROCOP BENEDICT HENNIGER OF EBERG, 1802
Shields and insignia. Rev. Legend.

3. 1 Ducat 1802 .... 150.00

BULGARIA

Kings of —
VLADIMIR, 972-1015
Bust. Rev. Bust of Christ.

1. 1 Solidus ND 1500.00

FERDINAND, 1887-1918

Head. Rev. Arms.

2. 100 Leva 1894 .... 200.00
3. 20 Leva 1894 ....*...... 35.00
4. 10 Leva 1894 ....*...... 22.50

*Head. Rev. Crowned oval shield. On the 25th year of reign.
The date 1912 is in very small numerals under the shield.*

5. 100 Leva 1912 .... 250.00
6. 20 Leva 1912 ....*...... 40.00

Uniformed bust. Rev. Arms with small crown counterstamped at bottom.
7. 4 Ducats 1910, 12 .... 200.00

BORIS III, 1918-1943

Uniformed bust. Rev. Arms with small crown counterstamped at bottom.
8. 4 Ducats 1926 .... 200.00

COURLAND

Dukes of —

JAMES
Bust. Rev. Arms.

1. 1 Ducat 1646 . . . . **200.00**

FREDERICK CASIMIR, 1682-1698

Bust. Rev. Eagle.

2. 1 Ducat 1689 . . . . **200.00**

ERNST JOHN
Bust. Rev. Arms.

3. 1 Ducat 1764 . . . . **150.00**

PETER BIRON, 1769-1795

Head. Rev. Two shields.

4. 1 Ducat 1780 . . . . **100.00**

CROATIA

Head of the Duke of Aosta as king. Rev. Value over shield. This coin was not placed in circulation.

1. 500 Kuna 1941 . . . . **Rare**

CZECHOSLOVAKIA

(Formerly the ancient kingdom of Bohemia, which see).

Half-length figure of St. Wenceslas. Rev. Shield.

1. 2 Ducats 1923-38 . . . . *. **27.50**
2. 1 Ducat 1923-38 . . . . **12.50**
3. 1 Ducat 1923. With a number from 1 to 1,000 next to date. **30.00**

St. Wenceslas on horse. Rev. Shield.

4. 10 Ducats 1929-38 . . . . **150.00**
5. 5 Ducats 1929-38 . . . . *. **75.00**

COMMEMORATIVES AND SPECIAL ISSUES

Saint holding plow drawn by Devil. Rev. Arms. On the 10th year of the Republic.

6. 4 Ducats 1928 . . . . *. **50.00**
7. 2 Ducats 1928 . . . . **30.00**

Standing figure with banner. Rev. Knight on horse. On the 1000th year of the introduction of Christianity into Bohemia.

8. 5 Ducats 1929 . . . . *. **200.00**
9. 4 Ducats 1929 . . . . **125.00**
10. 1 Ducat 1929 . . . . **50.00**

Head of Dr. Miroslav Tyrs. Rev. Eagle. On the Sokol movement.

11. 1 Ducat 1932 . . . . **40.00**

Head of Dr. Antonin Svehla. Rev. Sower. Homage issue.

12. 1 Ducat 1933 . . . . **40.00**

St. Elizabeth praying. Rev. Mining scenes. On the reopening of the Kremnica Mines.

13. 10 Ducats 1934 . . . . *. **350.00**
14. 5 Ducats 1934 . . . . **200.00**
15. 2 Ducats 1934 . . . . **125.00**
16. 1 Ducat 1934 . . . . **75.00**

Bust of Wallenstein. Rev. Crowned shield. To commemorate the ancient Wallenstein coinage.

17. 10 Ducats 1934 . . . . **400.00**
18. 5 Ducats 1934 . . . . **250.00**

DANZIG

A. Polish Kings of —

SIGISMUND I, 1506-1548

Bust. Rev. City arms.

1. 1 Ducat 1546, 47, 48 . . . . **100.00**

SIGISMUND II, 1548-1572

Bust right or left. Rev. City arms.

2. 1 Ducat 1549-58 .... 100.00

STEPHAN BATHORI, 1576-1587

Bust. Rev. City arms.

3. 1 Ducat 1578-87 .... 100.00

Christ standing. Rev. City arms.

4. 1 Siege Ducat 1577 .... 150.00

SIGISMUND III, 1587-1632

Bust. Rev. City arms.

5. 10 Ducats 1613, 14 .... 350.00
6. 5 Ducats 1614, ND 200.00
7. 4 Ducats 1617 .... 200.00
8. 3 Ducats 1617 .... 150.00
9. 2 Ducats 1619 .... 100.00
10. 1 Ducat 1588-1632 ....* 75.00

LADISLAS IV, 1632-1648

Bust. Rev. City arms.

11. 4 Ducats 1640, 41 ....* 300.00
12. 3 Ducats 1640, 41 .... 200.00
13. 2 Ducats 1634-47 .... 150.00
14. 1½ Ducats 1634, 47 .... 125.00
15. 1 Ducat 1633-48 .... 75.00

Bust. Rev. City view.

16. 10 Ducats 1644, ND 400.00
17. 8 Ducats 1644 .... 350.00
18. 6 Ducats ND 350.00
19. 5 Ducats 1645 .... 350.00
20. 4 Ducats 1645 .... 250.00
21. 3 Ducats 1634-47 ....* 200.00

JOHN CASIMIR, 1648-1668

Bust. Rev. City arms.

22. 2 Ducats 1652-58, ND ....* 200.00
23. 1½ Ducats 1661 .... 150.00
24. 1 Ducat 1649-68 .... 75.00

Plain or crowned bust. Rev. City view.

25. 12 Ducats 1650 .... 750.00
26. 6 Ducats ND ....* 300.00
27. 5 Ducats 1654, 56, ND 175.00
28. 4 Ducats, 1650, ND 150.00
29. 3 Ducats 1650, 58, ND 150.00
30. 2 Ducats 1651 .... 100.00

MICHAEL KORYBUT, 1669-1673

Bust. Rev. City arms.

31. 1 Ducat 1670-73 .... 125.00

Crowned bust. Rev. City view.

32. 3 Ducats ND 150.00

JOHN SOBIESKI, 1674-1696

Plain or crowned bust. Rev. City arms.

33. 4 Ducats 1692 .... 300.00
34. 2 Ducats 1692, ND 200.00
35. 1 Ducat 1676-92 ....* 100.00

Bust. Rev. City view.

36. 5 Ducats ND 300.00
37. 4 Ducats ND 250.00
38. 3 Ducats ND 200.00

AUGUST II OF SAXONY, 1697-1733

Bust. Rev. City arms.

DANZIG (cont'd)

39. 2 Ducats 1698 .... 200.00
40. 1 Ducat 1698 ....* 100.00

AUGUST III OF SAXONY, 1733-1763
Bust. Rev. City arms.

41. 1 Ducat 1734 .... 125.00

B. Free City of —

Neptune with trident. Rev. Arms between two columns.

42. 25 Gulden 1923 .... 140.00

Neptune with trident. Rev. Arms supported by lions.

43. 25 Gulden 1930 .... 400.00

DENMARK

Kings of —

(For additional coins of the Danish Kings, see under Norway).

HANS, 1481-1513

Ruler on throne. Rev. Arms.

1. 3 Nobles 1496 ....* ...... Rare
2. 2 Nobles 1502 .... Rare
3. 1 Noble 1496, 1502 .... Rare

Ruler standing. Rev. Triple lion shield.

4. 1 Goldgulden ND 400.00
5. ½ Goldgulden ND 250.00

CHRISTIAN II, 1513-1523
Ruler on throne. Rev. Arms.

6. 1 Noble 1516, 18 .... Rare

Ruler standing. Rev. Triple lion shield.

7. 1 Goldgulden ND. Square 300.00

Ruler on throne. Rev. Crowned shield. Posthumously struck in 1535 and 1536.

8. 2 Goldgulden ND ....* 750.00
9. 1 Goldgulden ND 250.00

FREDERICK I, 1523-1533

Ruler standing. Rev. Four shields around central shield.

10. 1 Goldgulden 1527 .... 250.00

Small crowned bust. Rev. Triple lion shield.

11. 1 Goldgulden 1531 .... 250.00

Busts of the King and Queen. Rev. Arms.

12. 1 Noble 1532 .... Rare

Ruler on throne. Rev. Arms.

13. 1 Noble ND .... Rare

St. Andrew standing with cross. Rev. Cross of shields. Struck for Schleswig.

14. 1 Goldgulden 1531, ND 400.00

CHRISTIAN III, 1534-1559

Crowned head. Rev. Arms.

15. 1 Goldgulden 1557 .... 200.00

Cross of arms. Rev. Orb in circle. Struck for Schleswig.

16. 1 Goldgulden ND 300.00

St. Andrew standing with cross. Rev. Cross of shields. Struck for Schleswig.

17. 2 Goldgulden 1546 .... 500.00
18. 1 Goldgulden 1536, 46, ND ....* 300.00

FREDERICK II, 1559-1588
Crowned F. Rev. Value.

19. 1 Goldgulden 1563. Square 750.00
20. 1 Krone 1563. Square 1000.00

Crowned F. Rev. Fortuna standing on globe.

21. 1 Goldgulden 1563. Crudely shaped 500.00

Arms. Rev. Value.

22.	1 Ducat 1564. Square	500.00
23.	1 Krone 1564. Square	500.00
24.	1 Goldgulden 1564. Square	500.00

FS monogram crowned. Rev. Value.

25.	1 Portugaloser 1584	2000.00
26.	1 Rosenoble 1584 ....*	1500.00
27.	2 Ducats 1584	500.00
28.	1 Angelot 1584	500.00
29.	1 Krone 1584	400.00
30.	1 Goldgulden 1584 ....*	400.00
31.	1 Hungarian Gulden 1584	400.00

CHRISTIAN IV, 1588-1648
Ruler standing. Rev. Arms.

32.	1 Goldgulden 1591, 92, 93, 1607	125.00

Ruler standing. Rev. Triple lion shield.

33.	1 Goldgulden 1603, 07, 08, 11 ....*	125.00
34.	1 Ducat 1637	175.00

Ruler standing. Rev. Thirteen shields around central arms.

35.	3 Goldgulden 1608	1250.00
36.	2 Goldgulden 1608 ....*	750.00

Ruler standing. Rev. Legend in square.

37.	1 Ducat 1640, 42, 46	125.00

Ruler standing. Rev. Hebrew legend.

38.	2 Ducats 1644, 45, 46, 48 ....*	200.00
39.	1 Ducat 1644, 45, 46, 47, 48	125.00
40.	½ Ducat 1644, 45, 46, 47	50.00
41.	¼ Ducat 1646, 47, 48	35.00

Ruler standing. Rev. C4 crowned.

42.	¼ Ducat ND	35.00

Large crowned bust. Rev. Triple lion shield.

43.	1 Goldgulden 1604-32	125.00

Crowned bust. Rev. Value.

44.	8 Daler 1604. Square	750.00
45.	6 Daler 1604. Square ....*	500.00
46.	4 Daler 1604. Square	400.00
47.	3 Daler 1604. Square	250.00

Large crowned bust. Rev. Elephant.

48.	1 Rosenoble 1611-29	400.00
49.	½ Rosenoble 1611	250.00

Plain bust. Rev. Two figures holding crown over arms and C4.

50.	Gold coin, 22.64 Grams ND	500.00
51.	Gold coin, 10.75 Grams ND	200.00
52.	Gold coin, 8.1 Grams ND	150.00

Crowned bust. Rev. Similar to above.

53.	Gold coin, 4.65 Grams ND	125.00

Triple lion shield. Rev. Crown.

54.	2 Krones 1619-48 ....*	200.00
55.	1 Krone 1619	125.00
56.	½ Krone 1619	125.00

C4 crowned. Rev. Arms.

57.	2 Ducats 1627	250.00
58.	1 Ducat 1627	150.00

C4 crowned. Rev. Legend.

58a.	½ Ducat 1642	75.00
58b.	¼ Ducat 1647, ND	50.00

Large cross. Rev. Arms.

59.	2 Portugalosers 1592	Rare
60.	1 Portugaloser 1591, 92	1250.00
61.	½ Portugaloser 1591, 92, 93	400.00
62.	¼ Portugaloser 1592, 93 ....*	250.00

Ruler on throne. Rev. Arms.

63.	1 Portugaloser 1603	1500.00

Ruler standing. Rev. Fortuna on globe. Struck for Gluckstadt.

64.	1 Portugaloser 1623	1250.00

Large cross. Rev. Crowned heart.

65.	¼ Portugaloser 1629	300.00

Ruler on horse. Rev. Arms.

66.	1 Portugaloser ND	....	1000.00

Large bust. Rev. Ruler on horse in circle of shields.

67.	1 Portugaloser ND	....	1250.00
68.	¼ Portugaloser ND	....	500.00

FREDERICK III, 1648-1670

Laureate bust. Rev. Vase with flowers.

69.	5 Ducats 1648. Square	....		750.00
70.	4 Ducats 1648. Square	....		500.00
71.	3 Ducats 1648. Square	....		400.00
72.	2 Ducats 1648. Square	....		250.00
73.	1 Ducat 1648. Square	....	*	175.00
74.	½ Ducat 1648. Square	....		100.00

Laureate bust. Rev. Legend in circle.

75.	1 Ducat 1649, 50, 51, 53	....	*	85.00
76.	½ Ducat 1652	....		65.00

Laureate bust. Rev. Fortuna on globe.

77.	1 Ducat 1660-69	....	150.00

Laureate bust. Rev. Arms.

78.	1 Portugaloser 1666	....		1000.00
79.	5 Ducats 1665	....		400.00
80.	1 Ducat 1667, 68, 69	....	*	125.00
81.	1 Krone 1667	....		125.00

Laureate bust. Rev. Large crown.

82.	5 Ducats 1665, 66	....		350.00
83.	3 Ducats 1667	....		250.00
84.	2 Ducats 1657	....		200.00
85.	2 Krones 1666	....	*	200.00
86.	1 Krone 1666	....		125.00

Laureate bust. Small oval arms on cross.

87.	2 Portugalosers 1666		Rare
88.	½ Portugaloser 1665, 67	....	600.00
89.	12 Ducats 1665	....	1500.00

Laureate bust. Rev. Crown and value.

90.	18 Marks 1668	....	200.00

Laureate bust. Rev. Three shields on cross within circle of shields.

91.	2 Portugalosers ND	....	Rare
92.	10 Ducats 1669. Thick	....	1000.00

Laureate head. Rev. Double cross formed by F3 monogram.

93.	2 Ducats 1670	....	250.00

Laureate bust. Rev. Crown and orb between sceptre and sword.

94.	2 Ducats ND	....	150.00

Crowned bust. Rev. Square formed by four F's. The diameter of these coins is the same, the value being determined by the thickness and corresponding weight.

95.	10 Ducats 1653	....		1500.00
96.	5 Ducats 1653, 62	....		1000.00
97.	3 Ducats 1662	....		350.00
98.	2 Ducats 1653, 62	....		250.00
99.	1 Ducat 1653-66, ND	....	*	75.00
100.	½ Ducat 1659, 64	....		50.00
101.	¼ Ducat 1660, 64	....		50.00

Laureate head. Rev. Similar to above.

102.	1 Ducat 1664, 67	....	100.00

Crowned bust. Rev. Circle of shields around central arms.

103.	1 Portugaloser 1653, 55, 56	....	1000.00
104.	½ Portugaloser 1653, 55, 57, 61	....	400.00
105.	3 Ducats 1661	....	300.00

Crowned bust. Rev. Cross of crowned F's.

106.	1 Ducat 1653	....	200.00

Crowned bust. Rev. Three shields on crowned cross.

107.	1 Ducat 1669, 70	....	125.00

DENMARK (cont'd)

Crowned bust. Rev. Ship.

108.	4 Ducats 1657, 58, 64	.... *	350.00
109.	3 Ducats 1666, 67	....	300.00
110.	2 Ducats 1657-67	....	200.00

Crowned bust. Rev. Crowned shield on cross.

111.	1 Portugaloser 1662, 63, 64	....	1000.00
112.	½ Portugaloser 1663, 64	....	500.00
113.	5 Ducats 1662	.... *	500.00
114.	4 Ducats 1663	....	400.00
115.	2 Ducats 1662, 63	....	250.00

Crowned bust. Rev. View of Fort Aggershus.

116.	1 Portugaloser ND	....	1500.00

Triple lion shield. Rev. Crown.

117.	2 Krones 1657, 59	....	175.00
118.	1 Krone 1655, 57, 59, 60	.... *	125.00

Triple lion shield. Rev. Crowned F3 over lion.

119.	½ Portugaloser 1658	....	500.00

Crowned F3. Rev. Sword cutting off hand reaching for crown.

120.	2 Portugalosers 1659	....	2000.00
121.	1 Portugaloser 1659	.... *	1250.00
122.	½ Portugaloser 1659	....	500.00
123.	6 Ducats 1659	....	500.00
124.	4 Ducats 1659	....	350.00
125.	3 Ducats 1659	....	250.00

Crowned F3. Rev. Value.

126.	6 Marks 1669	....	125.00
127.	3 Marks 1665, 68, 70	....	40.00

Crown over double F3 monogram. Rev. Arms.

128.	¼ Ducat 1670	....	50.00

Crossed sword and sceptre between crown and orb. Rev. Cross of St. Andrew.

129.	1 Portugaloser 1663	....	1500.00
130.	6 Ducats 1663	....	500.00

CHRISTIAN V, 1670-1699

Crowned bust. Rev. Three crowns over triple C5 monogram.

131.	2 Ducats 1673	....	150.00
132.	1 Ducat 1672, 73, 74, 76	.... *	100.00

Laureate bust. Rev. Crowned C5 monogram.

133.	5 Ducats 1692	....	350.00
134.	2 Ducats 1670, 92, 94, ND	.... *	150.00
135.	1 Ducat 1672-94, ND	....	75.00
136.	½ Ducat 1675	....	50.00
137.	¼ Ducat 1675	....	25.00

Laureate bust. Three shields on cross.

138.	1 Ducat 1671-92	....	125.00

Laureate bust. Rev. Three crowns over triple C5 monogram.

139.	1 Ducat 1679, 80, 85	....	75.00

Laureate bust. Rev. C's and 5's around radiate triangle.

140.	5 Ducats 1692	....	500.00
141.	2 Ducats 1692, 94	.... *	250.00
142.	1 Ducat 1694	....	150.00

Laureate bust. Rev. Long cross over arms.

143.	1 Ducat 1692	....	125.00

Laureate bust. Rev. Six crowns around C5 monograms.

144. 2 Ducats ND 150.00

Armored bust. Rev. Crowned arms.

145. 1 Ducat 1681, 83 .... 100.00

Bust. Rev. Fortress.

146. 1 Ducat 1682 .... 125.00

Long haired bust. Rev. Arms in circle of shields.

147. 10 Ducats 1691 .... 1000.00
148. 5 Ducats 1687 .... 400.00
149. 3 Ducats 1687 .... 250.00
150. 2 Ducats 1687 .... 200.00
151. 1 Ducat 1687, ND ....* 125.00

Long haired bust. Rev. Crowned oval arms.

152. 2 Ducats 1691 ....* 175.00
153. 1 Ducat 1691, 92 ....* 75.00

Long haired bust. Rev. Triple C5 monogram.

154. 1 Ducat 1691, 92, 93, 96, ND 75.00

Bust. Rev. Large crown.

155. 10 Ducats 1693, 96 .... 1000.00
156. 3 Ducats 1694 .... 200.00
157. 2½ Ducats 1696 .... 200.00
158. 2 Ducats 1693, 94, 96 .... 175.00
159. 1 Ducat 1693, 94, 96 ....* 75.00
160. ½ Ducat 1694, 96 .... 40.00
161. ¼ Ducat 1694 .... 30.00

Bust. Rev. Legend. From gold of the Koenigsberg Mines.

162. 2 Ducats 1697 ....* 350.00
163. 1 Ducat 1697 .... 300.00

Helmeted bust. Rev. View of Fort Christiansborg in Guinea, Africa.

164. 4 Ducats 1688 .... 500.00
165. 2 Ducats 1688 ....* 250.00
166. 1 Ducat 1688 .... 150.00

Bust. Rev. Ship in Christiansborg harbor.

167. 2 Ducats 1699 ....* 250.00
168. 1 Ducat 1699 .... 150.00

Laureate head. Rev. Elephant.

169. 3 Ducats 1678 .... 300.00
170. 2 Ducats 1673 ....* 250.00

Laureate head. Rev. Value and date.

171. 3 Marks (¼ Ducat) 1676 .... 60.00

Laureate head. Rev. Six crowns around C5 monograms. The Rev. is shown.

172. 3 Ducats 1678 .... 250.00
173. 2 Ducats 1678 ....* 200.00

Ruler standing. Rev. Fortuna on globe.

174. 1 Ducat 1682 .... 125.00

Ruler standing. Rev. C5 monogram crowned.

175. 10 Ducats ND 750.00

DENMARK (cont'd)

Ruler on horse. Rev. Elephant.

176.	3 Ducats 1673	....	300.00
177.	2 Ducats 1673	....	250.00

Ruler on horse. Rev. Crowned circular arms.

178.	1 Rider 1696	...............................*	125.00
179.	2 Ducats ND	....	125.00
180.	1 Ducat 1696	....	100.00
181.	½ Ducat 1696	....	50.00

Ruler on horse. Rev. Triple C5 monogram.

182.	4 Ducats ND	....	200.00
183.	2 Ducats ND	....	125.00
184.	1 Ducat 1692, ND	.........................*	75.00
185.	½ Ducat ND	....	50.00

Ruler on horse. Rev. Conjoined knight and lion. Without any legends.

186.	2½ Ducats ND	....	125.00
187.	1 Ducat ND	....	100.00
188.	½ Ducat ND	....	40.00

Ruler on horse. Rev. Double C5 monogram. Without any legends.

189.	2 Ducats ND	....	125.00
190.	1 Ducat ND	....	75.00
191.	½ Ducat ND	....	50.00

Ruler on horse. Rev. Six crowns around C5 monograms. Without any legends.

192.	4 Ducats ND	....	250.00
193.	2 Ducats ND	....	150.00
194.	1½ Ducats ND	....	125.00

Crown over C5. Rev. Elephant.

195.	4 Ducats 1683	....	400.00
196.	2 Ducats 1673	.........................*	250.00
197.	1½ Ducats 1673	....	200.00
198.	1 Ducat 1673	....	125.00

Crown over double C5 monogram. Rev. Crowned arms.

199.	1 Ducat 1691	....	75.00

Crown over initials. Rev. Value and date.

200.	3 Marks 1675	....	50.00

Six crowns around C5 monograms. Rev. Elephant.

201.	3 Ducats 1673	....	200.00

Pyramid with or without base. Rev. View of Copenhagen harbor.

202.	2 Ducats ND	...............................*	150.00
203.	1 Ducat ND	....	100.00

FREDERICK IV, 1699-1730

Bust. Rev. Bust of Christian V. Coronation coins struck in 1699. The indicated 3 Ducat piece is 28 millimetres, all the others are 21 millimetres and of varying thickness, the value being determined by weight.

204.	4 Ducats ND	....	450.00
205.	3 Ducats ND (size 21)	....	300.00
206.	3 Ducats ND (size 28)	....	450.00
207.	2 Ducats ND	....	200.00
208.	1 Ducat ND	.........................*	150.00

Bust. Rev. Three shields and three monograms around star.

209.	2 Ducats 1708, 09	....	150.00
210.	1 Ducat 1708, 09, ND	.........................*	75.00

Bust. Rev. Three shields and three monograms around radiate triangle.

211.	10 Ducats 1699	....	1000.00
212.	5 Ducats 1699, 1700	....	350.00
213.	4¾ Ducats, 1699	....	350.00
214.	2 Ducats 1708	....	125.00
215.	1 Ducat 1708, 09, ND	....	75.00

Bust. Rev. Crown over DMA, and below "Christiansborg".

216.	18 Marks 1701	....	2500.00

Bust. Rev. Large crown and value (for the "Rixdalers").

217.	1 Ducat 1705, 06	...............................*	75.00
218.	4 Rixdaler (2 Courant Ducats) 1714	....	200.00
219.	2 Rixdaler (1 Courant Ducat) 1714, 15, 16	....	125.00
220.	1 Rixdaler (½ Courant Ducat) 1715	....	60.00

Bust. Rev. Crowned arms in wreath.

221.	2 Ducats 1709	....	125.00
222.	1 Ducat 1709, 23, 26	...............................*	75.00
223.	½ Ducat 1719	....	50.00

Bust. Rev. Crowned circular arms.

DENMARK (cont'd)

224. 1 Ducat 1718, 19 .... 75.00
225. ½ Ducat 1710, 19 ....* 50.00

Bust. Rev. Double F4 monogram.

226. 3 Ducats 1700 ....* 250.00
227. 2 Ducats 1701, 04 .... 150.00
228. 1 Ducat 1700, ND 75.00
229. ½ Ducat ND 40.00
230. ¼ Ducat ND 75.00

Ruler on horse. Rev. Cross of three shields and three monograms.

231. 2 Ducats ND 125.00
232. 1 Ducat 1702, ND ....* 75.00
233. ½ Ducat ND 40.00
234. ¼ Ducat ND 30.00

Ruler on horse. Rev. Arms.

235. 2 Ducats 1710, 11 ....* 125.00
236. 1 Ducat 1710, 11 .... 75.00

Ruler on horse. Rev. Double F4 monogram.

237. 2 Ducats ND 125.00
238. 1 Ducat ND 75.00
239. ½ Ducat ND 50.00
240. ¼ Ducat ND 30.00

Bust. Rev. View of Fort Christiansborg.

241. 2 Ducats 1701, 04 .... 250.00
242. 1 Ducat 1701, 02, 04, 08, 25, ND 100.00

Bust. Fortress and ship at Christiansborg.

243. 1 Ducat 1701 .... 175.00

Bust. Rev. Ship and radiate sun, and below, "Christiansborg".

244. 5 Ducats 1704 .... 750.00

*Bust. Rev. Radiate sun over ship and below, "SOC. IND. OCC."
(The Danish West Indies Company).*

245. 2 Ducats 1708 .... 500.00

CHRISTIAN VI, 1730-1746

Double C6 monogram. Rev. Fortress at Christiansborg.

246. 1 Ducat 1730, 38, 40 .... 100.00

Bust. Rev. Arms on cross.

247. 1 Ducat 1732 .... 150.00

FREDERICK V, 1746-1766
Bust. Rev. Bust of Christian VI. Coronation coins struck in 1746.

248. 2 Ducats ND 150.00
249. 1 Ducat ND 100.00

*Bust. Rev. Crowned arms with ornaments and below, "EX AURO
SINICO". Struck from Chinese gold.*

250. 2 Ducats 1746 .... 250.00
251. 1 Ducat 1746 ....* 150.00

Laureate head. Rev. Type as above. Struck from Chinese gold.

252. 2 Ducats 1746 .... 250.00
253. 1 Ducat 1746 .... 150.00

Bust. Rev. Ancient galley with banner. Struck from Chinese gold.

254. 2 Ducats 1746 .... 300.00
255. 1 Ducat 1746 ....* 200.00

Laureate head. Rev. Type as above. Struck from Chinese gold.

256. 1 Ducat 1746 .... 200.00

Bust. Rev. Crowned oval arms.

257. 2 Ducats 1747 .... 150.00

Bust. Rev. Draped arms and below "EBEN EZER".

258. 1 Ducat 1758 .... 150.00

DENMARK (cont'd)

Bust in helmet. Rev. Crown and value.

259. 12 Marks 1757, 58 .... 75.00

Laureate head. Rev. Fortress and ship at Christiansborg.

260. 2 Ducats 1746 .... 200.00
261. 1 Ducat 1746 ....* 125.00

Laureate head. Rev. Crowned oval arms.

262. 2 Ducats 1747 .... 150.00
263. 1 Ducat 1747 .... 75.00

Laureate head. Rev. Ship.

264. 2 Ducats 1753 .... 200.00
265. 1 Ducat 1753, 54, 56 ....* 100.00

Head. Rev. Crown and value.

266. 12 Marks 1757-65 .... 50.00

Ruler standing. Rev. Crowned oval arms.

267. 2 Ducats 1747 .... 175.00
268. 1 Ducat 1747 ....* 100.00

Ruler standing. Rev. Fortress at Christiansborg.

269. 2 Ducats 1747 .... 175.00
270. 1 Ducat 1747 ....* 125.00

Ruler on horse. Rev. Embellished arms with initials DWC for Danish West Indies Company.

271. 2 Ducats 1749 ....* 200.00
272. 1 Ducat 1749 .... 150.00

Ruler on horse. Rev. Double F5 monogram.

273. 2 Ducats 1748 .... 150.00
274. 1 Ducat 1748 ....* 75.00

F's and V's around triangle. Rev. Crown and value.

275. 12 Marks 1757, 63 .... 75.00

CHRISTIAN VII, 1766-1808

Bust. Rev. Crowned C7 monograms around triangle.

276. 1 Christian d'or 1775, ND 150.00

Bust. Rev. "29 Januarii" in wreath.

277. 1 Ducat 1771 .... 150.00

Bust. Rev. Crown and value.

278. 12 Marks 1781, 82, 83, 85 .... 50.00

Wild man standing. Rev. Legend in square.

279. 1 Ducat 1771 .... 100.00

Wild man standing. Rev. Value, weight and fineness in square tablet.

280. 1 Species Ducat 1791, 92, 94, 1802 .... 60.00

FREDERICK VI, 1808-1839

Head. Rev. Value.

281. 2 Frederick d'or 1826, 27 .... 125.00
282. 1 Frederick d'or 1827 ....* 100.00

DENMARK (cont'd)

Head. Rev. Arms flanked by value.

283. 2 Frederick d'or 1828-36 .... 80.00
284. 1 Frederick d'or 1828-38 .... 50.00

Head. Rev. Arms supported by wild men.

285. 2 Frederick d'or 1836, 37, 38, 39 .... 100.00

CHRISTIAN VIII, 1840-1848

Head. Rev. Arms supported by wild men.

286. 2 Christian d'or 1841-47 .... 80.00
287. 1 Christian d'or 1843-47 ....*...... 50.00

FREDERICK VII, 1848-1863

Head. Rev. Arms supported by wild men.

288. 2 Frederick d'or 1850-63 ....*...... 80.00
289. 1 Frederick d'or 1853 .... 100.00

CHRISTIAN IX, 1863-1906

Head. Rev. Arms supported by wild men.

290. 2 Christian d'or 1866, 67, 69, 70 ....*...... 85.00
291. 1 Christian d'or 1869 .... 100.00

Head. Rev. Seated female.

292. 20 Kroner 1873-1900 ....*...... 25.00
293. 10 Kroner 1873-1900 .... 17.50

FREDERICK VIII, 1906-1912

Head. Rev. Arms.

294. 20 Kroner 1908-12 ....*...... 22.50
295. 10 Kroner 1908, 09 .... 15.00

CHRISTIAN X, 1912-1947

Head. Rev. Arms.

296. 20 Kroner 1913-31 ....*...... 22.50
297. 10 Kroner 1913-17 .... 15.00

ESTHONIA (REVAL)

Swedish Rulers of —

CHRISTINA, 1632-1654

Bust. Rev. City shield.

1. 1 Ducat 1650 .... 400.00

FINLAND

A. Coinage under the Czars of Russia

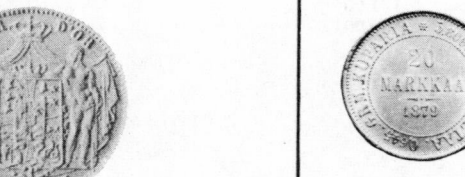

Crowned eagle. Rev. Value.

1. 20 Markkaa 1878-1913 .... 30.00
2. 10 Markkaa 1878-1913 .... 20.00

B. Coinage of the Republic

Lion. Rev. Value.

3. 200 Markkaa 1926 ....*...... 50.00
4. 100 Markkaa 1926 .... 30.00

FRANCE

A. Kings of —

(The coins from St. Louis IX through Henry IV are followed by an L and a number. These numbers identify the same coins in the French work by Lafaurie).

ST. LOUIS IX, 1266-1270

Shield in lobed circle. Rev. Floriated cross.

1. 1 Ecu d'or ND. L-197 .... 8000.00

PHILIP IV, 1285-1314

King on Gothic throne. Rev. Floriated cross in quadrilobe.

2. 1 Chaise d'or ND. L-213 .... 400.00

King seated. Rev. Floriated cross in quadrilobe.

3. 1 Masse d'or ND. L-212 .... 400.00

King seated. Rev. Floriated cross.

4. 1 Petit Royal d'or ND. L-217 .... 850.00
5. 1 Denier d'or ND. L-214 ....*..... 500.00

King standing. Rev. Floriated cross in quadrilobe.

6. 1 Petit Royal d'or ND. L-215 .... 1750.00

Lamb. Rev. Floriated cross in quadrilobe.

7. 1 Agnel d'or ND. L-216 .... 125.00

LOUIS X, 1314-1316

Lamb. Rev. Floriated cross in quadrilobe.

8. 1 Agnel d'or ND. L-240 .... 300.00

PHILIP V, 1316-1322

Lamb. Rev. Floriated cross in quadrilobe.

9. 1 Agnel d'or ND. L-241 .... 125.00

CHARLES IV, 1322-1328

King standing under Gothic dais. Rev. Floriated cross in quadrilobe.

10. 1 Royal d'or ND. L-244 ....*...... 100.00
11. ½ Royal d'or ND. L-245 .... 2000.00

Lamb. Rev. Floriated cross in quadrilobe.

12. 1 Agnel d'or ND. L-243 .... 125.00

PHILIP VI, 1328-1350

King seated on Gothic throne. Rev. Floriated cross in quadrilobe.

13. 1 Parisis d'or ND. L-252 .... 500.00

King seated on Gothic throne, a lion at feet. Rev. Floriated cross in quadrilobe.

14. 1 Lion d'or ND. L-253 .... 200.00

King seated on throne under draped pavillion. Rev. Floriated cross in quadrilobe, diamond in center.

15. 1 Pavillion d'or ND. L-254 .... 200.00

King with two sceptres on Gothic throne under dais. Rev. Floriated cross in enclosure.

16. 1 Double d'or ND. L-256 ....*...... 300.00
17. 1 Single d'or ND ....Unknown

King on Gothic throne. Rev. Floriated cross in quadrilobe, diamond in center.

18. 1 Chaise d'or ND. L-261 .... **100.00**

Armored King with shield on Gothic throne. Rev. Floriated cross in quadrilobe.

19. 1 Ecu d'or ND. L-262 .... **75.00**

King standing under Gothic dais. Rev. Floriated cross in quadrilobe.

20. 1 Royal d'or ND. L-251 .... **100.00**

St. George on horse. Rev. Floriated cross in quadrilobe.

21. 1 George-Florin ND. L-260 .... **2000.00**

Angel standing. Rev. Floriated cross in quadrilobe.

22. 1 Ange d'or ND. L-258 ....* **250.00**
23. ½ Ange d'or ND .... Unknown

Large crown. Rev. Floriated cross in quadrilobe.

24. 1 Couronne d'or ND. L-255 .... **1250.00**

JOHN THE GOOD, 1350-1364

Armored King with shield on Gothic throne. Rev. Floriated cross in quadrilobe.

25. 1 Ecu d'or ND. L-292 .... **100.00**

King standing under dais flanked by lis. Rev. Floriated cross in quadrilobe.

26. 1 Denier d'or ND. L-293 .... **5000.00**

King standing under dais. Rev. Floriated cross, diamond in center.

27. 1 Royal d'or ND. L-296 .... **125.00**

Armored King on horse. Rev. Floriated cross in quadrilobe.

28. 1 Franc a Cheval ND. L-297 .... **100.00**

Lamb. Rev. Floriated cross in ornate circle.

29. 1 Mouton d'or ND. L-294 ....* **150.00**
30. ½ Mouton d'or ND. L-295 .... **2000.00**

St. John standing. Rev. Fleur-de-lis.

31. 1 Florin ND. L-358 .... **75.00**

CHARLES V, 1364-1380

King standing under dais. Rev. Floriated cross, diamond in center.

32. 1 Royal d'or ND. L-369 .... **1000.00**

King standing under dais. Rev. Floriated cross in ornate circle.

33. 1 Franc a Pied ND. L-371 .... **50.00**

Armored King on horse. Rev. Floriated cross in quadrilobe.

34. 1 Franc a Cheval ND. L-370 .... **100.00**

FRANCE (cont'd)

CHARLES VI, 1380-1422

King on throne, two lions at feet. Rev. Floriated cross in ornate enclosure.

35.	1 Chaise d'or ND. L-428	.................*......	2500.00
36.	½ Chaise d'or ND. L-429	....	4000.00

Arms between madonna and angel. Rev. Roman cross.

37.	1 Salut d'or ND. L-413	...................*......	1500.00
38.	½ Salut d'or ND	....	Unknown

Lamb. Rev. Floriated cross in ornate enclosure.

39.	1 Mouton d'or ND. L-380	....	50.00

Crowned arms. Rev. Floriated cross in quadrilobe.

40.	1 Ecu d'or ND. L-378	...................*......	40.00
41.	½ Ecu d'or ND. L-379	....	2500.00

Crowned arms flanked by two coronets. Rev. Floriated cross in quadrilobe.

42.	1 Ecu d'or ND. L-426	....	150.00

Crowned helmet over shield. Rev. Cross in ornate enclosure.

43.	1 Heaume d'or ND. L-398	....	10000.00
44.	½ Heaume d'or ND. L-399	...................*......	500.00

HENRY V OF ENGLAND, 1415-1422

Lamb. Rev. Floriated cross in ornate enclosure.

45.	1 Mouton d'or ND. L-434	....	600.00

Arms between madonna and angel. Rev. Roman cross.

46.	1 Salut d'or ND. L-437	....	3000.00
47.	½ Salut d'or ND	....	Unknown

HENRY VI OF ENGLAND, 1422-1453

Angel over two shields. Rev. Roman cross.

48.	1 Angelot ND. L-488	....	250.00

Madonna and angel over two shields. Rev. Roman cross.

49.	1 Salut d'or ND. L-447	....	50.00

CHARLES VII, 1422-1461

Armored king on horse. Rev. Floriated cross in quadrilobe.

50.	1 Franc a Cheval ND. L-455	....	7000.00

King standing. Rev. Floriated cross in quadrilobe.

51.	1 Royal d'or ND. L-459	....	75.00

Lamb. Rev. Floriated cross in ornate enclosure.

52.	1 Mouton d'or ND	....	Unknown

Arms between madonna and angel. Rev. Roman cross.

53.	1 Salut d'or ND. L-461	....	1500.00

Large crowned shield. Rev. Floriated cross in quadrilobe.

54.	1 Ecu d'or ND. L-457	....	35.00

Crowned shield flanked by two lis or crowns. Rev. Floriated cross, a crown in each angle.

55.	1 Ecu Neuf ND. L-510	....	35.00
56.	½ Ecu Neuf ND. L-511. (Crowns not in angles)	....	30.00

Crowned shield flanked by two lis. Rev. Floriated cross, a crown or briquette in each angle.

57. 1 Ecu Briquette ND. L-512 .... 125.00

LOUIS XI, 1461-1483

St. Michael slaying dragon. Rev. Floriated cross.

58. 3 Angelots ND. L-526 .... 5000.00
59. ½ Angelot ND. L-528 .... 3000.00

Crowned arms flanked by crowned lis. Rev. Floriated cross in quadrilobe.

60. 1 Ecu d'or ND. L-524 .... 45.00

Crowned arms. Rev. Large floriated cross.

61. ½ Ecu d'or ND. L-525 .... 75.00

Crowned arms, small radiate sun above. Rev. Floriated cross.

62. 1 Ecu au Soleil ND. L-529 ....* 30.00
63. ½ Ecu au Soleil ND. L-530 .... 75.00

Quartered arms of Dauphine. Rev. Ornate cross.

64. 1 Ecu Delphinil ND. L-531 .... 2000.00

CHARLES VIII, 1483-1498

Crowned arms, small radiate sun above. Rev. Floriated cross.

65. 3 Ecus au Soleil ND. L-555 .... 4000.00
66. 1 Ecu au Soleil ND. L-554 ....* 35.00
67. ½ Ecu au Soleil ND. L-556 ....* 30.00

Crowned arms flanked by two ermines, sun above. Rev. Ornate cross.

68. 1 Ecu au Soleil de Bretagne ND. L-557 ....* 75.00
69. ½ Ecu au Soleil de Bretagne ND. L-557 .... 2000.00

Arms of Dauphine. Rev. Floriated cross.

70. 1 Ecu au Soleil de Dauphine ND. L-558 .... 60.00

LOUIS XII, 1498-1515

Crowned arms, small radiate sun above. Rev. Floriated cross.

71. 1 Ecu d'or au Soleil ND. L-592 .... 35.00
72. ½ Ecu d'or au Soleil ND. L-593 .... 50.00

Crowned arms flanked by two porcupines. Rev. Cross.

73. 1 Ecu d'or au Porcepic ND. L-598 ....* 50.00
74. ½ Ecu d'or au Porcepic ND. L-599 .... 800.00

Crowned arms flanked by two ermines, sun above. Rev. Ornate cross.

75. 1 Ecu au Soleil de Bretagne ND. L-594 ....* 75.00
76. ½ Ecu au Soileil de Bretagne ND. L-595 .... 800.00

Crowned arms flanked by two ermines, a porcupine below. Rev. Ornate cross.

77. 1 Ecu au Porcepic de Bretagne ND. L-600a 75.00

Arms of France and Dauphine quartered, sun above. Rev. Floriated cross.

78. 1 Ecu au Soleil du Dauphine ND. L-597 .... 100.00

Arms of France and Dauphine flanked by two porcupines. Rev. Cross.

79. 1 Ecu au Porcepic du Dauphine ND. L-601 .... 150.00

Crowned arms, small radiate sun above. Rev. Cross of Jerusalem.

80. 1 Ecu au Soleil de Provence ND. L-596 .... 1000.00

FRANCIS I, 1515-1547

Crowned arms flanked by two lis. Rev. Two crowns and two F's in angles of cross.

81. 1 Ecu d'or au Soleil ND. L-638 .... 40.00

Crowned arms flanked by two crowned F's. Rev. Two F's and two lis in angles of cross.

82. 1 Ecu d'or au Soleil ND. L-642 .... 200.00

Crowned arms flanked by a G and a lis. Rev. Two F's and two lis in angles of cross.

83. 1 Ecu d'or au Soleil ND. L-644 .... 150.00

Crowned arms, sun above, mint mark below. Rev. Floriated cross.

84. 1 Ecu d'or au Soleil ND. L-739 .... * 40.00
85. ½ Ecu d'or au Soleil ND. L-740 .... 200.00

Crowned arms, sun above, mint mark below. Rev. Two F's and two lis in angles of cross.

86. 1 Ecu d'or au Soleil ND. L-741 .... 35.00
87. ½ Ecu d'or au Soleil ND. L-742 .... 75.00

Crowned arms, small radiate sun above. Rev. Floriated cross.

88. 1 Ecu d'or au Soleil ND. L-634 .... * 35.00
89. ½ Ecu d'or au Soleil ND. L-635 .... 75.00

Crowned arms, small radiate sun above. Rev. Two crowned F's in angles of cross.

90. 1 Ecu d'or au Soleil ND. L-636 .... * 35.00
91. ½ Ecu d'or au Soleil ND. L-637 .... 200.00
92. 1 Ecu d'or au Soleil ND. The F's not crowned. L-644 bis .. 200.00

Crowned arms, small radiate sun above. Rev. Two F's and two lis in angles of cross.

93. 1 Ecu d'or ND. L-639 .... * 35.00
94. ½ Ecu d'or ND. L-640 .... 100.00

Same type as above but with a small cross added to both the Obv. and Rev.

95. 1 Ecu d'or a la Petite Croix ND. L-746 .... 80.00
96. ½ Ecu d'or a la Petite Croix ND. L-747 .... 200.00

Crowned arms, small radiate sun above. Rev. Four F's in angles of cross.

97. 1 Ecu d'or au Soleil ND. L-641 .... 150.00

Crowned arms flanked by two salamanders. Rev. Two F's and two salamanders in angles of cross.

98. 1 Ecu d'or au Salamandres ND. L-744, 745 .... 200.00

Crowned arms. Rev. Plain cross.

99. 1 Ecu d'or a la Croisette ND. L-749 .... * 50.00
100. ½ Ecu d'or a la Croisette ND. L-750 .... 200.00

Crowned arms flanked by two F's. Rev. Plain cross. This coin is doubtful.

101. 1 Ecu d'or a la Croisette ND. L-751 ....

Arms of France and Dauphine. Rev. Floriated cross.

102. 1 Ecu d'or du Dauphine ND. L-645 .... 50.00

Arms of France and Dauphine. Rev. Two crowned F's in angles of cross.

103. 1 Ecu d'or du Dauphine ND. L-646 .... 50.00

Arms of France and Dauphine. Rev. One dolphin and one lis in angles of cross.

104. 1 Ecu d'or du Dauphine ND. L-647 .... 100.00

  Arms of France and Dauphine. Rev. Two crowns in angles of cross.

105. 1 Ecu d'or du Dauphine ND. L-648 .... 50.00

  Arms of France and Dauphine. Rev. Crowned F and dolphin in angles of cross.

106. 1 Ecu d'or du Dauphine ND. L-649 .... 50.00

  Arms of France and Dauphine. Rev. Two dolphins in angles of cross.

107. 1 Ecu d'or du Dauphine ND. L-650 .... 50.00

  Crowned arms of France and Dauphine. Rev. Two F's and two lis in angles of cross.

108. 1 Ecu d'or du Dauphine a la Petite Croix ND. L-753 .... 700.00

  Same arms as above. Rev. Floriated cross.

109. 1 Ecu d'or du Dauphine. L-752 .... 1000.00

  Arms of France and Dauphine. Rev. Plain cross.

110. 1 Ecu d'or du Dauphine a la Croisette. L-754 .... 250.00

  Crowned arms flanked by two ermines. Rev. Two F's and two ermines in angles of cross.

111. 1 Ecu d'or de Bretagne ND. L-651 .... 75.00

  Crowned arms flanked by an F and an ermine. Rev. Two F's and two ermines in angles of cross.

112. 1 Ecu d'or de Bretagne ND. L-652 .... 75.00

HENRY II, 1547-1559

  Crowned bust. Rev. Crowned arms.

113. 1 Ecu d'or 1549. L-807 ....*...... 600.00
114. ½ Ecu d'or 1549. L-808 .... 700.00

  Bust. Rev. Cross of four H's with two crescents and two lis in angles (see also under Francis II and Charles IX).

115. 2 Henri d'or 1553-62. L-809 .... 300.00
116. 1 Henri d'or 1550-62. L-810 ....*..... 200.00
117. ½ Henri d'or 1550-60. L-811 .... 200.00

  Bust. Rev. Cross of four H's, with four lis in angles (see also under Francis II and Charles IX).

118. 2 Henri d'or 1550-61. L-812 .... 300.00
119. 1 Henri d'or 1550-59. L-813 ....*...... 200.00

  Laureate bust. Rev. Gallia seated.

120. 2 Henri d'or ND. L-816 .... 1500.00
121. 1 Henri d'or ND. L-817 .... 1000.00
122. ½ Henri d'or ND. L-818 ....*...... 1000.00

  Crowned arms flanked by two crescents. Rev. Two H's and two crescents in angles of cross. The ½ Ecu is known only as an Essai in double thickness. The normal weight ½ Ecu is unknown.

123. 1 Ecu d'or aux Croissants 1552. L-814 ....*...... 700.00
124. ½ Ecu d'or aux Croissants 1552 ....Unknown

  Crowned arms. Rev. Plain cross.

125. 1 Ecu d'or a la Croisette ND. L-806 .... 200.00

FRANCIS II, 1559-1560

(There are no distinctive coins of Francis II. During his short reign of seventeen months, the coinage of Henry II was continued without change. Therefore, coins dated 1559 or 1560 actually bear the name or portrait of Henry II, although they may have been struck under Francis II).

CHARLES IX, 1560-1574

(The early coins of this reign are not distinctive, in that like those of Francis II, they continue to bear the name or portrait of Henry II. Therefore, certain coins dated 1560, 1561 or 1562, although they purport to be coins of Henry II, were actually struck under Charles IX. The distinctive coinage of Charles IX follows).

FRANCE (cont'd)

Crowned arms. Rev. Floriated cross. (The coins dated 1575 were struck under Henry III although they bear the name of Charles IX).

126. 1 Ecu d'or 1562-75. L-890 ....*...... 50.00
127. ½ Ecu d'or 1561-75. L-891 .... 60.00

Arms of France and Dauphine. Rev. Floriated cross.

128. 1 Ecu d'or du Dauphine 1562-74. L-893 ....*...... 100.00
129. ½ Ecu d'or du Dauphine ....Unknown

Crowned arms without the King's name. Rev. Floriated cross. Struck by the Protestants in Rouen.

130. 1 Ecu au Soleil 1562. L-890c 100.00

HENRY III, 1574-1589

Crowned arms flanked by two H's. Rev. Ornate floriated cross. (For certain coins dated 1575, see under Charles IX).

131. 2 Ecu d'or 1589. L-959 .... 2500.00
132. 1 Ecu d'or 1578, ND. L-963 ....:.............*...... 150.00
133. ½ Ecu d'or 1578. L-964 .... 400.00

Crowned arms. Rev. Lobed floriated cross.

134. 1 Ecu d'or 1575-89. L-960 ....*...... 75.00
135. ½ Ecu d'or 1575-89. L-961 .... 100.00

Crowned arms. Rev. Floriated cross, mint mark in center.

136. 1 Ecu d'or 1575, 88. L-960x, 962 .... 75.00

CHARLES X, 1589-1590

Crowned arms. Rev. Floriated cross. (Coins with his name dated after 1590 were struck during the reign of Henry IV).

137. 1 Ecu d'or 1590-95. L-1015 .... 75.00
138. ½ Ecu d'or 1590-94. L-1016 ....*...... 200.00

HENRY IV, 1589-1610

Crowned arms flanked by two H's. Rev. Two H's and two lis in angles of floriated cross.

139. 2 Ecu d'or 1589. L-1047 .... 2500.00

Crowned arms. Rev. Lobed, floriated cross.

140. 1 Ecu d'or 1590-1610. L-1048 ....*...... 200.00
141. ½ Ecu d'or 1590-1610. L-1049. .... 200.00

Crowned arms. Rev. Floriated cross with an H under each of the four lis.

142. 1 Ecu d'or 1589-1604. L-1051. ....*...... 300.00
143. ½ Ecu d'or 1589-1603. L-1052. .... 300.00

Crowned arms in beaded circle. Rev. Floriated cross in beaded circle.

144. 1 Ecu d'or 1589-1610. L-1054. ....*...... 250.00
145. ½ Ecu d'or 1589-1603. ....Unknown

LOUIS XIII, 1610-1643

Crowned arms. Rev. Lobed floriated cross.

146. 1 Ecu d'or 1637-43. ....*...... 50.00
147. ½ Ecu d'or 1615-40. .... 50.00

Crowned arms in circle. Rev. Floriated cross in circle.

148. 1 Ecu d'or 1615. ....*...... 60.00
149. ½ Ecu d'or 1615. .... 100.00

FRANCE (cont'd)

Crowned arms. Rev. Floriated cross.

150.   1 Ecu d'or ND. 40.00

Arms of France and Dauphine. Rev. Floriated cross.

151.   1 Ecu d'or 1641. ....   500.00
152.   ½ Ecu d'or 1641. ....   750.00

Draped, laureate bust. Rev. Cross of eight L's.

153.   10 Louis d'or 1640. .... 6000.00

Laureate head. Rev. Cross of eight L's.

154.   10 Louis d'or 1640. .... 4000.00
155.   8 Louis d'or 1640. .... 3500.00
156.   4 Louis d'or 1640. .... 4500.00
157.   2 Louis d'or 1640-43. ....   300.00
158.   1 Louis d'or 1640-43. .... * ...   100.00
159.   ½ Louis d'or 1640-43. ....   60.00

LOUIS XIV, 1643-1715

Crowned arms. Rev. Lobed, floriated cross.

160.   1 Ecu d'or au Soleil 1643-51. ....   50.00
161.   ½ Ecu d'or au Soleil 1643-51. ....   200.00

Child head with short curl. Rev. Cross of eight L's.

162.   2 Louis d'or 1644. .... 1000.00
163.   1 Louis d'or 1644. ....   100.00
164.   ½ Louis d'or 1644. .... * ...   150.00

Child head with long curl. Rev. Cross of eight L's.

165.   2 Louis d'or 1644-52. ....   500.00
166.   1 Louis d'or 1644-53. .... * ...   75.00
167.   ½ Louis d'or 1644-46. ....   100.00

Youthful laureate head. Rev. Cross of eight L's.

168.   1 Louis d'or 1659-68. .... * ...   100.00
169.   ½ Louis d'or 1660-68. ....   300.00

Youthful plain head. Rev. Cross of eight L's.

170.   1 Louis d'or 1668-80. .... * ...   100.00
171.   1 Louis d'or 1668. Older head. 100.00
172.   ½ Louis d'or 1669-80. ....   300.00

Older laureate head. Rev. Cross of eight L's.

172-a. 1 Louis d'or 1683-89. ....   150.00

Old laureate head. Rev. Crowned arms.

173.   2 Louis d'or 1690-93. ....   200.00
174.   1 Louis d'or 1690-93. .... * ...   75.00
175.   ½ Louis d'or 1690-93. ....   75.00

Old laureate head. Rev. Arms of France and Navarre-Bearn.

176.   1 Louis d'or 1690. .... 1250.00

Old laureate head. Rev. Four L's around mint mark.

177.   2 Louis d'or 1693-95. .... * ...   200.00
178.   1 Louis d'or 1693-95. ....   75.00
179.   ½ Louis d'or 1693-95. ....   75.00

Old laureate head. Rev. Eight L's over crossed insignia.

180.   2 Louis d'or 1701, 02. ....   200.00
181.   1 Louis d'or 1701, 02. ....   100.00
182.   ½ Louis d'or 1701, 02 .... * ...   100.00

Old laureate head. Rev. Four lis in angles of crossed insignia.

183.   2 Louis d'or 1704-09. ....   275.00
184.   1 Louis d'or 1704-09. .... * ...   125.00
185.   ½ Louis d'or 1704-09. ....   150.00

FRANCE (cont'd)

Old laureate head. Cross of eight L's, sun in center.

186.	2 Louis d'or 1709-11	....	250.00
187.	1 Louis d'or 1709-11	...........................*	75.00
188.	½ Louis d'or 1709-11	....	75.00

Cross of four lis. Rev. Two angels holding arms.

189.	1 Lis d'or 1656	....	200.00

LOUIS XV, 1715-1774
Child head. Rev. Cross of eight L's.

190.	1 Louis d'or 1715	....	2000.00
191.	½ Louis d'or 1715	....	1750.00

Child head. Rev. Crowned arms over crossed insignia.

192.	2 Louis d'or 1716	....	1000.00
193.	1 Louis d'or 1716	...........................*	200.00
194.	½ Louis d'or 1716	....	500.00

Crowned child head. Rev. Cross of four shields.

195.	2 Louis d'or 1717, 18	....................*	200.00
196.	1 Louis d'or 1717, 18	....	500.00
197.	½ Louis d'or 1717, 18	....	500.00

Young laureate head. Rev. Maltese cross.

198.	1 Louis d'or 1718, 19	....	100.00
199.	½ Louis d'or 1718, 19	....................*	500.00

Laureate head. Rev. Crown over two L's.

199-a.	2 Louis d'or 1720, 22	....	500.00
200.	1 Louis d'or 1720, 22	....................*	100.00
201.	½ Louis d'or 1720, 22	....	500.00

Laureate head. Rev. Two script L's in palms, crown above.

202.	2 Louis d'or 1723-25	....	400.00
203.	1 Louis d'or 1723-25	....................*	100.00
204.	½ Louis d'or 1723-25	....	500.00

Draped bust. Rev. Crown over two shields.

205.	1 Louis d'or 1726-28	....................*	50.00
206.	½ Louis d'or 1726-28	....	40.00

Large head with band. Rev. Crown over two shields.

207.	2 Louis d'or 1740-65	....	100.00
208.	1 Louis d'or 1740-65	....	50.00
209.	½ Louis d'or 1740-65	....................*	40.00

Old laureate head. Rev. Crown over two shields.

210.	2 Louis d'or 1765-74	....................*	300.00
211.	1 Louis d'or 1765-74	....	175.00

LOUIS XVI, 1774-1793

Uniformed bust. Rev. Crowned arms within palms.

212.	1 Louis d'or 1774	....	250.00

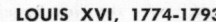

Uniformed bust. Rev. Crown over two oval shields.

213.	2 Louis d'or 1775-84	....	150.00
214.	1 Louis d'or 1774-84	....................*	75.00
215.	½ Louis d'or 1775-84	....	200.00

FRANCE (cont'd)

Bare head. Rev. Crown over two oval shields. This coin was not placed in circulation.

216. 1 Louis d'or 1785. .... 1000.00

Bare head. Rev. Crown over two square shields.

217. 2 Louis d'or 1786-92. ....* 75.00
218. 1 Louis d'or 1786-92. .... 40.00
219. 1 Louis d'or 1786. Horn on head. BB mm. 300.00

Bare head. Rev. Angel writing.

220. 24 Livres (Louis d'or) 1792, 93. .... 175.00

THE FIRST REPUBLIC

Angel writing. Rev. Value in wreath.

221. 24 Livres 1793. .... 120.00

NAPOLEON BONAPARTE, 1801-1815

Bare head with title of First Consul. Rev. Value and "Republique Francaise." Struck under the First Republic.

222. 40 Francs. Years 11, 12 (1803, 04). ....* 75.00
223. 20 Francs. Years 11, 12 (1803, 04). ....* 30.00

Bare head with title of Emperor. Rev. Value and "Republique Francaise."

224. 40 Francs. Years 13, 14, 1806, 07. A mm. ....* 60.00
225. 40 Francs. 1806, 07. I mm. 75.00
226. 40 Francs. 1807. M mm. 75.00
227. 40 Francs. Year 14, 1806, 07. U mm. 100.00
228. 40 Francs. Year 14, 1806, 07. W mm. 75.00
229. 20 Francs. Years 13, 14, 1806, 07. A mm. 30.00
230. 20 Francs. Years 13, 14, 1806. I mm. 30.00
231. 20 Francs. 1807. M mm. 35.00
232. 20 Francs. Years 13, 14, 1806. Q mm. 35.00
233. 20 Francs. Year 14, 1806, 07. U mm. .... ' 45.00
234. 20 Francs. Year 14, 1806, 07. W mm. 40.00

Laureate head with title of Emperor. Rev. Value and "Republique Francaise."

235. 40 Francs. 1807, 08. A mm. 65.00
236. 40 Francs 1808. H mm. 75.00
237. 40 Francs 1808. M mm. 75.00
238. 40 Francs 1808. U mm. 175.00
239. 40 Francs 1808. W mm. 75.00
240. 20 Francs 1807, 08. A mm. ....* ... 30.00
241. 20 Francs 1808. K mm. 60.00
242. 20 Francs 1808. M mm. 35.00
243. 20 Francs 1808. Q mm. 40.00
244. 20 Francs 1808. U mm. 40.00
245. 20 Francs 1808. W mm. 35.00

Laureate head with title of Emperor. Rev. Value and "Empire Francaise."

246. 40 Francs 1809-13. A mm. 60.00
247. 40 Francs 1809, 10, 12. W mm. 65.00
248. 40 Francs 1809. M mm. 75.00
249. 40 Francs 1809. U mm. 200.00
250. 40 Francs 1810, 11. K mm. 65.00
251. 40 Francs 1813. CL mm. 90.00
252. 20 Francs 1809-15. A mm. 25.00
253. 20 Francs 1809-15. L mm. 25.00
254. 20 Francs 1809-13. K mm. 25.00
255. 20 Francs 1809, 10, 11. H mm. 35.00
256. 20 Francs 1809-15. W mm. 25.00
257. 20 Francs 1809-12. M mm. 25.00
258. 20 Francs 1809-13. U mm. ....* ... 35.00
259. 20 Francs 1810-14. Q mm. 25.00
260. 20 Francs 1812, 13. R mm. 40.00
261. 20 Francs 1813, 14. CL mm. 50.00
262. 20 Francs 1813. Fish and mast mm. 40.00

LOUIS XVIII, 1814-1824

Uniformed bust. Rev. Arms.

263. 20 Francs 1814, 15. A mm. 25.00
264. 20 Francs 1814, 15. L mm. 27.50
265. 20 Francs 1814, 15. K mm. 27.50
266. 20 Francs 1814, 15. W mm. 27.50
267. 20 Francs 1814, 15. Q mm. 27.50
268. 20 Francs 1815. B mm. 40.00
269. 20 Francs 1815. R mm. (London) ....* ... 60.00

Bare head. Rev. Arms.

270. 40 Francs 1816-24. A mm. ....* ... 50.00
271. 40 Francs 1816, 17. L mm. 65.00
272. 40 Francs 1822. H mm. 75.00
273. 40 Francs 1816, 18, 19. W mm. 60.00
274. 40 Francs 1816. Q mm. 60.00
275. 40 Francs 1816. B mm. 75.00
276. 20 Francs 1816, 24. A mm. 25.00
277. 20 Francs 1816, 17, 18. L mm. 22.50

FRANCE (cont'd)

278.	20 Francs 1816, 17. K mm.	27.50
279.	20 Francs 1822. H mm.	40.00
280.	20 Francs 1816-24. W mm.	20.00
281.	20 Francs 1824. MA monogram mm.	40.00
282.	20 Francs 1818, 19, 20. T mm.	30.00
283.	20 Francs 1816-24. Q mm.	22.50
284.	20 Francs 1816. B mm.	30.00

CHARLES X, 1824-1830

Head. Rev. Arms.

285.	40 Francs 1824-30. A mm. ....*......	50.00
286.	40 Francs 1830. MA monogram mm.	75.00
287.	20 Francs 1825-30. A mm.	25.00
288.	20 Francs 1825-30. W mm.	30.00
289.	20 Francs 1828. T mm.	35.00
290.	20 Francs 1826. Q mm.	32.50

LOUIS PHILIPPE I, 1830-1848

Bare head. Rev. Value and date.

291.	20 Francs 1830, 31. A mm.	30.00
292.	20 Francs 1831. B mm.	30.00
293.	20 Francs 1831. T mm.	60.00
294.	20 Francs 1831. W mm.	30.00

Laureate head. Rev. Value and date.

295.	40 Francs 1831-39. A mm. ....*......	50.00
296.	40 Francs 1834, 35. L mm.	60.00
297.	40 Francs 1832, 33. B mm.	75.00
298.	20 Francs 1832-48. A mm.	25.00
299.	20 Francs 1834, 35. L mm.	30.00
300.	20 Francs 1832-46. W mm.	25.00
301.	20 Francs 1832. T mm.	60.00
302.	20 Francs 1832-35. B mm.	25.00

LOUIS NAPOLEON BONAPARTE, PRESIDENT, 1848-1852
(President of the Second Republic, and later Emperor Napoleon III)

Bare head. Rev. Value and date.

303.	20 Francs 1852.	25.00

NAPOLEON III, 1852-1870

Bare head. Rev. Arms.

304.	100 Francs 1855-59. A mm.	90.00
305.	100 Francs 1855-60. BB mm.	115.00
306.	50 Francs 1855-59. A mm.	40.00
307.	50 Francs 1855-60. BB mm.	50.00
308.	20 Francs 1853-60. A mm. ....*...	17.50
309.	20 Francs 1855, 56. D mm.	22.50
310.	20 Francs 1855-60. BB mm.	17.50
311.	10 Francs 1854-60. A mm.	10.00
312.	10 Francs 1855-60. BB mm.	10.00
313.	5 Francs 1854-60. A mm.	10.00
314.	5 Francs 1859, 60. BB mm.	12.50

Laureate head. Rev. Arms.

315.	100 Francs 1862-70. A mm.	90.00
316.	100 Francs 1862-69. BB mm.	100.00
317.	50 Francs 1862-68. A mm.	45.00
318.	50 Francs 1862-69. BB mm.	55.00
319.	20 Francs 1861-70. A mm. ....*...	17.50
320.	20 Francs 1861-70. BB mm.	17.50
321.	10 Francs 1861-68. A mm.	10.00
322.	10 Francs 1861-69. BB mm.	10.00
323.	5 Francs 1862-68. A mm.	10.00
324.	5 Francs 1862-69. BB mm.	12.50

SECOND AND THIRD REPUBLICS—1848-1852 and 1870-1940

Angel writing. Rev. Value and date.

325.	100 Francs 1878-1913	90.00
326.	50 Francs 1878-1904	100.00
327.	20 Francs 1848, 49 (2nd Rep.)	20.00
328.	20 Francs 1871-98 (3rd Rep.) ....*...	16.00

Head of Ceres. Rev. Value in circle.

329.	20 Francs 1849, 50, 51 (2nd Rep.) ....*...	20.00
330.	10 Francs 1850, 51 (2nd Rep.)	15.00
331.	10 Francs 1878, 89 (3rd Rep.)	100.00
332.	10 Francs 1895, 96, 99	20.00
333.	5 Francs 1878, 89	100.00

Head of the Republic. Rev. Rooster.

334.	20 Francs 1899-1914 ....*...	16.00
335.	10 Francs 1899-1914	9.00

Winged head of the Republic. Rev. Value.

336.	100 Francs 1929, 33, 35, 36	50.00

B. Cities and Provinces of —

AQUITAINE

A. English Rulers of —

EDWARD III, 1317-1355

Ruler walking. Rev. Cross.

1. 1 Guyennois ND 250.00

Ruler seated. Rev. Cross.

2. 1 Ecu d'or ND 125.00

St. John. Rev. Lily.

3. 1 Florin ND 150.00

Leopard. Rev. Cross.

4. 1 Leopard ND 150.00

EDWARD THE BLACK PRINCE, 1355-1375

Ruler standing under dais. Rev. Cross.

5. 1 Pavillion d'or ND ....*...... 300.00
6. ½ Pavillion d'or ND 1500.00

Ruler walking. Rev. Cross.

7. 1 Guyennois ND 250.00

Ruler seated. Rev. Cross.

8. 1 Chaise d'or ND 200.00

Crowned bust facing. Rev. Cross.

9. 1 Hardi ND 250.00

Leopard. Rev. Cross.

10. 1 Leopard ND 200.00

RICHARD II, 1377-1399
Crowned bust facing. Rev. Cross.

11. 1 Hardi ND 300.00
12. ½ Hardi ND 1000.00

HENRY IV, 1399-1413
Crowned bust facing. Rev. Cross.

13. 1 Hardi ND. 2000.00

HENRY V, 1417-1422
Lamb. Rev. Cross.

14. 1 Mouton d'or ND 150.00

Virgin and angel with shields. Rev. Cross.

15. 1 Salut d'or ND 1500.00

HENRY VI, 1422-1436

Angel over two shields. Rev. Cross.

16. 1 Angelot ND 250.00

Virgin and angel over two shields. Rev. Cross.

17. 1 Salut d'or ND 100.00

B. French Rulers of —

CHARLES, 1468-1474
Ruler on horse. Rev. Cross

18. 1 Franc a Cheval ND 1000.00

Crowned bust facing. Rev. Cross.

19. 1 Hardi ND. 250.00
20. ½ Hardi ND. 2000.00

Ruler standing with leopard. Rev. Arms on cross.

21. 1 Fort d'or ND. 2500.00

ARLES

Archbishops of —

GAILLARD DE SAUMATE, 1317-1323
St. John. Rev. Lily. G. Arel Archp.

1. 1 Florin ND. 250.00

STEPHAN DE LA GARDE, 1350-1359
St. John. Rev. Lily. S. Arel Archp.

2. 1 Florin ND. 50.00

WILLIAM II DE LA GARDE, 1360-1374
Ruler standing. Rev. Cross.

3. 1 Franc a Pied ND. 1000.00

JOHN FERRER, 1499-1521
Arms. Rev. Cross.

4. 1 Ecu d'or ND. 1000.00

AVIGNON

Popes of Rome at —

JOHN XXII, 1316-1334

St. John. Rev. Lily.

1. 1 Florin ND. 200.00

INNOCENT VI, 1352-1362
Pope seated. Rev. Crossed Keys.

2. 1 Zecchino ND. 500.00

URBAN V, 1362-1370

St. John. Rev. Lily.

3. 1 Florin ND. 200.00

CLEMENT VII, 1378-1394
Tiara and arms. Rev. St. Peter.

4. 1 Zecchino ND. 300.00

Tiara. Rev. Crossed Keys.

5. 1 Zecchino ND. 500.00

JOHN XXIII, 1410-1415
Tiara. Rev. Cross.

6. 1 Zecchino ND. 350.00

Pope seated. Rev. Tiara over arms.

7. 1 Ecu d'or ND. 400.00

Pope seated. Rev. Cross.

8. 1 Zecchino ND. 400.00

MARTIN V, 1417-1431

Tiara over shield. Rev. Crossed keys.

9. 1 Zecchino ND. 300.00

SIXTUS IV, 1471-1484
Tiara over arms. Rev. St. Peter.

10. 1 Zecchino ND. 350.00

Tiara. Rev. Two keys.

11. ½ Ecu d'or ND. 500.00

INNOCENT VIII, 1484-1492
Tiara. Rev. Crossed keys.

12. 1 Zecchino ND. 400.00

JULIUS II, 1503-1513

Legate's shield and arms. Rev. Cross.

13. 1 Ecu d'or ND. 300.00

JULIUS III, 1550-1555
Papal arms. Rev. Legate's arms.

14. 1 Ecu d'or ND. 400.00

PIUS IV, 1555-1559
Papal arms. Rev. Legate's arms.

15. 1 Ecu d'or 1562. With name of Alexander Farnese as legate   500.00
16. 1 Ecu d'or ND. With name of Charles Bourbon as legate ..   500.00

ST. PIUS V, 1565-1572
Pope seated. Rev. Cross.

17. 1 Ecu d'or ND. 400.00

Papal arms. Rev. Legate's arms.

18. 1 Ecu d'or ND 500.00

Two shields. Rev. View of Avignon.

19. 1 Ecu d'or 1570 .... 800.00

GREGORY XIII, 1572-1585
Two shields. Rev. View of Avignon.

20. 1 Ecu d'or ND. 800.00

Pope seated. Rev. Cross.

21. 1 Ecu d'or ND. 400.00

Papal arms. Rev. Two shields.

22. 1 Ecu d'or ND. 300.00

CLEMENT VIII, 1592-1605
Legate's arms. Rev. View of Avignon.

23. 8 Ecu d'or 1596 .... 5000.00
24. 4 Ecu d'or 1590 .... 2000.00

Bust. Rev. Legate's arms.

25. 10 Zecchini 1599 .... 5000.00
26. 4 Ecu d'or 1597, 98, 1602 ....*...... 2500.00
27. 2 Ecu d'or 1596, 98, 1600 .... 1000.00

PAUL V, 1605-1621

Bust. Rev. Legate's arms.

28. 4 Ecu d'or 1611 ....*...... 2000.00
29. 2 Ecu d'or 1608 .... 800.00

GREGORY XV, 1621-1623
Bust. Rev. Arms.

30. 8 Ecu d'or 1622 .... 3500.00

URBAN VIII, 1623-1644

Bust. Rev. Arms.

31.	4 Ecu d'or 1632-43	*	750.00
32.	2 Ecu d'or 1640		300.00

INNOCENT X, 1644-1655
Bust. Rev. Legate's arms.

33.	4 Ecu d'or 1644-50		750.00
34.	2 Ecu d'or 1644		400.00

ALEXANDER VII, 1655-1667

Bust. Rev. Legate's arms.

35.	4 Ecu d'or 1657, 58, 62, 63	*	750.00
36.	2 Ecu d'or 1664		400.00

BAR
Dukes of —
EDWARD III, 1411-1415
Crowned bust facing. Rev. Lily.

1. 1 Florin ND 350.00

BEARN
Counts of —
GASTON, 1436-1471
Ruler on horse. Rev. Cross.

1. 1 Ecu d'or ND 400.00

St. John. Rev. Lily.

2. 1 Florin ND 100.00

FRANCIS PHOEBUS, 1479-1483

Arms. Rev. Cross.

3.	1 Ecu d'or ND	*	400.00
4.	½ Ecu d'or ND		1500.00

CATHERINE, 1483-1484
Arms. Rev. Cross.

5. 1 Ecu d'or ND 350.00

BESANCON
CHARLES V OF SPAIN
Ruler standing. Rev. Cross.

1. 1 Florin 1541 ....Unknown

Laureate head. Rev. Eagle.

2.	4 Pistolets 1579		700.00
3.	2 Pistolets 1579-1673	*	500.00

Crowned bust. Rev. Eagle.

4. 1 Pistolet 1578, 1653, 54 ...... 125.00

Ruler standing. Rev. Eagle.

5. 2 Pistolets 1664 ...... 750.00

Ruler standing. Rev. Legend in cartouche.

6.	2 Ducats 1642, 54		150.00
7.	1 Ducat 1655		75.00
7a.	½ Ducat 1655		50.00

PHILIP IV OF SPAIN
Armored bust. Rev. Name and date.

8. 4 Pistolets 1664 ...... 1250.00

BOUILLON
Dukes of —
WILLIAM ROBERT DE LA MARCK, 1574-1588

Arms. Rev. Cross.

1. 1 Pistole 1587 ...... 1000.00

CHARLOTTE, 1589-1591
Arms. Rev. Plain or elaborate cross.

2.	1 Ecu d'or 1589, 91		600.00
3.	1 Pistole 1591		600.00

HENRY DE LA TOUR AND CHARLOTTE, 1591-1594
Arms. Rev. Cross of four towers.

4. 1 Pistole 1592 ...... 700.00

HENRY DE LA TOUR, 1591-1623
Bust. Rev. Arms.

5. 1 Ecu d'or 1614 ...... 150.00

Crowned arms. Rev. Cross of four towers.

6. 1 Ecu d'or 1597 ...... 150.00

Crowned arms. Rev. Cross.

7.	2 Ecu d'or 1614, ND		500.00
8.	1 Ecu d'or 1598, 1610, ND		150.00

FRANCE-BOUILLON (cont'd)

GEOFFREY MAURICE, 1652-1691
Bust. Rev. Arms.

9. 1 Souverain d'or (1652-1691) 200.00
10. ½ Souverain d'or (1652-1691) 150.00

BRITTANY

Dukes of —

PERIOD 800-1000
Bust. Rev. Cross.

1. Electrum 1 Sou ND 300.00

CHARLES DE BLOIS, 1341-1364
Ruler standing. Rev. Cross.

2. 1 Royal d'or ND 500.00

JOHN IV, 1345-1399
Ruler on horse. Rev. Cross.

3. 1 Ecu d'or ND 500.00

JOHN V, 1399-1442
Ruler on horse. Rev. Cross.

4. 1 Ecu d'or ND 300.00

FRANCIS I, 1442-1450

Ruler on horse. Rev. Cross.

5. 1 Ecu d'or ND 200.00

FRANCIS II, 1458-1488
Ruler on horse. Rev. Cross.

6. 1 Ecu d'or ND 200.00

ANNE, 1488-1491

Duchess on throne. Rev. Cross.

7. 1 Ecu d'or ND 1250.00

BURGUNDY

Dukes of —

EUDES IV, 1315-1350

St. John. Rev. Lily.

1. 1 Florin ND 100.00

Ruler standing. Rev. Cross.

2. 1 Ecu d'or ND 1000.00

PHILIP I, 1350-1361
St. John. Rev. Lily.

3. 1 Florin ND 100.00

PHILIP III, 1419-1467
Horseman. Rev. Arms on cross.

4. 1 Ecu d'or ND 150.00

CAMBRAI

A. Archbishops of —

GUY IV, 1342-1348

St. John. Rev. Lily. "FLOR PSV CA or FLOR EPI CA."

1. 1 Florin ND 75.00

PETER IV, 1349-1368

Lamb. Rev. Floriated cross.

2. 1 Agnel d'or ND 500.00

Ruler on horse. Rev. Cross.

3. 1 Franc à cheval ND 200.00

Ruler standing. Rev. Cross.

4. 1 Royal d'or ND 500.00

ROBERT OF GENEVA, 1368-1372

Ruler standing. Rev. Cross.

5. 1 Franc à pied ND 300.00

Ruler on horse. Rev. Cross.

6. 1 Franc à cheval ND 200.00

GERARD III, 1372-1378
Ruler on horse. Rev. Cross.

7. 1 Franc à cheval ND 500.00

MAXIMILIAN OF BERGHES, 1556-1570

Arms. Rev. Cross.

8. 1 Ecu d'or ND 150.00

Double eagle. Rev. Eagle shield.

9. 1 Goldgulden ND 50.00

LOUIS OF BERLAYMONT, 1570-1596
Eagle shield. Rev. Double eagle.

10. 1 Goldgulden 1578 .... 50.00

B. Cathedral Chapter of —
St. John. Rev. Lily. "FLOR. CAPI. CA."

11. 1 Florin ND 100.00

CHATEAU-RENAUD

Princes of —

FRANCIS AND LOUISE MARGUERITE, 1605-1614
Bust of Francis. Rev. Arms.

1. 1 Florin ND 150.00

LOUISE MARGUERITE, 1614-1631
Arms between two crosses of Jerusalem. Rev. Cross.

2. 1 Ecu d'or ND 400.00

CHATELET-VAUVILLERS

NICHOLAS II, 1525-1562
Arms. Rev. Cross.

1. 1 Ecu Sol 1554, ND 1000.00

DOLE (DOLA)

Spanish Kings of —

PHILIP II, 1556-1598
Crowned arms. Rev. Floriated cross.

1. 1 Ecu Pistolet 1563 .... 1000.00

PHILIP IV, 1621-1665
Floriated cross. Rev. Crowned arms between two small crowns.

2. 1 Corona or Ducat 1632 .... 1000.00

DOMBES

Princes of —

JOHN II, 1459-1482

Bust. Rev. Prince on horse.

1. 1 Franc à Cheval ND 1000.00

PETER II, 1482-1503
Bust. Rev. Prince on horse.

2. 1 Franc à Cheval ND 500.00

LOUIS II, 1560-1582

Crowned arms. Rev. Cross.

3. 2 Ecu d'or or 1 Pistole 1574, 78 .... 250.00
4. 1 Ecu d'or or ½ Pistole 1574, 75 ......*...... 175.00

FRANCIS II, 1582-1592
Prince kneeling before St. Mark. Rev. Christ.

5. 1 Zecchino ND 700.00

Arms. Rev. Cross.

6. 1 Pistole 1587 ....Unknown

MARIE, 1608-1626
Arms. Rev. Cross.

7. 1 Ecu d'or 1616 .... 500.00
8. ½ Ecu d'or 1611 .... 500.00

GASTON AND MARIE, 1626-1627
Arms. Rev. Cross.

9. 1 Ecu d'or 1627 .... 500.00

GASTON, 1627-1650

Crowned shield. Rev. Lobed, floriated cross.

10. 2 Ecu d'or 1640 .... 250.00
11. 1 Ecu d'or 1640, 41 ....*...... 150.00

Laureate bust. Rev. Cross of eight L's. Posthumous issue.

12. 2 Louis d'or 1652 ....*...... 1500.00
13. 1 Louis d'or 1652 .... 1500.00

ANNE MARIE LOUISE DE MONTPENSIER, 1650-1693
Ruler and Saint standing. Rev. Christ. Venetian style.

14. 1 Ducat ND 250.00

EVREUX

Counts of —

CHARLES OF NAVARRE, 1343-1387
Ruler standing before Gothic canopy. Rev. Cross.

1. 1 Ecu d'or ND 300.00

LIGNY

Counts of —

JOHN, 1353-1364
Bust of St. Peter with lion shield. Rev. Cross.

1. 1 Ecu d'or ND 300.00

GUY, 1364-1371

Ruler standing under dais. Rev. Cross.

2. 1 Ecu d'or ND 250.00

WALERAN III, 1371-1415
Lamb. Rev. Cross.

3. 1 Agnel d'or ND 750.00

Ruler standing under dais. Rev. Cross.

4. 1 Ecu d'or ND 250.00

LORRAINE

Dukes of —

JOHN I, 1346-1389

St. John standing. Rev. Lily.

1. 1 Florin ND 250.00

RENE II, 1473-1508
St. Nicholas. Rev. Arms.

2. 1 Goldgulden ND 225.00
3. ½ Goldgulden ND 225.00

ANTHONY, 1508-1544
Bust. Rev. Arms.

4. 6 Ducats ND 1500.00
5. 1 Goldgulden 1526, 33 .... 500.00

CHARLES III, 1545-1608
Arms. Rev. Cross.

6. 2 Pistoles 1587 .... 300.00
7. 1 Pistole 1587 .... 150.00
8. ½ Pistole 1587 .... 150.00

Crowned bust. Rev. Arms.

9. ½ Pistole ND 250.00

Plain bust. Rev. Arms.

10. 4 Pistoles 1587 .... 750.00
11. 2 Pistoles 1587, 88 ....*..... 350.00
12. 1 Ducat 1566-88 .... 350.00
13. ½ Ducat ND 250.00

Bust. Rev. Circle of seven shields.

14. 1 Ducat 1588 .... 300.00

HENRY II, 1608-1624
St. Nicholas. Rev. Arms.

15. 1 Goldgulden ND 100.00
16. ½ Goldgulden ND 200.00

Bust. Rev. Arms.

17. 1 Goldgulden 1611, ND 200.00

CHARLES IV, 1625-1670

Arms. Rev. Cross.

18. 2 Pistoles 1631 ....*..... 250.00
19. 1 Pistole 1639, ND 300.00

Laureate head. Rev. Interlinked C's.

20. 1 Pistole 1661, 62, 68, 69 .... 200.00

LEOPOLD I, 1697-1729
Laureate head. Rev. Two L's.

21. 5 Taler 1702 .... 200.00

Laureate head. Rev. Arms.

22. 10 Taler 1724 ....*..... 500.00
23. 5 Taler 1719 .... 200.00
24. 2½ Taler 1718 .... 200.00

FRANCIS III, 1729-1736

Bust. Rev. Arms supported by eagles.

25. 2 Ducats 1736 ....*..... 400.00
26. 1 Ducat 1736 .... 200.00

FRANCE (cont'd)

METZ

St. Stephan standing. Rev. Arms.

1. 1 Goldgulden 1620-45, ND 50.00

Bust of St. Stephan. Rev. Arms.

2. 1 Goldgulden 1639, 45, ND 400.00

MONTELIMART

Barons of —

GAUCHER ADEMAR, 1346-1369
St. John. Rev. Lily.

1. 1 Florin ND 1000.00

MONTPELLIER

Lords of —

SANCHO OF MAJORCA, 1311-1324

Ruler seated. Rev. Double cross.

1. 1 Petit Royal d'or ND 750.00

NAVARRE

Kings of —

CHARLES II, 1349-1387
Crowned bust. Rev. Floriated cross.

A. 1 Gold Real ND 750.00

JOHN II, 1441-1479

Arms. Rev. Cross.

1. 1 Ecu d'or ND 250.00
2. ½ Ecu d'or ND ....*...... 200.00

FRANCIS PHOEBUS, 1479-1483
Crowned bust. Rev. Arms.

2a. 1 Ecu d'or ND 500.00
3. ½ Ecu d'or ND 300.00

JOHN AND CATHERINE, 1484-1512

Arms. Rev. Small cross in quadrilobe.

---

4. 1 Ecu d'or ND ....*...... 150.00
5. ¼ Ecu d'or ND 300.00

Two busts facing each other. Rev. Arms.

6. 1 Ducat ND 350.00

Crown over initials "I-K." Rev. Cross.

6a. ½ Ecu d'or ND 300.00

FERDINAND II OF ARAGON, 1512-1516
Crowned bust. Rev. Crowned arms.

7. 4 Ducats ND 500.00
8. 2 Ducats ND 350.00
9. 1 Ducat ND 150.00
10. ½ Ducat ND 125.00

HENRY OF ALBRET, 1516-1555
Crowned arms. Rev. Floriated cross.

11. 1 Ecu au Soleil ND 200.00

Crowned arms. Rev. Short cross.

12. 1 Ecu d'or ND 300.00

JOAN, 1562-1572
Cross. Rev. Crowned arms.

13. 1 Ecu au Soleil 1561 .... 250.00

Crowned S between two I's. Rev. Crowned arms.

14. 1 Ecu d'or 1565 .... 1000.00

HENRY II, 1572-1610

Busts of Henry and Margaret. Rev. Crowned arms.

15. 2 Ducats 1577 ....*...... 700.00
16. 1 Ducat 1576, 77 .... 500.00

Crowned arms. Rev. Cross and four H's.

17. 1 Ecu d'or 1575-78 .... 200.00

NICE

Arms. Rev. Legend. Siege coin.

1. 1 Scudo d'oro 1543 .... 500.00

ORANGE

Princes of —

RAYMOND III AND IV, 1335-1393
St. John. Rev. Lily.

1. 1 Florin ND 65.00

Ruler standing. Rev. Cross.

2. 1 Franc à Pied ND 150.00

JOHN II, 1475-1502
Helmet. Rev. Cross.

3. 1 Ecu d'or ND 700.00

PHILIP WILLIAM, 1584-1618

Armored bust. Rev. Arms.

4. 1 Pistole 1607 .... 450.00
5. ½ Pistole 1607 .... 350.00
6. 4 Ecu d'or 1616 ....*...... 600.00

MAURICE, 1618-1625
Bust. Rev. Arms.

7. 1 Grand Ecu d'or 1618 .... 350.00

FREDERICK HENRY, 1625-1647

Bust. Rev. Arms.

8. 1 Grand Ecu d'or 1641, 45 ....*...... 300.00
9. ½ Grand Ecu d'or 1643 .... 300.00

Knight standing. Rev. Tablet. Dutch type.

10. 1 Ducat (1625-47) 500.00

WILLIAM HENRY, 1650-1702
Prince kneeling before Christ. Rev. Madonna.

11. 1 Zecchino ND 300.00

PERPIGNAN

French Kings of —

LOUIS XI, 1461-1483
Arms of France. Rev. Cross and P.

1. 1 Ecu au Soleil ND 150.00

CHARLES VIII, 1483-1498
Arms of France. Rev. Cross and P.

2. 1 Ecu au Soileil ND 250.00

PROVENCE

Counts of —

CHARLES I OF ANJOU, 1246-1285

Bust. Rev. Arms.

1. 1 Augustale d'or ND 1000.00

K. Rev. Arms.

2. 1 Sou d'or ND 250.00

K. Rev. Cross.

3. 1 Double Tarin ND 150.00

The Annunciation. Rev. Arms.

4. 1 Salut d'or ND 150.00
5. ½ Salut d'or ND ....*...... 500.00

CHARLES II OF ANJOU, 1285-1309
The Annunciation. Rev. Arms.

6. 1 Salut d'or ND 150.00

JOANNA OF NAPLES, 1343-1352

Ruler standing. Rev. Cross.

7. 1 Franc à Pied ND 150.00

Crowned bust facing. Rev. Arms.

8. 1 Florin ND 1500.00

St. John. Rev. Arms.

9. 1 Florin ND 100.00

St. John. Rev. Lily.

10. 1 Florin ND 75.00

Crown. Rev. Cross.

11. 1 Florin ND 500.00

LOUIS AND JOANNA, 1347-1382
St. John. Rev. Lily.

12. 1 Florin ND 75.00

LOUIS I, 1382-1384

Crowned arms. Rev. Cross in enclosure.

13. 1 Ecu d'or ND 75.00

Ruler standing. Rev. Cross.

14. 1 Franc à Pied ND 200.00

FRANCE-PROVENCE (cont'd)

St. John. Rev. Arms.

15. 1 Florin ND 100.00

RENE, 1434-1480
Crowned arms. Rev. Cross of Jerusalem.

16. 1 Ecu d'or ND 600.00
17. ½ Ecu d'or ND 600.00
18. ¼ Ecu d'or ND 300.00

Bust of St. Magdalene. Rev. Cross.

19. 1 Magdalin ND 250.00

CHARLES III, 1480-1482
St. Magdalene standing. Rev. Cross with two bars.

20. 1 Magdalin (½ Ecu) ND 750.00

Bust of St. Magdalene. Rev. Cross with two bars.

21. 1 Magdalin ND 250.00

RETHEL
Counts of —
LOUIS III DE MALE, 1346-1384

Lamb. Rev. Cross.

1. Mouton d'or ND 500.00

CHARLES II GONZAGA, 1601-1637
Bust and date. Rev. Crowned arms.

2. Gold 1 Ecu 1608 . . . . 1500.00

Ruler standing. Rev. Crowned arms.

3. 1 Florin ND 350.00

Ruler standing. Rev. Legend in cartouche.

4. 1 Florin ND 350.00

Arms. Rev. Double eagle.

5. 1 Florin ND 200.00

Crowned arms. Rev. Cross of Jerusalem.

6. 1 Florin 1608 . . . . 250.00

ROUSILLON
Spanish Kings of —
FERDINAND II, 1479-1516
Crowned bust. Rev. Crowned arms between P-P.

1. 1 Principat ND 350.00

CHARLES AND JOHANNA, 1516-1556
Crowned busts facing each other. Rev. Crowned arms between P-P.

2. 2 Ducats 1522 . . . . 1250.00

SAINT POL
Counts of —
GUY VI, 1360-1371
Count on horse. Rev. Cross and name of Count of Saint Pol.

1. 1 Franc à Cheval ND 350.00

STRÀSBOURG

Madonna. Rev. Orb.

1. 2 Goldgulden ND (1600) 150.00
2. 1 Goldgulden ND (1600) . . . .*. 100.00

Arms. Rev. Legend in wreath.

3. 4 Ducats ND (1650) 300.00
4. 1 Ducat ND (1650) 100.00

Madonna. Rev. Arms. Issued by the Cathedral Chapter.

5. 1 Ducat 1632 . . . . 150.00

Seated female and child. Rev. Arms over three shields. Issued under Bishop John v. Manderscheid, 1569-1592.

6. 6 Goldgulden 1575 . . . . Unique

VERDUN
Bishops of —
ERIC OF LORRAINE, 1593-1611
Bust. Rev. Arms.

1. 1 Florin 1608 . . . . 300.00

CHARLES OF LORRAINE-CHALIGNY, 1611-1622
Bust. Rev. Arms.

2. 1 Florin 1613 . . . . 300.00

VIENNOIS
Dauphins of —
GUIGES VIII, 1319-1333
St. John. Rev. Lily.

1. 1 Florin ND 150.00

HUMBERT II, 1333-1349
St. John. Rev. Lily.

2. 1 Florin ND 125.00

CHARLES V, 1349-1364
St. John. Rev. Lily.

3. 1 Florin ND 125.00

Ruler on horse. Rev. Cross.

4. 1 Franc à Cheval ND 200.00

CHARLES VI, 1380-1409
Crowned arms. Rev. Elaborate cross.

5. 1 Ecu d'or ND 250.00

CHARLES VII, 1422-1440
Crowned arms. Rev. Cross.

6. 1 Ecu d'or ND . . . . .Unknown

LOUIS, 1440-1456
Arms. Rev. Cross.

7. 1 Ecu d'or ND 125.00

GERMANY

A. Empire of —, 1871-1915

General Types for all the States

Obverse: Head of the ruler except for the free cities of Bremen, Hamburg and Lubeck, which have the city arms.

Reverse: "Deutsches Reich," value, date and eagle. Three varieties of this reverse design were used and the date on the coin automatically indicates the type of reverse:

FIRST REVERSE, 1871-1873 inclusive: Small eagle, and below, both the date and abbreviated value.

SECOND REVERSE, 1874-1889 inclusive: Small eagle, and below, the complete value with the date appearing at the right.

THIRD REVERSE, 1890-1915 inclusive: Large eagle.

(The illustrations above show a typical obverse as well as the three reverses in their correct numerical order.)

NOTE: The valuations in this section are for Uncirculated specimens of the commonest dates.

ANHALT

Dukes of —

FREDERICK I, 1871-1904

1.	20 Marks	1875	50.00
2.	20 Marks	1896, 1901	50.00
3.	10 Marks	1896, 1901	40.00

FREDERICK II, 1904-1918

4.	20 Marks	1904	45.00

BADEN

Grand Dukes of —

FREDERICK I, 1852-1907

5.	20 Marks	1872, 73	25.00
6.	20 Marks	1874	30.00
7.	20 Marks	1894, 95	25.00
8.	10 Marks	1872, 73	20.00
9.	10 Marks	1875-81, 88	20.00
10.	10 Marks	1890, 91, 93, 96, 97, 98, 1900, 01. Head left..	20.00
11.	10 Marks	1902-07. Head right	25.00
12.	5 Marks	1877	30.00

FREDERICK II, 1907-1918

13.	20 Marks	1911-14	22.50
14.	10 Marks	1909-13	20.00

BAVARIA

Kings of —

LOUIS II, 1864-1886

15.	20 Marks	1872, 73	22.50
16.	20 Marks	1874-76, 78	22.50
17.	10 Marks	1872, 73	17.50
18.	10 Marks	1874-81	20.00
19.	5 Marks	1877, 78	30.00

OTTO, 1886-1913

20.	20 Marks	1895, 1900, 05, 13	22.50
21.	10 Marks	1888	27.50
22.	10 Marks	1890, 93, 96, 98, 1900. "Von" in title	22.50
23.	10 Marks	1901-07, 09-12. "V" in title	20.00

LOUIS III, 1913-1918

24.	20 Marks	1914	60.00

BREMEN

Free City of —

25.	20 Marks	1906	37.50
26.	10 Marks	1907	45.00

BRUNSWICK

Dukes of —

WILLIAM, 1831-1884

27.	20 Marks	1875	45.00

HAMBURG

Free City of —

28.	20 Marks	1875-81, 83, 84, 87, 89	20.00
29.	20 Marks	1893-95, 97, 99, 1900, 13	20.00
30.	10 Marks	1873	50.00
31.	10 Marks	1874. Arms of 1873	32.50
32.	10 Marks	1875-80, 1888. New type arms	20.00
33.	10 Marks	1890, 93, 96, 98, 1900-03, 05-13	20.00
34.	5 Marks	1877	30.00

HESSE

Grand Dukes of —

LOUIS III, 1848-1877

35.	20 Marks	1872, 73	30.00
36.	20 Marks	1874	35.00
37.	10 Marks	1872-73	22.50
38.	10 Marks	1875-77	22.50
39.	5 Marks	1877	35.00

LOUIS IV, 1877-1892

40.	20 Marks	1892	50.00
41.	10 Marks	1878-80. H mm	25.00
42.	10 Marks	1888. A mm	27.50
43.	10 Marks	1890	35.00
44.	5 Marks	1877	37.50

ERNST LOUIS, 1892-1918

45.	20 Marks	1893. Young head	40.00
46.	20 Marks	1896-1901, 03. Older head with one S in title ..	40.00
47.	20 Marks	1905, 06, 08, 11. With 2 S's in title	35.00
48.	10 Marks	1893. Young head	35.00
49.	10 Marks	1896, 98. Older head	30.00

LUBECK

Free City of —

50.	10 Marks	1901, 04. Small arms	40.00
51.	10 Marks	1905, 06, 09, 10. Large arms	35.00

MECKLENBURG - SCHWERIN

Grand Dukes of —

FREDERICK FRANZ II, 1842-1883

52.	20 Marks	1872	50.00
53.	10 Marks	1872	60.00
54.	10 Marks	1878	45.00

FREDERICK FRANZ III, 1883-1897

55.	10 Marks	1890	45.00

FREDERICK FRANZ IV, 1897-1918

56.	20 Marks	1901	85.00
57.	10 Marks	1901	60.00

MECKLENBURG - STRELITZ

Grand Dukes of —

FREDERICK WILLIAM, 1860-1904

58.	20 Marks	1873	150.00
59.	20 Marks	1874	150.00
60.	10 Marks	1873	185.00
61.	10 Marks	1874, 80	75.00

ADOLF FREDERICK, 1904-1914

62.	20 Marks	1905	175.00
63.	10 Marks	1905	150.00

OLDENBURG

Grand Dukes of —

NICHOLAS FREDERICK PETER, 1853-1900

64.	10 Marks 1874	125.00

PRUSSIA

Emperors of Germany and Kings of —

WILLIAM I, 1861-1888

65.	20 Marks 1871-73. A mm	20.00
66.	20 Marks 1872, 73. B mm	20.00
67.	20 Marks 1872, 73. C mm	20.00
68.	20 Marks 1874-79, 81-88. A mm	20.00
69.	20 Marks 1874, 75, 77. B mm	25.00
70.	20 Marks 1874, 76-78. C mm	20.00
71.	10 Marks 1872, 73. A mm	15.00
72.	10 Marks 1872, 73. B mm	15.00
73.	10 Marks 1872, 73. C mm	15.00
74.	10 Marks 1874, 75, 77-80, 82, 83, 86, 88. A mm	15.00
75.	10 Marks 1874-78. B mm	15.00
76.	10 Marks 1874-79. C mm	20.00
77.	5 Marks 1877, 78. A mm	30.00
78.	5 Marks 1877. B mm	30.00
79.	5 Marks 1877. C mm	30.00

FREDERICK III, 1888

80.	20 Marks 1888	20.00
81.	10 Marks 1888	15.00

WILLIAM II, 1888-1918

82.	20 Marks 1888, 89	25.00
83.	20 Marks 1890-1913. A mm ....*	20.00
84.	20 Marks 1905, 06, 08, 09, 10, 12. J mm	22.50
85.	20 Marks 1913-15. Uniformed bust	25.00
86.	10 Marks 1889	60.00
87.	10 Marks 1890, 92-1907, 09-12 ....*	15.00

REUSS, OLDER LINE

Princes of —

HENRY XXII, 1859-1902

88.	20 Marks 1875	450.00

REUSS, YOUNGER LINE

Princes of —

HENRY XIV, 1867-1886

89.	20 Marks 1881	75.00
90.	10 Marks 1882	75.00

SAXONY

Kings of —

JOHN, 1854-1873

91.	20 Marks 1872, 73	25.00
92.	10 Marks 1872, 73	20.00

ALBERT, 1873-1902

93.	20 Marks 1874, 76-78	22.50
94.	20 Marks 1894, 95	22.50
95.	10 Marks 1874, 75, 77, 78, 79, 81, 88	20.00
96.	10 Marks 1891, 93, 96, 98, 1900, 01, 02	20.00
97.	5 Marks 1877	30.00

GEORGE, 1902-1904

98.	20 Marks 1903	30.00
99.	10 Marks 1903, 04	20.00

FREDERICK AUGUST III, 1904-1918

100.	20 Marks 1905, 13, 14	22.50
101.	10 Marks 1905-07, 1909-12	20.00

SAXON-ALTENBURG

Dukes of —

ERNST, 1853-1908

102.	20 Marks 1887	75.00

SAXON-COBURG-GOTHA

Dukes of —

ERNST II, 1844-1893

103.	20 Marks 1872	300.00
104.	20 Marks 1886	60.00

ALFRED, 1893-1900

105.	20 Marks 1895	65.00

CARL EDWARD, 1900-1918

106.	20 Marks 1905	65.00
107.	10 Marks 1905	65.00

SAXON-MEININGEN

Dukes of —

GEORGE II, 1866-1914

108.	20 Marks 1872	250.00
109.	20 Marks 1882. Head right	200.00
110.	20 Marks 1889. Head left	150.00
111.	20 Marks 1900, 05	250.00
112.	20 Marks 1910, 14. New older head	200.00
113.	10 Marks 1890, 98	175.00
114.	10 Marks 1902, 09, 14. New older head	175.00

SAXON-WEIMAR

Grand Dukes of —

CARL ALEXANDER, 1853-1901

115.	20 Marks 1892, 96	65.00

WILLIAM ERNST, 1901-1918

116.	20 Marks 1901	80.00

SCHAUMBURG-LIPPE

Princes of —

ADOLF GEORGE, 1860-1893

117.	20 Marks 1874	225.00

GEORGE, 1893-1911

118.	20 Marks 1898, 1904	75.00

SCHWARZBURG-RUDOLSTADT

Princes of —

GUNTHER, 1890-1918

119.	10 Marks 1898	75.00

SCHWARZBURG-SONDERSHAUSEN

Princes of —

CARL GUNTHER, 1880-1909

120.	20 Marks 1896	125.00

WALDECK

Princes of —

FREDERICK, 1893-1918

121.	20 Marks 1903	150.00

WURTTEMBERG

Kings of —

CARL, 1864-1891

122.	20 Marks 1872, 73	22.50
123.	20 Marks 1874, 76	30.00
124.	10 Marks 1872, 73	20.00
125.	10 Marks 1874-81, 1888	20.00
126.	10 Marks 1890, 91	30.00
127.	5 Marks 1877, 78	30.00

WILLIAM II, 1891-1918

128.	20 Marks 1894, 97, 98, 1900, 05, 13, 14	22.50
129.	10 Marks 1893, 96, 98, 1900-07, 09-13	17.50

B. Republic of —

Private Commemorative Issues, 1955-1957

A series of large handsome coins struck on the old Ducat standard to commemorate the anniversaries of various cities or of historical events. They are dated 1955, 1956 or 1957 and about ten different types have so far been struck.

130.	30 Ducat pieces	400.00
131.	20 Ducat pieces	300.00
132.	10 Ducat pieces	150.00
133.	4 Ducat pieces	50.00

C. Coinage of the German Cities and States before the Empire.

AACHEN (AIX)

Seated Madonna with name of Reynald of Julich. Rev. Charlemagne standing.

1. ½ Goldgulden ND. (1402-23) .... **Rare**

Madonna standing with name of Reynald of Julich. Rev. Charlemagne standing.

2. ½ Goldgulden ND. (1402-23) .... **Rare**

Charlemagne seated. Rev. Eagle with name of Maximilian II.

3. 1 Goldgulden 1572 .... 200.00

Charlemagne seated. Rev. Eagle with name of Rudolph II.

4. 1 Goldgulden 1585, 91, 92 .... 175.00

Charlemagne seated. Rev. Eagle with name of Ferdinand II.

5. 1 Goldgulden 1634 .... 125.00

Bust of Charlemagne. Rev. Ferdinand III standing.

6. 1 Ducat 1641, 43, 45 .... 75.00

Ferdinand III standing. Rev. Value in tablet.

7. 1 Ducat 1646 .... 65.00

Bust of Charlemagne. Rev. Madonna standing.

8. 1 Ducat ND. (1637-57) .... **Rare**

Madonna standing. Rev. Value in tablet.

9. 1 Ducat ND 175.00

Emperor Francis standing. Rev. Value in tablet.

10. 1 Ducat 1753 .... 125.00

ANHALT

Princes of —

WOLDEMAR VI AND BROTHERS, 1471-1508
St. Anne standing. Rev. Arms.

1. 1 Goldgulden ND .... **Rare**

JOHN GEORGE AND BROTHERS, 1603-1618
Two busts. Rev. Three busts.

2. 4 Ducats 1614 .... 600.00
3. 3 Ducats 1614, 16 .... 400.00

Three helmets. Rev. Arms.

4. 1 Ducat 1615, 16, 18, ND 125.00
5. ½ Ducat 1616, 18 .... 100.00

ANHALT-BERNBURG

Dukes of —

VICTOR FREDERICK, 1721-1765

Arms. Rev. Bear on wall.

1. 1 Ducat 1730-61 .... 40.00

Bust. Rev. Arms.

2. 5 Taler 1744 .... 100.00
3. 2½ Taler 1744 .... 100.00

ALEXIUS FREDERICK CHRISTIAN, 1796-1834

Bust. Rev. Arms.

4. 5 Taler or 1 Pistole 1796 .... 60.00

Bear on wall. Rev. Value and date.

5. 1 Harz-gold Ducat 1825 .... 100.00

ANHALT-COETHEN

Dukes of —

AUGUST LOUIS, 1728-1755
Arms supported by bears. Rev. Bear with shield.

1. 1 Ducat 1747, 51 .... 50.00

Head. Rev. Bear with shield.

2. 1 Ducat 1751 .... 85.00

ANHALT-PLOETZKAU

Dukes of —

AUGUST, 1603-1653
Altar with Phoenix. Rev. Fountain.

1. 3 Goldgulden 1620 .... 275.00
2. 2 Goldgulden 1620 .... 200.00
3. 1 Goldgulden 1615, 17, 20 .... 125.00

ANHALT-ZERBST

Princes of —

CHARLES WILLIAM, 1667-1718
Bust. Rev. C.W.

1. ½ Ducat ND 50.00

JOHN LOUIS AND CHRISTIAN AUGUST, 1742-1747

Two busts. Rev. Arms.

2. 1 Ducat 1742 ....*...... 40.00
3. 1 Ducat 1745. On the marriage of Catherine II of Russia, and with different legend 100.00

FREDERICK AUGUST, 1747-1793
Bust. Rev. Arms.

4. 1 Ducat 1764 .... 100.00

ARENBERG

Dukes of —

LOUIS ENGELBERT, 1778-1781

Head. Rev. Arms.

1. 1 Ducat 1783 .... 125.00

ASPEREMONT

Barons of —

FERDINAND

Ruler standing. Rev. Arms.

1. 1 Ducat ND (1650) 150.00

AUGSBURG

A. City Coinage.

Legend. Rev. Ship. On the Reformation.

1. 1 Ducat 1717 .... 40.00

City View. Rev. Legend. On the Augsburg Confession.

2. 1 Ducat 1730 .... 40.00

B. Coinage with the heads or names of the Holy Roman Emperors.

St. Udalric seated. Rev. Orb. Name of Maximilian I.

3. 1 Goldgulden 1515 .... 175.00

Bust of Charles V. Rev. Arms.

4. 1 Goldgulden 1527, 31 .... 150.00

St. Udalric seated. Rev. Orb. Name of Charles V.

5. 1 Goldgulden 1520 .... 175.00

Eagle. Rev. Arms. Name of Charles V.

6. 1 Goldgulden ND (1517-58) 35.00

Bust of Ferdinand I. Rev. Arms.

7. 1 Goldgulden 1558 .... 150.00

Eagle. Rev. Arms. Name of Ferdinand I.

8. 1 Goldgulden 1562, 63 .... 100.00

Bust of Maximilian II. Rev. Arms.

9. 1 Goldgulden 1562, 66 .... 100.00

Bust of Rudolph II. Rev. Arms.

10. 1 Goldgulden 1582 .... 125.00

Eagle Rev. Pyre. Name of Rudolph II.

11. 1 Goldgulden 1609 .... 125.00

Seated female. Rev. Eagle. Name of Matthias II.

12. 1 Goldgulden 1613 .... 60.00

Bust of Ferdinand II. Rev. Arms.

13. 1 Goldgulden 1619 .... 125.00

Eagle. Rev. Arms. Name of Ferdinand II.

14. 1 Goldgulden 1623, 28 .... 125.00

St. Afra and St. Ulric standing. Rev. Eagle. Name of Ferdinand II.

15. 2 Ducats 1626 .... 200.00

St. Afra and pyre. Rev. Eagle. Name of Ferdinand II.

16. 4 Ducats 1630 .... 300.00
17. 1 Ducat 1629-38 .... 40.00

St. Afra and St. Ulric standing. Rev. Double eagle. Name Ferdinand II.

18. 1 Goldgulden 1627, 28 .... 150.00

Bust of Ferdinand III. Rev. Arms.

19. 2 Ducats 1641, 43 .... 100.00
20. 1 Ducat 1637-45, 45-57 .... * 40.00

Busts of Ferdinand III and Eleanor. Rev. Arms.

21. 2 Ducats 1657 .... 125.00

St. Afra and pyre. Rev. Eagle. Name of Ferdinand III.

22. 1 Ducat 1638, 39, 42 .... 50.00

Bust of Ferdinand IV. Rev. Legend in wreath. On his coronation.

23. 1 Ducat 1653 .... 150.00

Legend. Rev. Eagle and trophies. Homage for Ferdinand IV.

24. 1 Ducat 1653 .... 40.00

Bust of Leopold I. Rev. Arms.

25. 1 Ducat 1658-77 .... 40.00

Bust of Leopold I. Rev. Pyre in wreath.

26. 1 Ducat 1677-92 .... 40.00

Bust of Leopold I. Rev. Arms between river gods.

27. 2 Ducats 1700 .... 125.00
28. 1 Ducat 1695, 97, 99, 1701 .... 40.00

Bust of Leopold I. Rev. Female and pyre.

29. 1 Ducat 1701, 02 .... 50.00

Busts of Leopold I and Margaret. Rev. Arms.

30. 3 Ducats 1672 .... 200.00
31. 2 Ducats 1672 .... 125.00

Bust of Leopold I. Rev. Bust of Eleanor.

32. 1 Ducat 1689, 90 .... 100.00

Busts of Leopold and Eleanor. Rev. Arms.

33. 3 Ducats 1691 .... 200.00
34. 2 Ducats 1691 .... 125.00

Bust of Joseph I. Rev. Crown and insignia. On his coronation.

35. 1 Ducat 1690 .... 40.00

Bust of Joseph I. Rev. Eagle.

36. 1 Ducat 1690 .... 35.00

Two genii over legend. Rev. Sword. Joseph I as Emperor.

37. 1½ Ducats 1690 .... 50.00

Two genii over legend. Rev. Crown. Joseph I as Crown Prince.

38. 1 Ducat 1690 .... 40.00

Bust of Joseph I. Rev. Female and pyre.

39. 1 Ducat 1705, 07 .... 50.00

Bust of Joseph I. Rev. Pyre between river gods and eagle.

40. 1 Ducat 1708, 11 .... 50.00

Bust of Charles VI. Rev. Pyre between river gods and eagle.

41. 1 Ducat 1711 .... 50.00

Bust of Charles VI. Rev. Pyre between river gods and eagle.

42. 1 Ducat 1714, 15 .... 40.00

Bust of Charles VI. Rev. Flying eagle. On his coronation.

43. 1 Ducat 1711 .... 50.00

Bust of Charles VI. Rev. Pyre between river gods.

44. 2 Ducats 1738 .... 100.00
45. 1 Ducat 1737, 38 .... 40.00

Bust of Charles VI. Rev. Female and pyre.

46. 1 Ducat 1726 ....*...... 50.00
47. ½ Ducat 1717 .... 30.00

Bust of Charles VII. Rev. Female and pyre.

48. 1 Ducat 1742 .... 75.00

Bust of Charles VII. Rev. Arms.

49. 1 Ducat 1743 .... 75.00

Bust of Francis I. Rev. As indicated.

50. 3 Ducats 1745. City view 200.00
51. 2 Ducats 1745. City view 125.00
52. 3 Ducats 1745. Arms 200.00
53. 2 Ducats 1745. Arms 125.00

Bust of Francis I. Rev. Eagle and pyre between river gods.

54. 1 Ducat 1745 .... 60.00

Bust of Francis I. Rev. Arms.

55. 1 Ducat 1762, 63 .... 50.00

Bust of Joseph II. Rev. Arms.

56. 1 Ducat 1767 .... 50.00

C. Bishops of —

ALEXANDER SIGISMUND OF PALATINATE, 1690-1737

Bust. Rev. Two shields.

57. 2 Ducats 1708 ....*...... 175.00
58. 1 Ducat 1708 .... 100.00

JOSEPH OF HESSE, 1740-1768
Bust with cap. Rev. Two shields.

59. 1 Ducat 1744 .... 125.00

D. Swedish Kings of —

Conjoined heads of Gustav Adolphe and Queen. Rev. Two shields.

60. 2 Ducats 1632 .... 200.00

Facing or profile bust of Gustave Adolphe. Rev. Arms.

61. 1 Ducat 1632, 33, 34, 35 .... 75.00

BADEN

Margraves, and later, Grand Dukes of —

A. The Baden Line (Baden-Baden)

CHRISTOPHER, 1475-1527

St. Peter. Rev. Four shields and cross.

1. 1 Goldgulden ND ....*...... 40.00
2. 1 Goldgulden 1505-09 .... 75.00

St. Bernard standing. Rev. Arms.

3. 1 Goldgulden 1513, 18, 19 .... 400.00

WILLIAM, 1622-1677
St. George on horse. Rev. Circle of arms.
4. 1 Goldgulen ND 500.00

Bust. Rev. Arms.
5. 1 Ducat 1674 .... 300.00

LOUIS GEORGE AND FRANCISCA SIBYLLA AUGUSTA, 1707-1761

Conjoined busts. Rev. Two shields. On the Peace of Rastatt.
6. 1 Ducat 1714 .... 35.00

B. The Durlach Line (Baden-Durlach)
GEORGE FREDERICK, 1604-22
Bust. Rev. Quartered Arms.
7. 2 Ducats 1610 .... 400.00
8. 1 Goldgulden 1609 .... 300.00

Ruler standing. Rev. Arms.
9. 1 Ducat 1622 ....Unknown

CHARLES WILLIAM, 1709-1738

Armored Bust. Rev. Arms supported by griffins.
10. 1 Ducat 1721 .... 65.00
11. ½ Ducat 1721 ....*...... 40.00

Bust. Rev. Four shields and four initials around central shield.
12. 1 Carolin 1733, 34 .... 150.00
13. ½ Carolin 1734 .... 100.00

Large bust. Rev. Draped arms.
14. 1 Ducat 1736 .... 150.00
15. 1 Carolin 1734, 35 .... 150.00

Arms. Rev. Legend in square tablet.
16. 2 Ducats 1737 .... 300.00

Arms. Rev. Legend in circle.
17. 1 Ducat 1737 .... 60.00

Arms. Rev. Legend in cartouche.
18. ½ Ducat 1737 .... 40.00

CHARLES FREDERICK AND MAGDALENE WILHELMINA, 1738-1745

Crowned oval shield. Rev. Two shields surmounted by vase.
19. 1 Ducat 1738 .... 50.00

Crowned oval shield. Rev. Two shields surmounted by flame.
20. 1 Ducat 1738 .... 50.00

Crowned oval shield. Rev. Three line legend and date.
21. 1 Ducat 1738 .... 50.00

Crowned oval shield. Rev. Standing female and column.
22. 1 Ducat 1738 .... 50.00

CHARLES FREDERICK, 1746-1811
Large armored bust. Rev. Arms surrounded by legend and date.
23. 1 Ducat 1747 .... 125.00

Large armored bust. Rev. Arms flanked by date.
24. 1 Ducat 1751 .... 85.00

Large armored bust. Rev. Two shields crowned.
25. ½ Ducat 1747 .... 80.00

Crowned shield. Rev. Legend and date in circle.
26. ¼ Ducat 1747 .... 30.00

Large Head. Rev. Shield with supporters.
27. 1 Rhine-gold Ducat 1765, 67, 68 .... 400.00

Bust of Amalie Frederika of Hesse. Rev. Two shields. On the birth of twin princesses.
27a. 1 Ducat 1776 .... 35.00

Two baby heads facing each other. Rev. Legend. On the birth of twin princesses.
27b. 1 Ducat 1776 .... 35.00

Bust. Rev. Draped arms. On the birth of Prince Charles.
28. 1 Ducat 1786 .... 35.00

Head. Rev. River god.
29. 1 Rhine-gold Ducat 1807 .... 75.00

GERMANY-BADEN (cont'd)

LOUIS, 1818-1830

Head. Rev. Arms.

30.	10 Gulden 1819, 21, 23, 24, 25	. . . . *	85.00
31.	5 Gulden 1819, 21, 22, 24-28	. . . . *	35.00
32.	5 Taler or 500 Kreuzer 1830	. . . .	50.00

LEOPOLD, 1830-1852

Obv. as indicated. Rev. Arms.

33.	1 Rhine-gold Ducat 1832-42. Small head	. . . .	40.00
34.	1 Rhine-gold Ducat 1843-46. Larger head	. . . .	40.00
35.	1 Rhine-gold Ducat 1847-52. Largest head	. . . .	40.00

FREDERICK, 1852-1907

Head. Rev. Arms.

36.	1 Rhine-gold Ducat 1854	. . . .	75.00

BAMBERG

A. City of —

Two females standing. Rev. Legend. On the Union with Bavaria.

1.	1 Ducat 1802	. . . .	75.00

B. Bishops of —

GEORGE III SCHENK OF LIMBURG, 1505-1522

St. Henry standing. Rev. Two shields.

2.	1 Goldgulden 1506, 11, 12, 13, 14	. . . .	125.00

St. Henry and St. Kunigunde with church model. Rev. Two shields.

3.	1 Goldgulden 1507, ND	. . . .	125.00

JOHN PHILIP OF GEBSATTEL, 1599-1609

St. Henry and St. Kunigunde with church model. Rev. Two shields.

4.	2 Ducats 1601	. . . .	300.00
5.	1 Ducat 1600, 01, 02	. . . . *	125.00

JOHN GODFREY OF ASCHHAUSEN, 1609-1622
Arms. Rev. Legend. On his death.

6.	1 Goldgulden 1622	. . . .	150.00

JOHN GEORGE II FUCHS OF DORNHEIM, 1623-1633
Bust. Rev. St. Henry and St. Kunigunde with church model.

7.	1 Ducat 1628, 31	. . . .	100.00
8.	1 Goldgulden 1624, 28	. . . .	85.00

FRANCIS, COUNT OF HATZFELD, 1633-1642

Madonna seated. Rev. Arms.

9.	1 Ducat 1635, 37, 38, 40	. . . .	65.00

MELCHIOR OTTO VOIT OF SALZBURG, 1642-1653

Bust. Rev. Arms.

10.	1 Ducat 1647	. . . .	65.00

PHILIP VALENTINE VOIT OF RINECK, 1653-1672
Bust. Rev. Two shields.

11.	1 Ducat 1657	. . . .	50.00

LOTHAR FRANCIS, 1693-1729
(See under Mayence.)

FREDERICK CHARLES, 1729-1746
(See under Wurzburg.)

JOHN PHILIP ANTHONY OF FRANKENSTEIN, 1746-1753
Bust. Rev. Arms.

12.	1 Ducat 1750	. . . .	40.00

Knight standing. Rev. Arms.

13.	1 Ducat 1746	. . . .	40.00

FRANCIS CONRAD, COUNT OF STADION, 1753-1757

Bust. Rev. Arms. On the Homage of Bamberg.

14.	1 Ducat 1753	. . . .	40.00

ADAM FREDERICK, COUNT OF SEINSHEIM, 1757-1779

Bust. Rev. Knight standing. On the Homage of Bamberg.

15.	1 Ducat 1757	. . . .	40.00

FRANCIS LOUIS OF ERTHAL, 1779-1795

Bust. Rev. Female and pyramid. On the Homage of Bamberg.

16. 1 Ducat 1779 .... 40.00

CHRISTOPHER FRANCIS OF BUSECK, 1795-1802

Bust over legend. Rev. Female at altar. On the Homage of Bamberg.

17. 1 Ducat 1795, ND 40.00

BAVARIA

Dukes, and later, Kings of —

LOUIS IV, 1413-1447
Arms on cross. Rev. Three shields.

1. 1 Goldgulden ND 60.00

Lamb. Rev. Floriated cross.

2. 1 Mouton d'or ND 75.00

ALBERT IV, 1465-1508
Duke kneeling before Madonna standing. Rev. Arms.

3. 1 Goldgulden 1506 .... 80.00

Duke kneeling before Madonna seated. Rev. Arms.

4. 1 Goldgulden 1506 .... 80.00

WILLIAM IV, 1508-1550
Duke kneeling before Madonna seated. Rev. Arms. With titles of Albert.

5. 1 Goldgulden 1508, 09, 10 .... 75.00

WILLIAM IV AND LOUIS X, 1516-1545
Madonna seated. Rev. Arms.

6. 1 Goldgulden ND 150.00

Madonna standing. Rev. Arms.

7. 1 Goldgulden 1525, 32 .... 200.00

ALBERT V, 1550-1579
Bust. Rev. Arms.

8. 2 Ducats 1565, 68 .... 125.00

Bust with hat. Rev. Arms.

9. 1 Ducat ND 100.00

Duke kneeling. Rev. Lion with arms.

10. 2 Ducats ND 200.00
11. 1 Ducat ND 100.00

WILLIAM V, 1579-1598
Arms. Rev. Date. On his wedding.

12. 1 Ducat 1568 .... 100.00

St. Henry standing. Rev. Arms.

13. 1 Ducat 1596 .... 150.00

MAXIMILIAN I, 1598-1651

Elector before Madonna. Rev. Arms.

14. 2 Ducats 1642, 44, 45, 47 ....*...... 75.00
15. 1 Ducat 1638, 42-47 .... 40.00

Madonna. Rev. Arms.

16. 2 Ducats 1618 ....*...... 75.00
17. 1 Goldgulden 1625 .... 50.00
18. 1 Ducat 1632, 40 .... 100.00

Elector standing. Rev. View of Munich.

19. 5 Ducats 1640 ....*...... 150.00
20. 1 Ducat 1645 .... 50.00

Elector standing. Rev. Madonna.

21. 2 Ducats 1645 .... 75.00
22. 1 Ducat 1644, 46 .... 100.00

Elector at table. Rev. Madonna over view of Munich.

23. 4 Ducats 1610 .... 300.00

FERDINAND MARIA, 1651-1679
Elector standing. Rev. Madonna and shield.

24. 1 Ducat 1655-71 .... 50.00

Elector standing. Rev. View of Munich.

25. 1 Ducat 1677, 78 .... 50.00

Bust. Rev. Madonna and shield.

26. 1 Goldgulden 1674-79 .... **50.00**

Bust. Rev. Arms.

27. ½ Ducat 1672, 78 .... **35.00**
28. ¼ Ducat 1672, 73, 76 .... **25.00**

Busts of Ferdinand and Adelaide. Rev. Arms. On their wedding.

29. 3 Ducats 1652 .... **100.00**

Madonna. Rev. Shield. On the birth of Prince Max Emanuel.

30. ½ Ducat 1662 .... **25.00**

Bust of Adelaide. Rev. Arms. On the birth of Princess Louise.

31. 1 Ducat 1663 .... **50.00**

Family kneeling. Rev. Two shields. On the birth of Prince Louis Amadeus.

32. 4 Ducats 1665 .... **100.00**

Sun, moon and earth. Rev. Three shields. On the birth of Prince Cajetan Maria.

33. 2 Ducats 1670 .... **75.00**

St. Nicholas seated. Rev. Arms. On the birth of Prince Joseph Clemens.

34. 1 Ducat 1671 .... **50.00**

Two shields. Rev. Column. On the birth of Princess Violanta Beatrix.

35. 2 Ducats 1673 .... **75.00**

MAXIMILIAN EMANUEL, 1679-1726

Bust. Rev. Madonna standing.

36. 2 Ducats 1685, 87 ....*...... **85.00**
37. 1 Ducat 1687, 97 .... **40.00**

Bust. Rev. Madonna over arms.

38. 1 Goldgulden 1691, 98 .... **40.00**

Bust. Rev. Bust of Madonna over arms.

39. 1 Goldgulden 1699, 1700, 02, 03, 15 ....*...... **35.00**
40. 1 Goldgulden 1704. With pyre under bust. (Occupation of Augsburg) **100.00**

Head. Rev. Arms. Struck for the Lowlands.

41. 2 Souverain d'or 1712 .... **150.00**

Head. Rev. Madonna seated.

42. 2 Max d'or 1717 .... **75.00**
43. 1 Max d'or 1715-26 ....*...... **40.00**
44. ½ Max d'or 1715-25 .... **25.00**

Palm tree. Rev. Shields of Bavaria and Poland. On the birth of Prince Charles Albert.

45. 2 Ducats 1697 .... **50.00**

Three sunflowers. Rev. Legend. On the birth of Prince Ferdinand Maria.

46. 2 Ducats 1699 .... **50.00**

Crowned lion. Rev. Arms. Struck for the Lowlands.

47. 1 Souverain d'or 1711-13 .... **65.00**

CHARLES ALBERT, 1726-1744

Head. Rev. Madonna seated.

48. 1 Carolin 1726-32 ....*...... **50.00**
49. ½ Carolin 1726-31 .... **30.00**
50. ¼ Carolin 1726-31 .... **20.00**

Bust. Rev. Madonna seated.

51. 1 Carolin 1732-35 .... **50.00**
52. ½ Carolin 1732-37 .... **30.00**
53. ¼ Carolin 1732-35 .... **20.00**

Bust. Rev. Arms supported by lions.

54. 1 Ducat 1737 ....Unknown

Head. Rev. Eagle. On the Vicariat.

55. 2 Goldgulden 1740 .... **85.00**
56. 1 Goldgulden 1740 .... **40.00**

Bust. Rev. Eagle. On the Vicariat.

57. 1 Ducat 1740 .... **50.00**

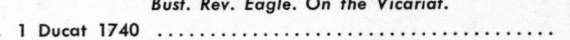

Madonna. Rev. Arms supported by lions.

58. 2 Ducats 1737 ....Unknown
59. 1 Ducat 1737, 39 ....*...... **40.00**

"AB". Rev. Legend. On his wedding.

60. 1 Ducat 1722 .... **30.00**

MAXIMILIAN JOSEPH III, 1745-1777

Bust. Rev. Eagle. On the Vicariat.

61. 1 Ducat 1745 .... 65.00

Bust. Rev. Madonna.

62. 1 Max d'or 1747, 51 .... 60.00

Busts of Maximilian and Marie Anne. Rev. Landscape. On their wedding.

63. 1 Ducat 1747 .... 50.00

Bust. Rev. Carriage. Homage of the representatives of the people.

64. 1 Ducat 1747 .... 50.00

Busts of Maximilian and Marie Anne. Rev. Bavaria before Pyramid.

65. 5 Ducats 1747 .... 150.00

Bust. Rev. River god.

66. 1 Danube-gold Ducat 1756, 60, 62 .... 90.00
67. 1 Inn-gold Ducat 1756, 60, 62 .... 90.00
68. 1 Isar-gold Ducat 1756, 60, 62 .... 120.00

Bust. Rev. Arms supported by lions.

69. 1 Ducat 1755-75 .... 40.00

CHARLES THEODORE, 1777-1799

Head. Rev. Arms.

70. 3 Ducats 1787 .... 125.00
71. 2 Ducats 1787 .... 75.00
72. 1 Ducat 1778-98 ....*...... 35.00

Head. Rev. River god, city in background.

73. 1 Danube-gold Ducat 1779, 80, 93 .... 80.00
74. 1 Inn-gold Ducat 1779, 80, 93, 98 .... 80.00
75. 1 Isar-gold Ducat 1779, 80, 93, 98 .... 80.00

Head. Rev. Double Eagle. On the Vicariat.

76. 3 Ducats 1790, 92 ....*...... 125.00
77. 2 Ducats 1790, 92 .... 75.00
78. 1 Ducat 1790, 92 .... 50.00

MAXIMILIAN JOSEPH (IV, 1799-1806), (I, 1806-1825)
Head. Rev. Arms.

79. 1 Ducat 1799-1805 .... 30.00

Head. Rev. Wurzburg shield under palm-tree.

80. 1 Goldgulden 1803 .... 40.00

Bust or head. Rev. Arms supported by lions.

81. 1 Ducat 1806. Bust 50.00
82. 1 Ducat 1811-25. Head 40.00

Head. Rev. Wurzburg city view.

83. 1 Goldgulden 1815 .... 50.00

Head. Rev. Wurzburg shield.

84. 1 Goldgulden 1817, ND 40.00

Head. Rev. River god.

85. 1 Danube-gold Ducat 1821 .... 75.00
86. 1 Inn-gold Ducat 1821 .... 75.00
87. 1 Isar-gold Ducat 1821 .... 75.00

Head. Rev. Speyer city view.

88. 1 Rhine-gold Ducat 1821 .... 75.00

LOUIS I, 1825-1848

Head. Rev. Arms supported by lions.

89. 1 Ducat 1826-48 .... 30.00

Head. Rev. River god.

90. 1 Danube-gold Ducat 1830 .... 75.00
91. 1 Inn-gold Ducat 1830 .... 75.00
92. 1 Isar-gold Ducat 1830 .... 75.00

Young or old head. Rev. Speyer city view.

93. 1 Rhine-gold Ducat 1830, 42, 46 .... 50.00

Head. Rev. Legend.

94. 1 Goldgulden 1826 .... 100.00

GERMANY-BAVARIA (cont'd)

Head. Rev. Wurzburg city view.

95. 1 Goldgulden ND (1827, 43) 40.00

Head. Rev. Wurzburg shield.

96. 1 Goldgulden ND (1843) 40.00

MAXIMILIAN II, 1848-1864

Head. Rev. Arms.

97. 1 Ducat 1849-56 .... 25.00

Head. Rev. Wurzburg shield.

98. 1 Goldgulden ND (1850) 40.00

Head. Rev. Wurzburg city view.

99. 1 Goldgulden ND (1850) 40.00

Head. Rev. Speyer city view.

100. 1 Rhine-gold Ducat 1850-56, 63 .... 40.00

Head. Rev. Arms.

101. 1 Mining-Ducat 1855. Goldkronach 500.00

Head. Rev. Value.

102. 1 Krone 1857-64 .... 85.00
103. ½ Krone 1857-64 ....* 50.00

LOUIS II, 1864-1886

Head. Rev. Value.

104. 1 Krone 1864-69 ....* 125.00
105. ½ Krone 1864-69 .... 75.00

Head. Rev. Wurzburg city view.

106. 1 Goldgulden ND (1864) 35.00

Head. Rev. Wurzburg shield.

107. 1 Goldgulden ND (1864) 35.00

Head. Rev. Crown in wreath.

108. 1 Ducat ND (1864) 25.00

BENTHEIM

Counts of —

MORITZ, 1625-1674
Bust. Rev. Arms.

1. 1 Ducat 1656 .... 300.00

ERNST WILLIAM, 1643-1693
Arms. Rev. Value.

2. 2 Ducats 1669 .... 250.00
3. 1 Ducat 1669 .... 125.00

BRANDENBURG-ANSBACH

Margraves of —

JOAQUIM ERNST, 1603-1625

Margrave standing. Rev. Arms.

1. 4 Ducats 1622 ....* 600.00
2. 2 Ducats 1622 .... 500.00
3. 1 Ducat 1609, 19, 20, 23, 24 .... 40.00

Facing armored bust. Rev. Arms.

4. 1 Goldgulden 1610, 11, 19-21, 23, 24 .... 50.00

Margrave on horse. Rev. Cross and five shields.

5. 1 Goldgulden 1623 .... 150.00

FREDERICK, ALBERT AND CHRISTIAN, 1625-1634
Three busts. Rev. Arms.

6. 1 Ducat 1625-30, 32 .... 40.00

ALBERT, 1634-1667
Bust. Rev. Arms.

7. 2 Ducats 1660 .... 300.00
8. 1 Ducat 1651, 52, 63 .... 40.00

JOHN FREDERICK, 1667-1686
Bust. Rev. Arms.

9. 3 Ducats 1672 .... 350.00
10. 2 Ducats 1672, 77, 83 .... 100.00
11. 1 Ducat 1672 .... 50.00
12. 1 Ducat 1680, 83. PIETATE ET IVSTITIA 40.00

Bust. Rev. Crossed initials.

13. 1 Ducat 1684 .... 50.00

Arms. Rev. Piety and Justice.

14. 2 Ducats 1683 .... 100.00
15. ¾ Ducat 1674 .... 100.00
16. ¼ Ducat 1680, 84 .... 20.00

WILLIAM FREDERICK, 1703-1723
Bust. Rev. Arms.

17. 1 Ducat 1715 .... 70.00

Bust. Rev. Two shields.

18. ¼ Ducat 1717 .... 50.00

CHRISTIANE CHARLOTTE, 1723-1729

Bust. Rev. Crown over linked C's.

19. 1 Ducat 1726 .... 50.00

CHARLES WILLIAM FREDERICK, 1729-1757
Bust. Rev. Eagle.

20. 2 Ducats 1729. Thick or broad 100.00
21. 1 Ducat 1729 .... 75.00

Bust. Rev. Two shields.

22. 1 Ducat 1740, 47, 50 .... 35.00

Bust. Rev. Eagle with shield.

23. 1 Ducat 1744 .... 40.00

Bust. Rev. Eagle over arms.

24. 1 Ducat 1753 .... 40.00

Falconier on horse. Rev. Falcon.

25. 1 Hunting Ducat ND 80.00

Bust. Rev. Arms.

26. 1 Carolin 1734, 35 .... 80.00
27. ½ Carolin 1734, 35 .... 50.00

ALEXANDER, 1757-1791
Two shields. Rev. Legend. On his wedding.

28. 2 Ducats 1754 .... 50.00
29. 1 Ducat 1754 .... 35.00

Bust. Rev. Eagle shield.

30. 1 Ducat 1757 .... 40.00

Bust. Rev. Arms.

31. 1 Ducat 1762 .... 60.00

Bust. Rev. Crown above three arms.

32. 1 Ducat 1763 .... 35.00
33. 1 Ducat 1777 ....*...... 125.00

Bust. Rev. Star of Order.

34. 1 Ducat 1779 .... 35.00

Bust. Rev. Eagle shield with chain of Order.

35. 1 Carolin 1758, 66 .... 200.00

Margrave on horse. Rev. Shields and trophies.

36. 1 Ducat 1765 .... 35.00

Head. Rev. Eagle with two shields. On the union of Ansbach and Culmbach.

37. 1 Ducat 1769 .... 40.00

Busts of Alexander and George Frederick. Rev. Altar. On the union of Ansbach and Culmbach.

38. 1 Ducat 1769 .... 40.00

Knight at altar. Rev. Legend. On the homage.

39. 1 Ducat 1769 .... 35.00

BRANDENBURG-BAYREUTH

Margraves of —

CHRISTIAN, 1603-1655
Margrave standing. Rev. Arms.

1. 4 Ducats 1609 .... 175.00
2. 2 Ducats 1609 .... 80.00
3. 1 Ducat 1609, 28-32 .... 50.00

Bust. Rev. Arms.

4. 1 Ducat 1631, 41, 42, 44, ND 35.00

Bust. Rev. Arms. On the 50th year of his reign.

5. 1 Ducat 1653 .... 150.00

CHRISTIAN ERNST, 1655-1712
Bust. Rev. Arms.

6. 1 Ducat 1659, 62, 77, 94, 1708, ND 60.00
7. ½ Ducat 1685 .... 30.00

Busts of the Margrave and his wife. Rev. View of Cronach Mine.

8. 2 Ducats 1695 .... 600.00

GEORGE WILLIAM, 1712-1726
Bust. Rev. Arms.

9. 2 Ducats 1720 .... 400.00
10. 1 Ducat 1720-22 .... 200.00

Bust. Rev. Legend. On his death.

11. 2 Ducats 1726 .... 300.00
12. 1 Ducat 1726 .... 100.00

GEORGE FREDERICK CHARLES, 1726-1735
Swan and tree. Rev. Legend. On the homage.

13. 1 Ducat 1727 .... 35.00

FREDERICK, 1735-1763
Bust. Rev. Arms.

14. 1 Ducat 1735, 46 .... 50.00

Margrave on horse. Rev. Order.

15. 1 Ducat 1746 .... 40.00

FREDERICK CHRISTIAN, 1763-1769
Bust. Rev. Arms.

16. 1 Ducat 1763 .... 40.00

Bust. Rev. Bible, cross and sword. On his birthday.

17. 1 Ducat 1764 .... 50.00

Margrave on horse. Rev. Crown over Order.

18. 1 Ducat 1767 .... 40.00

BRANDENBURG-FRANCONIA

Margraves of —

FREDERICK V, 1361-1397

Arms in enclosure. Rev. St. John.

1. 1 Goldgulden ND 100.00

JOHN III, 1404-1420
Arms in enclosure. Rev. St. John.

2. 1 Goldgulden ND 500.00

FREDERICK VI, 1404-1440
Eagle. Rev. St. John.

3. 1 Goldgulden ND 200.00

ALBERT ACHILLES, 1464-1486

St. John. Rev. Cross with five shields.

4. 1 Goldgulden ND. Mint: Schwabach 30.00

FREDERICK AND SIGISMUND, 1486-1495
St. John. Rev. Cross with four shields.

5. 1 Goldgulden ND. Mint: Schwabach 30.00

FREDERICK IV, 1495-1515
St. John. Rev. Cross with four shields.

6. 1 Goldgulden 1497-1515, ND. Mint: Schwabach 35.00

CASIMIR AND GEORGE, 1515-1527
St. John. Rev. Cross with four shields.

7. 1 Goldgulden 1515-26. Mint: Schwabach 35.00

GEORGE, 1527-1536
Cross with five shields. Rev. St. John.

8. 1 Goldgulden 1528-35 .... 50.00

GEORGE AND ALBERT, 1536-1543
Cross with five shields. Rev. St. John.

9. 1 Goldgulden 1538, 40, 41 .... 100.00

ALBERT ALCIBIADES, 1527-1554
Eagle. Rev. Blank. Square necessity coin.

10. 1 Ducat 1553 .... 200.00

Armored bust. Rev. Cross with five shields.

11. 1 Goldgulden 1549 .... 350.00

GEORGE FREDERICK, 1543-1603
Margrave standing. Rev. Arms.

12. 1 Ducat 1557. Mint: Schwabach 350.00

Facing bust. Rev. Cross with five shields.

13. 1 Goldgulden 1571. Mint: Schwabach 350.00

Margrave standing. Rev. Eagle.

14. 1 Ducat 1587-91, 94-97. Mint: Koenigsberg 40.00

BRANDENBURG-PRUSSIA

(See under Prussia)

BRAUNAU ·

Arms. Rev. Blank. Octagonal siege coins of the Austrian War of Succession.

1. 2 Ducats 1743 .... 350.00
2. 1 Ducat 1743 .... 150.00
3. ½ Ducat 1743 .... 100.00

BREISACH ·

Legend. Rev. Imperial orb over three shields.

1. 1 Ducat 1633. Square siege coin 500.00

BREMEN

A. City Coins with the heads or names of the Holy Roman Emperors

Eagle. Rev. Arms. Charles V.

1. 1 Goldgulden 1542, 46, 49 .... 300.00

Eagle. Rev. Arms. Matthias II.

2. 1 Goldgulden 1613 .... 250.00

Eagle. Rev. Arms supported by lions. Ferdinand II.

3. 1 Goldgulden 1635, 37 .... 100.00

Eagle. Rev. Arms. Ferdinand II.

4. 1 Goldgulden 1627, 35 .... 100.00

Ferdinand II standing. Rev. Arms.

5. 2 Ducats 1640, 52 .... 175.00
6. 1 Ducat 1640-52 ....* 85.00

Eagle. Rev. Arms supported by lions. Ferdinand III.

7. 2 Goldgulden 1649 ....* 400.00
8. 1 Goldgulden 1640 .... 125.00

Key. Rev. St. Peter. Leopold I.

9. ¼ Ducat ND 25.00

Eagle. Rev. Arms supported by lions. Leopold I.

10. 5 Ducats 1661 .... 250.00
11. 3 Ducats 1667 .... 200.00

Leopold I standing. Rev. Arms.

12. 5 Ducats ND 400.00
13. 3 Ducats 1659 .... 400.00
14. 2 Ducats 1659, 67 .... 175.00
15. 1 Ducat 1659, 67 ....* 85.00

Head of Leopold I. Rev. Arms.

16. 1 Ducat 1672 .... 100.00

Bust of Leopold I. Rev. Arms supported by lions.

17. 4 Ducats ND 600.00

Eagle. Rev. Arms supported by lions. Joseph I.

18. 1 Ducat 1710 .... 75.00

Eagle. Rev. Arms supported by lions. Charles VI.

19. 1 Ducat 1723 .... 100.00

Eagle. Rev. Arms supported by lions. Francis I.

20. 2 Ducats 1746 .... 150.00
21. 1 Ducat 1745, 46 ....* 60.00

B. Archbishops of —

HENRY II OF SCHWARZBURG, 1463-1497

St. Peter standing. Rev. Arms on cross.

22. 1 Goldgulden ND 75.00

JOHN III RODE, 1497-1511
St. Peter standing. Rev. Arms on cross.

23. 1 Goldgulden ND 75.00
24. ½ Goldgulden ND 150.00

St. Peter seated. Rev. Arms.

25. 1 Goldgulden ND 100.00

CHRISTOPHER OF BRUNSWICK, 1511-1558
St. Peter standing. Rev. Arms on cross.

26. 1 Goldgulden ND 75.00

St. Peter seated. Rev. Arms.

27. 1 Goldgulden 1521 .... 125.00

GEORGE OF BRUNSWICK, 1558-1566
St. Peter standing. Rev. Arms.

28. 1 Goldgulden ND 100.00

HENRY III OF LAUENBURG, 1567-1585
Bust. Rev. Arms.

29. 1 Ducat 1583 .... 200.00

St. Peter. Rev. Arms.

30. 1 Goldgulden 1584, ND 75.00

JOHN FREDERICK OF HOLSTEIN-GOTTORP, 1596-1634
Bust. Rev. Cross.

31. 10 Ducats ND 600.00

St. Peter standing. Rev. Arms.

32. 1 Goldgulden 1612, 18 .... 75.00

BREMEN AND VERDEN

Swedish Rulers of —

Bust of Christina. Rev. Arms.

1. 10 Ducats 1650 .... 3000.00

BRESLAU

A. City of —

St. Wenceslas. Rev. Lion.

1. 1 Goldgulden 1517-31, ND 100.00

St. John. Rev. Arms.

2. 1 Goldgulden 1531, 34 .... 100.00

St. Wenceslas. Rev. Arms.

3. 2 Ducats 1542 .... 250.00
4. 1 Ducat 1531-60 ....* 80.00

Arms. Rev. Shield of Pfintzig. On the Shooting Fete.

5. 2 Ducats 1560 .... 150.00

Maximilian II standing. Rev. Arms.

6. 1 Ducat 1572, 73 .... 50.00

Rudolph II standing. Rev. Arms.

7. 1 Ducat 1577 .... 65.00

Louis II standing. Rev. Arms.

8. 1 Ducat 1577 .... 75.00

Arms. Rev. Legend. On the Shooting Fetes.

9.	3 Ducats (1527-1614) Round	200.00
10.	3 Ducats (1527-1614) Square	175.00
11.	2 Ducats 1527, 77, 1614	125.00
12.	1 Ducat 1614 ....*	60.00

Bust of Matthias II. Rev. Arms.

13.	5 Ducats 1612	300.00
14.	5 Ducats 1612. Square	400.00
15.	4 Ducats 1612 ....*	300.00
16.	3 Ducats 1612	250.00
17.	3 Ducats 1612. Square	300.00
18.	2 Ducats 1611-13	125.00
19.	2 Ducats 1612, 13. Square	150.00
20.	1 Ducat 1611-13	65.00

Bust of Matthias II. Rev. Crowned F over arms.

20a.	2 Ducats 1617. Round and broad	100.00
20b.	2 Ducats 1617. Square and smaller ....*	125.00
20c.	1 Ducat 1617	40.00

Bust of Frederick V of Bohemia. Rev. Arms.

21.	2 Ducats 1620	250.00

Bust of Frederick V. Rev. Lion.

22.	1 Ducat 1620	175.00

Bust of Ferdinand II. Rev. Arms.

23.	3 Ducats 1622	150.00
24.	1 Ducat 1622	65.00
25.	½ Ducat 1622	50.00

Bust of Ferdinand II. Rev. Scales.

26.	2 Ducats 1630	100.00
27.	1 Ducat 1630 ....*	65.00

Bust of Ferdinand III. Rev. Arms.

28.	5 Ducats 1651	200.00

B. Bishops of —

JACOB OF SALZA, 1520-1539

St. John. Rev. Arms.

29.	1 Ducat 1524-39	100.00

Bust. Rev. Arms.

30.	3 Ducats 1531	250.00

BALTHASAR OF PROMNITZ, 1539-1562
Bust with hat. Rev. Arms.

31.	5 Ducats 1551	600.00

St. John. Rev. Three shields.

32.	1 Ducat 1540-60	85.00

CASPAR OF LOGAU, 1562-1574

St. John. Rev. Arms.

33.	1 Ducat 1562-73	100.00

MARTIN GERSTMANN, 1574-1585
St. John. Rev. Arms.

34.	2 Ducats 1574-77	200.00
35.	1 Ducat 1574-85	85.00

ANDREW JERIN, 1585-1596

St. John. Rev. Arms.

36.	1 Ducat 1585-92, ND	85.00

JOHN VI OF SITSCH, 1600-1608

St. John. Rev. Arms.

37.	3 Ducats 1603. Square	275.00
38.	2 Ducats 1603. Square	150.00
39.	1 Ducat ND ....*	100.00

CHARLES OF AUSTRIA, 1608-1624

Bust. Rev. Two shields.

40.	1 Ducat 1611, 12	85.00

Two shields. Rev. Legend. On the Shooting Fete.

41.	3 Ducats 1612	175.00
42.	2 Ducats 1612	125.00
43.	1 Ducat 1612 ....*	75.00

Bust. Rev. Three shields.

44.	10 Ducats 1615, 18	600.00
45.	7 Ducats 1614, 18	400.00
46.	6 Ducats 1614	300.00
47.	5 Ducats 1616	250.00
48.	4 Ducats 1618	250.00
49.	3 Ducats 1614, 18	175.00
50.	1 Ducat 1614	85.00

Bust. Rev. Arms.

51.	1 Ducat 1618	100.00
52.	½ Ducat 1618	35.00

Bust. Rev. Arms and two small shields.

53.	5 Ducats ND	250.00
54.	2 Ducats ND	150.00
55.	1 Ducat ND	85.00

CHARLES FERDINAND OF POLAND, 1625-1655

Bust right or left. Rev. Two shields or arms.

56.	15 Ducats 1631, 32	Rare
57.	10 Ducats 1631, 38, 39, 42	650.00
58.	6 Ducats 1632, 39	400.00
59.	6 Ducats 1632. Square	500.00
60.	5 Ducats 1632, 39	300.00
61.	5 Ducats 1632. Square	400.00
62.	4 Ducats 1632 ....*	250.00
63.	3 Ducats 1632, 53. Round. 200.00. Octagonal	300.00
64.	2 Ducats 1632, 53. Round. 125.00. Octagonal	175.00
65.	1 Ducat 1635	100.00

SEBASTIAN OF ROSTOCK, 1664-1671
Bust. Rev. Arms.

66.	10 Ducats 1667	650.00
67.	2 Ducats 1655	200.00
68.	1 Ducat 1655	125.00

FREDERICK OF HESSE, 1671-1682

Bust. Rev. Arms.

69.	3 Ducats 1674	200.00
70.	2 Ducats 1679-82 ....*	125.00
71.	1 Ducat 1679-82	80.00

FRANCIS LOUIS OF NEUBURG, 1683-1732

Bust. Rev. Arms.

72.	10 Ducats 1701	650.00
73.	6 Ducats 1730	400.00
74.	2 Ducats 1690, 93	125.00
75.	1 Ducat 1686-1732 ....*	65.00
76.	¼ Ducat ND	30.00
77.	⅙ Ducat ND	20.00

PHILIP OF SINZENDORF, 1732-1749

Bust. Rev. Arms.

78.	8 Ducats 1733	500.00
79.	1 Ducat 1738 ....*	60.00

PHILIP GOTTHARD OF SCHAFFGOTSCH, 1747-1795
Bust. Rev. Arms.

80.	5 Ducats 1748	300.00
81.	1 Ducat 1748-77	40.00

JOSEPH OF HOHENLOHE, 1795-1817

Bust. Rev. Arms.

82.	1 Ducat 1796	75.00

BRETZENHEIM

Princes of —
CHARLES AUGUST, 1769-1823

Bust. Rev. Arms on cross.

1.	1 Ducat 1790	125.00

BRUNSWICK

City of —

Double Eagle. Rev. Lion.

1.	1 Goldgulden 1622, 29	150.00
2.	1 Ducat 1627, 48, 49, ND	100.00

Double Eagle. Rev. Arms.

3.	1 Goldgulden 1628, 31	150.00

Double Eagle. Rev. Value.

4.	1 Ducat 1626	150.00

Double Eagle. Rev. Value on tablet.

5. 1 Ducat 1628-60 .... 125.00

BRUNSWICK-CALENBERG

Dukes of —

ERIC I, 1491-1540
Arms. Rev. Double Eagle.

1. 1 Goldgulden 1539 .... 200.00

BRUNSWICK-GRUBENHAGEN

Dukes of —

WOLFGANG AND PHILIP II, 1567-1595
Arms. Rev. Bear and date.

1. 1 Goldgulden 1588 .... 150.00

BRUNSWICK-LUNEBURG

Dukes of —

JULIUS ERNST OF DANNENBERG, 1598-1636
Bust. Rev. Arms.

1. 1 Goldgulden 1619 .... 200.00
2. 1 Ducat 1625 .... 150.00

CHRISTIAN OF MINDEN, 1599-1633

Bust. Rev. Arms.

3. 1 Ducat 1621-1633 .... 85.00

St. Andrew. Rev. Arms. Struck from Andreasberg gold.

4. 1 Goldgulden 1624, 29 .... 125.00

AUGUST, 1610-1636
Bust. Rev. Arms.

5. 1 Ducat 1634 .... 200.00

Ruler on horse. Rev. Arms.

6. 1 Goldgulden 1618 .... 125.00

Standing ruler. Rev. Arms.

7. 1 Goldgulden ND 125.00

FREDERICK, 1636-1648

Standing ruler. Rev. Arms.

8. 1 Ducat 1636-48, ND 50.00

Armored bust. Rev. Arms.

9. 1 Ducat 1647, 48, ND 60.00

GEORGE OF CALENBERG, 1635-1641

Bust. Rev. Arms.

10. 1 Ducat 1636, 37, 38, ND 60.00

Arms. Rev. Orb.

11. 1 Goldgulden 1635 .... 75.00

CHRISTIAN LOUIS OF CELLE, 1646-1665
Bust. Rev. Arms.

12. 1 Ducat 1646 .... 65.00

Arms. Rev. Horse.

13. 1 Ducat 1650, 61 .... 40.00

GEORGE WILLIAM OF CELLE, 1665-1705
Bust. Rev. Horse.

14. 4 Ducats 1688 .... 300.00
15. 2 Ducats 1685, 88, 90, 99 .... 85.00
16. 1 Ducat 1685, 90 .... 40.00
17. ½ Ducat 1685, 90 .... 30.00
18. ¼ Ducat 1690 .... 25.00

Bust. Rev. Arms.

19. 10 Ducats 1665 .... 600.00
20. 2 Ducats 1675, 99 .... 85.00
21. 1 Ducat 1664, 75 .... 40.00

Arms. Rev. Horse.

22. 2 Ducats 1675, 99, 1700 .... 85.00
23. 1 Ducat 1684-97, ND ....* 40.00
24. ½ Ducat 1685-90 .... 25.00

JOHN FREDERICK OF CALENBERG, 1665-1679
Bust. Rev. Arms.

25. 1 Ducat 1659-1685 .... 40.00

Bust. Rev. Palm tree on rock.

26. 4 Ducats 1673 .... 400.00
27. 2 Ducats 1673 .... 150.00
28. 1 Ducat 1668-79 ....* 50.00

ERNST AUGUST, 1692-1698
Bust. Rev. Landscape.

29. 20 Ducats 1680 .... Rare

Bust. Rev. Arms.

30. 10 Ducats 1681, 85 .... 600.00
31. 1 Ducat 1681, 85, 94 .... 50.00

Bust. Rev. Arms under hat.

32. 2 Ducats 1694 .... 125.00
33. 1 Ducat 1694, 98 ....* 60.00

GERMANY-BRUNSWICK-LUNEBURG (cont'd)

Bust. Rev. Horse.

34.	2 Ducats 1695	100.00
35.	1 Ducat 1695, 98	40.00
36.	½ Ducat 1695	30.00
37.	¼ Ducat 1695	25.00

Bust. Rev. Legend. On his death.

38.	1 Ducat 1698	50.00

GEORGE I OF ENGLAND, 1698-1727

Bust. Rev. Arms.

39.	2 Ducats 1698	125.00
40.	1 Ducat 1712-23 ....*	50.00
41.	1 Harz-gold Ducat 1712, 14	50.00

Laureate bust. Rev. Four shields crossed.

42.	2 Ducats 1716, 18	100.00
43.	1 Ducat 1715-27 ....*	35.00
44.	1 Harz-gold Ducat 1723	75.00

Laureate bust. Rev. Legend. On his death.

45.	4 Ducats 1727	200.00
46.	2 Ducats 1727	75.00

Laureate head. Rev. Horse.

47.	½ Ducat 1724	40.00
48.	¼ Ducat 1724	25.00

Arms. Rev. Horse.

49.	5 Taler 1699	75.00
50.	2½ Taler 1699	65.00
51.	2 Ducats 1698-1707	65.00
52.	1 Ducat 1698-1712	35.00
53.	1 Harz-gold Ducat 1710, 13, 14, 15 ......*	40.00

Four shields crossed. Rev. Wild man.

54.	1 Ducat 1726	50.00

GEORGE II OF ENGLAND, 1727-1760

Bust. Rev. Four shields crossed.

55.	1 Harz-gold Ducat 1729	75.00

Bust. Rev. Arms.

56.	1 Ducat 1730, 47	40.00

57.	1 Harz-gold Ducat 1730, 47 ....*	50.00
58.	½ Ducat 1730, 34, 37 ....*	35.00
59.	¼ Ducat 1737	20.00

Arms. Rev. Two values as indicated.

60.	4 Goldgulden or 8 Taler 1749, 50, 52	125.00
61.	2 Goldgulden or 4 Taler 1749-55 ....*	75.00
62.	1 Goldgulden or 2 Taler 1749-55	50.00
63.	½ Goldgulden or 1 Taler 1749-56	30.00
64.	¼ Goldgulden or ½ Taler 1754-57	25.00

Bust. Rev. Value.

65.	1 Ducat 1751	60.00

Arms. Rev. Horse.

66.	1 Ducat 1730-38	35.00
67.	1 Harz-gold Ducat 1730-56 ....*	35.00

Arms. Rev. Value.

68.	5 Taler 1758	50.00

Horse. Rev. Value.

69.	1 Harz-gold Ducat 1751	65.00

Four shields crossed. Rev. Horse.

70.	1 Ducat 1728, 30	50.00

Crowned initials. Rev. Horse.

71.	¼ Ducat 1730	25.00

GEORGE III OF ENGLAND, 1760-1820
Bust. Rev. Arms.

72.	1 George d'or 1768	75.00

Arms. Rev. Horse.

73.	1 Harz-gold Ducat 1767-1818	35.00

Arms. Rev. Value.

74.	5 Taler 1813, 14, 15	100.00

Horse. Rev. Value.

75.	1	Pistole 1803 ....*	65.00
76.	10	Taler 1813, 14	85.00
77.	5	Harz-gold Taler 1814	100.00
78.	2½	Taler 1814, 15 ....*	75.00
79.	1	Harz-gold Ducat 1815, 18 ....*	40.00

(For coins of the succeeding English Kings, see under Hannover and under Charles II of Brunswick-Wolfenbuttel.)

BRUNSWICK-WOLFENBUTTEL

Dukes of —

(Old Line, 1514-1634 and New Line, 1635-1884.)

HENRY II, 1514-1568

Bust. Rev. Fortuna standing.

1.	1	Goldgulden 1558	100.00

Bust. Rev. Arms.

2.	1	Ducat 1558	100.00

Arms. Rev. Wild man.

3.	1	Ducat 1558	85.00

JULIUS, 1568-1589

Busts of Julius and Hedwig. Rev. Arms.

4.	2	Ducats ND	250.00

FREDERIC ULRIC, 1613-1634

Bust. Rev. Arms.

5.	1	Goldgulden 1625, 26	65.00

Half length figure. Rev. Arms and wild man.

6.	10	Ducats 1615	Rare

Standing ruler. Rev. Arms.

7.	1	Goldgulden 1630	50.00

Wild man and tree. Rev. Arms.

8.	1	Ducat 1615-1629	50.00
9.	1	Goldgulden 1615, 21	50.00

Wild man with broken tree. Rev. Arms.

10.	1	Goldgulden 1615, 21, 29, 31	50.00

CHRISTIAN OF HALBERSTADT, 1616-1626

Armored arm with sword. Rev. Legend.

11.	10	Ducats 1622	Rare
12.	2	Ducats 1622	Rare
13.	1	Ducat 1622	750.00

AUGUST, 1635-1666

Armored bust. Rev. Arms.

14.	1	Ducat 1638, 39	50.00

Facing bust with cap. Rev. Arms.

15.	1	Ducat 1658	75.00

RUDOLPH AUGUST, 1666-1704

Armored bust. Rev. Galley.

16.	1	Ducat 1680	350.00

Bust. Rev. Legend. On his death.

17.	¾	Ducat 1704	50.00

Arms. Rev. Horse.

18.	2	Ducats 1669	125.00
19.	1	Ducat 1669, 79	40.00

RUDOLPH AUGUST AND ANTONY ULRIC, 1685-1704

Two busts. Rev. Arms.

20.	1	Ducat 1691, 99	75.00

Bust on each side.

21.	1	Ducat 1698, 99, 1701, ND	65.00

ANTONY ULRIC, 1704-1714

Bust. Rev. Arms.

22.	1	Ducat 1705	60.00

Bust. Rev. Horse.

23.	2	Ducats 1707, 11		125.00
24.	1	Ducat 1707, 12 ....*	60.00
25.	1	Harz-gold Ducat 1710	75.00
26.	½	Ducat 1708, 09 ....*	25.00

Initials. Rev. Horse.

27.	1	Ducat 1707, 09, 11		40.00
28.	½	Ducat 1708, 09 ....*	30.00
29.	2	Harz-gold Ducats 1712	150.00
30.	1	Harz-gold Ducat 1710, 12	85.00

Prince Antony Ulric in cradle. Rev. Legend.

31.	2	Ducats 1714	100.00

ELIZABETH JULIANA, 1656-1704
Bust. Rev. Legend. On her death.

32. 1 Ducat 1704 .... **100.00**

Bust. Rev. Salzdahlum Castle. On her death.

33. 2 Ducats 1704 .... **200.00**

FERDINAND ALBERT I, DIED 1687

Bust. Rev. Arms.

34. 2 Ducats 1678 ....* **200.00**
35. 1 Ducat 1680 .... **100.00**

LOUIS RUDOLPH, 1714-1735

Bust. Rev. Angel over city view of Blankenburg. On the Reformation.

36. 1 Ducat 1717 .... **65.00**

Bust. Rev. Horse and city view of Blankenburg.

37. 1 Ducat 1720 .... **60.00**

Bust. Rev. Arms.

38. 1 Ducat 1714 .... **75.00**

Bust. Rev. Horse.

39. 12 Ducats 1715 .... **Rare**
40. 1 Ducat 1725-34 .... **40.00**
41. 1 Harz-gold Ducat 1732 .... **75.00**

Bust of Albert Ernst of Oettingen. Rev. Legend.

42. 1 Friendship Ducat ND **60.00**

Head. Rev. Helmet and horse.

43. 1 Ducat 1726 .... **50.00**

Head. Rev. Helmet.

44. 1 Ducat 1718-33 .... **40.00**

Head. Rev. Star.

45. 1 Ducat 1730, 33 .... **60.00**

Bust or head. Rev. Wild man with or without arms.

---

46. 2 Ducats 1731, 32 ND **85.00**
47. 1 Ducat 1733 ....* **50.00**

Head. Rev. Legend. On his death.

48. 1 Ducat 1735 .... **40.00**

Arms. Rev. Horse.

49. 1 Ducat 1715 .... **40.00**

Arms. Rev. Wild man.

50. 1 Ducat 1717-26 .... **35.00**

Initials. Rev. Horse.

51. 1 Ducat 1715, 18 ....* **40.00**
52. ½ Ducat 1715 .... **30.00**
53. ¼ Ducat 1717-34, ND **20.00**

Initials. Rev. Wild man.

54. 1 Ducat 1720 .... **40.00**
55. ½ Ducat 1718-28 ....* **25.00**
56. ½ Ducat ND. Square ....* **60.00**
57. ¼ Ducat 1728 .... **20.00**

Horse. Rev. Wild man.

57a. 1 Ducat 1733 .... **125.00**

Initials. Rev. Helmet.

58. ½ Ducat 1726, 27 .... **25.00**

AUGUST WILLIAM, 1714-1731

Bust. Rev. Horse.

59. 2 Ducats 1716, 19, 22, 28 ....* **125.00**
60. 1 Harz-gold Ducat 1721, 28, 29, 30 .... **60.00**
61. 1 Ducat 1714-30 .... **50.00**

Bust. Rev. Legend.

62. 2 Ducats 1730. Birthday issue **125.00**
63. 1 Ducat 1731. Death issue **60.00**

Bust. Rev. Legend. On the Reformation.

64. 1 Ducat 1717, 28 .... **40.00**

GERMANY-BRUNSWICK-WOLFENBUTTEL (cont'd)

Arms. Rev. Wild man.

65.	1 Ducat 1725, 28	40.00

Arms. Rev. Horse.

66.	1 Harz-gold Ducat 1730	75.00

Wild man. Rev. Legend. On the jubilee of the dynasty.

67.	2 Ducats 1730	125.00

Initials. Rev. Horse.

68.	2 Harz-gold Ducats 1727 .... *......	Rare
69.	1 Ducat 1716	50.00
70.	½ Ducat 1715-21 .... *......	30.00
71.	¼ Ducat 1717, 18	25.00

Bust. Rev. Legend. On the Augsburg Confession.

72.	1 Ducat 1730	40.00

FERDINAND ALBERT II, 1735

Bust. Rev. Horse.

73.	1 Ducat 1735 .... *......	150.00
74.	1 Harz-gold Ducat 1735	150.00

Bust. Rev. Legend. On his death.

75.	1 Ducat 1735	100.00

Initials. Rev. Horse.

76.	1 Ducat 1735	100.00

ELIZABETH CHRISTINA, 1733-1797

Initials. Rev. Legend. On her wedding.

77.	1 Ducat 1733	60.00

CHARLES I, 1735-1780

Armored bust. Rev. Arms.

77a.	10 Taler 1742	175.00
77b.	5 Taler 1742 .... *......	100.00

Armored bust. Rev. Horse.

78.	1	Harz-gold Ducat 1736	75.00
79.	1	Ducat 1736, 39 .... *......	50.00
80.	10	Taler 1742-63	100.00
81.	5	Taler 1742-68	50.00
82.	2½	Taler 1742-77	40.00

Head. Rev. Horse.

83.	1	Ducat 1737-65 .... *......	35.00
84.	1	Harz-gold Ducat 1737, 39, 49	50.00
85.	2	Pistoles 1767. (10 Taler)	150.00
86.	1	Pistole 1767. (5 Taler)	85.00
87.	½	Pistole 1767. (2½ Taler)	50.00

Initials. Rev. Legend. On his wedding.

88.	1 Ducat 1733	40.00

CHARLES WILLIAM FERDINAND, 1780-1806

Arms. Rev. Value.

89.	1	Ducat 1780	50.00
90.	1	Harz-gold Ducat 1781-1801 ...... *......	40.00
91.	10	Taler 1800, 05	100.00
92.	5	Taler 1782-1805 .... *......	60.00
93.	2½	Taler 1796-1806 .... *......	50.00

FREDERICK WILLIAM, 1806-1815

Arms. Rev. Value.

94.	10	Taler 1813, 14	....	100.00
95.	5	Taler 1814, 15	.............................*......	65.00
96.	2½	Taler 1815	....	125.00
97.	1	Harz-gold Ducat 1814, 15	....	40.00

CHARLES II, 1815-1830

Arms. Rev. Value. Struck during the regency of George IV of England. The coinage before 1822 shows his name as George only. The coinage of 1822 shows his name as George IV. Other coins of George IV will be found under Hannover.

98.	10	Taler 1817-22	....	85.00
99.	5	Taler 1816-22	.............................*......	50.00
100.	2½	Taler 1816-22	....	40.00

Arms. Rev. Value. Without the name of George and showing the title of Charles II as "Herzog."

101.	10	Taler 1828-30	...........................*......	85.00
102.	5	Taler 1825-30	....	60.00
103.	2½	Taler 1825-28	....	40.00
104.	1	Harz-gold Ducat 1825	.................*......	50.00

Uniformed bust. Rev. Arms.

| 105. | 10 | Taler 1827-29 | ....*...... | 100.00 |
| 106. | 2½ | Taler 1829 | .... | 60.00 |

WILLIAM, 1831-1884

Horse. Rev. Value.

| 107. | 10 Taler 1831 | .... | 75.00 |

Arms supported by wild men. Rev. Value.

108.	10	Taler 1833, 34	.........................*......	85.00
109.	5	Taler 1832	....	175.00
110.	2½	Taler 1832	....	75.00

Head. Rev. Arms.

| 111. | 10 | Taler 1850-57 | ....*...... | 85.00 |
| 112. | 2½ | Taler 1851 | .... | 75.00 |

Head. Rev. Value.

| 113. | 1 Krone 1857, 58, 59 | .... | 100.00 |

BUCHEIM

Counts of —

JOHN CHRISTIAN, 1619-1657
Bust. Rev. Arms.

| 1. | 1 Ducat 1650 | .... | 150.00 |

COLOGNE

A. City coinage

Christ on throne. Rev. Orb.

| 1. | 1 Goldgulden ND (1400-1500) | .... | 60.00 |

Christ seated. Rev. Arms.

| 2. | 1 Goldgulden 1515-34. | .... | 50.00 |

The three Magi. Rev. St. Ursula in ship.

| 3. | 6 Ducats ND (1600) | .... | 400.00 |
| 4. | 4 Ducats 1612 | .... | 400.00 |

St. Ursula standing. Rev. Shield on cross.

| 5. | 1 Goldgulden ND (1600) | .... | 100.00 |

Value on tablet. Rev. Arms.

| 6. | 1 Ducat 1634 | .... | 75.00 |

B. Coinage with the heads or names of the Holy Roman Emperors

Eagle. Rev. Arms. Maximilian II.

| 7. | 1 Goldgulden 1567-73 | .... | 40.00 |

Eagle. Rev. Arms. Rudolph II.

| 8. | 1 Goldgulden 1577-1611 | .... | 40.00 |

Eagle. Rev. Arms. Ferdinand II.

| 9. | 1 Goldgulden 1619-34 | .... | 40.00 |

Ferdinand II standing. Rev. Arms.

| 10. | 1 Ducat 1634-36 | .... | 60.00 |

Ferdinand III standing. Rev. Arms.

11.	1 Ducat 1643-57	40.00

Bust of Leopold I. Rev. Arms.

12.	1 Ducat 1661-72	50.00

Leopold I standing. Rev. Arms.

13.	1 Ducat 1689, 93	50.00

Eagle. Rev. Wine glass. Leopold I.

14.	1 Ducat 1672	75.00

Bust of Joseph I. Rev. Arms.

15.	1 Ducat 1705, 08	50.00

Eagle. Rev. Arms. Joseph I.

16.	1 Ducat 1705	40.00

Bust of Charles VI. Rev. Eagle.

17.	1 Ducat 1724	50.00

Bust of Charles VI. Rev. Arms.

18.	1 Ducat 1717-39	40.00

Bust of Charles VI. Rev. Arms with supporters.

19.	12 Ducats 1727	Rare
20.	1 Ducat 1727, 31	50.00

Arms. Rev. Eagle. Charles VI.

21.	1 Ducat 1716	50.00

Arms. Rev. Wine bottle. Charles VI.

22.	1 Ducat 1716	50.00

Bust of Charles VII. Rev. Two shields.

23.	1 Ducat 1742	85.00

Bust of Francis I. Rev. Arms.

24.	1 Ducat 1750, 53, ND	50.00

Bust of Joseph I. Rev. Arms.

25.	1 Ducat 1767	75.00

C. Archbishops of —

WALRAM OF JULICH, 1346-1349
Ruler on throne. Rev. Cross.

26.	1 Ecu d'Or ND	250.00

St. John. Rev. Lily.

27.	1 Florin ND	100.00

WILLIAM OF GENNEP, 1349-1362
St. John. Rev. Lily.

28.	1 Florin ND	75.00
29.	½ Florin ND	60.00
30.	¼ Florin ND	25.00

ADOLPH II OF MARK, 1363-1364
St. John. Rev. Lily.

31.	1 Florin ND	150.00

ENGELBERT III OF MARK, 1364-1368
St. John. Rev. Lily.

32.	1 Florin ND	100.00

KUNO OF FALKENSTEIN, 1368-1371
St. John on throne. Rev. Arms.

33.	1 Goldgulden ND	60.00

St. Peter. Rev. Arms.

34.	1 Goldgulden ND	60.00

St. Peter under canopy. Rev. Arms.

35.	1 Goldgulden ND	75.00

FREDERICK III OF SAARWERDEN, 1371-1414
St. Peter under canopy. Rev. Arms.

36.	1 Goldgulden ND	40.00

St. Peter on throne. Rev. Arms.

37.	1 Goldgulden ND	40.00

St. John. Rev. Arms and two shields.

38.	1 Goldgulden ND	40.00

St. John. Rev. Arms.

39.	1 Goldgulden ND	40.00

THEODORE II OF MOERS, 1414-1463
Ruler standing. Rev. Arms.

40.	1 Goldgulden 1458, ND	60.00

Christ. Rev. Four shields.

41.	1 Goldgulden ND	50.00

St. Peter. Rev. Arms.

42.	1 Goldgulden ND	50.00

St. John. Rev. Arms and two shields.

43.	1 Goldgulden ND	35.00

Arms on cross. Rev. Three shields.

44.	1 Goldgulden ND	40.00
45.	1 Goldgulden 1436-56	65.00

RUPERT OF PALATINATE, 1463-1480
Christ on throne. Rev. Cross and four shields.

46.	1 Goldgulden ND	50.00

Christ standing. Rev. Four shields.

47.	1 Goldgulden ND	50.00

Ruler standing. Rev. Arms.

48.	1 Goldgulden ND	40.00

HERMAN IV OF HESSE, 1480-1508
St. Peter. Rev. Arms.

49.	1 Goldgulden ND	35.00

Christ on throne. Rev. Arms.

50.	1 Goldgulden 1491-1508	65.00

PHILIP II OF DAUN, 1508-1515
Christ on throne. Rev. Arms.

51.	1 Goldgulden 1508-15, ND	35.00

HERMAN V OF WIED, 1515-1546

Christ on throne. Rev. Arms.

52.	1 Goldgulden 1515-31 . . . . *	50.00
53.	½ Goldgulden 1516	75.00

ADOLPH III OF SCHAUENBURG, 1547-1556
Christ on throne. Rev. Arms.

54.	1 Goldgulden 1547-49	35.00

ANTHONY OF SCHAUENBURG, 1556-1558
Christ on throne. Rev. Arms.

55.	1 Goldgulden 1556, 57	65.00

GERMANY-COLOGNE (cont'd)

JOHN GEBHARD OF MANSFELD, 1558-1562
Christ on throne. Rev. Arms.

56. 1 Goldgulden 1558 .... 40.00

FREDERICK IV OF WIED, 1562-1567
Christ on throne. Rev. Arms.

57. 1 Goldgulden 1563, 64, 65 .... 75.00

SALENTIN OF ISENBURG, 1567-1577
Bust with long beard. Rev. Arms.

58. 2 Ducats 1577 .... 200.00
59. 1 Ducat 1573, 75 .... 40.00
60. 1 Goldgulden 1575 .... 50.00

St. Peter standing. Rev. Arms.

61. 1 Goldgulden 1570 .... 35.00

GEBHARD OF WALDBURG, 1577-1583
Bust. Rev. Arms.

62. 1 Goldgulden 1583 .... 200.00

St. Peter. Rev. Arms.

63. 1 Goldgulden 1581, 82, 83 .... 50.00

ERNST OF BAVARIA, 1583-1612
St. Peter. Rev. Arms.

64. 1 Goldgulden ND 50.00

FERDINAND OF BAVARIA, 1612-1650
Arms of Bavaria. Rev. Shield.

65. 1 Goldgulden 1634, 37 .... 75.00

Madonna. Rev. Arms.

66. 1 Ducat ND 75.00

Arms. Rev. Value in square.

67. 1 Ducat 1640 .... 50.00

MAX HENRY OF BAVARIA, 1650-1688
Bust. Rev. Arms.

68. 1 Ducat 1644, 65, ND 60.00

JOSEPH CLEMENT OF BAVARIA, 1688-1723

Joseph and Mary with the three Magi. Rev. Arms. Struck from Westphalian gold.

69. 3 Ducats 1696 .... 200.00

Bust. Rev. Arms.

70. 1 Ducat 1694, 1722 .... 50.00

Bust with hat. Rev. Arms.

71. 1 Ducat 1715 .... 65.00

Bust. Rev. Madonna seated.

72. 1 Ducat 1694, 98 .... 50.00

Bust. Rev. The three Magi.

73. 1 Ducat 1723 .... 75.00

CLEMENT AUGUST OF BAVARIA, 1723-1761
Bust. Rev. Adoration of the three Magi.

74. 1 Ducat 1726, 42, 44 .... 60.00

Bust. Rev. Seven shields on mantle.

75. 1 Carolin 1735 .... 125.00
76. ½ Carolin 1735, 36 .... 75.00

Bust. Rev. Madonna seated.

77. 1 Ducat 1750 .... 65.00

Facing or profile bust. Rev. Sun and legend.

78. 1 Ducat 1750 .... 65.00

CONSTANCE

A. City of —

Eagle and CONST. Rev. Orb. Name of Maximilian.

1. 1 Goldgulden ND. (1486-1508) 200.00

Eagle and CONSTANC. Rev. Similar to above.

2. 1 Goldgulden ND. (1486-1508) 200.00

Arms. Rev. Double eagle. Name of Ferdinand II or III.

3. 2 Ducats ND. (1618-57). Square 750.00
4. 1 Ducat 1629, 52, ND. Round or square 250.00

B. Bishops of —

JOHN FRANCIS II SCHENK OF STAUFFENBERG, 1704-1740

Two shields. Rev. Arms.

5. 2 Ducats 1737 .... 200.00
6. 1 Ducat 1737 ....*...... 100.00

FRANCIS CONRAD OF RODT, 1750-1775
Bust. Rev. Arms.

7. 1 Ducat 1761 .... 125.00

CORVEY

Abbots of —

CHARLES OF BLITTERSDORF, 1722-1737
St. Vitus. Rev. Arms.

1. 1 Ducat 1724, ND 125.00

CASPAR OF BOSELAGER, 1737-1758

St. Vitus. Rev. Arms.

2. 1 Ducat 1743, 53 .... 100.00

PHILIP OF SPIEGEL, 1758-1776
St. Vitus. Rev. Arms.

3. 1 Ducat 1758, 59 .... 75.00

COSEL

(Several so-called "Love Ducats" were struck under Saxon auspices, but they are more jetons than coins.)

DARMSTADT

Legend on each side. On the Reformation.

1. 1 Ducat 1817 .... 75.00

DIEPHOLT

St. Stephen. Rev. Eagle.

1. 1 Goldgulden ND. (1600) 125.00

DIETRICHSTEIN

Princes of —

FERDINAND, 1655-1698
Bust with wig. Rev. Arms.

1. 10 Ducats 1695 .... Rare
2. 1 Ducat 1695, 96 .... 125.00

CHARLES LOUIS, DIED 1732
Bust. Rev. Arms.

3. 1 Ducat 1726 .... 125.00

DORTMUND

(Coinage with the names, heads or standing figures of the Holy Roman Emperors.)

St. John standing. Rev. Orb. Name of Sigismund.

1. 1 Goldgulden ND (1410-39) 125.00

Frederick III standing. Rev. Orb.

2. 1 Goldgulden ND (1470-80) 60.00

Maximilian standing. Rev. Orb.

3. 1 Goldgulden ND (1500) 85.00

Ferdinand II standing. Rev. Orb.

4. 1 Ducat 1632 .... 100.00

Ferdinand III standing. Rev. Arms.

5. 1 Ducat 1636, 37, 39 .... 100.00

Ferdinand III standing. Rev. Eagle over legend.

6. 1 Ducat 1635-55 .... 100.00

Leopold I standing. Rev. Eagle

7. 1 Ducat 1660, 63 .... 125.00

Bust of Charles VI. Rev. Eagle.

8. 1 Ducat 1717 .... 150.00

Bust of Charles VII. Rev. Eagle.

9. 2 Ducats 1742. Square ....*...... 300.00
10. 1 Ducat 1742. Square 150.00

EAST FRISIA

Counts, and later, Princes of —
UDO OF NORDEN, 1421-1433

St. Luderus. Rev. Lion shield.

1. 1 Goldgulden ND (1433) 250.00

ULRIC, 1441-1466
St. Peter. Rev. Orb.

2. 1 Goldgulden ND 50.00

St. John. Rev. Orb.

3. 1 Goldgulden ND 50.00

ENNO I, 1446-1491
St. John. Rev. Orb.

4. 1 Goldgulden ND 50.00

EDZARD I, 1491-1528
St. John. Rev. Orb.

5. 1 Goldgulden ND 40.00

ENNO II, 1528-1540
Christ with globe. Hev. Harpyrie shield.

6. 1 Goldgulden ND 60.00

St. John. Rev. Orb.

7. 1 Goldgulden ND 40.00

GERMANY-EAST FRISIA (cont'd)

Bust with hat. Rev. Arms.

8. 1 Goldgulden 1529 .... 125.00

EDZARD II AND JOHN, 1566-1591
Bust of Emperor Maximilian II. Rev. Arms.

9. 1 Goldgulden 1568, 69 .... 100.00

Bust of Emperor Rudolph II. Rev. Arms.

10. 1 Goldgulden 1571-90 .... 60.00

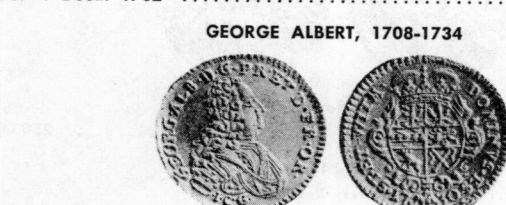

Charlemagne standing. Rev. Arms.

11. 1 Goldgulden 1574 .... 75.00

Charlemagne on throne. Rev. Cross.

12. 1 Goldgulden ND 75.00

EDZARD II, 1591-1599
Bust of Emperor Rudolph II. Rev. Arms.

13. 1 Goldgulden 1594 .... 50.00

St. Luderus. Rev. Arms.

14. 1 Goldgulden ND 50.00

ENNO III, 1599-1625
Bust. Rev. Cross.

15. 1 Goldgulden 1615 .... 50.00

Christ standing. Rev. Arms.

16. 1 Goldgulden ND 50.00

Arms. Rev. Cross.

17. ½ Ducat ND 40.00

CHRISTIAN EBERHARD, 1690-1708
Bust. Rev. Arms.

18. 1 Ducat 1702 .... 85.00

GEORGE ALBERT, 1708-1734

Bust. Rev. Arms.

19. 1 Ducat 1715, 30, 31 .... 50.00

CHARLES EDZARD, 1734-1744
Armored bust. Rev. Arms.

20. 1 Ducat 1737 .... 75.00

EGGENBERG

Princes of —

JOHN CHRISTIAN AND JOHN SEYFRIED, 1649-1713
Two busts. Rev. Arms.

1.	15 Ducats 1652	......	Rare
2.	10 Ducats 1652, 54	......	500.00
3.	5 Ducats 1652, 58	......	300.00
4.	1 Ducat 1654	......	100.00

EICHSTAETT

Bishops of —

GABRIEL, 1496-1535
St. Walburga standing. Rev. Arms.

1. 1 Goldgulden 1511 .... 400.00

MARTIN OF SCHAUMBERG, 1560-1590

St. Willibald standing. Rev. Arms.

2. 4 Goldgulden 1560 .... Rare
3. 1 Goldgulden 1560 ....*...... 150.00

St. Willibald standing. Rev. Eagle and name of Maximilian II.

4. 2 Ducats 1570 .... 300.00

JOHN CONRAD OF GEMMINGEN, 1595-1612
Arms. Rev. Eagle and name of Rudolph II.

5. 14 Ducats 1596 .... Rare
6. 8 Ducats 1596 .... Rare
7. 6 Ducats 1596 .... 450.00

JOHN CRISTOPHER OF WETTERSTETTEN, 1612-1636
St. Willibald standing. Rev. 2 shields.

8. 1 Ducat 1633, 34 .... 75.00

St. Walburga standing. Rev. 2 shields.

9. 1 Ducat 1633 .... 85.00

Saint standing. Rev. eagle and name of Ferdinand II.

10. 1 Ducat 1635 .... 75.00

JOHN EUCHARIUS SCHENK OF CASTELL, 1685-1697
Bust. Rev. Arms supported by lions.

11. 6 Ducats 1694 .... 200.00

Bust. Rev. Eagle flying over arms.

12. 10 Ducats ND .... Rare

FRANCIS LOUIS SCHENK OF CASTELL, 1725-1736
Bust. Rev. Arms. Oval shaped.

13. 1 Ducat 1736 .... 200.00

JOHN ANTONY II OF FREYBERG, 1736-1757
Bust. Rev. Arms.

14. 1 Ducat 1755 .... 100.00

St. Willibald standing. Rev. Arms.

15. 1 Ducat 1738 .... 75.00

St. Walburga standing. Rev. Arms.

16. 1 Ducat 1738 .... 75.00

EINBECK

City gate. Rev. Double eagle. Name of Ferdinand II.

1. 1 Goldgulden 1629 .... 250.00

ELBING

A. Swedish Kings of —

Bust of Gustav Adolphe. Rev. Arms.

1. 1 Ducat 1630 .... 250.00

Bust of Charles X. Rev. Arms.

2. 1 Ducat 1657 .... 350.00

B. Polish Kings of —

Bust of John Casimir. Rev. Arms.

3. 1 Ducat 1661 .... 125.00

Bust of Michael Korybut. Rev. Arms.

4. 2 Ducats 1672 .... 250.00
5. 1 Ducat 1671 .... 125.00

EMDEN

St. Peter. Rev. Orb.

1. 1 Goldgulden ND. (1470) 75.00

Knight standing. Rev. Value in tablet or cartouche.

2. 2 Ducats 1694 .... 250.00
3. 1 Ducat 1635-98, ND ....*...... 100.00

View of the city. Rev. Hands and sceptre.

4. 3¼ Ducats ND 250.00
5. 2½ Ducats 1737, 43, 46 .... 150.00
6. 2¼ Ducats 1750 .... 150.00
7. 2 Ducats ND 125.00

Arms. Rev. Hands with bundle of arrows.

8. 4 Ducats ND. (1700) 250.00

ERFURT

A. City of —

Wheel and date. Rev. Arms.

1. 1 Goldgulden 1620, 22, 70, ND 200.00

B. Swedish Kings of —

Radiant Jehovah in Hebrew characters. Rev. Long legend.

2. 10 Victory Ducats 1631. Struck by Gustav Adolphe 2000.00

King in bed. Rev. King in triumphal chariot. On the death of Gustav Adolphe.

3. 4 Ducats 1634 .... 500.00

Bust of Gustav Adolphe. Rev. Crown over legend.

4. 1 Ducat 1632, 33, 34 .... 75.00

Bust of Gustav Adolphe. Rev. Arms.

5. 8 Ducats 1632 ....*...... 2000.00
6. 1 Ducat 1634 .... 125.00

ESSEN

Abbessess of —

ANNA SALOME, 1646-1688
Arms. Rev. Madonna.

1. 1 Ducat 1672 .... 300.00

FRANCES CHRISTINE, 1717-1776

Arms. Rev. Madonna.

2. 1 Ducat 1754 .... 125.00

FRANKFURT

A. City coinage

Angel. Rev. Legend. On the Reformation.

1. 1 Goldgulden 1617 ....*...... 75.00
2. 1 Goldgulden 1617. Square 125.00

Two hands in prayer. Rev. Comet. On the appearance of a comet.

3. 1 Ducat 1618. Square 125.00

Eagle. Rev. Value on tablet, in cartouche or plain.

4. 2 Ducats 1633-37 .... 50.00
5. 1 Ducat 1633-1749, ND 30.00
6. ½ Ducat 1740 .... 30.00

Eagle. Rev. View of the city in a storm.

7. 2 Ducats 1705, 10 .... 85.00

Eagle. Rev. Tower in a stormy sea.

8. 2 Ducats 1710, 11 ....* 75.00
8a. 1 Ducat 1710, 11 .... 50.00

Bible on rock at sea. Rev. Legend. On the Reformation.

9. 1 Ducat 1717 .... 50.00

Eagle. Rev. Floriated cross.

10. 1 Ducat 1762 .... 60.00

City view. Rev. Legend. Struck under French occupation.

11. 1 Ducat 1796 .... 40.00

Legend on each side. On the Reformation.

12. 1 Ducat 1817 .... 30.00

Eagle. Rev. Value.

13. 1 Ducat 1853, 56 .... 30.00

B. Coinage with the heads or names of the Holy Roman Emperors

St. John. Rev. Lily. Charles IV.

14. 1 Florin ND. (1347-78) 175.00

St. John. Rev. Eagle on shield. Rupert of Palatinate.

15. 1 Goldgulden ND. (1400-10) 150.00

St. John. Rev. Orb. Sigismund.

16. 1 Goldgulden ND. (1410-33) 30.00

Charlemagne standing. Rev. Arms. Sigismund.

17. 1 Goldgulden ND. (1410-33) 150.00

St. John. Rev. Orb. Albert II.

18. 1 Goldgulden ND. (1438-39) 40.00

St. John. Rev. Orb. Frederick III.

19. 1 Goldgulden ND 30.00
20. 1 Goldgulden 1491, 92, 93 .... 65.00

St. John. Rev. Orb. Maximilian I.

21. 1 Goldgulden 1494-1515, ND 50.00

St. John. Rev. Lily. Charles V.

22. 1 Goldgulden 1521, 22 .... 100.00

St. John. Rev. Orb. Charles V.

23. 1 Goldgulden 1527 .... 125.00

St. John. Rev. Eagle. Rudolph II.

24. 1 Goldgulden 1611, 12 .... 50.00

Bust of Matthias II. Rev. Crown.

25. 3 Ducats 1612 .... 175.00
26. 2 Ducats or Goldgulden 1612 ....* 125.00
27. 1 Goldgulden 1612 .... 75.00

Matthias II on horse. Rev. Eagle.

28. 10 Ducats ND. (1612) 500.00
29. 5 Ducats ND. (1612) 300.00

Matthias II on horse. Rev. Circle of shields.

30. 5 Ducats ND. (1612) 300.00
31. 3 Ducats ND. (1612) 175.00

St. John. Rev. Eagle. Matthias II.

32. 1 Goldgulden 1617, 18, 19 .... 50.00

Ferdinand II on throne. Rev. Crown.

33. 3 Ducats 1619 .... 175.00
34. 1 Goldgulden 1619 ....* 65.00

Bust of Ferdinand II. Rev. Wreath over crown.

34a. 2 Ducats ND. Square 150.00

Legend. Rev. Arm with Crown. Ferdinand II.

35.	2 Ducats 1619	125.00
36.	1 Ducat 1619	60.00

Crowned F. Rev. Legend. Ferdinand II.

36a.	½ Ducat 1619	22.50

St. John. Rev. Eagle. Ferdinand II.

37.	1 Goldgulden 1620, 21, 22	50.00

St. John. Rev. Orb. Ferdinand II.

38.	1 Goldgulden 1620, 24, 25	50.00

Hand with sceptre and arm with sword. Rev. Legend. On the coronation of Leopold I.

39.	4 Ducats 1658	200.00
40.	2 Ducats 1658	125.00
41.	1 Ducat 1658	65.00
42.	½ Ducat 1658	40.00

Bust of Charles VI. Rev. Insignia.

43.	2 Ducats 1711	100.00

Globe. Rev. Legend. Charles VI.

44.	1½ Ducats 1711	75.00
45.	¾ Ducat 1711	50.00

Legend. Rev. City view. On the election of Charles VI.

46.	2 Ducats 1711	100.00

Bust of Charles VII. Rev. Female at altar.

47.	4 Ducats 1742	175.00
48.	2 Ducats 1742	100.00
49.	1 Ducat 1742	35.00

Bust of Charles VII. Rev. Bust of Maria Amalia.

50.	1 Ducat ND. (1742)	100.00

Eagle. Rev. Legend. On the coronation of Charles VII.

51.	1 Ducat 1742	65.00

Bust of Francis I. Rev. Insignia on table.

51a.	1 Ducat 1745	35.00

Eagle. Rev. Legend. On the election of Francis I.

52.	1 Ducat 1745	50.00

Altar. Rev. Legend. On the coronation of Francis I.

53.	1½ Ducats 1745	75.00
54.	¾ Ducat 1745	50.00

Bust of Joseph II. Rev. Peace standing near fallen soldier.

55.	2 Ducats 1764	*	65.00
55a.	1 Ducat 1764		35.00

Globe. Rev. Legend. On the coronation of Joseph II.

56.	1½ Ducats 1764	75.00
57.	¾ Ducat 1764	50.00

Head of Leopold II. Rev. Altar.

58.	1 Ducat 1790	60.00

Crossed insignia. Rev. Legend. On the coronation of Leopold II.

59.	1½ Ducats 1790	75.00
60.	¾ Ducat 1790	50.00

Head of Francis II. Rev. Altar.

61.	2 Ducats 1792	125.00
62.	1 Ducat 1792	60.00

Crossed insignia. Rev. Legend. On the coronation of Francis II.

63.	1½ Ducats 1792	75.00
64.	¾ Ducat 1792	50.00

FREIBURG

Madonna. Rev. Arms.

1.	1 Goldgulden 1622	600.00

Two shields and eagle. Rev. City view.

2.	1 Ducat 1717	200.00

FREISING

Bishops of —

JOHN FRANCIS OF KAPPING AND LICHTENEGG, 1695-1727

St. Corbianus. Rev. Arms. On the Milennium.

1.	2 Ducats 1724	200.00

CLEMENT WENCESLAUS OF SAXONY, 1763-1768

Bust. Rev. Arms.

2.	1 Ducat 1765, 66	100.00

FUERSTENBERG

Princes of —

JOSEPH, 1704-1762

Bust with wig. Rev. Arms with owl below.

1.	1 Ducat 1750, 51	150.00

GERMANY-FUERSTENBERG (cont'd)

CHARLES EGON I, DIED 1788

Bust. Rev. Arms.

2. 1 Ducat 1772 .... 75.00

FUGGER

Counts of —

ANTONY, 1493-1560

Arms. Rev. Eagle.

1. 1 Goldgulden ND 50.00

MAXIMILIAN, 1619-1637
Arms. Rev. Eagle.

2. 13 Ducats 1621 .... Rare
3. 10 Ducats 1621 .... Rare
4. 1 Goldgulden ND 125.00

Three shields. Rev. Eagle.

5. 1 Ducat 1622 .... 125.00

FULDA

Bishops of —

BALTHASAR OF DERNBACH, 1570-1606
Eagle. Rev. Arms and name of Rudolph II.

1. 20 Ducats 1606 .... Rare

BERNARD GUSTAV OF BADEN, 1671-1678

St. Boniface. Rev. Initials.

2. 2 Ducats 1672 .... 250.00
3. 1 Ducat 1672 .... 100.00
4. ½ Ducat 1672 ....* 40.00
5. ¼ Ducat 1672 .... 35.00

PLACIDUS OF DROSTE, 1678-1700
Bust with hat. Rev. Arms.

6. 10 Ducats 1680 .... 600.00
7. 8 Ducats 1688 .... 500.00
8. 7 Ducats 1688 .... 400.00
9. 2 Ducats 1692 .... 200.00
10. 1 Ducat 1692 .... 85.00

CONSTANTINE OF BUTLAR, 1714-1726

Bust. Rev. Arms.

11. 1 Ducat 1715-26 .... 60.00

Bust. Rev. Two shields.

12. 1 Ducat 1716, 21 .... 65.00

ADOLPH OF DALBERG, 1726-1737

Bust. Rev. Arms.

13. 2 Ducats 1728, 30 ....* 125.00
14. 1 Ducat 1726, 28, 30 .... 60.00

Bust. Rev. Crossed initials.

15. 1 Carolin or 10 Gulden 1734, 35 .... 125.00
16. ½ Carolin or 5 Gulden 1734 .... 75.00

AMANDUS OF BUSECK, 1737-1756

Bust. Rev. Arms.

17. 8 Ducats 1738 .... 400.00
18. 1 Ducat 1738 ....* 65.00

Bust. Rev. Sun and legend. On the Jubilee.

19. 1 Ducat 1744 .... 50.00

ADALBERT OF SCHLEIFRAS, 1756-1759

Bust. Rev. Arms.

20. 2 Ducats 1759 .... 150.00

HENRY VIII OF BIBRA, 1759-1788

Arms. Rev. Legend.

21. 1 Ducat 1779 .... 300.00

Bust. Rev. Legend.

22. 1 Ducat 1779 .... 50.00

Bust. Rev. Arms.

23. 1 Ducat 1779 .... 65.00

FURTH

Swedish Kings of —

Gustav Adolphe standing. Rev. Arms.

1. 1 Ducat 1632 .... 1000.00

GLATZ

Counts of —

JOHN OF PERNSTEIN, 1537-1549

Two shields. Rev. Bohemian lion.

1. 1 Ducat 1540, 41, 44, 46 .... 125.00

ERNST OF BAVARIA, 1549-1554
Three shields. Rev. Bohemian lion.

2. 1 Ducat 1549, 50, 54 .... 125.00

GOSLAR

Arms under helmet. Rev. Double eagle. Name of Ferdinand II.

1. 1 Goldgulden 1628, ND 250.00

Bust of Ferdinand II. Rev. Arms.

2. 1 Ducat ND. (1620) 125.00

Ferdinand II standing. Rev. Arms.

3. 1 Ducat ND. (1620) 500.00

GOTTINGEN

Double Eagle. Rev. Arms.

1. 4 Ducats 1660 .... Rare

HAGENAU

Rose in shield. Rev. Double eagle. Name of Rudolph II.

1. 1 Goldgulden 1604, 08, 10, 11 .... 500.00

St. John. Rev. Eagle.

2. 1 Goldgulden ND 750.00

HALBERSTADT

CATHEDRAL CHAPTER OF THE BISHOPRIC
St. Stephan standing. Rev. Arms.

1. 1 Goldgulden 1628, 29, ND 60.00

St. Stephan standing. Rev. Shield.

2. 2 Goldgulden 1631 .... 150.00

HALLE-IN-SUEBIA

Bust of Joseph I. Rev. Three shields.

1. 1 Ducat 1705 .... 40.00

Bust of Charles VI. Rev. Three shields.

2. 1 Ducat 1712 .... 40.00

Three shields. Rev. Legend. On the Peace of Baden.

3. 1 Ducat 1714 .... 50.00
4. ¼ Ducat 1714 .... 25.00

Bust of Charles VII. Rev. Three shields.

5. 1 Ducat 1742 .... 50.00

Bust of Francis I. Rev. Three shields.

6. 1 Ducat 1746 .... 50.00

Bust of Joseph II. Rev. Three shields.

7. 1 Ducat 1777, ND 40.00

HAMBURG

A. City coinage

City gate. Rev. Cross.

1. 10 Ducats or 1 Portugaloser ND. (1553-1673) 500.00
2. 5   Ducats or ½ Portugaloser ND. (1553-1673) ..*...... 300.00
3. 2½ Ducats or ¼ Portugaloser ND. (1553-1673) 150.00

Christ blessing couple. Rev. The Wedding at Cana.

4. 10 Ducats ND 700.00

Madonna on each side.

5. 2 Ducats 1649, 60, 66 .... 125.00
6. 1 Ducat 1497-1667, ND 40.00

Madonna. Rev. Arms.

7. 2 Ducats 1669-94 ....*...... 125.00
8. 1 Ducat 1668-75 .... 40.00
9. ½ Ducat 1675 .... 50.00

Elbe River god. Rev. Father Time.

10. 1 Ducat ND. (1700) 60.00

Hammonia standing. Rev. Tablet.

11. 1 Ducat 1807 .... 75.00

City gate. Rev. Tablet.

12. 2 Ducats 1808, 09, 10 ....*...... 75.00
13. 1 Ducat 1808-11 .... 40.00

Knight standing. Rev. Tablet.

14. 1 Ducat 1811-50. Old style 30.00
15. 1 Ducat 1851-72. New style ....*...... 25.00

B. Coinage with the heads or names of the Holy Roman Emperors

St. Peter. Rev. Orb. Sigismund I.
16. 1 Goldgulden ND. (1435-37) 40.00

St. Peter. Rev. Orb. Frederick III.
17. 1 Goldgulden ND. (1440-93) 40.00

St. Peter. Rev. Orb. Maximilian I.
18. 1 Goldgulden ND. (1493-1519) 75.00

St. Peter. Rev. Orb. Charles V.
19. 1 Goldgulden 1553 .... 60.00

St. Peter. Rev. Orb. Ferdinand I.
20. 1 Goldgulden 1553, 61 .... 50.00

St. Peter. Rev. Orb. Maximilian II.
21. 1 Goldgulden 1566 .... 50.00

St. Peter. Rev. Orb. Rudolph II.
22. 1 Goldgulden 1581-89, ND 40.00

St. Peter. Rev. Orb. Matthias II.
23. 1 Goldgulden 1617, 19 .... 50.00

St. Peter. Rev. Orb. Ferdinand II.
24. 1 Goldgulden 1628 .... 50.00

Eagle. Rev. Arms. Leopold I.
25. 5 Ducats 1696 .... 300.00
26. 2 Ducats 1689-1707 .... 40.00
27. ½ Ducat ND. (1692-1704) 25.00
28. ¼ Ducat 1680, ND 20.00
29. 1 Goldgulden 1675 .... 60.00

Madonna. Rev. Eagle. Leopold I.
30. 2½ Ducats ND. (1692-1705) 175.00

Madonna and shield. Rev. Eagle. Leopold I.
31. 1 Ducat 1694, 1702 .... 50.00

Bust of Joseph I. Rev. Arms.
32. 2 Ducats 1705 .... 150.00
33. 1 Ducat 1705-10 .... 60.00

Eagle. Rev. Arms. Joseph I.
34. 2 Ducats 1705 .... 125.00
35. 1 Ducat 1706-11 .... 50.00
36. ¼ Ducat 1729 .... 25.00

Eagle. Rev. Arms. Charles VI.
37. 2 Ducats 1713-40 .... 85.00
38. 1 Ducat 1713-40 .... 40.00

Eagle. Rev. Arms. Charles VII.
39. 2 Ducats 1742, 44, 45 .... 125.00
40. 1 Ducat 1742, 43, 44, 45 .... 60.00

Eagle. Rev. Arms. Francis I.
41. 2 Ducats 1746-64 .... 80.00
42. 1 Ducat 1746-65 .... 40.00

Eagle. Rev. Arms. Joseph II.
43. 2 Ducats 1764-72 .... 80.00
44. 1 Ducat 1765-72 .... 40.00

Eagle. Rev. Tablet. Joseph II.
45. 2 Ducats 1766-90 .... 75.00
46. 1 Ducat 1773-90 .... 40.00

Eagle. Rev. Tablet. Leopold II.
47. 2 Ducats 1790-92 .... 125.00
48. 1 Ducat 1791, 92 .... 75.00

Eagle. Rev. Arms. Francis II.
49. 4 Ducats 1797 .... 500.00

Eagle. Rev. Tablet. Francis II.
50. 2 Ducats 1793-1806 ....*...... 75.00
51. 1 Ducat 1793-1806 .... 40.00

C. Private Bank Issues (Portugalosers)

(Each of the following coins is a 1 Portugaloser piece or 10 Ducats. Smaller pieces are indicated as "½ P" or "¼ P". The descriptions of the Obv. and Rev. designs are separated by a dash).

52. Madonna-Cross. ND (1500-1700) 500.00
53. Same but ½ P 275.00
54. Same but ¼ P 150.00
55. City view on each side. 1653 .... 400.00
56. City view-City plan. 1664 .... 400.00
57. City view-Four shields. 1665, 75, 89 .... 350.00
58. City view-Table. 1667 .... 400.00
59. City view-Apollo and Diana. 1672 .... 400.00
60. City view-Mercury and landscape. ND 350.00
61. City view-Ship. 1675 .... 300.00
62. Three figures-Dockside. 1677 .... 300.00
63. Mine-Mercury and Neptune. ½ P 1679, ND 175.00
64. Fidelity at table-Pax. 1681 .... 300.00
65. Elbe River god-City Goddess. ½ P 1683 .... 175.00
66. Rostrum-Sun and seascape. ND 300.00
67. City gate-Eagle. ½ P 1687 .... 250.00
68. City view and hen-Column. 1688 .... 300.00
69. City gate-Bourse. 1690 .... 300.00
70. City Goddess-Bourse. 1691 .... 300.00
71. Same but ½ P ND 150.00
72. Altar-City plan. 1693 .... 300.00
73. Four columns-Monument. 1694 .... 300.00
74. City gate-Altar. 1695 .... 300.00
75. Double Eagle-Arms. ½ P. 1695 .... 250.00
76. Tree-Three beehives. 1714 .... 400.00
77. Fortuna-Mercury. 1716 .... 300.00
78. Arms-Vine. ½ P. 1716 .... 150.00
79. Arms-Pyramid. 1717 (Reformation) 350.00
80. Building-Fountain. 1719 .... 300.00
81. Same but ½ P. 1741 .... 150.00
82. City Goddess-Column. 1723 .... 300.00
83. Naval figure-Altar. 1723 .... 300.00
84. Moneta at Anvil-Table. 1726 .... 300.00
85. Altar-Olive tree. ND 300.00
86. City Goddess-Arms. 1730 (Augsburg Confession) 350.00
87. City gate-Neptune and Elbe River god. 1732 .... 300.00
88. Pallas-Vine. ½ P. 1735 .... 125.00
89. Courtroom-Ship. 1736 .... 300.00
90. Germania at Altar-City gate. 1748 .... 300.00

HAMLIN

City church. Rev. Double eagle. Name of Leopold I.

1. 1 Goldgulden 1638-68 .... 150.00

Ferdinand III standing. Rev. City church.

2. 1 Ducat 1656 .... 150.00

HANAU-LICHTENBERG

Counts of —

JOHN REINHARD I, 1599-1625

Arms. Rev. Double Eagle.

1. 1 Goldgulden 1613, 14, 17, 18, ND 65.00

FREDERICK CASIMIR, 1641-1685
Jehova and wreath. Rev. Arms.

2. 1 Ducat 1647 .... 65.00

Arms. Rev. Legend in cartouche.

3. 1 Ducat 1647 .... 65.00

PHILIP REINHARD, 1666-1712
Bust. Rev. Arms.

4. 1 Ducat ND 85.00

JOHN REINHARD II, 1712-1736
Bust. Rev. Arms.

5. 1 Ducat 1733, ND 85.00

HANNOVER

A. City of —

Castle gate. Rev. Legend.

1. 3½ Goldgulden 1590 .... 350.00

Castle gate. Rev. Eagle.

2. 3 Ducats 1666 .... 275.00
3. 3 Goldgulden 1654 .... 275.00
4. 1 Ducat 1640, 66, 67 ....*...... 100.00
5. 1 Goldgulden 1616-33 .... 125.00

B. English Kings of —

(For earlier issues of the English Kings, see under Brunswick-Luneburg).

GEORGE IV, 1820-1830

Head. Rev. Value.

6. 10 Taler 1821-30 ....*...... 80.00
7. 5 Taler 1821-30 .... 60.00
8. 2½ Taler 1821-30 .... 60.00

Horse. Rev. Value.

9. 5 Harz-gold Taler 1821 .... 125.00
10. 1 Harz-gold Ducat 1821, 24, 27 .... 50.00

(For other coins with the name and title of George IV, see under Charles II of Brunswick-Wolfenbuttel.)

WILLIAM IV, 1830-1837

Head. Rev. Arms.

11. 10 Taler 1832-37 .... 100.00
12. 5 Taler 1835 ....*...... 125.00
13. 2½ Taler 1832-37. Rev. Value ....*...... 65.00

Horse. Rev. Value.

14. 1 Harz-gold Ducat 1831 .... 75.00

C. Hannoverian Kings of —

ERNST AUGUST, 1837-1851

Small head. Rev. Arms in circle.

15. 10 Taler 1838. B mm ...., 125.00
16. 10 Taler 1839, 44. S mm 90.00
17. 5 Taler 1839. S mm ....*...... 75.00
18. 2½ Taler 1839, 40, 43. S mm 60.00

Large head. Rev. Plain arms. All with B mm.

19. 10 Taler 1846-51 .... 80.00
20. 5 Taler 1845-51 ....*...... 50.00
21. 5 Harz-gold Taler 1849, 50 ....*...... 100.00
22. 2½ Taler 1845-50 .... 50.00

GERMANY-HANNOVER (cont'd)

GEORGE V, 1851-1866

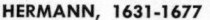

Head. Rev. Arms.

23.	10	Taler 1853-56	100.00
24.	5	Taler 1853, 55, 56 ....*.....	75.00
25.	5	Harz-gold Taler 1853 ....*.....	150.00
26.	2½	Taler 1853, 55	75.00

Head. Rev. Value.

27.	1	Krone 1857-66	100.00
28.	½	Krone 1857-66	75.00

HATZFELD

Princes of —

SEBASTIAN, 1569-1631
Bust. Rev. Two virtues standing.

1.	1	Ducat 1597	175.00

HERMANN, 1631-1677

Bust. Rev. Madonna.

2.	1	Ducat ND	150.00

HESSE-CASSEL

A. Landgraves, and later, Electors of —

WILLIAM II, 1493-1509
St. Elizabeth. Rev. Five shields crossed.

1.	1	Goldgulden 1506-08	350.00

• WILLIAM I AND PHILIP
St. Elizabeth. Rev. Five shields crossed.

2.	1	Goldgulden 1510	400.00

PHILIP, 1509-1567
St. Elizabeth. Rev. Lion shield within four small shields.

3.	1	Goldgulden 1510, 11	350.00

Arms. Rev. Legend.

4.	½	Goldgulden 1564	100.00

MAURICE, 1592-1632
Bust. Rev. Flags and symbols.

5.	1	Goldgulden 1618	150.00

Arms. Rev. Four shields.

6.	1	Ducat 1624	250.00
7.	1	Goldgulden 1624, 26 ....*......	200.00

Lion. Rev. Two flags.

8.	4	Ducats 1627	300.00

Legend. Rev. Crossed flags. On his death.

9.	2	Ducats 1632	200.00
10.	1	Ducat 1632	125.00

WILLIAM V, 1627-1637
Bust. Rev. Arms.

11.	1	Goldgulden 1627	200.00

Arms. Rev. Willow tree in storm.

12.	2	Ducats 1632	175.00
13.	1	Goldgulden 1628-34 ....*......	75.00

Lion. Rev. Willow tree in storm.

14.	2	Goldgulden 1637	200.00
15.	1	Goldgulden 1635-37 ....*......	65.00

Lion. Rev. Willow tree.

16.	2	Ducats 1637	125.00
17.	1	Ducat 1637	75.00

Legend. Rev. Willow tree. On his death.

18.	2	Ducats 1637	150.00
19.	1	Ducat 1637	75.00

AMALIA ELIZABETH, REGENT, DIED 1651
Arms. Rev. Rock in storm.

20.	1	Mining Ducat ND	200.00

Legend. Rev. Rock. On her death.

21.	2	Ducats 1651	300.00

WILLIAM VI, 1637-1663
Bust. Rev. Arms.

22.	1	Ducat 1661, 63	200.00

Bust. Rev. Legend. On his death.

23.	1	Ducat 1663	150.00

Lion. Rev. Willow tree in storm.

24.	1	Goldgulden 1638	150.00

Arms. Rev. Ship.

25.	1¼	Ducats 1654	175.00
26.	1	Goldgulden 1652, 53	150.00

HEDWIG SOPHIA, 1649-1683
Arms. Rev. Legend. On her death.

27.	2	Ducats 1683	85.00

ELIZABETH HENRIETTA, DIED 1683
Bust. Rev. Crown on pedestal. On her death.

28.	2	Ducats 1683	85.00

WILLIAM VII, 1663-1670
Arms. Rev. Legend. On his death.

29.	1	Ducat 1670	150.00

CHARLES, 1670-1730
Bust. Rev. Spring.

30.	½	Ducat ND	40.00

Bust. Rev. Lion and "Eddergold".

31.	½	Edder-gold Ducat ND	150.00

Head. Rev. Lion on pedestal with book.

32. 2 Ducats ND		150.00
33. 1 Ducat 1720, ND ....*		40.00
34. 1 Ducat 1720. Without book on Rev.		60.00
35. ¼ Ducat 1720		20.00

Head. Rev. Arms.

36. 2 Ducats ND		100.00
37. 1 Ducat 1724, 25, ND ....*		40.00

Head. Rev. Swan.

38. ¼ Ducat ND		15.00

Arms. Rev. Swan.

39. 1 Ducat 1686		150.00

Legend. Rev. Edder River Landscape.

40. 1 Edder-gold Ducat 1677		400.00

FREDERICK I
(See below under B.)

WILLIAM VIII, 1751-1760
Bust. Rev. Arms.

41. 1 Ducat 1751, 54		100.00

Initials. Rev. Lion.

42. ¼ Ducat 1752		15.00

FREDERICK II, 1760-1785

Head. Rev. Star of Order.

43. 2 Louis d'Or 1773, 75-77, 80, 85		85.00
44. 1 Louis d'Or 1771, 77, 78, 83, 84, 85 ....*		40.00

Armored bust. Rev. Landscape with river-god.

45. 1 Edder-gold Ducat 1775		125.00

GEORGE WILLIAM, PRINCE
Bust. Rev. Arms.

46. 1 Ducat 1768		100.00

Bust of Wilhelmine Caroline. Rev. Legend.

47. 1 Ducat 1764		75.00

WILLIAM IX (I), 1785-1821
Head. Rev. Star of Order.

48. 1 Louis d'Or 1786, 87, 88, 90		40.00

Head. Rev. Lion and trophies.

49. 5 Taler 1791-1801		40.00
50. 5 Taler 1803, 05, 06. With title as elector William I..*		50.00

Head. Rev. Arms.

51. 5 Taler 1814-20		150.00

WILLIAM II, 1821-1831

Bust. Rev. Arms.

52. 5 Taler 1821-29		75.00

WILLIAM II AND FREDERICK WILLIAM, 1831-1847

Arms. Rev. Legend.

53. 10 Taler 1838, 40, 41		80.00
54. 5 Taler 1834-47 ....*		40.00

Legend on each side.

55. ½ Edder-gold Ducat 1835		75.00

FREDERICK WILLIAM I, 1847-1866

Head. Rev. Arms.

56. 5 Taler 1851		40.00

B. Swedish Kings of —
FREDERICK I, 1730-1751

Bust. Rev. Swedish arms.

57. 1 Ducat 1731, 46, 49, 50		125.00

Head. Rev. Swedish arms.

58. 1 Ducat 1737, 46 .... 125.00

Crown over linked FR. Rev. Lion-shield.

59. 1 Ducat 1737 .... 125.00

Crown over linked FR. Rev. Swedish arms.

60. 1 Ducat 1737 .... 150.00

Head. Rev. Lion standing.

61. ½ Edder-gold Ducat 1731 ....* 100.00
62. ½ Ducat 1748 ....* 75.00
63. ¼ Ducat ND 40.00

Bust. Rev. Lion standing.

64. ½ Edder-gold Ducat 1731 .... 150.00

Crown over linked FR. Rev. Lion standing.

65. ¼ Ducat 1744, 50 .... 40.00

HESSE-DARMSTADT

Landgraves, and later, Grand Dukes of —

LOUIS V, 1596-1626
Arms. Rev. Three helmets.

1. 1 Goldgulden 1621 .... 200.00
2. 1 Ducat 1623 .... 200.00

GEORGE II, 1626-1661
Bust. Rev. Arms.

3. 1 Ducat 1651, 55, 56, 58 .... 100.00
4. 1 Goldgulden 1656 .... 100.00

Oak tree. Rev. Legend. On his death.

5. 1 Ducat 1661 .... 150.00
6. ½ Ducat 1661 .... 75.00

Legend. Rev. Laurel tree. On his death.

7. ½ Ducat 1661 .... 50.00

LOUIS VI, 1661-1678
Bust. Rev. Arms.

8. 1 Ducat 1675 .... 150.00

ERNST LOUIS, 1678-1739
Bust. Rev. Arms.

9. 2 Ducats 1703, 06-10. Arms supported by lions 125.00
10. 2 Ducats 1704. Arms with 5 helmets 125.00
11. 1 Ducat 1702-06, 17, 18. Arms suported by lions 60.00
12. ½ Ducat 1703. Arms supported by lions 35.00
13. ½ Ducat 1703. Arms between branches 35.00
14. ¼ Ducat 1705 .... 25.00

Bust. Rev. Female at altar. On the Reformation.

15. 1 Ducat 1717 .... 100.00

Bust. Rev. Crossed initials.

16. 4 Ducats 1717 .... 350.00
17. 2 Ducats ND 100.00
18. 1 "Alchemy" Ducat ND 125.00
19. 1 Carolin 1733, ND ....* 50.00
20. ½ Carolin 1733, ND 35.00
21. ¼ Carolin 1733, ND 25.00

Arms. Rev. Value.

22. ¼ Ducat 1703 ....* 25.00
23. ⅛ Ducat 1705 .... 20.00

Lion. Rev. Value.

24. ½ Ducat 1710 .... 60.00

LOUIS VIII, 1739-1768
Crossed initials. Rev. Lion.

25. 1 Ducat 1740, 41 .... 40.00

Monogram. Rev. Lion with arms.

26. 1 Ducat 1742, 43, 53, ND 35.00

Bust. Rev. Arms with palm-branches.

27. 1 Ducat 1746, 48, 49, 51, 53, 55, ND 35.00

Bust. Rev. Lion with arms.

28. 1 Ducat 1746 .... 40.00

Crossed initials. Rev. Lion-shield within 7 shields.

29. 2 Ducats 1760 .... 80.00
30. 1 Ducat 1760, 61 ....* 35.00

Monogram. Rev. Horse and city view.

31. 1 Ducat ND 125.00

Monogram. Rev. Lion with monogram-shield.

32. 1 Ducat ND 35.00

Horse and city view. Rev. Lion with monogram-shield.

33. 1 Ducat 1741 .... 125.00

Stag and hunter. Rev. Stag and 3 dogs.

34. 2 Ducats ND 250.00

GERMANY-HESSE-DARMSTADT (cont'd)

Crossed initials. Rev. Stag.

35. 1 Ducat ND 60.00

Crossed initials. Rev. Boar.

36. 1 Ducat ND 60.00

Monogram NB. Rev. Legend ALLES IN DER WELT etc.

37. 1 Ducat ND 40.00

LOUIS IX, 1768-1790
Bust. Rev. Arms, lions and value.

38. 1 Ducat 1758, 72 .... 65.00

LOUIS X (I), 1790-1830

Head. Rev. Arms.

39. 10 Gulden 1826, 27 .... 50.00

LOUIS II, 1830-1848

Head. Rev. Arms.

40. 10 Gulden 1840, 41, 42 .... 50.00
41. 5 Gulden 1835, 40, 41 ....* 30.00
42. 5 Rhine-gold Gulden 1835 ....* 300.00

HESSE-HOMBURG

Landgraves of —

FREDERICK II, DIED 1708
Bust. Rev. Mountain.

1. 1 Ducat 1690, ND (3 different bust-dies) 150.00

HESSE-MARBURG

Landgraves of —

LOUIS III, 1567-1604
Bust. Rev. Arms.

1. 1 Goldgulden 1591 .... 250.00

HILDESHEIM

A. City of —

Bust of Charles V with hat. Rev. Arms.

1. 5 Ducats 1528 .... 200.00

Bust of Charles V. Rev. Arms.

2. 4½ Goldgulden 1605, ND 200.00

Orb. Rev. Arms.

3. 1 Goldgulden 1573 .... 85.00

Arms. Rev. Eagle. Name of Rudolph II.

4. 1 Goldgulden 1602, 03, 06 .... 75.00

Rudolph II on horse. Rev. Eagle.

5. 10 Goldgulden ND. (1576-1610) .... Rare

Madonna. Rev. Arms.

6. 1 Goldgulden 1624 .... 80.00

Arms. Rev. Eagle. Name of Ferdinand II.

7. 4 Goldgulden 1626 .... 200.00
8. 1 Goldgulden 1623, 27, 28 .... 75.00
9. ½ Goldgulden 1623, 27 .... 60.00

Arms. Rev. Eagle. Name of Leopold I.

10. 1 Goldgulden 1672 .... 100.00

B. Bishops of —

JODOCUS EDMUND OF BRABECK, 1688-1702
Bust. Rev. Arms.

11. 1 Ducat 1694 .... 100.00

SEDE VACANTE, 1761-1763
Arms. Rev. Value in cartouche.

12. ½ Pistole 1763 .... 60.00

FREDERICK WILLIAM OF WESTPHALIA, 1763-1789

Bust right or left. Rev. Arms and value.

13. 10 Taler or 2 Pistoles 1766 .... 200.00
14. 5 Taler or 1 Pistole 1764, 65 ....* 75.00
15. 1 Ducat 1778 .... 60.00

Arms. Rev. Value in cartouche.

16. ½ Pistole 1763 .... 40.00

Arms. Rev. Value.

17. 1 Ducat 1784 .... 50.00

HOHENLOHE

Counts, and later, Princes of —

ANONYMOUS
Bust of Rudolph II. Rev. Arms.

1. 1 Ducat 1608 .... 125.00

GERMANY-HOHENLOHE (cont'd)

Arms. Rev. Eagle.

2. 1 Goldgulden 1615 .... 85.00

JOHN FREDERICK I OF OHRINGEN, 1676-1702

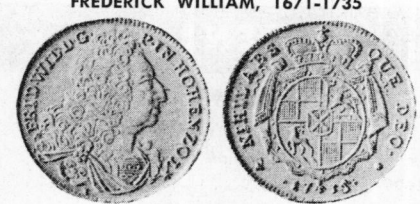

Knight on horse. Rev. Arms.

3. 2 Ducats 1699 .... 125.00
4. 1 Ducat 1699 ....*...... 75.00

WOLFGANG JULIUS OF NEUENSTEIN, 1676-1698

Bust. Rev. Knight on horse.

5. 1 Ducat 1697 .... 75.00

CHARLES LOUIS OF WEICKERSHEIM, 1708-1756
Bust. Rev. Arms.

6. 1 Ducat 1737 .... 75.00

JOHN FREDERICK II OF OHRINGEN, 1708-1765
Bust. Rev. Three shields.

7. 1 Ducat 1760 .... 60.00

CHARLES PHILIP OF NEUENSTEIN, 1733-1763
Bust. Rev. Arms.

8. 1 Goldgulden 1735 .... 50.00

PHILIP ERNST OF SCHILLINGSFUERST, 1697-1750
Bust. Rev. Arms.

9. 1 Ducat 1750 .... 60.00

JOSEPH ANTHONY OF WALDENBURG
Bust. Rev. Phoenix.

10. 1 Ducat 1747 .... 75.00

LOUIS GOTTFREID OF PFEDELBACH, 1685-1728
Arms. Rev. Legend. On the Reformation.

11. 1 Ducat 1717 .... 75.00

LOUIS OF LANGENBERG, PHILIP AND CHARLES AUGUST OF KIRCHBERG
Legend. Rev. Three female figures.

12. 1 Ducat 1751 .... 65.00

LOUIS FREDERICK CHARLES OF OHRINGEN, 1765-1805
Bust. Rev. Arms.

13. 1 Ducat 1770 .... 50.00

FREDERICK LOUIS OF INGELFINGEN, 1796-1806
Bust. Rev. Value.

14. 1 Ducat 1796 .... 65.00

HOHENZOLLERN-HECHINGEN

Princes of —

FREDERICK WILLIAM, 1671-1735

Bust. Rev. Arms.

---

1. 1 Carolin 1734, 35 ....*...... 125.00
2. ½ Carolin 1734, 35 .... 75.00

INGOLSTADT

St. John. Rev. Orb. With name of Frederick III.

1. 1 Goldgulden ND (1470-90) 60.00

ISENBURG

Princes of —

CHARLES, 1803-1815

Head. Rev. Value.

1. 2 Ducats 1811 .... 250.00
2. 1 Ducat 1811 ....*...... 150.00

JULICH-CLEVE-BERG

A. Dukes of Julich

REYNALD IV, 1402-1423
Duke on throne. Rev. Cross.

1. 2 Goldgulden ND 200.00

St. John. Rev. Four shields.

2. 1 Goldgulden ND 40.00

St. Peter. Rev. Lion.

3. 1 Goldgulden ND 100.00

B. Dukes of Cleve

JOHN, 1347-1368
St. John. Rev. Lily.

4. 1 Florin ND 100.00

ADOLPH VII, 1394-1448
Helmeted arms on each side.

5. 1 Goldgulden ND 150.00

JOHN I, 1448-1481
Madonna. Rev. Helmet over two shields.

6. ½ Goldgulden ND 85.00

Standing ruler. Rev. Shield on cross.

7. 1 Goldgulden ND 125.00

JOHN II, 1481-1521
Standing ruler. Rev. Shield on cross.

8. 1 Goldgulden ND 100.00

Half length bust. Rev. Cross and four shields.

9. 1 Goldgulden ND 100.00

Bust of St. John. Rev. Five shields.

10. 1 Goldgulden 1511, 17 .... 150.00

St. John. Rev. Cross.

11. 1 Philips-gulden 1501 .... 200.00

St. John. Rev. Helmeted arms.

12. 1 Goldgulden ND 85.00

St. John. Rev. Arms on cross.

13. 1 Goldgulden ND 85.00

St. Martin standing. Rev. Arms.

14. 1 Goldgulden 1503 .... 200.00

C. Dukes of Berg

WILLIAM I, 1296-1308
Ship. Rev. St. Michael.

15. 1 Angel or Angelot ND 200.00

ADOLPH VIII, 1308-1348
St. Stephen. Rev. Arms.

16. 1 Goldgulden ND 125.00

WILLIAM II, 1360-1408
Half length bust. Rev. Shield.

16a. 1 Goldgulden ND 125.00

ADOLPH IX, 1408-1423
St. John. Rev. Orb.

16b. 1 Goldgulden ND 100.00

D. Dukes of Julich - Berg

ADOLPH IX, 1423-1437
St. John. Rev. Orb. Name of Sigismund I.

17. 1 Goldgulden ND 85.00

GERHART VI, 1437-1475
St. John. Rev. Orb.

18. 1 Goldgulden ND 85.00

WILLIAM IV, 1475-1511
Arms on cross. Rev. Three shields.

19. 1 Goldgulden ND 85.00

Bust of St. Hubert. Rev. Arms on cross.

20. 1 Goldgulden 1501, ND 35.00

St. Hubert standing. Rev. Arms.

21. 1 Goldgulden 1503 .... 35.00

St. Hubert standing. Rev. Five shields. The last three dates are posthumous.

22. 1 Goldgulden 1511, 12, 13, 14 .... 40.00

E. Dukes of Julich, Cleve and Berg

JOHN III, 1511-1539
St. Hubert. Rev. Arms.

23. 1 Goldgulden 1511-16 .... 100.00

WILLIAM V, 1539-1592
Five shields. Rev. Double eagle.

24. 1 Goldgulden 1567, 72, 81, 87 .... 100.00

JOHN WILLIAM I, 1592-1609
Five shields. Rev. Double eagle

25. 1 Goldgulden 1604, 08, 09, ND 100.00

INTERREGNUM, 1609-1624
Five shields. Rev. Double eagle.

26. 1 Goldgulden 1613, ND 85.00

SIEGE OF JULICH, 1610
Eight punch marks. Rev. Blank. Octagonal necessity coin.

27. 40 Taler 1610 .... Rare

F. Palatine Dukes of Julich, Cleve and Berg

WOLFGANG WILLIAM, 1624-1653

Bust. Rev. Arms and value.

28. 1 Ducat 1636, 43, 50 .... 40.00

PHILIP WILLIAM, 1653-1679

Bust. Rev. Arms.

29. 1 Ducat 1654-77 .... 40.00

Bust. Rev. Sun over legend.

30. 1 Ducat 1676 .... 40.00

JOHN WILLIAM II, 1679-1716

Bust. Rev. Orb. on Shield.

31. 1 Ducat 1682-1710 .... * 50.00
32. ¼ Ducat 1710, 11 .... 25.00

Bust. Rev. Circle of nine shields.

33. 2 Ducats 1707 .... * 85.00
34. 1 Ducat 1707, 08 .... 60.00

Bust. Rev. Three shields.

35. 2 Ducats 1708, 09, 11 .... 100.00
36. 1 Ducat 1708, 09, 11 .... 50.00

Head. Rev. Two shields on double eagle. Vicariat issue.

37. 5 Ducats 1711 .... 350.00
38. 3 Ducats 1711 .... 200.00
39. 2 Ducats 1711 .... * 150.00
40. 1 Ducat 1711 .... 85.00

Bust. Rev. Bust of Marie Anne.

41. 2 Ducats ND 125.00

CHARLES PHILIP, 1716-1742
Bust. Rev. Initials.

42. 10 Ducats 1717 .... Rare
43. 5 Ducats 1717 .... 350.00
44. 1 Ducat 1720 .... 100.00
45. 1 Goldgulden 1718 .... 150.00

Head. Rev. Five shields.

46. 1 Carolin 1732 .... 150.00

GERMANY-JULICH-CLEVE-BERG (cont'd)

Head. Rev. Arms.

47. 1 Carolin 1733 ....* 150.00
48. ½ Carolin 1733 .... 75.00
49. ¼ Carolin 1735 .... 30.00

CHARLES THEODORE, 1742-1799

Bust. Rev. Arms.

50. 1 Ducat 1749, 50 .... 65.00

Bust. Rev. Three shields.

51. 2 Ducats 1750 .... 125.00

Bust. Rev. Cross of St. Hubert.

52. 1 Ducat 1750 .... 65.00

KAUFBEUREN

Bust of Charles V. Rev. Orb.

1. 1 Goldgulden ND (1517-58) 75.00

Charles V standing. Rev. Pillars of Hercules.

2. 1 Ducat 1542, 43 .... 200.00

Orb. Rev. Arms.

3. 1 Goldgulden 1541, 46 .... 200.00

Arms. Rev. Cross.

4. 1 Ducat ND (1600) 50.00

Seated female. Rev. Legend. On the Augsburg Confession.

5. 1 Ducat 1730 .... 50.00

KEMPTEN

A. Abbots of —

RUPERT OF BODMAN, 1678-1728

Four helmeted shields. Rev. St. Hildegarde in shield.

1. 2 Ducats 1693 ....* 175.00
2. 1 Ducat 1692, 95 .... 75.00

ENGELBERT OF SIRGENSTEIN, 1747-1760
Bust. Rev. Arms.

3. 2 Ducats 1748 .... 150.00
4. 1 Ducat 1748 .... 100.00

B. City of —

St. Magnus standing. Rev. Double eagle.

5. 1 Goldgulden 1511-48 .... 150.00

Angel. Rev. Legend. On the Reformation.

6. 1 Ducat 1717 .... 60.00

Obelisk. Rev. Sun over castle. On the Augsburg Confession.

7. 1 Ducat 1730 .... 50.00

KOENIGSEGG

Counts of —

FRANCIS HUGO

Armored bust. Rev. Arms.

1. 1 Ducat 1756 .... 75.00

LANDAU

Arms, legend and punch marks. Rev. Blank. Square with clipped corners. Struck while besieged by the French.

1. 4 Doppia 1713 .... 2,500.00
2. 1 Doppia 1713 .... 1,000.00

LEININGEN

Counts of —

EMICHO V, 1375-1442

Half length figure under canopy. Rev. Arms in cartouche.
1. 1 Goldgulden ND 750.00

LEININGEN-WESTERBURG

Counts of —

LOUIS, 1597-1622

Bust. Rev. Arms.

1. 1 Goldgulden 1614, 17, 18, 19 .... 85.00

LEIPZIG

Bust of Frederick the Bellicose. Rev. City view. On the 300th year of the Academy.

1. 1 Ducat 1709 .... 100.00

Bust of Martin Luther. Rev. Altar. On the Reformation.

2. 2 Ducats 1717 .... 75.00
3. 1 Ducat 1717 .... 40.00

LEUTKIRCH

City View. Rev. Church.

1. 1 Peace Ducat 1748 .... 50.00

LIMBURG-SONTHEIM

Barons of —

FREDERICK, 1530-1596
Armored bust. Rev. Ship.

1. 2 Ducats ND 250.00

LIPPE-DETMOLD

Counts of —

(The coinage of Lippe-Schaumburg will be found under Schaumburg-Lippe.)

SIMON VII, 1613-1627

Eagle. Rev. Arms. Name of Matthias.

1. 1 Goldgulden 1619 .... 200.00

SIMON HENRY, 1666-1697
Bust. Rev. Arms.

2. 3 Ducats 1685, 92 .... 250.00
3. 1½ Ducats 1685, 92 .... 150.00
4. 1 Ducat 1673, 85 .... 125.00

FREDERICK ADOLPH, 1697-1718
Bust. Rev. Arms.

5. 10 Ducats 1712, 15 .... Rare
6. 5 Ducats 1711, 15, 16 .... 400.00
7. 2 Ducats 1714 .... 200.00
8. 1 Ducat 1711-16, ND 100.00

Bust. Rev. Legend.

9. 1 Ducat 1710, ND 125.00

Bust. Rev. Value.

10. ¼ Ducat 1714, 15 .... 50.00

SIMON HENRY ADOLPH, 1718-1734
Bust. Rev. Arms.

11. 4 Ducats 1719 .... 300.00
12. 1 Ducat 1718, 19 .... 75.00

SIMON AUGUST, 1734-1782
Head. Rev. Arms.

13. 1 Ducat 1765. Birthday issue 100.00
14. 1 Ducat 1767 .... 100.00

Busts of the Count and Countess. Rev. Two hands. On their wedding.

15. 1 Ducat 1769 .... 100.00

FREDERICK WILLIAM LEOPOLD, 1782-1802
Two shields. Rev. Legend. On the birth of the Crown Prince.

16. 1½ Ducats 1796 .... 150.00

LOEWENSTEIN-ROCHEFORT

Princes of —

MAXIMILIAN CHARLES, 1672-1718
Flying eagle. Rev. Legend. On the birth of Leopold.

1. 1 Ducat 1716 .... 200.00

Bust. Rev. Arms.

2. 1 Ducat 1692 .... 250.00

CHARLES THOMAS, 1735-1789

Bust. Rev. Arms.

3. 1 Ducat 1754 .... 60.00

LOEWENSTEIN-WERTHEIM

Princes of —

CHARLES LOUIS, 1737-1779

Bust. Rev. Arms.

1. 1 Ducat 1767 .... 40.00

JOHN LOUIS WOLRAD, 1730-1790
Bust. Rev. Lion.

2. 1 Ducat ND 125.00
3. ¼ Ducat ND 35.00

Bust. Rev. Arms.

4. 1 Ducat 1768, 69, 71 .... 75.00

Bust. Rev. Figure kneeling at altar. On the 50th year of reign.

5. 1 Ducat 1780 .... 200.00

DOMINICK CONSTANTINE, 1789-1806
Bust. Rev. Allegory. On his birthday.

6. 1 Ducat 1791 .... 60.00

FREDERICK CHARLES, 1799-1806

Bust. Rev. Arms.

7. 2 Ducats 1799. Thick flan 250.00
8. 1 Ducat 1799 ....*...... 65.00

LUBECK

A. City of —

Double eagle. Rev. Blank.

1. ½ Ducat or Bracteate ND (1300) 250.00

"English" king in ship. Rev. Sun and eagle.
2. 1 Rosenoble ND (1327-77) 250.00

St. John. Rev. Lily.
3. 1 Ducat ND (1400-1500) 50.00

St. John. Rev. Emperor seated.
4. 1½ Ducats ND (1400-1500) 500.00

St. John. Rev. Madonna.
5. 1 Ducat 1497 .... 250.00

St. John on each side.
6. 1 Ducat ND (1500) 50.00

Orb. Rev. Double eagle.
7. 1 Goldgulden 1583-1675 .... 75.00
8. ¼ Ducat ND (1650) 25.00

Double eagle. Rev. Arms.
9. 1 Goldgulden 1589-1637 .... 75.00

Birth of Christ. Rev. The Resurrection.
10. 10 Ducats ND (1619-27) 500.00
11. 5 Ducats ND (1619-27) 250.00

St. John. Rev. Cross.
12. ½ Portugaloser or 5 Ducats 1636 .... 500.00

Royal figure seated. Rev. Double eagle.
13. ½ Portugaloser or 5 Ducats 1628 .... 500.00

Royal figure standing. Rev. Double eagle.
14. 4 Ducats 1638 .... 275.00
15. 2 Ducats 1656-1716 .... * 85.00
16. 1 Ducat 1631-1759 .... 50.00
17. ½ Ducat 1679-1714 .... 35.00
18. ¼ Ducat 1679-1728 .... 25.00

Rock on sea. Rev. All-seeing eye.
19. 1 Ducat 1707 .... 50.00

Double eagle. Rev. Legend. On the Reformation.
20. 2 Ducats 1717 .... 75.00
21. 1 Ducat 1717 .... * 40.00

Bust of Charles VI. Rev. Double eagle.
22. 1 Ducat 1729, 30 .... 60.00

Religion standing. Rev. Double eagle. On the Augsburg Confession.
23. 1 Ducat 1730 .... 50.00

Tablet. Rev. Double eagle. With names of the Holy Roman Emperors.
24. 1 Ducat 1790-1801 .... 40.00

B. Bishops of —

EBERHARD, 1567-1586
Bust. Rev. Arms.
25. 10 Ducats ND .... Rare

JOHN ADOLPH, 1585-1596
Arms. Rev. Cross.
26. 1 Portugaloser or 10 Ducats ND .... Rare
27. ½ Portugaloser or 5 Ducats ND 300.00

JOHN FREDERICK, 1607-1634
St. Peter. Rev. Arms.
28. 1 Goldgulden 1612 .... 125.00

Bust. Rev. Arms.
29. 1 Portugaloser or 10 Ducats ND .... Rare

CHRISTIAN ALBERT, 1655-1666
Armored bust. Rev. Arms. Posthumously struck.
30. 1 Ducat 1689 .... 125.00

AUGUST FREDERICK, 1666-1705
Armored bust. Rev. Arms.
31. 1 Ducat 1688, 89 .... 85.00

CHRISTIAN AUGUST, 1705-1726
Armored bust. Rev. Lion.
32. 1 Ducat 1724, 26 .... 75.00

FREDERICK AUGUST, 1750-1785
Bust. Rev. Arms. For illustration, see Oldenburg No. 3.
33. 1 Pistole 1776 .... 100.00

LUNEBURG

St. John. Rev. Orb.
1. 2 Goldgulden 1592 .... 200.00
2. 1 Goldgulden ND (1470-1500) .... * 65.00
3. 1 Goldgulden 1581-99 .... 100.00

St. John. Rev. Double eagle.

4.	2 Goldgulden 1600	175.00
5.	1 Goldgulden 1600-35	75.00

St. John. Rev. Arms on cross.

6.	3 Goldgulden ND (1600-50)	250.00
7.	2½ Goldgulden ND (1600-50)	200.00

Bust of St. John. Rev. Orb.

8.	1 Goldgulden 1626, 29	85.00

St. John. Rev. Face in crescent.

9.	2 Goldgulden ND (1650)	200.00
10.	1 Goldgulden ND (1650) ....*......	75.00
11.	1 Ducat 1645, 47	85.00

St. John. Rev. Crescent, hunters and fishermen.

12.	6 Ducats ND (1650)	400.00

Castle gate. Rev. Double cross.

13.	½ Portugaloser 1567, ND	400.00

Castle gate. Rev. Double eagle.

14.	2 Goldgulden ND (1576-1610)	200.00

Lion. Rev. Double eagle.

15.	1 Goldgulden ND (1576-1610)	100.00

MAGDEBURG

A. General City coinage

Arms. Rev. Cross.

1.	10 Ducats ND (1573-1606)	1,500.00
2.	5 Ducats ND (1573-1606)	400.00

Emperor Otto I on horse. Rev. Eagle.

4.	4 Ducats 1599	500.00

Arms. Rev. Value in square.

4.	1 Ducat 1673	125.00

City view. Rev. Arms.

5.	2 Ducats 1675	250.00

B. Coinage with the names of the Holy Roman Emperors

Female over city gate. Rev. Eagle. Maximilian II.

6.	1 Goldgulden 1571, 74, 76	150.00

Female over city gate. Rev. Eagle. Rudolph II.

7.	2 Goldgulden 1594	300.00
8.	1 Goldgulden 1571, 85, 1600, 05, 06	125.00

Female over city gate. Rev. Eagle. Matthias.

9.	1 Goldgulden 1617	150.00

Arms with helmet. Rev. Eagle. Matthias.

10.	1 Goldgulden ND	200.00

Arms with helmet. Rev. Eagle. Ferdinand II.

11.	1 Goldgulden 1624	150.00

Female over city gate. Rev. Eagle. Ferdinand II.

12.	1 Goldgulden 1622, 24, 26-30	85.00

Female over city gate. Rev. Eagle. Ferdinand III.

13.	2 Ducats 1639	175.00

Eagle. Rev. Value on tablet. Ferdinand III.

14.	1 Ducat 1638, 41, 42	100.00

C. Archbishops of —

JOAQUIM FREDERICK, 1566-1598

Bust. Rev. Arms.

15.	2 Ducats 1590	350.00

Eagle. Rev. Arms.

16.	1 Goldgulden 1586	300.00

CHRISTIAN WILLIAM, 1598-1631

Bust. Rev. Arms.

17.	1 Goldgulden 1615, 23, ND	200.00
18.	½ Goldgulden ND	150.00

Bust. Rev. Three shields in circle of fourteen shields.

19.	2 Goldgulden ND	250.00

CATHEDRAL CHAPTER, 1638

St. Mauritius. Rev. Arms.

20.	1 Ducat 1638	125.00

AUGUST, 1638-1680

Legend. Rev. St. Mauritius. On his enthronement.

21.	1 Ducat 1638	70.00

Facing bust. Rev. Arms of Magdeburg.

22.	1 Ducat 1640, 41	70.00

Bust. Rev. Arms of Saxony.

23.	1 Ducat 1671	100.00

Initials. Rev. Legend. On the death of Anna Marie.

24.	1 Ducat 1669	75.00

MANSFELD

Counts of —

A. The Vorderort Line BORNSTEDT

BRUNO II, WILLIAM I AND JOHN GEORGE IV, 1604-1607

Three shields. Rev. St. George.

1.	1 Goldgulden 1606	150.00

BRUNO II, WILLIAM I, JOHN GEORGE IV AND VOLRAT VI, 1605-1615

Three shields. Rev. St. George.

2.	1 Goldgulden 1611	150.00

BRUNO II, WILLIAM I, JOHN GEORGE IV, VOLRAT VI AND JOBST, 1609-1615

Three shields. Rev. St. George.

3.	1 Goldgulden 1615, ND	65.00

WOLFGANG III AND JOHN GEORGE II, 1631-1638

St. George. Rev. Value on tablet.

4. 1 Ducat 1631, 32, 35, 38 .... 65.00

CHARLES ADAM, 1638-1662
St. George. Rev. Value on tablet.

5. 1 Ducat 1656 .... 100.00

FRANCIS MAXIMILIAN, 1644-1692
St. George. Rev. Arms and value.

6. ¼ Ducat 1670, 71 .... 50.00

FRANCIS MAXIMILIAN AND HENRY FRANCIS, 1644-1692

St. George. Rev. Crowned arms.

7. 1 Ducat 1687 .... 60.00

HENRY, PRINCE OF FONDI, 1717-1780
Armored bust. Rev. Crowned arms.

8. 1 Ducat 1747 .... 150.00

Crowned arms on mantle. Rev. St. George.

9. 1 Ducat 1774 .... 80.00

FRANCIS GUNDACAR, 1780-1806
Crowned arms on mantle. Rev. St. George.

10. 1 Ducat 1792 .... 80.00

B. The Vorderort Line EISLEBEN

JOHN GEORGE I, PETER ERNST I AND CHRISTOPHER II, 1558-1579
St. George. Rev. Three shields.

11. 1 Goldgulden ND 65.00

JOHN GEORGE II, 1619-1647
St. George. Rev. Three shields.

12. 1 Goldgulden 1632, 35-37 .... 80.00

C. The Vorderort Line FRIEDEBURG

PETER ERNST I, BRUNO II, HOYER CHRISTOPHER, GEBHARD VIII AND JOHN GEORGE IV
Three shields. Rev. St. George.

13. 1 Goldgulden 1587 .... 125.00

PETER ERNST I, BRUNO II, GEBHARD VIII AND JOHN GEORGE IV, 1587-1601
Three shields. Rev. St. George.

14. 1 Goldgulden 1597 .... 125.00

PETER ERNST I, BRUNO II, WILLIAM I AND JOHN GEORGE IV, 1601-1604
Three shields. Rev. St. George.

15. 1 Goldgulden 1603 .... 125.00

D. The Vorderort Line ARTERN

VOLRAT VI, JOBST II AND WOLFGANG III, 1615-1617
Three shields. Rev. St. George.

16. 1 Goldgulden 1616, 17 .... 100.00

VOLRAT VI, JOBST II, WOLFGANG III AND BRUNO III, 1616-1619
Three shields. Rev. St. George.

17. 1 Goldgulden 1617, 18 .... 100.00

VOLRAT VI AND JOBST II
St. George. Rev. Three shields.

18. 1 Goldgulden 1619 .... 80.00

VOLRAT VI, WOLFGANG III AND JOHN GEORGE II, 1620-1627
St. George. Rev. Three shields.

19. 1 Goldgulden 1620, 21, 26 ....*...... 70.00
20. ½ Goldgulden 1620 .... 150.00

PHILIP ERNST, WOLFGANG III AND JOHN GEORGE II

St. George. Rev. Three shields.

21. 1 Goldgulden 1630 .... 100.00

E. The Hinterort Line

VOLRAT V, JOHN I AND CHARLES I, 1560-1566
Arms. Rev. Helmet.

22. 1 Goldgulden 1563 .... 300.00

DAVID, 1603-1628
St. George. Rev. Crowned arms.

23. 1 Ducat 1619 .... 200.00

St. George. Rev. Legend above arms.

24. 1 Goldgulden 1606, 18 .... 200.00

Arms with helmet. Rev. St. George.

25. 1 Goldgulden 1622 .... 250.00

ERNST VI AND FREDERICK CHRISTOPHER, 1579 AND 1603-1611
Arms with helmet. Rev. St. George. Title of Rudolph II.

26. 1 Goldgulden 1607 .... 200.00

FREDERICK CHRISTOPHER AND DAVID, 1620-1628
St. George. Rev. Arms with helmet.

27. 1 Ducat 1622 .... 250.00

CHRISTIAN FREDERICK, 1632-1666
St. George. Rev. Value on tablet.

28. 1 Ducat 1644, 47, 52 .... 125.00

MAYENCE (MAINZ)

A. Archbishops of —

GERLACH OF NASSAU, 1346-1371
St. John. Rev. Lily.

1. 1 Goldgulden ND 30.00
2. 1 Goldgulden ND. Mint: Eltville 100.00

Archbishop standing. Rev. Arms in enclosure.

3. 1 Goldgulden ND. Mint: Bingen 30.00

Archbishop standing. Rev. Rupert of Palatinate standing.

4. 1 Goldgulden ND. Mint: Bingen 150.00

SEDE VACANTE, 1371
St. Martin standing. Rev. Wheel shield in enclosure.

5. 1 Goldgulden ND. Mint: Bingen 80.00

JOHN I OF LUXEMBURG, 1371-1373
Archbishop standing. Rev. Arms in enclosure.

6. 1 Goldgulden ND. Mint: Bingen 30.00

Archbishop on throne. Rev. Wheel shield in enclosure.

7. 1 Goldgulden ND. Mint: Hoechst 30.00

ELECTION DISPUTE AFTER THE DEATH OF JOHN I, 1373
St. Martin on throne. Rev. Wheel shield in enclosure.

8. 1 Goldgulden ND (Anonymous). Mint: Bingen 30.00

ADOLPH I OF NASSAU, 1373-1390

St. Martin on throne. Rev. Wheel shield in enclosure.

9. 1 Goldgulden ND. Mints: Bingen, Hoechst 30.00

St. John standing. Rev. 4 Arms in enclosure.

10. 1 Goldguldedn ND. Mints: Bingen, Hoechst 30.00
11. 1 Goldgulden ND. Mint: Udenheim 60.00

Archbishop standing. Rev. Arms in enclosure.

12. 1 Goldgulden ND. Mint: Oberlahnstein 150.00

CONRAD II OF WEINSBERG, 1390-1396
Archbishop on throne. Rev. Wheel shield in enclosure.

13. 1 Goldgulden ND. Mint: Bingen 30.00

St. John standing. Rev. Wheel shield in enclosure.

14. 1 Goldgulden ND. Mint: Bingen 30.00

St. John standing. Rev. Arms of Mainz-Nassau in enclosure.

15. 1 Goldgulden ND. Mint: Bingen 50.00

St. John standing. Rev. 4 Arms in enclosure.

16. 1 Goldgulden ND. Mints: Bingen, Hoechst 30.00

ELECTION DISPUTE, 1396-1397
St. Martin on throne. Rev. Wheel shield in enclosure.

17. 1 Goldgulden ND. Mints: Bingen, Hoechst 40.00

JOHN II OF NASSAU, 1397-1419
Archbishop on throne. Rev. Wheel shield in enclosure.

18. 1 Goldgulden ND. Mint: Bingen 30.00

St. John standing. Rev. Arms of Mainz-Nassau and small arms of Cologne and Trier.

19. 1 Goldgulden ND. Mints: Bingen, Hoechst 30.00

St. John standing. Rev. 5 Arms in enclosure.

20. 1 Goldgulden ND. Mints: Bingen, Hoechst 30.00

St. Peter standing. Rev. 5 Arms in enclosure.

21. 1 Goldgulden ND. Mints: Bingen, Hoechst 30.00

Bust of St. Peter under canopy. Rev. 5 Arms in enclosure.

22. 1 Goldgulden ND 30.00

St. Martin on throne. Rev. Wheel shield in enclosure.

23. 1 Goldgulden ND. Mint: Hoechst 30.00

CONRAD III OF DHAUN, 1419-1434
Archbishop standing. Rev. Wheel shield in enclosure.

24. 1 Goldgulden ND. Mints: Bingen, Hoechst 30.00

St. Peter standing. Rev. 5 Arms in enclosure.

25. 1 Goldgulden ND. Mints: Bingen, Hoechst 30.00

St. Peter standing. Rev. 4 Arms in enclosure.

26. 1 Goldgulden ND. Mint: Bingen 30.00

THEODORE I OF ERBACH, 1434-1459
Archbishop standing. Rev. Wheel shield in enclosure.

27. 1 Goldgulden ND. Mints: Bingen, Hoechst 30.00

Arms on cross. Rev. 3 shields.

28. 1 Goldgulden 1436-38, ND. Mints: Bingen, Hoechst 30.00

THEODORE II OF ISENBURG, 1459-1461 and 1475-1482
Christ on throne. Rev. Floriated cross with 4 shields.

29. 1 Goldgulden ND. (1459-61). Mint: Mayence 40.00

Arms on cross. Rev. 3 shields.

30. 1 Goldgulden ND. (1475-82). Mints: Mayence, Hoechst, Rhenish 50.00

ADOLPH II OF NASSAU, 1461-1475
Christ on throne. Rev. Floriated cross with 4 shields.

31. 1 Goldgulden ND. Mint: Mayence 30.00

BERTHOLD OF HENNEBERG, 1484-1504
Arms on cross. Rev. Christ on throne.

32. 1 Goldgulden 1490. Mint: Rhenish 60.00

4 Arms in enclosure. Rev. Christ on throne.

33. 1 Goldgulden 1491-1504 .... 60.00

JAMES OF LIEBENSTEIN, 1504-1508
4 Arms in enclosure. Rev. Christ on throne.

34. 1 Goldgulden 1504-08 .... 40.00

URIEL OF GEMMINGEN, 1508-1514
4 Arms in enclosure. Rev. Christ on throne over wheel shield.

35. 1 Goldgulden 1506, 09, 12, 14, ND 40.00

Christ on throne over family shield. Rev. 4 Arms in enclosure.

36. 1 Goldgulden ND 80.00

ALBERT OF BRANDENBURG, 1514-1545
Christ on throne. Rev. 4 Arms in enclosure.

37. 1 Goldgulden 1515, 34-43, ND 30.00

DANIEL BRENDEL OF HOMBURG, 1555-1582
Arms. Rev. Floriated cross and 4 shields.

38. 1 Goldgulden 1571, 72 .... 150.00

WOLFGANG OF DALBERG, 1582-1601
Arms. Rev. 4 Arms in enclosure.

39. 1 Goldgulden 1586, 87, 88, 93, 95 .... 60.00

Arms with infulae. Rev. 4 Arms in enclosure.

40. 1 Goldgulden 1596 .... 150.00

GEORGE FREDERICK OF GREIFFENKLAU, 1626-1629

Arms. Rev. Floriated cross, 3 shields and orb.

41. 1 Goldgulden 1626, 27 .... 70.00

Arms. Rev. St. Martin on horse.

42. 1 Goldgulden 1628 .... 100.00

Arms. Rev. Value in tablet.

43. 1 Ducat 1628, 29 .... 30.00
44. 1 Ducat 1628. Square 150.00

ANSELM CASIMIR WAMBOLDT OF UMSTADT, 1629-1647
Facing bust. Rev. Arms.

45. 2 Ducats 1629 (from the ducat die) 150.00
46. 1 Ducat 1629 .... 100.00

Facing bust. Rev. Crowned arms.

47. 2 Ducats 1642 .... 75.00

Bust right. Rev. Crowned arms.

48. 2 Ducats 1642, 44, 46, 47 .... 75.00
49. 1 Ducat 1633, 38, 44, ND 35.00

Bust right. Rev. Arms.

50. 2 Ducats 1636 (from the ducat die) 100.00
51. 1 Ducat 1636, 38 .... 35.00

Bust right. Rev. Arms with 3 helmets.

52. 2 Ducats 1642 .... 75.00

Arms with 3 helmets. Rev. Legend in wreath.

53. 2 Ducats 1638, 39, ND 75.00

Arms. Rev. Legend on tablet.

54. 1 Ducat 1636, 41 .... 35.00

Crowned arms. Rev. Legend between branches.

55. 1 Ducat 1642, 46 .... 35.00

Crowned arms in wreath. Rev. Legend between branches.

56. 1 Ducat 1645, 46 .... 35.00

JOHN PHILIP OF SCHOENBORN, 1647-1673
Facing bust. Rev. Arms.

57. 1 Ducat 1648-66 .... 35.00

Bust right or left. Rev. Arms.

58. 1 Ducat 1667, 68, 70, 71 .... 35.00

LOTHAR FREDERICK OF METTERNICH, 1673-1675
Bust. Rev. Arms.

59. 1 Ducat 1673 .... 150.00

DAMIAN HARTARD v. d. LEYEN, 1675-1678
Bust. Rev. Arms.

60. 1 Ducat 1676 .... 75.00

ANSELM FRANCIS OF INGELHEIM, 1679-1695

Bust. Rev. Arms.

61. 2 Ducats 1680 ....*...... 100.00
62. 1 Ducat 1684 .... 40.00

LOTHAR FRANCIS OF SCHOENBORN, 1695-1729
Concordia seated. Rev. Arms under canopy. On the Peace of Ryswick.

63. 2 Ducats ND (1696) 75.00
64. 1 Ducat ND (1696) 35.00

Arms. Rev. Altar and value.

65. 2 Ducats 1696 .... 75.00
66. 1 Peace Ducat 1696 ....*...... 35.00

Minerva standing. Rev. Arms. On the Peace of Ryswick.

67. 2 Ducats 1696 ....*...... 75.00
68. 1 Ducat 1696 .... 35.00

Bust. Rev. Arms.

69. 1 Ducat 1716, 28 .... 125.00
70. ¾ Ducat 1712 .... 50.00

FRANZ LUDWIG OF PFALZ-NEUBURG, 1729-1732
Bust. Rev. Lion being led by hand from heaven.

70a. 1 Ducat 1730 .... 40.00

PHILIP CHARLES OF ELTZ, 1731-1743
Bust. Rev. Arms.

71. 2 Ducats 1738 .... 125.00
72. 1 Ducat 1738 .... 50.00

JOHN FREDERICK CHARLES OF OSTEIN, 1743-1763
Bust. Rev. Arms.

73. 2 Ducats 1745, 48 .... 100.00
74. 1 Ducat 1745, 47, 53 .... 40.00

Bust. Rev. Arms supported by dogs.

75. 2 Ducats 1760 ....*...... 100.00
76. 1 Ducat 1759, 60 .... 50.00

EMERIC JOSEPH OF BREIDBACH, 1763-1774
Bust. Rev. Arms.

77. 1 Ducat 1768, 69, 71 .... 40.00

Bust. Rev. Legend.

78. 1 Rhine-gold Ducat 1772 .... 85.00

FREDERICK CHARLES JOSEPH OF ERTHAL, 1774-1802

Bust. Rev. Arms.

79. 1 Ducat 1795 .... 40.00

Bust. Rev. City view.

80. 1 Ducat 1795 .... 45.00

CHARLES OF DALBERG, 1802-1813
(See under Rhine Confederation.)

B. Cathedral Chapters of —

St. Martin on horse and S-M-E. Rev. Shield with wheel in enclosure.
81. 1 Goldgulden ND (1300-1400) 350.00

St. Martin on horse and S-M-E. Rev. Arms.
82. 1 Goldgulden ND 200.00
83. ½ Goldgulden ND 200.00

St. Martin on horse. Rev. Shield with wheel in enclosure.
84. 2 Goldgulden ND (shield with ornaments) 300.00
85. 2 Goldgulden ND (smaller shield) 300.00
86. 1 Goldgulden ND 200.00

St. Martin on horse. Rev. Angel with arms.
87. 1 Goldgulden. 1584, ND 200.00

C. Swedish Rulers of —

Facing bust of Christina. Rev. Arms.
88. 2 Ducats ND (1634) 500.00

(Note: For the coinage of St. Alban in Mayence, see under Saint Alban.)

MECKLENBURG

Dukes of —

JOHN ALBERT, 1547-1576
Bust with hat. Rev. Cross with five arms.
1. 1 Ducat 1554 .... 200.00

MECKLENBURG-GUSTROW

Dukes of —

JOHN ALBERT II, 1611-1636
Duke standing. Rev. Arms.
1. 3 Ducats 1633 .... 250.00
2. 2 Ducats 1633 .... 200.00
3. 1 Ducat 1633 .... 100.00

GUSTAV ADOLPH, 1636-1695

Bust. Rev. Arms.
4. 1 Ducat 1666, 68. Mint: Wismar ....*...... 100.00
5. 1 Ducat 1671, 72, 74, 75, 80, 85-89. Mint: Gustrow 100.00

MECKLENBURG-SCHWERIN

Dukes, and later Grand Dukes of —

ADOLPH FREDERICK, 1592-1658
Bust. Rev. Arms.
1. 1 Goldgulden 1615 .... 150.00

Half length bust. Rev. Arms.
2. 1 Goldgulden 1616 .... 150.00

Bust. Rev. Arms.
3. 1 Goldgulden 1625 .... 125.00

Facing bust. Rev. Arms.
4. 1 Ducat 1639 .... 80.00

CHRISTIAN LOUIS I, 1658-1692
Bust. Rev. Arms.
5. 2 Ducats 1681 .... 250.00
6. 1 Ducat 1670, 71, 81, 88 .... 150.00

FREDERICK WILLIAM, 1692-1713
Initials. Rev. Arms.
7. 1 Ducat 1696. NON EST MORTALE QVOD OPTO 125.00
8. 1 Ducat 1703. PROVIDE ET CONSTANTER 100.00

Bust. Rev. Arms.
9. 2 Ducats 1703. PROVIDE ET CONSTANTER 175.00
10. 1 Ducat 1696. NON EST MORTALE QVOD OPTO 125.00
11. 1 Ducat 1701. QVO DEVS ET FORTVNA DVCVNT 75.00
12. 1 Ducat 1703, 05. PROVIDE ET CONSTANTER ....*...... 75.00

Bust. Rev. Initials.
13. 1 Ducat 1696 .... 125.00

Arms. Rev. Ox head.
14. 1 Ducat 1701 ....*...... 75.00
15. ¼ Ducat 1701 .... 25.00

Bust. Rev. The Duke and Duchess in boat.
16. 2 Ducats 1704 .... 175.00
17. 1 Ducat 1703, 04 ....*...... 75.00

Bust. Rev. Value.
18. ¼ Ducat ND 20.00

CHRISTIAN LOUIS II, 1747-1756
Bust. Rev. Arms.
19. 2 Pistoles 1752 .... 100.00
20. 1 Pistole 1754 .... 60.00

Bust. Rev. Value.
21. ¼ Ducat 1756 .... 25.00

FREDERICK, 1756-1785

Bust. Rev. Value.
22. 2 Taler 1769, 78, 82, 83 .... 35.00

GERMANY-MECKLENBURG-SCHWERIN (cont'd)

FREDERICK FRANCIS, 1785-1837

Arms. Rev. Value.

23. 2 Taler 1792, 97 .... 35.00

Head. Rev. Arms.

24.	10	Taler 1828, 31, 32, 33	140.00
25.	5	Taler 1828, 31-33, 35 ....*......	75.00
26.	5	Taler 1828. Mint visit	200.00
27.	2½	Taler 1831, 33, 35	50.00
28.	2	Taler 1830	200.00
29.	1	Ducat 1830 ....*......	200.00

PAUL FREDERICK, 1837-1842

Head. Rev. Arms.

30.	10	Taler 1839 ....*......	150.00
31.	5	Taler 1840	80.00
32.	2½	Taler 1840 ....*.....	40.00

MECKLENBURG-STRELITZ

Dukes of —

ADOLPH FREDERICK III, 1708-1752

Bust. Rev. Faith before temple. On the Reformation.

1. 1 Ducat 1717. A DEO 125.00

Bust. Rev. Jerusalem on mountain. On the Reformation.

2. 1 Ducat 1717. NEC INGENS etc. 200.00

Bust. Rev. City on rock in ocean. On the Reformation.

3. 1 Ducat 1717. CONSILIO STAT etc. 200.00

Bust. Rev. Arms.

4. 5 Taler 1747, 49 .... 75.00

Initials. Rev. Ox head.

5. 5 Taler 1748 .... 70.00

Initials. Rev. Value.

6. 2 Taler 1746, 47 .... 40.00
7. 1 Taler 1746, 47, 49 .... 35.00

ADOLPH FREDERICK IV, 1752-1794

Head. Rev. Arms.

8. 1 Pistole 1754 .... 100.00

Bust. Rev. Arms.

9. 1 Pistole 1754 .... 100.00

MINDEN

Bishops of —

HERMAN OF SCHAUENBURG, 1566-1582
Arms. Rev. Double eagle.

1. 1 Goldgulden ND 500.00

ANTON OF SCHAUENBURG, 1585-1599
Arms. Rev. Double eagle.

2. 1 Goldgulden 1589, 95 .... 250.00

MOERS

Counts of —

FREDERICK II, 1375-1417
Three shields in enclosure. Rev. St. John.

1. 1 Goldgulden ND 400.00

FREDERICK III, 1417-1448
Five shields in enclosure. Rev. St. John.

2. 1 Goldgulden ND 250.00

Arms in enclosure. Rev. St. John.

3. 1 Goldgulden ND. Mint:Falkenberg 300.00

Arms in enclosure. Rev. St. Andrew over shield.

4. 1 Goldgulden ND. Mint: Moers 300.00

MUNSTER

Bishops of —

JOHN III OF PALATINATE-SIMMERN, 1457-1466
Bust of St. Paul. Rev. Arms on cross.

1. 1 Goldgulden ND 300.00

HENRY III OF SCHWARZBURG, 1466-1496

St. Paul seated. Rev. Three shields.

2. 1 Goldgulden ND 150.00

CONRAD II OF RIETBERG, 1497-1508
St. Paul standing. Rev. Eagle shield in enclosure.

3. 1 Goldgulden ND 200.00
4. ½ Goldgulden ND 125.00

St. Paul seated. Rev. Three shields.

5. 1 Goldgulden ND 175.00
6. ½ Goldgulden ND 100.00

ERICH I OF SAXE-LAUENBURG, 1508-1522
Knight on horse. Rev. Arms in enclosure.

7. 1 Goldgulden ND 300.00

FRANCIS OF WALDECK, 1532-1553
St. Peter and St. Paul. Rev. Four shields in enclosure.

8. 1 Goldgulden ND 175.00

St. Paul seated. Rev. Four shields in enclosure.

9. 1 Goldgulden ND 175.00

JOHN IV OF HOYA, 1566-1574
St. Paul standing. Rev. Four shields in enclosure.

10. 1 Goldgulden 1570 .... 175.00

FERDINAND OF BAVARIA, 1612-1650

Arms. Rev. Value.

11. 2 Ducats 1640. Square 125.00
12. 1 Ducat 1638-47 ....* 50.00

St. Paul standing. Rev. Arms.

13. 1 Ducat 1633, 34 .... 75.00

CHRISTOPHER BERNARD OF GALEN, 1650-1678
Madonna. Rev. Arms.

14. 2 Ducats ND 175.00
15. 1 Ducat ND 125.00

Arms. Rev. Value.

16. 1 Ducat 1652, 65 .... 75.00

Arms. Rev. Legend. On his death.

17. 1 Goldgulden 1678 .... 80.00

FREDERICK CHRISTIAN OF PLETTENBERG, 1688-1706
Bust. Rev. Arms.

18. 1 Ducat 1695 .... 100.00

FRANCIS ARNOLD OF METTERNICH, 1704-1718

Bust. Rev. Arms.

19. 2 Ducats 1717 ....* 200.00
20. 1 Ducat 1717 .... 100.00

NASSAU

Counts, and later, Dukes of —

RUPERT, 1355-1390
St. John. Rev. Lily.

1. 1 Goldgulden ND 175.00

WALRAM, 1370-1393
St. Paul standing. Rev. Arms in enclosure.

2. 1 Goldgulden ND 175.00

PHILIP, 1371-1429
St. John. Rev. Arms in enclosure.

3. 1 Goldgulden ND 300.00

HENRY OF DILLENBURG, 1662-1702
Bust. Rev. Arms.

4. 1 Ducat 1688 .... 175.00

CHARLES AUGUST, 1719-1753

Arms. Rev. Prince standing.

5. 1 Ducat 1750 .... 75.00

Bust. Rev. Arms.

6. 1 Ducat 1750 .... 125.00

FREDERICK AUGUST AND FREDERICK WILLIAM, 1803-1816

Arms. Rev. Value on tablet.

7. 1 Ducat 1809 .... 50.00

WILLIAM, 1816-1839

Head. Rev. Arms.

8. 1 Ducat 1818 .... 50.00

NOERDLIINGEN

St. John. Rev. Orb. With name of Holy Roman Emperor as indicated.

1. 1 Goldgulden ND. Sigismund 30.00
2. 1 Goldgulden 1491-93, ND. Frederick III 30.00
3. 1 Goldgulden 1494-1501, 06-08, 11, 13, 16. Maximilian I . 30.00

NORDHAUSEN

Theodosius seated. Rev. Arms.

1. 1 Goldgulden 1619 .... 250.00

NOSTIZ

Counts of —

ANTON JOHN, 1683-1736

Bust. Rev. Arms supported by griffins.

1. 1 Ducat 1719 .... 125.00

NUREMBERG

A. General City Coinage

St. Sebaldus. Rev. Arms in trefoil.

1. 1 Goldgulden ND (1429) 200.00

St. Lawrence. Rev. Eagle.

2. 3 Goldgulden 1612 .... 600.00
3. 2 Goldgulden ND (1552), 1614, 86 .... 500.00
4. 1 Goldgulden ND (1429-1506), 1506-1686 .... * 50.00

St. Lawrence. Rev. Arms.

5. 1 Goldgulden 1614-23 .... 50.00

Two shields. Rev. Legend. On the Shooting Match.

6. 1 Goldgulden 1579 .... 200.00

St. Sebaldus with church model. Rev. Eagle.

7. 1 Goldgulden 1623-86 .... 50.00

St. Sebaldus with church model. Rev. Arms.

8. 1 Goldgulden 1629-30 .... 60.00

Eagle. Rev. Two shields.

9. 1 Ducat 1635, 40 .... 50.00

Eagle. Rev. Genius standing with two shields.

10. 1 Peace Ducat 1635 .... 60.00
11. 1 Ducat 1637-86 .... * 50.00

Arms. Rev. Tablet with value.

12. 1 Ducat 1635-45 .... 40.00

Legend and arms. Rev. Two hands over globe. On the Peace.

13. 4 Ducats 1650. Square 350.00
14. 3 Ducats 1650 .... 250.00
15. 3 Ducats 1650. Square 300.00
16. 2 Ducats 1650 .... * 85.00
17. 1 Ducat 1650 .... 40.00

Eagle and hand. Rev. Legend.

18. 1 Ducat 1650 .... 60.00

Arms. Rev. Tablet.

19. 1 Goldgulden 1660 .... 250.00

Genius with two shields. Rev. City view.

20. 5 Ducats 1677 .... 300.00

Light and screen. Rev. Legend. On the Reformation.

21. 2 Ducats 1717. Square .... * 150.00
22. 1 Ducat 1717 .... 65.00
23. 1 Goldgulden 1717 .... 50.00

Three shields. Rev. City view.

24. ½ Ducat 1773 .... 50.00

B. Coinage with the heads of the Holy Roman Emperors

Bust of Maximilian II. Rev. Two shields.

25. 2 Goldgulden 1570 .... 400.00
26. 1 Goldgulden 1570 .... 300.00

GERMANY-NUREMBERG (cont'd)

Bust of Rudolph II. Rev. Two shields.

27. 1 Goldgulden 1580 .... 150.00

Busts of Matthias and Anna. Rev. Three shields.
28. 2 Goldgulden 1612 .... 400.00
29. 1 Goldgulden 1612 ....* ... 60.00

Ferdinand II on horse. Rev. Genius with two shields.
30. 10 Ducats 1630 .... 850.00

Bust of Leopold I. Rev. Three shields.

31. 1 Goldgulden 1658 .... 200.00

Bust of Leopold I. Rev. Genius with two shields.
32. 10 Ducats ND (1670) 750.00
33. 6 Ducats ND (1670) 500.00
34. 5 Ducats ND (1670) ....* ... 400.00
35. 4 Ducats ND (1670) 300.00

Bust of Charles VI. Rev. Three shields.
36. 1 Ducat 1711 .... 250.00

Bust of Charles VI. Rev. Altar.

37. 1 Ducat 1712 .... 60.00

Bust of Charles VII. Rev. Noris standing.

38. 1 Ducat 1742 .... 200.00

Bust of Francis I. Rev. Noris standing.

39. 1 Ducat 1745 .... 75.00

Bust of Joseph II. Rev. Arms.

40. 1 Ducat 1766 .... 60.00

Bust of Leopold II. Rev. City view.

41. 1 Ducat 1790 .... 75.00

Bust of Francis II. Rev. City view.

42. 1 Ducat ND (1792) 60.00

C. The Lamb Coinage of Nuremberg

Arms. Rev. Lamb on globe.

43. 2 Ducats 1632 ....* ... 80.00
44. 1 Ducat 1632 .... 50.00
45. ½ Ducat 1700. Square 20.00
46. ¼ Ducat ND. Round 15.00
47. ¼ Ducat ND. Square 10.00
48. ⅛ Ducat ND. Round 10.00
49. ⅛ Ducat ND. Square 10.00
50. 1/16 Ducat ND. Round 10.00
51. 1/16 Ducat ND. Square 10.00
52. 1/32 Ducat ND. 10.00

Arms. Rev. Lamb under cross from heaven.

53. 3 Ducats 1649. Square 175.00
54. 1 Ducat 1633. Round ....* ... 100.00

161

Three shields. Rev. Lamb.

55.	2 Ducats 1649	....	70.00
56.	1 Ducat 1649	.....................*......	40.00
57.	½ Ducat 1692	....	25.00

Three shields. Rev. Lamb on globe.

58.	5 Ducats 1703	....	200.00
59.	4 Ducats 1703	....	150.00
60.	3 Ducats 1703. Round	.............*......	125.00
61.	3 Ducats 1700. Square	....	150.00
62.	2 Ducats 1700. Round	....	75.00
63.	2 Ducats 1700. Square	.............*......	85.00
64.	1 Ducat 1700. Round	....	25.00
65.	1 Ducat 1700. Square	....	30.00
66.	½ Ducat 1700. Round	....	12.50

City view. Rev. Lamb.

67.	2 Ducats 1806. With laurel wreath	....	350.00
68.	1 Ducat 1806	....................*......	125.00

D. Nuremberg Coinage of the Swedish Kings

GUSTAV ADOLPHE, 1611-1632

Bust facing. Rev. Arms.

69.	2 Ducats 1631. Thick	....	600.00
70.	1 Ducat 1631	................*......	450.00

Bust right. Rev. Arms.

71.	6 Ducats 1632	....	1250.00
72.	2 Ducats 1632. Thick	.............*......	600.00
73.	1 Ducat 1632	....	75.00

Bust. Rev. Legend in wreath.

74.	1 Ducat 1632	....	125.00

King standing. Rev. Arms.

75.	1 Ducat 1632	....	450.00

Bust facing. Rev. Legend in square. On his death.

76.	2 Ducats 1632	....	500.00

OBERSTEINBACH

Two shields. Rev. Altar. On the Reformation.

1.	1 Ducat 1717	....	50.00

OETTINGEN

Counts, and later, Princes of —

WOLFGANG I AND JOAQUIM, 1477-1520
Arms. Rev. St. Wolfgang.

1.	1 Goldgulden 1519, 20	....	750.00

CHARLES WOLFGANG AND LOUIS XV, 1522-1549
Arms. Rev. Adoration of the three Magi.

2.	1 Goldgulden 1522, 29, 34, 40, 41	....	750.00

CHARLES WOLFGANG AND MARTIN, 1522-1549
Arms. Rev. Adoration of the three Magi.

3.	1 Goldgulden 1529, 40	....	250.00

MARTIN, 1520-1549

Half length bust of Charles V. Rev. Arms.

4.	1 Goldgulden 1541	....	600.00

CHARLES WOLFGANG, LOUIS XV AND MARTIN, 1522-1549
Arms. Rev. Double eagle. Name of Charles V.

5.	2 Goldgulden 1546	....	750.00
6.	1 Goldgulden 1546	....	600.00

OETTINGEN-OETTINGEN

Princes of —

ALBERT ERNST I, 1659-1683
Bust. Rev. Arms.

1.	2 Goldgulden 1677	750.00
2.	1 Ducat 1675	125.00

Bust. Rev. Legend and arms.

3.	1 Goldgulden 1677	300.00

Monogram. Rev. Arms.

4.	½ Ducat ND. Square	200.00
5.	¼ Ducat ND	100.00

ALBERT ERNST II, 1683-1731

Armored bust. Rev. Arms.

6.	1 Ducat ND	400.00

Bust. Rev. Legend. On his death.

7.	1 Ducat ND (1731)	250.00

OLDENBURG

Counts, and later, Dukes of —

ANTON GUNTHER, 1603-1667

Bust. Rev. Arms.

1.	3 Ducats 1660. Facing bust	200.00
2.	1 Ducat 1664. Profile bust	60.00

FREDERICK AUGUST, 1773-1785

Bust. Rev. Arms. This is the same coin as Lubeck No. 33.

3.	1 Pistole 1776	100.00

OSNABRUCK

A. Bishops of —

JOHN III OF DIEPHOLZ, 1424-1437
St. Peter standing. Rev. Arms.

1.	1 Goldgulden ND	750.00

CONRAD IV OF RIETBERG, 1482-1508
St. Peter on throne. Rev. Arms in enclosure.

2.	1 Goldgulden ND	100.00

St. Peter standing. Rev. Arms in enclosure.

3.	1 Goldgulden ND ....*	100.00
4.	½ Goldgulden ND	150.00

ERICH II OF BRUNSWICK-GRUBENHAGEN, 1508-1532
St. Peter on throne. Rev. Arms in enclosure.

5.	1 Goldgulden 1515, 23, 30	175.00

St. Peter on throne. Rev. Cross with four arms.

6.	1 Goldgulden ND. Mint: Wiedenbruck	200.00

FRANCIS WILLIAM OF WARTENBERG, 1625-1661
St. Peter standing. Rev. Arms.

7.	1 Ducat 1637	175.00

Three shields on each side.

8.	1 Ducat ND	175.00

ERNST AUGUST I OF BRUNSWICK, 1662-1698

Bust. Rev. Arms.

9.	1 Ducat 1666-98	175.00

B. Swedish Kings of —

Bust of Gustav Adolphe II. Rev. Crown over legend.

10.	1 Ducat 1633	100.00

PADERBORN

Bishops of —

THEODOR ADOLPH OF THE RECK, 1650-1660
Facing bust. Rev. Arms.

1.	1 Ducat 1651, 53	175.00

FERDINAND II OF FURSTENBERG, 1661-1683
Bust. Rev. Arms.

2.	1 Ducat 1674	100.00

HERMAN WERNER OF METTERNICH, 1683-1704
Bust. Rev. Arms.

3.	1 Ducat 1684, 93	100.00

FRANCIS ARNOLD OF METTERNICH, 1704-1718
Bust. Rev. Arms.

4.	1 Ducat 1713	100.00

CLEMENT AUGUST OF BAVARIA, 1719-1761

Bust. Rev. Madonna and arms.

5.	1 Goldgulden 1720	75.00

GERMANY-PADERBORN (cont'd)

WILLIAM ANTON OF ASSEBURG, 1763-1782

Bust. Rev. Arms.

6. 5 Taler or 1 Pistole 1767 ....*...... 100.00
7. 1 Ducat 1776, 77 .... 125.00

PALATINATE (PFALZ)

Electors of —

RUPERT I, 1353-1390

St. John. Rev. Lily.

1. 1 Goldgulden ND. Mints: Bacharach, Heidelberg 30.00

St. John. Rev. Arms in enclosure.

2. 1 Goldgulden ND. Mints: Bacharach, Heidelberg, Oppenheim 30.00

RUPERT II, 1390-1398

St. John. Rev. Lion and wheel shield in enclosure.

3. 1 Goldgulden ND. Mint: Neustadt 100.00

St. John. Rev. 4 arms in enclosure.

4. 1 Goldgulden ND. Mints: Bacharach, Oppenheim 70.00

RUPERT III, 1398-1410

St. John. Rev. 5 arms in enclosure.

5. 1 Goldgulden ND. Mints: Bacharach, Neustadt 125.00

St. John. Rev. Eagle over 2 shields.

6. 1 Goldgulden ND. Mint: Heidelberg 200.00

LOUIS III, 1410-1436

St. Peter. Rev. 4 arms in enclosure.

7. 1 Goldgulden ND. Mints: Bacharach, Heidelberg 30.00

St. Peter. Rev. 5 arms in enclosure.

8. 1 Goldgulden ND. Mints: Bacharach, Heidelberg, Oppenheim 30.00

Christ on throne. Rev. Cross with 4 arms.

9. 1 Goldgulden ND. Mint: Bacharach 50.00

Elector standing. Rev. Arms in enclosure.

10. 1 Goldgulden ND. Mints: Bacharach, Heidelberg, Neustadt (rare), Oppenheim, Ruesselsheim (rare) 30.00

LOUIS IV, 1436-1449

Arms on cross. Rev. Three shields.

11. 1 Goldgulden 1436-38, ND. Mint: Bacharach 40.00

FREDERICK I, 1449-1476

Christ on throne. Rev. Cross with 4 arms.

12. 1 Goldgulden ND. Mints: Bacharach, Heidelberg 40.00

Arms on cross. Rev. Three shields.

13. 1 Goldgulden ND. Mint: Bacharach 40.00

Elector standing. Rev. Arms in enclosure.

14. 1 Goldgulden ND. Mint: Bacharach 80.00

PHILIP, 1476-1508

Christ on throne. Rev. Arms on cross.

15. 1 Goldgulden 1490, ND 125.00

Christ on throne. Rev. 4 arms in enclosure.

16. 1 Goldgulden 1492, 93, 97 .... 100.00

Madonna on crescent. Rev. Three shields.

17. 1 Goldgulden 1500, 02, 05 .... 75.00

Shield on cross. Rev. Three shields.

18. 1 Goldgulden ND. Mint: Bacharach 80.00

Shield with 3 arms on cross. Rev. Three shields.

19. 1 Goldgulden ND 60.00

LOUIS V, 1508-1544

Madonna. Rev. Three shields.

20. 1 Goldgulden 1508 .... 200.00

Christ on throne. Rev. 4 shields in enclosure.

21. 1 Goldgulden 1509, 13, 15 .... 75.00

OTTO HENRY AND PHILIP, 1505-1556
Madonna on crescent. Rev. Arms in enclosure.

22. 1 Goldgulden 1515. Mint: Neuburg 200.00

Bust of Madonna. Rev. Arms.

23. 1 Ducat 1516 .... 200.00

FREDERICK II, 1508-1566

Half length bust. Rev. 4 arms in enclosure.

24. 1 Goldgulden ND. Mint: Heidelberg 350.00

FREDERICK III, 1557-1576

Half length bust. Rev. Arms and 3 shields.

25. 1 Goldgulden 1567. Mint: Heidelberg 250.00

Bust. Rev. Arms.

26. 1 Goldgulden 1575 .... 250.00

FREDERICK IV, 1592-1610

Half length bust. Rev. Three shields.

27. 1 Goldgulden 1608 .... 300.00

FREDERICK V, 1610-1632

Elector on horse. Rev. Three shields.

28. 4 Ducats 1612 ....*...... 600.00
29. 2 Ducats 1612 .... 500.00
30. 1 Ducat 1612 .... 250.00

Lion. Rev. Three shields.

31. 1 Goldgulden 1621. Mint: Heidelberg 150.00

Lion. Rev. Arms.

32. 1 Goldgulden 1621. Mint: Heidelberg 150.00

CHARLES LOUIS, 1648-1680
Bust. Rev. Three shields. On the Vicariat.

33. 1 Ducat 1657 .... 125.00

Bust. Rev. Three shields.

34. 1 Ducat 1659, 62, 73 ....*...... 65.00
35. ½ Rhine-gold Ducat 1674 .... 175.00
36. ½ Ducat 1673 .... 80.00
36a. ¼ Rhine-gold Ducat 1674 .... 175.00

CHARLES, 1680-1685
Bust. Rev. Three shields.

37. 1 Ducat 1682 .... 300.00

JOHN WILLIAM, 1690-1716
Bust. Rev. Ten shields.

38. 2 Ducats 1707 .... 100.00
39. 2 Ducats 1707. "Hoc Bellonae Stipendium" 100.00
40. 1 Ducat 1707 .... 80.00
41. 1 Ducat 1707. "Hoc Bellonae Stipendium" 70.00

Bust. Rev. Imperial globe in shield.

42. 1 Ducat 1708 .... 125.00
43. ¼ Ducat 1711 .... 30.00

Bust. Rev. Three shields.

44. 1 Ducat 1708 .... 125.00

Bust. Rev. Double eagle. On the vicariat.

45. 3 Ducats 1711 .... 250.00
46. 2 Ducats 1711 ....*...... 100.00
47. 1 Ducat 1711 .... 50.00
48. ¼ Ducat 1711 .... 30.00

Bust. Rev. Arms.

49. 1 Ducat 1683, 86, 1703 .... 80.00
50. ½ Ducat 1705, 08 .... 50.00

Bust. Rev. Value.

51. ¼ Ducat 1708 .... 30.00

Head. Rev. Imperial globe in shield.

52. ¼ Ducat 1710 .... 30.00

CHARLES PHILIP, 1716-1742

Young bust of Prince Philip August. Rev. The Prince standing. Struck by the city of Mannheim.

53. 1 Ducat 1725 .... 75.00

Head. Rev. Three shields.

54. 1 Ducat 1737 .... 125.00

Bust. Rev. Double Eagle. On the vicariat.

55. 1 Ducat 1740 .... 100.00

Bust. Rev. City view of Mannheim.

56. 1 Rhine-gold Ducat ND 250.00

Bust. Rev. Three shields.

57. 1 Ducat 1721 .... 50.00

Elector on horse. Rev. Five shields crossed.

58. 1 Ducat 1721, 26 .... 40.00

Head. Rev. Five shields crossed between four initials.

59.   1 Carolin 1732 .... 150.00
59a. ½ Carolin 1732 .... 150.00

Head. Rev. Arms.

60. 1 Carolin 1733, 35 ....*...... 60.00
61. ½ Carolin 1733, 36 .... 35.00
62. ¼ Carolin 1735, 36 .... 25.00

Head. Rev. Crown over three arms supported by lions.

62a. 1 Carolin 1733 .... 400.00

Bust. Rev. Crown over three arms supported by lions.

62b. ½ Carolin 1732 .... 400.00

Bust. Rev. Four initials and arms.

63. 1 Pistole 1748, 49 (very rare), 50 .... 80.00

Bust. Rev. Three shields.

64. 2 Ducats 1750. Dm. (Düsseldorf) 100.00

Bust. Rev. Arms.

65. 1 Ducat 1749 (rare), 50, 51 .... 50.00

Bust. Rev. St. Hubertus Order.

66. 1 Ducat 1750 .... 40.00

Head. Rev. Arms.

67. 1 Ducat 1764 .... 150.00

Head. Rev. Three shields.

68. 1 Ducat 1769 .... 60.00

Head or bust. Rev. City view of Mannheim.

69. 1 Rhine-gold Ducat 1763, 64, 67, 78 .... 50.00

Conjoined heads of Charles and Elizabeth Augusta. Rev. Two shields.

70. 1 Ducat 1742. Struck at Mannheim 50.00

Small bust. Rev. Fortuna.

71. 1 Lottery Ducat ND 40.00

GERMANY-PALATINATE (PFALZ) (cont'd)

Arms of Heidelberg. Rev. Long legend.

72. 1 Homage Ducat 1746 .... 40.00

City shield of Mannheim. Rev. Legend.

73. 1 Homage Ducat 1744 .... 40.00

City shield of Mannheim. Rev. Legend. On the 50th year of reign.

74. 1 Ducat 1792 .... 30.00

(For other coins of Charles Theodore, see under BAVARIA)

PALATINATE-BIRKENFELD-ZWEIBRUCKEN

Counts of —

CHRISTIAN IV, 1735-1775
Bust. Rev. Arms.

1. 1 Ducat 1747, 51 .... 250.00

CHARLES AUGUST, 1775-1795
Head. Rev. Arms.

2. 2 Ducats 1788 .... 250.00

Head. Rev. Arms supported by lions.

3. 1 Ducat 1788, 90 .... 150.00

PALATINATE-MOSBACH

Counts of —

OTTO II, 1461-1499

Madonna. Rev. Arms.

1. 1 Goldgulden 1496 .... 250.00

PALATINATE-NEUBURG

Counts of —

PHILIP WILLIAM, 1653-1690

Bust. Rev. Sun. On his daughter's marriage.

1. 1 Ducat 1676 .... 75.00

Bust. Rev. Arms.

2. 1 Ducat 1654 .... 150.00

PALATINATE-SIMMERN

Counts of —

STEPHAN, 1410-1453

Count standing. Rev. Arms in enclosure.

1. 1 Goldgulden ND. Mints: Simmern, Wachenheim (rare) 125.00

FREDERICK I, 1453-1480

Count standing. Rev. Arms in enclosure.

2. 1 Goldgulden ND 150.00

RICHARD, 1569-1598

Count standing. Rev. Arms and value.

3. 2 Ducats 1576 .... 350.00
4. 1 Ducat 1576-79, 87 ....* 30.00

PALATINATE-SULZBACH

Counts of —

CHRISTIAN AUGUST, 1632-1708
Bust. Rev. Arms.

1 1 Ducat 1682 .... 200.00

GERMANY-PALATINATE-SULZBACH (cont'd)

Arms. Rev. Resurrection of Christ.

2. ¼ Ducat ND 50.00

PALATINATE-VELDENZ

Counts of —

GEORGE GUSTAVE, 1592-1634
Count standing. Rev. Arms.

1. 1 Ducat 1596 .... 250.00

LEOPOLD LOUIS, 1634-1694
Bust. Rev. Arms.

2. 1 Ducat 1673 .... 250.00

PALATINATE-ZWEIBRUCKEN

Counts of —

LOUIS, 1459-1489
Count standing. Rev. Arms in enclosure.

1. 1 Goldgulden ND. Mint: Wachenheim 175.00

Arms on cross. Rev. Three shields.

2. 1 Goldgulden ND. Mint: Wachenheim 225.00

JOHN II, 1604-1635

Arms. Rev. Double Eagle.

3. 1 Goldgulden 1611, 16-19, 24, ND 35.00

PASSAU

Bishops of —

VIGILIUS FROESCHL, 1500-1517
St. Stephan. Rev. Cross.

1. 1 Goldgulden 1508, ND 400.00

ERNST OF BAVARIA, 1517-1540
St. Stephan. Rev. Arms.

2. 1 Ducat 1522, 37 .... 350.00

URBAN OF TRENBACH, 1561-1598
St. Stephan. Rev. Double eagle.

3. 2 Ducats 1567 .... 400.00
4. 1 Ducat 1570 .... 250.00

SEBASTIAN OF POETTING, 1673-1689

5. ¼ Ducat 1674 .... 40.00
6. ⅙ Ducat 1674 .... 40.00

JOHN PHILIP OF LAMBERG, 1689-1712

Bust. Rev. Arms.

7. 2 Ducats 1698, 1701 .... 150.00
8. 1 Ducat 1698, 1705, 06, 08, 09 ....*...... 40.00

Monogram. Rev. Arms.

9. ½ Ducat 1709 .... 30.00

RAYMOND FERDINAND OF RABATTA, 1713-1722
Bust. Rev. Arms.

10. 1 Ducat 1716 .... 50.00

Initials. Rev. Fox with arms.

11. ½ Ducat 1716 .... 30.00

JOSEPH DOMINIC OF LAMBERG, 1723-1761

Bust. Rev. Arms.

12. 1 Ducat 1747 .... 50.00

LEOPOLD ERNST OF FIRMIAN, 1763-1783

Bust. Rev. Arms.

13. 1 Ducat 1779 .... 40.00

POMERANIA

A. Dukes of —

BOGISLAUS X, 1474-1523
Madonna. Rev. Arms on cross.

1. 1 Goldgulden 1499, ND 250.00

JOHN FREDERICK, 1569-1600
Half length bust. Rev. Arms.

2. 1 Ducat 1594, 96 .... 85.00

PHILIP JULIUS, 1592-1625
Bust. Rev. Arms.

3. 1 Goldgulden 1609, 11 .... 100.00

PHILIP II, 1606-1618
Bust. Rev. Arms.

4. 1 Goldgulden 1612, 13 .... 75.00

Arms supported by wild men. Rev. David with his harp.

5. 2 Goldgulden 1614 .... 150.00

Bust. Rev. David with his harp.

6. 2 Goldgulden 1614 .... 150.00

Bust. Rev. Crossed sword and pen.

7. 1 Goldgulden 1614, 15 .... 75.00

Bust. Rev. Light.

8. 2 Goldgulden 1615 .... 150.00
9. 1 Goldgulden 1615 .... 100.00

Bust. Rev. Stag.

10. 2 Goldgulden 1615 .... 200.00
11. 1 Goldgulden 1615, 16 .... 150.00

Bust. Rev. Snail.

12. 2 Goldgulden 1617 .... 200.00
13. 1 Goldgulden 1617, 18 .... 150.00

Bust. Rev. Wreath with SOLI DEO GLORIA.

14. 2 Goldgulden 1616 .... 150.00
15. 1 Goldgulden 1616-18 .... 75.00

Bust. Rev. Legend. On the Reformation.

16. 1 Goldgulden 1617 .... 150.00

Man with lamb. Rev. Legend. On the Reformation.

17. 1 Goldgulden 1617 .... 150.00

FRANCIS, 1618-1620
Bust. Rev. Griffin.

18. 1 Goldgulden 1618 .... 150.00

BOGISLAUS XIV, 1620-1637
Bust. Rev. Griffin in shield.

19. 1 Goldgulden 1632 .... Rare

Bust. Rev. Arms.

20. 1 Goldgulden 1628 .... 80.00

Bust and helmet. Rev. Griffin.

21. 1 Goldgulden 1629 .... 80.00

Duke standing. Rev. Arms.

22. 1 Ducat 1629, 31, 33-36, ND 50.00

Duke standing. Rev. Arms with three helmets.

23. 1 Ducat 1633, ND 50.00

Legend. Rev. Skull. On his burial.

24. 1 Ducat 1654 .... 75.00
25. ½ Ducat 1654 .... 40.00

B. Swedish Rulers of —

CHRISTINA, 1632-1654

Facing bust. Rev. Christ over arms.

26. 1 Ducat 1641 .... 150.00

Facing half length bust. Rev. Arms.

27. 1 Ducat 1642 .... 200.00

Facing bust. Rev. Arms.

28. 1 Ducat 1642, 46, 53 .... 100.00

Bust. Rev. Arms.

29. 2½ Ducats 1653 .... 800.00

CHARLES X, 1654-1660

Bust. Rev. Arms.

30. 2 Ducats 1658 .... 500.00

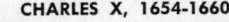

King standing. Rev. Arms.

31. 1 Ducat 1654, 56, 58, 59 .... 500.00

CHARLES XI, 1660-1697

Small bust in circle. Rev. Arms supported by wild men.

32. 2 Ducats 1661 ....*...... 400.00
33. 1 Ducat 1662 .... 400.00

Large bust not in circle. Rev. Arms supported by wild men.

34. 3 Ducats 1674 .... 750.00
35. 2 Ducats 1684, 90 .... 400.00
36. 1 Ducat 1672-75, 82, 84, 86, 89, 90, 95, 97 ......*...... 350.00
37. 1 Ducat 1666. Without the wild men ....*...... 500.00

Large bust. Rev. Crown, orb and crossed swords over sheaf.

38. 2 Ducats 1692-94, 96, 97, ND 300.00

CHARLES XII, 1697-1718

Half length bust. Rev. Lion between falling and broken columns.

39. 2 Ducats 1706 .... 350.00

Half length bust. Rev. Five line legend in wreath.

40. 2 Ducats 1706 .... 300.00

GERMANY-POMERANIA (cont'd)

Bust with long hair. Rev. Arms.

41. 1 Ducat 1706 .... 175.00

Bust with short hair. Rev. Arms.

42. 1 Ducat 1706, 09 .... 175.00

ADOLPH FREDERICK, 1751-1771

Head. Rev. Griffin and value.

43. 10 Taler 1759 .... 400.00
44. 5 Taler 1758 (very rare), 59 ....*...... 250.00

PRUSSIA

A. Brandenburg Electors of —

JOAQUIM AND ALBERT, 1499-1514
St. Paul standing. Rev. Cross and five shields.

1. 1 Goldgulden ND. Mint: Brandenburg 400.00
2. 1 Goldgulden ND. Mint: Berlin 300.00

JOAQUIM I, 1499-1535
St. Paul standing. Rev. Cross and five shields.

3. 1 Goldgulden 1516, 18, 19, 21. Mint: Frankfurt (Oder) .. 350.00

St. John standing. Rev. Cross and five shields.

4. 1 Goldgulden 1526. Mint: Frankfurt (Oder) 600.00

JOAQUIM II, 1535-1571
St. John. Rev. Cross and five shields.

5. 2 Goldgulden 1540 .... 1500.00
6. 1 Goldgulden 1538-40 .... 800.00

Eagle. Rev. Double eagle.

7. 1 Goldgulden 1552 .... 750.00

Five shields. Rev. Double eagle.

8. 1 Goldgulden 1557 .... 750.00

Bust. Rev. Arms.

9. 2 Ducats 1560 .... 1500.00
10. 1 Ducat 1560, 66 .... 800.00

Arms. Rev. Cross.

11. 10 Ducats 1570 .... 3000.00

JOHN GEORGE, 1571-1598
Eagle. Rev. Five shields.

12. 1 Goldgulden 1573, 87 .... 750.00

Armored bust. Rev. Arms and legend.

13. 2 Ducats 1584 .... 1500.00

Armored bust. Rev. Cross and shields.

14. 10 Ducats 1584, 87 .... 3000.00
15. 5 Ducats 1590 .... 2500.00

Armored bust. Rev. Arms.

16. 1 Ducat 1590 .... 750.00

JOAQUIM FREDERICK, 1598-1608
Elector standing. Rev. Eagle.

17. 2 Ducats 1606 .... 1200.00
18. 1 Ducat 1605, 06 .... 500.00

Half length bust. Rev. Cross.

19. 10 Ducats 1605 .... 3000.00

JOHN SIGISMUND, 1608-1619
Bust. Rev. Arms.

20. 1 Goldgulden 1615 .... 400.00

Facing bust. Rev. Arms.

21. 1 Goldgulden 1614, 17 .... 300.00

Half length bust. Rev. Arms.

22. 1 Goldgulden 1617 .... 500.00

Bust. Rev. Arms.

23. 1 Ducat ND 750.00

Elector standing. Rev. Eagle.

24. 1 Ducat 1611, 12, 14 .... 350.00

Elector standing. Rev. Arms.

25. 2 Ducats 1615 .... 800.00

Bust. Rev. Cross.

26. 10 Ducats 1612 .... 3000.00
27. 5 Ducats 1611, 13, 14 .... 2500.00

GEORGE WILLIAM, 1619-1640
I. Berlin Mint with or without Mintmaster's Initials LM
Elector on horse. Rev. Sceptre within two circles of 24 shields.

28. 10 Ducats 1620 (LM) 3000.00

Bust. Rev. Sceptre shield.

29. 1 Goldgulden 1620 (LM) 1200.00

Bust. Rev. Arms with 7 fields.

30. 1 Goldgulden 1622 .... 400.00

Bust. Rev. Arms with 12 fields.

31. 2 Goldgulden 1621 .... 750.00

Elector standing before desk with helmet. Rev. Five Arms.

32. 1 Ducat 1620 (LM) 1200.00

Elector standing before desk with helmet. Rev. Sceptre within circle of 8 shields.

33. 2 Ducats 1620 (LM) 400.00

Elector standing before desk with helmet. Rev. Arms.

34. 2 Ducats ND (LM) 750.00

II. Cologne Mint with Mintmaster's Initials LM or IP
Bust in elector's robes. Rev. Arms with 12 fields.

35. 2 Ducats 1626 (IP) from the ducat die 1000.00
36. 1 Ducat 1626 (IP) 750.00
37. 1 Goldgulden 1628 (LM) 750.00

Elector standing. Rev. Sceptre within circle of shields.

38. 1 Ducat 1639 (LM) 300.00

Armored bust with sceptre. Rev. Arms.

39. 1 Goldgulden 1628 (LM) 300.00

Bust in elector's robes with sceptre. Rev. Arms.

40. 2 Goldgulden ND (LM) 800.00

Bust in elector's robes with sceptre. Rev. Arms under elector's hat.

41. 2 Goldgulden 1628 (LM) 800.00

Elector standing at desk with helmet. Rev. Arms.

42. 2 Ducats 1634 (LM), 36 (LM) 175.00

Elector standing at desk with helmet. Rev. Oval arms.

43. 2 Ducats 1635 (LM) 350.00

Elector standing at desk with helmet. Rev. Eagle with shields.

44. 2 Ducats 1637 (LM), 38, 40 .... 150.00

Elector on horse. Rev. Eagle with 14 shields.

45. 10 Ducats 1634 (LM) 2500.00

46. 5 Ducats 1634 (LM) 2000.00

III. Koenigsberg Mint with initials DK or a heart
Elector standing. Rev. Arms under elector's hat.
47. 1 Ducat 1625 .... 400.00

Elector standing. Rev. Arms with 12 fields.
48. 1 Ducat 1627 (heart) 400.00

Elector standing. Rev. Arms with 5 fields under elector's hat.
49. 1 Ducat 1631, 32 (heart) 400.00

Bust with elector's hat. Rev. Arms with 5 fields under elector's hat.
50. 2 Ducats 1634 (heart) 800.00
51. 1 Ducat 1633, 34 (heart) 250.00
52. 1 Ducat 1635-40 (DK) ....*...... 125.00

Bust with elector's hat. Rev. Arms with 9 fields under elector's hat.
53. 1 Ducat 1635 (DK and heart) ....*...... 150.00
54. 1 Ducat 1638, 39 (DK) 150.00

Bust. Rev. Arms with 9 fields under elector's hat.
55. 1 Ducat 1639 (DK) 350.00

FREDERICK WILLIAM, 1640-1688
I. Berlin Mint with initials LM, AB, LCS, CT, IL, or CS
Half length bust in elector's robes with sceptre. Rev. Arms with 25 fields.
56. 5 Ducats 1650 (CT) 750.00

Elector standing at desk with helmet. Rev. Arms with 25 fields.
57. 5 Ducats 1652, 53, 55, 57 (CT) 750.00

Elector standing at desk with helmet. Rev. Arms with 10 fields.
58. 4 Ducats 1666 (IL) 800.00

Armored half length bust with sceptre. Rev. Arms with 25 fields.
59. 5 Ducats 1653 (CT) 600.00

Armored bust. Rev. Sceptre shield with the ribbon of the Order of the Garter between branches.
60. 4 Ducats 1675 (CS) 3000.00

Elector standing. Rev. Eagle with 12 shields.
61. 2 Ducats 1641 (LM) 500.00

Elector standing in wreath of flowers. Rev. Arms with 12 fields in wreath of flowers.
62. 2 Ducats 1641 (sometimes with LM) 200.00

Elector standing. Rev. Arms with 23 fields.
63. 2 Ducats 1643, 44 (AB) 200.00
64. 2 Ducats 1646 (CT) 200.00

Elector standing. Rev. Arms with 25 fields under elector's hat.
65. 2 Ducats 1650, 54 (CT) 200.00

Armored half length bust. Rev. Arms with 25 fields under elector's hat.
66. 2 Ducats 1654 (CT), 1665 (IL) 500.00

Bust. Rev. Arms between palm-branches.
67. 2 Ducats 1669 .... 400.00

Bust with elector's hat. Rev. Arms between palm-branches.
68. 2 Ducats 1670 .... 500.00

Elector standing at desk. Rev. 6 shields and sceptre.
69. 1 Ducat 1641 (LM) 300.00

Elector standing at desk. Rev. Arms with 9 fields.
70. 1 Ducat 1641 (LM) 300.00

Elector standing at desk. Rev. Arms with 12 fields.
71. 1 Ducat 1643 (AB) 300.00

Elector standing. Rev. Arms with 14 fields under elector's hat.
72. 1 Ducat 1651 (CT) 300.00

Elector standing knee-length. Rev. Arms with 14 fields under elector's hat.
73. 5 Ducats 1654 (CT, from the ducat die) 800.00
74. 1 Ducat 1654, 56 (CT) 300.00

Armored bust. Rev. Sceptre shield surrounded by 13 shields.
75. 1 Ducat 1662 (AB) 125.00
76. 1 Ducat 1665, 66 (IL) 300.00

Bust. Rev. Sceptre shield surrounded by 13 shields.
77. 1 Ducat 1667 (IL) 250.00

Draped bust. Rev. Sceptre shield between branches.
78. 1 Ducat 1668, 73, 74 (IL), 75 (CS), 77 (CS) 250.00

Naked bust. Rev. Sceptre shield between branches.
79. 1 Ducat 1669-72 (IL) 200.00

Armored bust. Rev. Sceptre shield between branches.
80. 1 Ducat 1679-82 (CS) 200.00
81. 1 Ducat 1683-85 (LCS) 150.00

Armored and draped bust. Rev. Sceptre shield between branches.
82. 1 Ducat 1685, 86 (LCS) 150.00

Armored half length bust. Rev. Sceptre shield between branches.
83. 1 Ducat 1686, 87 .... 250.00

Bust in elector's robes. Rev. Sceptre shield.
84. ¾ Ducat 1656 (CT) 400.00

Bust in elector's robes. Rev. Sceptre shield between branches.
85. ½ Ducat ND 400.00

Bust in elector's robes. Rev. Arms with 14 fields.
86. ½ Ducat 1655 (CT) 50.00

Helmeted head. Rev. Crown over flying eagle.
87. ½ Ducat 1668 (IL) 100.00
88. ¼ Ducat 1668 (IL) 100.00

Bust. Rev. Crown over flying eagle.
89. ¼ Ducat 1675 (IL) 100.00

Bust. Rev. Ship. Trade coins for Guinea, Africa.
90. 1 Ducat 1682 (CS) 175.00
91. 1 Ducat 1682, 83, 85, 86 (LCS) ....*...... 175.00

Armored half length bust. Rev. Ship. For Guinea.
92. 1 Ducat 1686-88 (LCS) 175.00

Facing bust. Rev. Legend. On his 35th birthday and on the birth of Prince Charles Emil.
93. 4 Ducats 1655 (AB) 350.00
94. 3 Ducats 1655 (CT) 250.00
95. 2 Ducats 1655 (with or without elector's hat) 150.00

Bust. Rev. City view of Stettin; above eagle and griffin. On the conquest of Stettin.
96. 2 Ducats 1677 (CS). FORTIOR HIS SIGNIS 100.00
97. 2 Ducats 1677 (CS). LUCE RESURGO NOVA 100.00

Elector on horse. Rev. Legend. On the conquest of Stettin.
98. ½ Ducat 1677 .... 80.00

Bust with elector's hat. Rev. Arms.
99. 1 Ducat 1646 (CT). For Prussia 125.00

Elector standing knee length. Rev. Crowned arms.

100. 1 Ducat 1665 (IL). For Prussia 300.00

Bust. Rev. Crowned arms.

101. 1 Ducat 1665 (IL). For Prussia 350.00

II. Halberstadt Mint with initials LCS
Bust. Rev. Sceptre between branches.

102. 1 Ducat 1679 (LCS) 750.00

III. Koenigsberg Mint with initials DK, HM, TT, CV, HS, BA, CM, CG, DS, NB
Bust. Rev. Arms.

103. 5 Ducats ND (1657, DK) 900.00
104. 4 Ducats ND (1657, DK) 800.00

Elector on horse. Rev. Rose in circle of shields.

105. 5 Ducats ND 800.00
106. 3 Ducats ND 500.00
107. 2 Ducats ND ....*...... 200.00

Head. Rev. Head of Prince Charles Emil. On the 14th birthday of the Prince.

108. 2 Ducats 1669 (CG) 250.00

Bust. Rev. Crowned arms.

109. 2 Ducats 1670-72 (TT) 250.00
110. 2 Ducats 1673, 74 (CV) 250.00
111. 2 Ducats 1675, 79, 82-84 (HS) 200.00
112. 2 Ducats 1686 (BA) 300.00

Bust with elector's hat. Rev. Arms.

113. 1 Ducat 1641, 48, 49 (DK) 150.00

Facing bust. Rev. Arms.

114. 1 Ducat 1643 (DK) 250.00

Bust. Rev. Arms.

115. 1 Ducat 1651 (CM) 175.00
116. 1 Ducat 1657 (DK), 1660 over 1657 .... 150.00

Bust in elector's robes. Rev. Arms.

117. 1 Ducat 1657 (NB), 1658 (without NB) 175.00

Armored bust. Rev. Arms.

118. 1 Ducat 1661-63 (HM) 125.00

Crowned bust with sword. Rev. Arms with 5 fields.

119. 1 Ducat 1664-66 ....*...... 100.00
120. 1 Ducat 1667 (CG) 150.00

Bust. Rev. Eagle.

121. 1 Ducat 1668 (CG and DS) 200.00
122. 1 Ducat 1673, 74 (CV) 350.00
123. ½ Ducat 1670, 71 (TT), 1685 (HS) ....*...... 80.00

Head. Rev. Crowned arms.

124. 1 Ducat 1669 (CG and DS) 100.00

Bust. Rev. Crowned arms.

125. 1 Ducat 1670-72 (TT) 175.00
126. 1 Ducat 1679, 81, 82 (HS) 200.00

Bust. Rev. Crowned oval arms.

127. 1 Ducat 1676, 83, 84 (HS) 150.00
128. 1 Ducat 1685, 86 (BA) 200.00

Bust. Rev. Crowned round arms.

129. 1 Ducat 1687 (HS) 200.00

IV. Magdeburg Mint with initials IE
Bust. Rev. Arms.

130. 5 Ducats 1683 (IE) 900.00

V. Luenen Mint
Facing bust. Rev. Arms with 4 fields.

131. 1 Ducat 1659 (M-M for Moneta Marcana) 750.00

Bust. Rev. Arms with 4 fields.

132. 1 Ducat 1660, 62 .... 350.00

Facing bust. Rev. Arms with 6 fields.

133. 1 Ducat 1664 .... 350.00

VI. Minden Mint with initials HB
Bust in elector's robes. Rev. Arms with 26 fields.

134. 1 Ducat 1652 (HB) 400.00

Bust. Rev. Arms with 5 fields.

135. 1 Ducat 1670 (HB) 300.00

VII. Ravensberg Mint struck at Bielefeld
Arms. Rev. Value on table.

136. 1 Ducat 1648 .... 600.00

Bust in elector's robes. Rev. Arms with 6 fields.

137. 1 Ducat 1648 .... 300.00

FREDERICK III, 1688-1701 (I, 1701-1713)
I. Berlin Mint with initials LCS, S, or RF
Bust. Rev. Crossed initials.

138. 1 Ducat 1688 .... 350.00
139. 1 Ducat 1697 (RF and LCS) 200.00
140. 1 Ducat 1697 (RF and LCS) Without Order of the Garter.. 350.00

Bust. Rev. Sceptre in shield.

141. 1 Ducat 1689, 90 (LCS) 200.00
142. 1 Ducat 1696 (LCS). Without Order of the Garter 200.00

Head. Rev. Crossed initials.

143. 2 Ducats 1698-1700 (RF and LCS) 300.00
144. 1 Ducat 1698, 99 (RF and LCS) 200.00

Bust with mantle. Rev. Ship. Trade coin for Guinea, Africa.

145. 1 Ducat 1688, 90 (LCS) 150.00

Bust. Rev. Ship. Trade coin for Guinea.

146. 1 Ducat 1692, 94-96 (S and LCS) 150.00

II. Koenigsberg Mint with initials HS, SD or CG
Laureate bust. Rev. Arms.

147.	1 Ducat 1691, 93 (HS)	300.00
148.	1 Ducat 1695, 97 (SD)	350.00
149.	1 Ducat 1700 (CG)	350.00

Laureate bust. Rev. Eagle.

150.	½ Ducat 1700 (CG)	100.00

III. Magdeburg Mint with initials ICS
Bust. Rev. Sceptre in shield.

151.	1 Ducat 1692 (ICS)	400.00

IV. Minden Mint with initials BH
Bust. Rev. Arms with 25 fields.

152.	1 Ducat 1691 (BH)	400.00

Bust. Rev. Sceptre in shield and eagle with crown.

153.	1 Ducat 1695 (BH)	400.00

Bust. Rev. Sceptre in shield.

154.	½ Ducat 1695 (BH)	200.00

(The coinage of Frederick III continues directly below under B, as Frederick I, King of Prussia.)

B. Kings of —

FREDERICK I, 1701-1713
Mints and the initials of the mint masters or engravers as they appear on the coins.

Berlin Mint: LCS, CS, L, CFL, M, R
Koenigsberg Mint: CG, GWM
Magdeburg Mint: HFH
Minden Mint: BH

Head. Rev. Cross of initials.

155.	2 Ducats 1701. Thick. LCS	600.00
156.	1 Ducat 1701. LCS ....*	200.00

Bust over legend. Rev. Crown. On his Coronation.

157.	1 Ducat 1701. Koenigsberg Mint	100.00

Head. Rev. Crowned eagle.

158.	1 Ducat 1701. CS ....*	200.00
159.	1 Ducat 1703, 04. CFL and CS	150.00

Bust. Rev. Initials in chain of Order.

160.	1 Ducat 1705-12. L and CS	125.00
161.	1 Ducat 1707-09. HFH	400.00
162.	1 Ducat 1706. BH	400.00

Head. Rev. Flying eagle.

163.	2 Ducats 1701. Thick. R and CS	600.00
164.	2 Ducats 1712. HFH	300.00
165.	1 Ducat 1710. R and CS	400.00
166.	½ Ducat 1712. HFH	100.00

Bust. Rev. Eagle shield.

167.	2 Ducats 1713. CG	600.00
168.	2 Ducats 1703, 04. Thick. CG	500.00
169.	1 Ducat 1702-12. CG ....*	100.00
170.	1 Ducat 1713. GWM and CG	400.00

Head. Rev. Crowned arms. Struck for Neuchatel.

171.	1 Ducat 1713. JP	400.00

Bust. Rev. Crown on altar. On his death.

172.	1 Ducat 1713. L with or without CS	100.00

FREDERICK WILLIAM AND SOPHIA DOROTHEA, 1706

Busts. Rev. Legend. On their wedding. Magdeburg Mint with initials HFH.

173.	2 Ducats 1706	250.00
174.	1 Ducat 1706 ....*	100.00
175.	½ Ducat 1706, 12	60.00
176.	¼ Ducat 1706, 12	35.00
177.	¼ Ducat 1706. With legend "Frid:Wilh:D.G.Rex. Boruss"...	100.00

FREDERICK WILLIAM I, 1713-1740
Mints and the initials of the mint masters or engravers as they appear on the coins.

Berlin Mint: IFS, IGN, EGN, L, M
Koenigsberg Mint: CG, M
Magdeburg Mint: HFH
Bust. Rev. Eagle flying to sun.

178.	1 Ducat 1713. L and IFS	100.00
179.	¼ Ducat 1713. HFH	30.00

Bust. Rev. Eagle.

180.	1 Ducat 1714. HFH	250.00
181.	1 Ducat 1733. EGN	80.00

Laureate head. Rev. Eagle flying to sun.

182.	2 Ducats 1713. HFH	400.00
183.	1 Ducat 1713. CG with or without M or L ......*	60.00
184.	1 Ducat 1713. HFH	70.00
185.	½ Ducat 1713. HFH	40.00
186.	¼ Ducat 1713. HFH	30.00

Bust. Rev. Initials and crown in chain of Order.

187.	1 Ducat 1714. L and IFS	175.00

Bust. Rev. Arms with five fields.

188.	1 Ducat 1714. L and IFS	300.00

Bust. Rev. Arms with six fields.

189.	1 Ducat 1715, 16. L and IFS	200.00
190.	1 Ducat 1714-17. CG with M or L	100.00
191.	1 Ducat 1714. HFH	60.00

Bust. Rev. Arms with twelve fields.

192.	1 Ducat 1714. HFH	200.00

Bust. Rev. Arms with forty fields.

193.	1 Ducat 1714. HFH	60.00
194.	¼ Ducat 1715. HFH	30.00

Laureate head. Rev. Arms with forty fields.

195.	½ Ducat 1714. HFH	40.00
196.	¼ Ducat 1715. HFH	30.00

Bust. Rev. Star of Order with legend.

197.	1 Ducat 1717. L and IFS	75.00
198.	1 Ducat 1733-40. EGN	60.00
199.	1 Ducat 1714. HFH	60.00

Bust. Rev. Star of Order without legend.

200.	1 Ducat 1714-16. IFS	....	75.00
201.	1 Ducat 1714. CG and M	....	300.00
202.	1 Ducat 1715. No initials	....	300.00
203.	1 Ducat 1714, 16. Plain bust. HFH	..........*	60.00
204.	1 Ducat 1717. Laureate bust. HFH	....	100.00
205.	¼ Ducat 1716. HFH	....	30.00

Laureate head. Rev. Star of Order.

206.	½ Ducat 1714. HFH	....	40.00
207.	¼ Ducat 1714, 16. HFH	....	30.00

Bust with pigtail. Rev. Oval arms.

208.	1 Ducat 1718-28. CG with or without M	....	60.00
209.	1 Ducat 1718. HFH with or without L	....	100.00

Bust with pigtail. Rev. Star of Order with legend.

210.	1 Ducat 1717, 18. HFH with or without M	....	75.00

Bust with or without L. Rev. Oval arms with six fields.

211.	2 Ducats 1724. IGN	....	400.00
212.	2 Ducats 1732. EGN	....	500.00
213.	1 Ducat 1716. M and IFS	....	125.00
214.	1 Ducat 1717, 18. IFS	....	125.00
215.	1 Ducat 1719-25. IGN	....	75.00
216.	1 Ducat 1725-32. EGN	....	75.00
217.	½ Ducat 1726. EGN	....	50.00

Bust. Rev. Flying eagle.

218.	2 Ducats 1733. EGN	....	400.00
219.	1 Ducat 1733, 34. EGN	....	75.00

Bust. Rev. Cross of initials.

220.	1 William D'or 1737-40. EGN on Obv. or Rev. ...*	125.00
221.	½ William D'or 1738-40. EGN	....	60.00

FREDERICK II, THE GREAT, 1740-1786

Mints, mint marks and the initials of mint masters or mint officials as they appear on the coins.

Berlin Mint: A mm, EGN, CHI, ALS
Breslau Mint: B mm, AHE, AE
Cleve Mint: C mm
Aurich Mint: D mm

Head. Rev. Justice standing. On the Homage of Koenigsberg.

222.	1 Ducat 1740. No initials	....	40.00

Head. Rev. Legend. On the Homage of Berlin.

223.	1 Ducat 1740. No initials	....	40.00

Armored bust. Rev. Crowned eagle shield.

224.	1 Ducat 1741-45. EGN	....	60.00
225.	1 Ducat 1743-48. AHE	....	70.00

Armored bust. Rev. Crowned initials in chain of Order.

226.	1 Ducat 1745. EGN	....	75.00

Armored bust. Rev. Flying eagle over trophies.

227.	1 Ducat 1745-49. EGN	....	60.00
228.	1 Ducat 1749. CHI	....	70.00

Armored bust. Rev. Eagle on globe over branches.

229.	2 Ducats 1749. EGN	....	400.00
230.	1 Ducat 1749. EGN	....	300.00

Armored bust. Rev. Eagle over trophies and value.

231.	1 Ducat 1753, 54. A mm	....	70.00

Bare bust. Rev. Eagle over trophies and value.

232.	1 Ducat 1754, 57. B mm	....	100.00

Armored bust. Rev. Cross of initials.

233.	1 Frederick D'or 1744-48. AE	....	80.00

Armored bust. Rev. Crowned eagle between trophies. The last coin was struck in lower grade gold during the Seven Year War.

234.	2 Frederick D'or 1749. ALS	....	125.00
235.	2 Frederick D'or 1750-52. A mm	....	125.00
236.	2 Frederick D'or 1747-49. W on shield. AHE	....	175.00
237.	1 Frederick D'or 1741-46. EGN	....	70.00
238.	1 Frederick D'or 1750-52, 59. A mm	..........*	50.00
239.	1 Frederick D'or 1749. Bust left. ALS	....	125.00
240.	1 Frederick D'or 1746-49. W on shield. AHE or AE	......	100.00
241.	1 Frederick D'or 1750. AE	....	100.00
242.	1 Frederick D'or 1750, 64. B on shield. B mm or AE	....	90.00
243.	½ Frederick D'or 1749. CHI	....	40.00
244.	½ Frederick D'or 1750-52. A mm	....	30.00
245.	1 Frederick D'or 1755, 56. A mm	....	100.00

Head. Rev. Crowned eagle shield.

246.	1 Frederick D'or 1750. A mm	....	100.00

Armored bust. Rev. Eagle and lions head between trophies.

247.	1 Frederick D'or 1752, 53. D mm	....	300.00

Head. Rev. Crowned eagle between trophies.

248.	2 Frederick D'or 1753, 55. A mm	....	150.00

Head. Rev. Eagle between trophies. The last three coins were struck in lower grade gold during the Seven Year War.

249.	1 Frederick D'or 1752-58, 63. A mm	....	50.00
250.	½ Frederick D'or 1752-56. A mm	....	30.00
251.	2 Frederick D'or 1756, 57. A mm	....	350.00
252.	1 Frederick D'or 1755, 56, 57. A mm	....	75.00
253.	½ Frederick D'or 1755. A mm	....	200.00

Head. Rev. Crown over Two F's.

254.	½ Frederick D'or 1750. A mm	....	60.00

Armored bust. Rev. Eagle over trophies.

255.	2 Frederick D'or 1751, 52. B mm	....	150.00

GERMANY-PRUSSIA (cont'd)

256.	2 Frederick D'or 1752, 53. C mm	300.00
257.	1 Frederick D'or 1750-57. B mm	65.00
258.	1 Frederick D'or 1751-53. C mm ....*.....	100.00
259.	½ Frederick D'or 1750-53. B mm ....*.....	50.00
260.	½ Frederick D'or 1753. C mm	100.00

Head. Rev. Eagle over trophies.

261.	1 Frederick D'or 1754, 55. C mm	300.00

Young laureate head. Rev. Eagle over trophies.

262.	2 Frederick D'or 1764-71, 75. A mm	125.00
263.	1 Frederick D'or 1764-76. A mm	50.00
264.	1 Frederick D'or 1764-75. B mm	65.00
265.	½ Frederick D'or 1765, 69, 70, 72-74. A mm	30.00
266.	½ Frederick D'or 1765-75. B mm	50.00

Old laureate head. Rev. Eagle over trophies.

267.	2 Frederick D'or 1776. A mm	140.00
268.	1 Frederick D'or 1775-86. A mm	50.00
269.	1 Frederick D'or 1776-78, 80-86. B mm	65.00
270.	1 Frederick D'or 1781. With date "D.20.August." B mm..	1500.00
271.	½ Frederick D'or 1784, 86. A mm	35.00
272.	½ Frederick D'or 1776, 77. B mm	150.00

FREDERICK WILLIAM II, 1786-1797
Bust. Rev. Eagle above trophies.

273.	1 Frederick D'or 1786, 88-97. A mm	40.00
274.	1 Frederick D'or 1787-97. B mm	40.00

Crowned eagle shield. Rev. Value.

275.	1 Ducat 1787, 90. A mm	40.00

FREDERICK WILLIAM III, 1797-1840

Eagle shield. Rev. Legend, "Fuerstenzeche."

276.	1 Rhine-gold Ducat 1803. B mm	1000.00

Bust. Rev. Eagle above trophies.

277.	2 Frederick D'or 1800-02, 06, 11, 13, 14. A mm *......	75.00
278.	1 Frederick D'or 1798-1813, 16. A mm	40.00
279.	1 Frederick D'or 1800-05. B mm	150.00
280.	½ Frederick D'or 1802-04, 06, 14, 16. A mm	30.00

Bust in uniform. Rev. Eagle above trophies.

282.	1 Frederick D'or 1817-19, 22. A mm	40.00
283.	½ Frederick D'or 1817. A mm	35.00

Head. Rev. Eagle above trophies.

284.	2 Frederick D'or 1825-32, 36-40. A mm	65.00
285.	1 Frederick D'or 1825, 27-34, 36-40. A mm	40.00
286.	½ Frederick D'or 1825, 27-29, 32, 33, 37-40. A mm	30.00

FREDERICK WILLIAM IV, 1840-1861

Head. Rev. Eagle above trophies.

287.	2 Frederick D'or 1841-46, 48, 49, 52. A mm ....*......	80.00
288.	1 Frederick D'or 1841-52. A mm	45.00
289.	½ Frederick D'or 1841-46, 49. A mm ....*......	35.00

Older head. Rev. Eagle above trophies.

290.	2 Frederick D'or 1853-55. A mm	80.00
291.	1 Frederick D'or 1853-55. A mm ....*......	45.00
292.	½ Frederick D'or 1853. A mm	40.00

Older head. Rev. Value in wreath.

293.	1 Krone 1858-60. A mm	100.00
294.	½ Krone 1858. A mm	100.00

WILLIAM I, 1861-1888

Head. Rev. Value in wreath. The B mm is for Hannover.

295.	1 Krone 1861-64, 66-70. A mm ....*......	120.00
296.	1 Krone 1867, 68. B mm	125.00
297.	½ Krone 1862-64, 66-69. A mm	70.00
298.	½ Krone 1868. B mm	200.00

QUEDLINBURG

Abbesses of —

DOROTHEA SOPHIA, 1618-1645
Arms of Quedlinburg. Rev. Arms of Saxony.

1. 1 Ducat ND 200.00

Crowned arms of Quedlinburg. Rev. Crowned arms of Saxony.

2. 1 Ducat ND 100.00

ANNE DOROTHEA, 1685-1704

Bust. Rev. Ship. On her death.

3. 2 Ducats 1704 .... 125.00

Bust. Rev. Setting sun. On her death.

4. 1 Ducat 1704 .... 70.00

RANTZAU

Counts of —

CHRISTIAN I, 1650-1663

Bust. Rev. Arms.

1. 2 Ducats 1656 .... 400.00
2. 1 Ducat 1655, 56, 58 ....* 125.00

DETLEF, 1663-1697
Bust. Rev. Arms.

3. 1 Ducat 1689 .... 175.00

RATZEBURG

Bishops of —

AUGUST OF BRUNSWICK, 1610-1636

Duke on horse. Rev. Arms.

1. 1 Goldgulden 1618 .... 150.00

Duke standing. Rev. Arms.

2. 1 Ducat ND 125.00

Bust. Rev. Arms.

3. 1 Ducat 1634 .... 150.00

REGENSBURG (RATISBON)

A. General City Coinage

Arms. Rev. St. Wolfgang.

1. 1 Goldgulden 1512 .... 500.00

Arms. Rev. Legend. In honor of Bernard of Saxony.

2. 1 Ducat 1633 .... 175.00

Arms. Rev. City view.

3. 1 Ducat 1634 .... 150.00

Legend and arms. Rev. Light and hands. On the Reformation.

4. 2 Ducats 1642 .... 75.00

Arms. Rev. Light. On the Reformation.

5. 1 Ducat 1642 .... 40.00

Double eagle. Rev. Wreath.

6. 1 Ducat 1653 .... 200.00

Arms. Rev. Double eagle.

7. 1 Ducat 1658 .... 175.00
7a. ½ Ducat ND. Square ....* 50.00
8. ¼ Ducat ND 25.00
9. ¼ Ducat ND. Square 25.00
10. ⅙ Ducat ND. Square 35.00
11. ⅛ Ducat ND. Square 25.00

Lamb on column. Rev. Legend. On the Reformation.

12. 1 Ducat 1717 .... 50.00

Arms over legend. Rev. Vine. On the Reformation.

13. 1 Ducat 1742 .... 60.00

Crossed keys. Rev. Crowned R.

14. 1/16 Ducat ND (1750) 20.00
15. 1/32 Ducat ND (1750) 15.00

Crossed keys. Rev. Double eagle.

16. 1/32 Ducat ND (1750) 15.00

B. Coinage with the heads or names of the Holy Roman Emperors

Arms. Rev. Double eagle. Matthias.

17. 1 Goldgulden 1617, 18 .... 175.00

Arms. Rev. Double eagle. Ferdinand II.

18.	2 Ducats 1632	200.00
19.	1 Ducat 1632	175.00

Arms. Rev. Double eagle. Ferdinand III.

20.	1 Ducat 1637-57	60.00

Arms. Rev. Double eagle. Leopold I.

21.	2 Ducats ND	150.00
22.	1 Ducat 1659-96 ....*......	70.00

Arms. Rev. Double eagle. Joseph I.

23.	1 Ducat 1706	75.00

Bust of Charles VI. Rev. Arms.

24.	2 Ducats ND	150.00
25.	1 Ducat 1712	75.00
26.	½ Ducat ND	75.00

Bust of Charles VI. Rev. City View.

27.	1 Ducat 1737, ND	60.00

Arms. Rev. Double eagle. Charles VI.

28.	½ Ducat ND (1740)	60.00

Bust of Charles VII. Rev. City view.

28a.	2 Ducats ND (thick) ....*......	200.00
28b.	1 Ducat ND	75.00

Bust of Charles VII. Rev. Arms.

29.	2 Ducats ND (1742-45)	175.00
30.	½ Ducat ND (1742-45)	80.00

Bust of Francis I. Rev. City view.

31.	3 Ducats ND (1745-65) ....*......	300.00
32.	2 Ducats ND (1745-65)	100.00
33.	1 Ducat ND (1745-65)	50.00
34.	½ Ducat ND (1745-65)	30.00
35.	¼ Ducat ND (1745-65)	20.00

Bust of Francis I. Rev. Eagle flying over arms.

36.	3 Ducats ND (1745-65)	300.00
37.	2 Ducats ND (1745-65)	250.00

Bust of Joseph II. Rev. Arms.

38.	3 Ducats ND (1765-90)	200.00
39.	1 Ducat ND (1765-90)	40.00

Bust of Joseph II. Rev. City view.

40.	1 Ducat ND (1765-90)	40.00

City view. Rev. Double eagle. Joseph II.

41.	2 Ducats ND (1765-90)	100.00

Head of Leopold II. Rev. City view.

42.	1 Ducat ND (1790-92)	75.00

City view. Rev. Double eagle. Francis II.

43.	1 Ducat ND (1792-1806)	50.00

C. Bishops of —

JOHN III OF PALATINATE, 1507-1538
Arms. Rev. St. Peter standing.

44.	1 Goldgulden 1523	500.00

Arms. Rev. Madonna.

45.	1 Ducat 1526	500.00

DAVID KOELDERER, 1567-1579
Arms. Rev. Double eagle.

46.	1 Goldgulden ND	500.00

ANTHONY IGNACE, COUNT FUGGER, 1769-1787
Bust. Rev. Arms.

47.	1 Ducat 1770	75.00

CHARLES OF DALBERG, 1804-1817
Bust. Rev. Arms.

48.	1 Ducat 1809	200.00

REUSS

Counts, and later, Princes of —

A. Older Line

HENRY III, 1733-1768
Bust. Rev. Arms.

1.	1 Ducat 1764	75.00

B. Younger Line

HENRY II, 1572-1635
Arms. Rev. Two helmets.

2.	1 Goldgulden 1619, 22	125.00

HENRY XII, 1744-1784

Initials. Rev. Arms. On the Peace of Hubertusburg.

3.	1 Ducat 1763	50.00

Bust. Rev. Arms.

4.	1 Ducat 1764	75.00

REUSS-ROTHENTHAL

Counts of —

HENRY V, 1668-1698
Bust. Rev. Arms.

1.	1 Ducat 1679	250.00

RHINE CONFEDERATION

CHARLES OF DALBERG, ARCHBISHOP OF MAYENCE, 1802-1813

Bust. Rev. Arms.

1. 1 Ducat 1809 .... 50.00

ROSENBERG

Lords of —

WILLIAM, 1581-1592
Bust right. Rev. Arms.

1. 4 Ducats 1585 .... 400.00
2. 2 Ducats 1585 .... 300.00

Arms. Rev. St. Christopher standing.

3. 2 Ducats 1584. Thick 350.00
4. 1 Ducat 1582-88, 90 .... * 100.00

PETER WOK, 1592-1599

Arms. Rev. St. Christopher standing.

5. 1 Ducat 1592-95 .... 100.00

ROSTOCK

(The coinage is with the names of the Holy Roman Emperors.)

Griffin. Rev. Double eagle. Rudolph II.
1. 1 Goldgulden 1606, 08-11, ND 80.00

Griffin. Rev. Double eagle. Matthias.
2. 1 Goldgulden 1613-17 .... 100.00

Griffin. Rev. Double eagle. Ferdinand II.
3. 2 Goldgulden 1623 .... 500.00
4. 1 Goldgulden 1625-31 .... 100.00

Arms. Rev. Double eagle. Ferdinand II.
5. 1 Ducat 1632-34, 36 .... 50.00

Tablet and value. Rev. Double eagle. Ferdinand III.
6. 2 Ducats 1639 .... 125.00

Arms. Rev. Double eagle. Ferdinand III.
7. 1 Ducat 1636, 39, 46, 55 .... 50.00

Arms. Rev. Double eagle. Leopold I.
8. 2 Ducats 1661, 95 .... 300.00
9. 1 Ducat 1661, 64, 65, 72, 77, 82, 94 .... 150.00

Griffin. Rev. Double eagle. Leopold I.
10. ½ Ducat 1695 .... 100.00

Griffin. Rev. Double eagle. Leopold I.
11. 1 Wedding Ducat 1704 .... 200.00

Griffin. Rev. Value. Leopold II.
12. ¼ Ducat 1696 .... 75.00

Arms. Rev. Double eagle. Francis I.
13. 1 Ducat 1762 .... 150.00

Arms. Rev. Double eagle. Joseph II.
14. 1 Ducat 1783 .... 80.00

Arms. Rev. Double eagle. Francis II.
15. 1 Ducat 1796 .... 50.00

ROTHENBURG

Legend. Rev. Fortress. On the Reformation.
1. 1 Ducat 1717 .... 80.00

ROTTWEIL

Eagle. Rev. Orb in enclosure. Maximilian I.
1. 1 Goldgulden ND (1486-1519) 650.00

ST. ALBAN

(In Mayence)

St. Alban standing. Rev. Shield and donkey.
1. 1 Goldgulden 1597 .... 100.00
2. 1 Goldgulden 1712, 16, 20, 25, 44, 78, 79, 80 ... * 50.00

SALM-DHAUN

CURATORIAL COINAGE, 1606-1617
Arms. Rev. Double eagle. Matthias.

1. 1 Goldgulden 1617 .... 200.00

WOLFGANG FREDERICK, DIED 1638
Arms. Rev. Double eagle. Matthias.

2. 1 Goldgulden 1619 .... 200.00

SALM-KYRBURG

Counts, and later, Princes of —

OTTO I, DIED 1607
Arms. Rev. Double eagle. Rudolph II.

1. 2 Ducats ND 400.00

JOHN PHILIP, OTTO LOUIS, JOHN CASIMIR AND OTTO
Arms with lion. Rev. Double eagle. Ferdinand II.

2. 1 Goldgulden ND 350.00

FREDERICK III, 1779-1794
Head. Rev. Arms.

3. 1 Carolin 1782 .... 175.00
4. 1 Ducat 1780, 82 .... 150.00

SAXONY

(The Albertine Line)

Electors, and later, Kings of —

ALBERT, 1464-1500
Orb in trefoil. Rev. St. John.

1. 1 Goldgulden ND 35.00

Shield on cross. Rev. Shield with double eagle supported by lions. Struck for Frisia.

2. 1 Goldgulden ND 300.00

GEORGE, 1500-1539
St. John. Rev. Orb in trefoil.

3. 1 Goldgulden ND 200.00

Arms. Rev. St. Boniface. Struck for Frisia.

4. 1 Goldgulden ND 300.00

GEORGE AND HENRY, 1500-1505
St. John. Rev. Orb in trefoil.

5. 1 Goldgulden ND 200.00

MAURICE, 1547-1553
Arms. Rev. Legend. On the Siege of Leipzig.

6. 10 Ducats 1547. Round 1500.00
7. 4 Ducats 1547. Square 600.00
8. 2 Ducats 1547. Square 300.00
9. 1 Ducat 1547. Square 175.00

Shield. Rev. Arms.

10. 2 Ducats 1552 .... 400.00
11. 1 Ducat ND 200.00

Elector standing. Rev. Five shields in quatrefoil.

12. 1 Goldgulden 1548 .... 350.00

AUGUST, 1553-1586
Bust with sword. Rev. Arms.

13. 2 Goldgulden 1554 .... 400.00

Bust with sword. Rev. Helmeted shield with lion.

14. 1 Goldgulden 1558 .... 300.00

Bust with sword. Rev. Two shields and orb.

15. 10 Goldgulden 1585 .... 1500.00

Bust. Rev. Arms.

16. 1 Goldgulden ND 200.00

Half length figure. Rev. Arms.

17. 1¼ Ducats ND 400.00
18. 1 Goldgulden ND 200.00

Half length figure. Rev. Five shields.

19. 1 Goldgulden 1585, ND 80.00

Arms within orb. Rev. Value.

20. 1 Goldgulden 1584 .... 175.00
21. 1 Goldgulden 1584. Square 200.00

CHRISTIAN I, 1586-1591

Armored bust. Rev. Cross and four shields.

22. 10 Ducats 1587, 90 .... 800.00
23. 5 Ducats 1587 .... 500.00
24. 2½ Ducats 1587 .... 300.00
25. 2 Ducats 1587, 90 ....* 250.00
26. 1 Ducat 1590 .... 125.00

Duke standing. Rev. Arms.

27. 1 Ducat 1589, 90 .... 175.00

FREDERICK WILLIAM, REGENT, 1591-1601
Bust. Rev. Arms.

28. 1 Ducat 1594 .... 200.00

SOPHIA, 1582-1622

Initials. Rev. "IHS."

29. 1 Ducat 1616 .... 22.50

CHRISTIAN II, 1601-1611
Half length figure. Rev. Cross and circle of shields.

30. 20 Ducats 1610 .... 1000.00
31. 10 Ducats 1606, 10 .... 600.00
32. 8 Ducats 1606 .... 500.00

JOHN GEORGE I, 1611-1656
Half length figure with sword, before helmet. Rev. Cross within circle of shields.

33. 5 Ducats 1614 .... 500.00

Half length figure with sword, a helmet in front. Rev. Arms.

34. 2 Ducats 1616 (swan) 75.00
35. 2 Ducats 1625 (HI) 125.00
36. 2 Goldgulden 1620 (swan) 300.00
37. 1 Goldgulden 1615 .... 200.00
38. 1 Goldgulden 1618-20 (swan) ....* 100.00
39. 1 Goldgulden 1625, 32 (HI) 200.00
40. 1 Goldgulden 1641 (CR) 200.00

Elector standing. Rev. Arms.

41.	2 Ducats 1620 (swan)	75.00
42.	2 Ducats 1628, 29, 32 (HI) ....*......	75.00
43.	2 Ducats 1635 (CM)	200.00
44.	2 Ducats 1636-39 (SD)	75.00
45.	2 Ducats 1640-46, 52, 54 (CR)	75.00
46.	1 Ducat 1622 (swan)	60.00
47.	1 Ducat 1627-30, 32-34 (HI)	40.00
48.	1 Ducat 1635 (CM)	60.00
49.	1 Ducat 1635-40 (SD)	40.00
50.	1 Ducat 1640-46, 48, 49, 52, 53, 55 (CR) ...	40.00
51.	½ Ducat 1651-53, 55 (CR)	50.00
52.	¼ Ducat 1651 (CR)	60.00

Bust of John George I. Rev. Bust of Frederick III. On the Reformation.

53.	2 Ducats 1617	50.00
54.	1 Ducat 1617	35.00

Elector on horse over arms. Rev. Legend. On the Vicariat.

55.	2 Ducats 1619	50.00
56.	1 Ducat 1619	35.00

Arms. Rev. St. George. On the baptism of Prince Henry.

57.	2 Ducats 1622	250.00
58.	1 Ducat 1622	100.00

Bust of John George I. Rev. Bust of John. On the Augsburg Confession.

59.	2 Ducats 1630 ....*......	50.00
60.	1 Ducat 1630	35.00

Legend. Rev. Patience standing. On the Peace of Prague.

61.	1 Ducat 1635	75.00

Facing bust with sword. Rev. Legend. On his death.

62.	2 Ducats 1656	150.00

JOHN GEORGE II, 1656-1680
Elector on horse. Rev. Legend. On the Vicariat.

63.	2 Ducats 1657	50.00
64.	1 Ducat 1657	30.00

Bust with sword; in front, elector's hat. Rev. Arms.

65.	2 Ducats 1659, 60, 62	100.00
66.	1 Ducat 1659, 60, 62, 64, 65, 72 ....*......	60.00
67.	½ Ducat 1659, 60, 62; 64, 65, 66	40.00

Bust. Rev. Arms.

68.	1 Goldgulden 1669	250.00

Elector on horse. Rev. Shield on obelisk.

69.	1 Ducat 1669	100.00

Elector on horse. Rev. Arms.

70.	1 Goldgulden 1670	300.00

Bust. Rev. Arms on palm branches.

71.	3 Ducats 1675, 79	250.00
72.	2 Ducats 1675, 76 ....*......	100.00

JOHN GEORGE III, 1680-1691

Bust. Rev. Arms on palm branches.

73.	2 Ducats 1681, 83, 85, 86, 88, 89, 91	125.00
74.	1½ Ducats 1681, 83, 84, 90, 91 ....*......	100.00

Bust with sword; in front, elector's hat. Rev. Arms on palm branches.

75.	1 Ducat 1681, 83, 84, 86, 87, 90, 91 ....*......	60.00
76.	½ Ducat 1683, 84, 88, 90, 91	40.00

Half length figure with sword, before elector's hat. Rev. Arms.

77.	2 Ducats 1685	250.00

Half length figure with sword. Rev. Arms.

78.	2 Ducats 1685	250.00

Bust. Rev. Crossed swords and four arms.

79.	1 Ducat 1686	75.00

Bust with sword, before helmet. Rev. Arms.

80.	2 Ducats 1691	250.00

Legend. Rev. Arms in clouds with flag. On his death.

81.	1 Ducat 1691	150.00

JOHN GEORGE IV, 1691-1694
Bust with sword, before elector's hat. Rev. Arms.

82.	1 Ducat 1691-94	75.00
83.	½ Ducat 1691-94	40.00

Bust. Rev. Crossed swords and four arms.

84.	2 Ducats 1692-94	125.00
85.	1½ Ducats 1692, 93	150.00

GERMANY-SAXONY (cont'd)

ANNA SOPHIA, DIED 1717
Ship. Rev. Legend under crown. On her death.

86.	1 Ducat 1717	70.00

FREDERICK AUGUST I (AUGUST II), 1694-1733
A. Coinage of the Dresden Mint.

Bust with sword. Rev. Arms.

87.	2 Ducats 1695 (IK)	250.00
88.	1 Ducat 1694 (IK)	100.00

Bust with sword. Rev. Lion with sword and arms.

89.	1 Ducat 1695-97 (IK)	75.00
90.	¼ Ducat 1696 (IK)	20.00

Bust. Rev. Lion with sword and arms.

91.	½ Ducat 1696 (IK)	30.00
92.	¼ Ducat 1696 (IK)	40.00

Elector standing to right, before desk. Rev. Elector's hat over two arms.

93.	2 Ducats 1696	80.00

Elector standing to left, before desk. Rev. Altar.

94.	2 Ducats 1696	60.00

Bust. Rev. Crowned arms.

95.	2 Ducats 1698, 1700-02, 04, 07, 11, 14 (ILH)	100.00
96.	2 Ducats 1717, 23, 27, 33 (IGS)	250.00
97.	1 Ducat 1698-1704, 06, 07, 10, 11, 13, 14 (ILH) ...	35.00
98.	1 Ducat 1716-18, 20-33 (IGS)	35.00
99.	1 Ducat 1733 from the ½ ducat die (IGS)	100.00
100.	½ Ducat 1699, 1701, 07, 10 (ILH)	40.00
101.	½ Ducat 1716, 17, 26, 29, 33 (IGS)	40.00
102.	¼ Ducat 1700, 10 (ILH)	20.00
103.	¼ Ducat 1717, 20-22, 27, 29, 33 (IGS)	20.00

Head. Rev. Crowned arms.

104.	1 Ducat 1721	200.00

Bust. Rev. Crowned initials.

105.	2 Ducats 1708, 09 (ILH)	100.00
106.	1 Ducat 1708, 09 (ILH)	60.00

Crowned initials. Rev. Crowned arms.

107.	2 Ducats 1710	250.00
108.	1 Ducat 1710	175.00
109.	½ Ducat 1710	40.00
110.	¼ Ducat from the ½ ducat die......................	60.00
111.	¼ Ducat 1710	30.00

B. Coinage of the Leipzig Mint.

Elector on horse. Rev. Arms on drapery.

112.	1½ Ducats 1697 (EPH)	200.00
113.	1 Ducat 1697 (EPH)	40.00
114.	1 Ducat 1697 (EPH) from the ½ ducat die	100.00
115.	1 Ducat 1697 (EPH) from the ¼ ducat die	100.00
116.	½ Ducat 1697 (EPH)	60.00
117.	¼ Ducat 1697 (EPH)	35.00

King on horse. Rev. Arms on trophies.

118.	2 Ducats 1702, 12 (EPH)	75.00
119.	1 Ducat 1702, 12 (EPH)	35.00

Bust. Rev. Crown over two arms.

120.	2 Ducats 1709 (EPH) from the ducat die	150.00
121.	1 Ducat 1702, 09 (EPH)	35.00
122.	½ Ducat 1702 (EPH)	40.00

Crowned bust on post. Rev. Crown over three arms.

123.	1 Ducat 1702 (EPH)	200.00

Crowned bust on post. Rev. Crowned initials and three arms.

124.	1 Ducat 1703 (EPH)	100.00
125.	1 Ducat 1703 (EPH) from the ½ ducat die	150.00
126.	½ Ducat 1703 (EPH)	150.00

C. Coinage on the Vicariat.

Elector on horse. Rev. Altar with insignia.

127.	2 Ducats 1711	50.00

Elector on horse. Rev. Two desks with insignia.

128.	2 Ducats 1711 (ILH)	40.00
129.	1 Ducat 1711 ....*......	30.00

Elector on horse. Rev. Sword and sceptre crossed.

130.	1 Ducat 1711	30.00

D. Commemorative Coinage

Elector on horse. Rev. Arms on drapery. Expedition to Hungary.

131.	2 Ducats 1695	200.00
132.	1 Ducat ND (1695), 1695	40.00

King on horse. Rev. Crown over legend. On the Coronation.

133.	2 Ducats 1697	50.00
134.	1 Ducat 1697 (O)	35.00

Bust. Rev. Crown. On the Coronation.

135.	2 Ducats 1697. FRID-AVG- etc.	50.00
136.	2 Ducats 1697. FRIDERICVS AVGVST etc.	50.00
137.	1 Ducat 1697	40.00

Arm with Polish sabre. Rev. Crown over legend. On the Coronation.

138.	1 Ducat 1697 (IK)	35.00

Bust, AVGVSTVS-II:REX POLONIAE. Rev. Crown. On the Coronation.

139.	1 Ducat ND. (1697) from the ½ ducat die	150.00
140.	½ Ducat ND (1697)	50.00

Bust of Frederick the Warlike with elector's hat and sword. Rev. City view of Leipzig. Jubilee of the University.

141.	2 Ducats 1709	150.00
142.	1 Ducat 1709	60.00

Rock and seven planets. Rev. Legend. From gold of the Freiberg mines.

143.	1 Ducat 1701	100.00

Rock and triangle. Rev. Legend. From gold of the Freiberg mines.

144.	1 Ducat 1709, 14	100.00

Head. Rev. Crown on cushion. Treaty of Lublin.

145.	1 Ducat 1715	60.00

Legend. Rev. Two hearts. On the wedding of his son to Maria Josepha of Austria.

146.	3 Ducats 1719 (IGS)	75.00
147.	2 Ducats 1719 (IGS)	50.00
148.	1 Ducat 1719 (IGS)	30.00

FREDERICK AUGUST II, 1733-1763
A. Coinage of the Dresden Mint.

Bust. Rev. Crowned arms.

149.	2 Ducats 1735-39 (FWôF)	250.00
150.	1 Ducat 1734 (IGS)	100.00
151.	1 Ducat 1735-45, 48-51, 55, 56 (FWôF)	40.00
152.	1 Ducat 1757 (IDB)	50.00
153.	1 Ducat 1760-63 (FWôF)	40.00
154.	1 Ducat 1757 (IDB) with FR (Fridericus Rex)	70.00
155.	½ Ducat 1735-37, 40, 43, 56 (FWôF)	25.00
156.	½ Ducat 1750. (AVGVSTVS III REX POL:	125.00

| 157. | ¼ Ducat 1734 (IGS) | 40.00 |
| 158. | ¼ Ducat 1735-37, 39, 40, 43 (FWôF) | 15.00 |

B. Coinage of the Leipzig Mint.

Crowned bust. Rev. Crowned arms.

159.	2	Ducats 1753, 54 (EDC)	75.00
160.	1	Ducat 1752 (IGG)	50.00
161.	1	Ducat 1753, 54, 56 (EDC)	50.00
162.	10	Taler 1753 (G)	80.00
163.	10	Taler 1754, 55, 56 (EDC)	80.00
165.	5	Taler 1753 (G)	60.00
165.	5	Taler 1754-56, 58 (EC)	50.00
166.	2½	Taler 1753 (G)	35.00

C. Coinage on the Vicariat.

Bust. Rev. Double eagle with arms.

| 167. | 1 Ducat 1740 | 40.00 |

Elector on horse. Rev. Throne.

| 168. | 1 Ducat 1741, 42 | 35.00 |

Bust. Rev. Crown over two arms.

| 169. | 1 Ducat 1745 | 50.00 |

Elector on horse. Rev. Flying eagle.

| 170. | 1 Ducat 1745 | 35.00 |

FREDERICK CHRISTIAN, 1763

Hymen floating. Rev. Legend. On his wedding with Antonia of Bavaria.

| 171. | 1 Ducat 1747 | 25.00 |

Bust. Rev. Crowned arms.

| 172. | 1 Ducat 1763 (FWôF) | 40.00 |

XAVIER, 1763-1768

Bust. Rev. Arms.

| 173. | 1 Ducat 1766-68 (EDC) | 40.00 |

FREDERICK AUGUST III (I. FROM 1806), 1763-1827

A. Coinage of the Dresden Mint.

Head. Rev. Arms.

| 174. | 1 Ducat 1764-78 (EDC) | 35.00 |
| 175. | 1 Ducat 1779-90 (IEC) | 35.00 |

Bust. Rev. Arms.

| 176. | 1 Ducat 1791-1804 (IEC) | 35.00 |
| 177. | 1 Ducat 1805, 06 (SGH) | 45.00 |

Armored bust. Rev. Two arms.

| 178. | 10 Taler 1777, 78 (EDC) | 100.00 |

Head. Rev. Two arms.

179.	10 Taler 1779-87, 90 (IEC)	80.00
180.	5 Taler 1777, 78 (EDC)	35.00
181.	5 Taler 1779, 82 (IEC)	35.00

Armored bust. Rev. Arms on branches.

182.	10 Taler 1791-1803 (IEC)	65.00
183.	10 Taler 1804-1806 (SGH)	80.00
184.	5 Taler 1802 (IEC)	75.00
185.	5 Taler 1806 (SGH)	65.00

B. Coinage of the Leipzig Mint.

Head. Rev. Arms.

| 186. | 1 Ducat 1764 (IFôF) | 40.00 |

C. Coinage on the Vicariat.

Bust. Rev. Double eagle with arms.

| 187. | 1 Ducat 1792 | 40.00 |

D. Coinage as Frederick August I.

Head. Rev. Arms.

188.	10 Taler 1806-17	*	85.00
189.	5 Taler 1806-17		60.00
190.	1 Ducat 1806-22		30.00
191.	1 Ducat 1806. Without D in the D.G. of legend	*	100.00

Uniformed bust. Rev. Arms.

192.	10 Taler 1818, 25-27		100.00
193.	5 Taler 1818, 25-27	*	80.00
194.	1 Ducat 1823-27		30.00

ANTON, 1827-1836

Head. Rev. Arms.

195.	10 Taler 1828-36	70.00
196.	5 Taler 1827-36	40.00
197.	1 Ducat 1827-36	30.00

FREDERICK AUGUST II, 1836-1854

Head. Rev. Arms in wreath.

| 198. | 1 Ducat 1836-38 | 30.00 |

Head. Rev. Draped arms.

199.	10	Taler 1836-53		70.00
200.	5	Taler 1837-54	*	40.00
201.	2½	Taler 1842-54		30.00

JOHN, 1854-1873

Head. Rev. Value.

| 202. | 1 Krone 1857-63, 65, 67, 68, 70, 71 | | 100.00 |
| 203. | ½ Krone 1857, 58, 62, 66, 68, 70 | * | 85.00 |

SAXON-ALTENBURG

Dukes of —

JOHN PHILIP AND HIS BROTHERS, 1602-1639

Four busts. Rev. Arms.

| 1. | 1 Goldgulden 1614, 19, 22 | 40.00 |

JOHN PHILIP AND FREDERICK WILLIAM II
Bust of John Philip. Rev. Arms.

2. 2 Ducats 1637, 38 . . . . **60.00**

Bust of John Philip. Rev. Bust of Frederick William.

3. 1 Ducat 1638 . . . . **40.00**

JOHN PHILIP

Bust. Rev. Legend. On his death.

4. 1 Ducat 1639 . . . . **150.00**

FREDERICK WILLIAM II, 1639-1669
Armored bust. Rev. Arms.

5. 1 Ducat 1640, 41, 42 . . . . **40.00**

Initials of Magdalene Sybil. Rev. Legend. On her death.

6. 1 Ducat 1668 . . . . **50.00**

Armored bust. Rev. Legend. On his death.

7. 1 Ducat 1669 . . . . **125.00**

SAXON-COBURG-GOTHA

Dukes of —

ERNST, 1826-1844

Head. Rev. Value and Arms

1. 1 Ducat 1831, 36, 42 . . . . **50.00**

SAXON-EISENACH

Dukes of —

JOHN WILLIAM, 1690-1729

Armored bust. Rev. Arms and four initials.

1. 1 Ducat 1700 . . . . **100.00**

Arms and four initials. Rev. Crane.

2. 1 Ducat 1716 . . . . **65.00**

SAXON-EISENBERG

Dukes of —

CHRISTIAN, 1675-1707
Armored bust. Rev. Two arms in clouds and heart on altar.

1. 1 Ducat 1682 . . . . **100.00**

Bust. Rev. Arms.

2. 2 Ducats 1682 . . . . **300.00**
3. ½ Ducat 1683. Thick **75.00**
4. ¼ Ducat 1683, ND . . . . * **40.00**

Armored bust. Rev. Table with sword and palm.

5. 1 Ducat 1686 . . . . **200.00**

Bust. Rev. Oval arms.

6. 2 Ducats 1697. Thick **150.00**
7. 1 Ducat 1697 . . . . * **100.00**
8. ½ Ducat ND **60.00**

Arms. Rev. Palm tree. "Alchemical" gold issue.

9. 1 Goldgulden 1684 . . . . **200.00**

SAXON-ERNESTINE

Electors of —

FREDERICK II, 1428-1464
St. John. Rev. Orb in trefoil.

1. 1 Goldgulden ND **50.00**

FREDERICK III, ALBERT AND JOHN
St. John. Rev. Orb in quatrefoil.

2. 1 Goldgulden 1498-1500, ND **40.00**

FREDERICK III, GEORGE AND JOHN, 1498-1507
St. John. Rev. Orb.

3. 1 Goldgulden 1498, 99, ND **40.00**

FREDERICK III, JOHN AND GEORGE
St. John. Rev. Orb.

4. 1 Goldgulden 1500, ND **40.00**

FREDERICK III, 1486-1525
Bust with hat. Rev. Cross.

5. 2 Ducats 1522 . . . . **300.00**

JOHN FREDERICK, 1532-1553
Bust. Rev. Double eagle. Name of Charles V.

6. 2 Goldgulden 1552 . . . . **350.00**

SAXON-GOTHA

Dukes of —

A. Old Gotha

JOHN FREDERICK, 1554-1595
Arms. Rev. Two angels with wreath.

1. 1 Ducat 1566, ND 300.00

Arms and date. Rev. Blank. On the Siege of Gotha.

2. 1 Ducat 1567. Square 150.00

JOHN CASIMIR, 1572-1633

Armored bust. Rev. Legend. On his death.

3. 2 Ducats 1633 .... 125.00

JOHN ERNST, 1572-1638
Bust. Rev. Arms.

4. 1 Ducat 1635, 36, 37 .... 40.00
5. 1 Ducat 1637, 38. With GOTT BESS etc. 40.00

Bust. Rev. Legend. On his death.

6. 1 Ducat 1638 .... 75.00

B. New Gotha

ERNST, 1640-1675

Name of Jehovah over legend. Rev. Arms over legend. On the Peace of Westphalia.

7. 2 Ducats 1650 .... 80.00
8. 1 Ducat 1650 .... 50.00
9. ½ Ducat 1650 ....* 35.00

Arms. Rev. Legend.

10. ½ Ducat 1673 .... 50.00
11. ¼ Ducat 1675 ....* 25.00

Bust. Rev. Legend. On his death.

12. 1 Ducat 1675 .... 75.00

FREDERICK I, 1675-1691
Bust. Rev. Arms.

13. 1 Ducat 1681 .... 75.00

Laureate head of Magdalene Sybil. Rev. Legend. On her death.

14. 1 Ducat 1681 .... 200.00

Fortuna on globe. Rev. Arms.

15. 1 Goldgulden 1684 .... 100.00

Bust. Rev. Four arms and four initials.

16. 1 Ducat 1689 .... 50.00
17. ½ Ducat 1689, 90 .... 50.00

Head with wig. Rev. Ship.

18. 1 Ducat 1690 .... 85.00
19. ½ Ducat 1690 .... 50.00

Head. Rev. Star of the Elephant Order, crossed initials and arms.

20. 1 Ducat 1690 .... 200.00

Bust. Rev. Arms.

21. ¼ Ducat 1682, 84 .... 25.00

Armored bust. Rev. Legend. On his death.

22. 1 Ducat 1691 .... 60.00

FREDERICK II AND JOHN WILLIAM, 1691-1707

Busts of Bernard and Henry. Rev. Two hands in clouds.

23. 1 Ducat 1692. Homage of Gotha 60.00

FREDERICK II, 1691-1732
Bust. Rev. Arms.

24. 2 Ducats 1699, 1707 .... 150.00
25. 1 Ducat 1694, 98, 99, 1707 .... 100.00
26. ½ Ducat 1702 .... 35.00

Bust. Rev. Legend. On the Reformation.

27. 2 Ducats 1717 .... 75.00

Bust. Rev. Oak tree. On the Reformation.

28. 1 Ducat 1717 .... 50.00

Bust. Rev. Legend. On the Augsburg Confession.

28a. 2 Ducats 1730 .... 200.00

FREDERICK III, 1732-1772

Bust. Rev. Arms.

29. 1 Ducat 1732 .... 65.00

Armored bust. Rev. Legend. On the religious peace.

30. 2 Ducats 1755 .... **125.00**

Armored bust. Rev. Arms. On the religious peace.

31. 1 Ducat 1755 .... **50.00**

SAXON-HILDBURGHAUSEN

Dukes of —

ERNST FREDERICK, 1715-1724
Bust. Rev. Legend. On the Reformation.

1. ½ Ducat 1717 .... **75.00**

ERNST FREDERICK CHARLES, 1745-1780
Bust. Rev. Arms.

2. 1 Ducat 1771 .... **175.00**

SAXON-LAUENBURG

Dukes of —

JULIUS HENRY, 1656-1665

Bust. Rev. Arms.

1. 2 Ducats 1662 .... **300.00**
2. 1 Ducat 1657, 62 ....*...... **125.00**

Bust. Rev. Madonna.

3. 1 Ducat 1659 .... **200.00**

JULIUS FRANCIS, 1666-1689

Bust. Rev. Arms.

4. 2 Ducats 1673, ND **250.00**
5. 1 Ducat 1670, 73, ND ....*...... **125.00**

SAXON-MEININGEN

Dukes of —

BERNARD, 1680-1706
Armored bust. Rev. Arms.

1. 1 Ducat 1687, 88 .... **75.00**

Armored bust. Rev. Meiningen Castle.

2. 2 Ducats 1692 .... **150.00**
3. 1 Ducat 1692 .... **100.00**

ERNST LOUIS I, 1706-1724

Busts of the Duke and his wife. Rev. Two shields.

4. 1 Ducat 1714. On the marriage **75.00**
5. 1 Ducat 1717. On the Reformation ....*..... **75.00**

SAXON-ROEMHILD

Dukes of —

HENRY, 1680-1710
Bust. Rev. Arms.

1. 1 Ducat 1698. Three varieties of the Rev. **250.00**

SAXON-SAALFELD

Dukes of —

JOHN ERNST VIII, 1680-1729
Armored bust. Rev. Arms.

1. 1 Ducat 1698, 1720, 21, 27 .... **65.00**
2. ½ Ducat 1725, 28 .... **40.00**
3. ¼ Ducat 1725, 27, 28 .... **25.00**

Armored bust. Rev. Bust of Luther. On the Reformation.

4. 2 Ducats 1717 .... **125.00**
5. 1 Ducat 1717 .... **50.00**

Armored half length bust. Rev. City view of Reichmansdorf.

6. 1 Mining Ducat 1717, 19, 21, 22, 26-28 .... **100.00**

CHRISTIAN ERNST AND FRANCIS JOSIAS, 1729-1745

Initials in shields. Rev. Arms supported by lions.

7. 1 Ducat 1740 .... **65.00**

Duke kneeling. Rev. Bust of his brother.

8. 1 Ducat 1745 .... **75.00**

Initials. Rev. Arms.

9. ¼ Ducat 1738, 43 .... **20.00**

CHRISTIAN ERNST, 1729-1745

Duke kneeling. Rev. Eagle and sun. On his death.

10.	2 Ducats ND	50.00
11.	1 Ducat ND ....*.....	25.00

FRANCIS JOSIAS, 1745-1764

Lion with initials in shield. Rev. Arms.

12.	1 Ducat 1746, 49	50.00

Initials in shield. Rev. Arms.

13.	¼ Ducat 1752	15.00

ERNST FREDERICK, 1764-1800

Bust. Rev. City view of Reichmansdorf.

14.	1 Mining Ducat 1766	200.00

SAXON-WEIMAR

Dukes of —

JOHN ERNST AND HIS SEVEN BROTHERS, 1605-1640
Four busts on each side.

1.	1 Goldgulden 1613-15, 19	50.00

JOHN ERNST AND HIS FIVE BROTHERS

Arms. Rev. Shield.

2.	1 Goldgulden 1623	75.00

BERNARD, DIED 1639
Arms. Rev. Christ standing.

3.	1 Goldgulden 1634	350.00

WILLIAM, 1630-1662
Arms. Rev. Jehovah and legend.

4.	1 Ducat 1651	60.00
5.	½ Ducat 1651, 52	35.00
6.	¼ Ducat 1651	15.00

Bust. Rev. Trophies and legend.

7.	2 Ducats 1654	300.00
8.	½ Ducat 1654 ....*.....	40.00

Arms. Rev. Legend.

9.	1 Ducat 1651	100.00

10.	½ Ducat 1651, 56 ....*.....		70.00
11.	¼ Ducat 1658		50.00

Arms of Henneberg. Rev. Legend.

12.	1 Ducat 1661	125.00

Bust. Rev. Jena Castle.

13.	1 Ducat 1661	100.00

Bust. Rev. Arms.

14.	¼ Ducat 1662	25.00

WILLIAM ERNST, 1683-1728
Bust. Rev. Weimar Castle.

15.	1 Ducat 1717	75.00

Table with book and lamp. Rev. Legend. On the Reformation.

16.	2 Ducats 1717	200.00
17.	1 Ducat 1717 ....*.....	50.00

ERNST AUGUST, 1728-1748
Hercules and lion. Rev. Mountain.

18.	1 Ducat ND	50.00

Initials in shield. Rev. Legend.

19.	1 Ducat 1745	80.00

Bust amid trophies. Rev. Rose bush and sheep.

20.	1 Ducat ND	75.00

FREDERICK III, ADMINISTRATOR
Bust. Rev. Felicitas standing.

21.	1 Ducat 1752	100.00

Bust. Rev. Arms.

22.	1 Ducat 1754	100.00

ERNST AUGUST CONSTANTINE, 1756-1758
Bust. Rev. City view of Eisenach.

23.	1 Ducat 1756. Homage of Eisenach	60.00

Bust. Rev. Hilarity.

24.	1 Ducat 1756	60.00

Initials. Rev. Hilarity standing.

25.	1 Ducat 1756	50.00

Armored bust. Rev. Arms and value.

26.	1 Pistole ND	250.00

ANNE AMALIA, 1758-1775
Bust. Rev. Arms.

27.	1 Ducat 1764	250.00

Bust. Rev. Arms and value.

28.	1 Pistole 1764	250.00

SAXON-WEISSENFELS

Dukes of —

JOHN ADOLPH, 1680-1697
Initials of Joan Magdalene, his wife. Rev. Legend. On her death.

1.	1 Ducat 1686	150.00

JOHN GEORGE, 1697-1712
Duke standing. Rev. Arms.

2.	1 Ducat 1698	200.00

GERMANY-SAXON-WEISSENFELS (cont'd)

Bust. Rev. Two shields.

3. 1 Ducat ND 200.00

CHRISTIAN, 1712-1736
Bust. Rev. Stag.

4. 1 Ducat 1726, ND 75.00

Bust. Rev. Luther kneeling. On the Reformation.

5. 1 Ducat 1717 .... 50.00

SAYN-SAYN

SAYN-SAYN

Counts of —

HENRY, 1568-1606
Arms. Rev. Double eagle. Rudolph II.

1. 2 Goldgulden 1592 .... 400.00
2. 1 Goldgulden 1590 .... 250.00

SAYN-WITTGENSTEIN

Counts of —

LOUIS, 1607-1634

Arms. Rev. Double eagle. Ferdinand II.

1. 1 Goldgulden ND 75.00

Arms. Rev. Orb.

2. 1 Goldgulden ND. (Zwitter) 125.00
3. 1 Goldgulden ND. Title of Ferdinand II. 100.00

Three shields. Rev. Double eagle. Ferdinand II.

4. 1 Goldgulden ND 75.00

Three shields. Rev. Orb.

5. 1 Goldgulden ND. SI DEUS PRO NOBIS etc. 175.00
6. 1 Goldgulden ND. Title of Ferdinand II. 150.00

Two shields. Rev. Orb. Ferdinand II.

7. 1 Goldgulden ND 100.00

JOHN, DIED 1657

Bust. Rev. Arms.

8. 1 Ducat 1654 .... 350.00

GUSTAV, 1658-1701
Bust with wig. Rev. Castle, rock and goat.

9. 2 Ducats 1687 .... 400.00

SCHAUENBURG

Counts of —

ADOLPH XIII, 1576-1601
Count on horse. Rev. Arms.

1. 20 Ducats 1592 .... 1,500.00

Three shields. Rev. Orb. Rudolph II.

2. 1 Goldgulden 1589, 92, 93, 95, 1600 .... 250.00

ERNST III, 1601-1622
Arms. Rev. Double eagle.

3. 1 Goldgulden 1603, 04, 08, 10, 12. Rudolph II. 250.00
4. 1 Goldgulden 1616. Matthias 250.00

Count on horse. Rev. Dragon over wall.

5. 20 Ducats ND 1,500.00

Count on horse. Rev. Arms.

6. 20 Ducats ND 1,500.00
7. 10 Ducats ND. 45 or 51 millimetres 750.00
8. 5 Ducats ND 500.00

SCHAUMBURG-LIPPE

Counts, and later, Princes of —

WILLIAM, 1748-1777

Head. Rev. Arms.

1. 10 Taler 1763 .... 125.00
2. 1 Ducat 1762 .... * 75.00

PHILIP ERNST, 1777-1787
Arms. Rev. Legend.

3. 1 Ducat 1777 .... 75.00

Bust. Rev. Tablet.

4. 1 Ducat 1783 .... 100.00

GEORGE WILLIAM, 1807-1860

Head. Rev. Arms.

5. 10 Taler 1829 .... 200.00

SCHLESWIG-HOLSTEIN

(See under Denmark, period 1523-1559)

SCHLESWIG-HOLSTEIN-GLUCKSBURG

Dukes of —

PHILIP ERNST, 1698-1729
Arms. Rev. Initials.

1. 1 Ducat 1716 .... 125.00

SCHLESWIG-HOLSTEIN-GOTTORP

Dukes of —

JOHN ADOLPH, 1590-1616
Duke standing. Rev. Arms.

1. 1 Ducat 1601 .... 125.00

FREDERICK III, 1616-1659

Bust. Rev. Arms.

2. 1 Goldgulden 1619 .... 150.00
3. 1 Ducat 1642 .... 100.00

Duke standing. Rev. Arms.

4. 1 Goldgulden 1627 .... 175.00

CHRISTIAN ALBERT, 1659-1694
Bust. Rev. Arms.

5. 5 Ducats 1674 .... 500.00
6. 1 Ducat 1664, 74, 89 .... 75.00

Bust. Rev. Orb.

7. 1 Goldgulden 1664 .... 175.00

Bust. Rev. Mountain.

8. 1 Ducat 1689 .... 75.00

FREDERICK IV, 1694-1702

Arms and lions. Rev. Holm Fortress.

9. 1 Ducat 1698 .... 175.00

Bust. Rev. Arms with two lions.

10. 1 Ducat 1698, 1700 .... 85.00

Bust. Rev. Arms.

11. 1 Ducat 1698 .... 175.00

Bust. Rev. Lions in shield and six arms.

12. 1 Ducat 1698 .... 125.00

CHARLES FREDERICK, 1702-1739
Head. Rev. Lion shield.

13. ¼ Ducat 1711 .... 25.00

Head. Rev. Arms supported by lions.

14. 1 Ducat 1705 .... 65.00

Head. Rev. Arms.

15. 1 Ducat 1706 .... 65.00

Bust. Rev. Arms.

16. 1 Ducat 1712 .... 85.00

Bust. Rev. Lion shield.

17. 1 Ducat 1710, 11, ND 75.00

Arms. Rev. Initials.

18. 1 Ducat 1710 .... 125.00

Lion shield. Rev. Initials.

19. ¼ Ducat 1708 .... 25.00

SCHLESWIG-HOLSTEIN-PLOEN

Dukes of —

JOHN ADOLPH, 1671-1704
Arms. Rev. Initials.

1. 1 Ducat 1677 .... 150.00

Bust. Rev. Arms.

2. 1 Ducat 1690 .... 150.00

FREDERICK CHARLES, 1722-1761

Bust. Rev. Arms.

3. 1 Ducat 1760. Year under arms ....*...... 125.00
4. 1 Ducat 1760. Value under arms 125.00

SCHLESWIG-HOLSTEIN-SONDERBÜRG

Dukes of —

JOHN THE YOUNGER, 1564-1622
Bust. Rev. Orb.

1. 1 Goldgulden 1619 .... 125.00

ALEXANDER, 1622-1627
Arms. Rev. Orb.

2. 1 Goldgulden 1624 .... 100.00

SCHWARZBURG

Counts of —

THE SONS OF ALBERT VII, 1605-1613
Three helmets. Rev. Arms.

1. 1 Goldgulden 1606 .... 150.00

Three helmets. Rev. Cross and five shields.

2. 1 Goldgulden 1606, 08. Mint: Erfurt 100.00
3. 1 Goldgulden 1611, 13, 16, 18. Mint: Saalfeld 100.00

SCHWARZBURG-RUDOLSTADT

Princes of —

GUNTHER XLIII, 1718-1740
Arms. Rev. Legend. From gold of the Goldisthal Mines.

1. 1 Ducat 1737 .... 300.00

LOUIS FREDERICK II, 1793-1807

Double eagle. Rev. Value.

2. 1 Ducat 1803 .... 75.00

SCHWARZBURG-SONDERSHAUSEN

Princes of —

CHRISTIAN WILLIAM, 1666-1721
Bust. Rev. Shield.

1. ¼ Ducat 1684, 86 .... 40.00

Bust. Rev. Arms between wild man and wild woman.

2. 1 Ducat 1679, 84, 89 .... 100.00

ANTON GUNTHER II, 1697-1716
Bust. Rev. Arms.

3. 1 Ducat 1680 .... 150.00

SILESIA

Evangelic States of —

Silesian eagle. Rev. "Jehova" beneath radiate clouds.

1. 1 Ducat 1634 .... 100.00

SILESIA-JAEGERNDORF

Dukes of —

GEORGE FREDERICK OF BRANDENBURG, 1543-1603
Duke standing. Rev. Arms.

1. 4 Ducats 1592. Thick 1000.00
2. 2 Ducats 1592. Thick 750.00
3. 1 Ducat 1561, 92, 95, 96 .... 300.00

Arms. Rev. Double eagle. Name of Ferdinand I.

4. 1 Ducat 1563 .... 350.00

Arms. Rev. Double eagle. Name of Rudolph II.

5. 1 Ducat 1578 .... 350.00

JOHN GEORGE OF BRANDENBURG, 1606-1621
Half-length bust. Rev. Oval arms with three helmets.

6. 12 Ducats ND 2000.00
7. 10 Ducats ND 1750.00
8. 5 Ducats ND 1000.00
9. 4 Ducats ND 1000.00

Half-length bust to right. Rev. Arms with three helmets.

10. 10 Ducats 1611 .... 1750.00
11. 8 Ducats 1611 .... 1500.00
12. 7 Ducats 1611 .... 1500.00
13. 5 Ducats 1611. Two sizes 1000.00
14. 4 Ducats ND 750.00

Bust. Rev. Arms with three helmets.

15. 4 Ducats 1610 .... 1000.00
16. 3 Ducats 1610 .... 750.00

Half-length bust facing. Rev. Arms with three helmets.

17. 10 Ducats 1611 .... 1750.00

Duke standing. Rev. Crowned oval arms.

18. 3 Ducats ND 500.00
19. 2 Ducats 1618, 20, 21, ND ....*...... 150.00

Duke standing. Rev. Arms with three helmets.

20. 1 Ducat 1610 .... 300.00

Duke standing. Rev. Crowned arms.

21. 1 Ducat 1611 .... 300.00

Half-length bust. Rev. Crowned arms.

22. 1 Ducat 1612, 20 .... 150.00
23. 1 Ducat 1614, 16, 17. With oval arms 150.00

Crowned arms. Rev. Legend.

24. 2 Ducats 1617. Thick 350.00
25. 1 Ducat 1620. Thick 200.00
26. ½ Ducat 1615, 17, 20-22 ....*...... 100.00

SILESIA-LIEGNITZ-BRIEG

Dukes of —

WENCESLAS, 1348-1364
Lily. Rev. St. John.

1. 1 Goldgulden ND 60.00

FREDERICK II, 1488-1547
Bust. Rev. Arms.

2. 5 Ducats 1545 .... 750.00
3. 1 Ducat 1543, 44 .... 150.00

JOAQUIM FREDERICK, 1587-1602

Bust. Rev. Arms.

4. 1 Ducat 1600 .... 100.00

Bust. Rev. Legend. On his death.

5. 5 Ducats 1602 .... 600.00
6. 2 Ducats 1602 .... 300.00

JOHN CHRISTIAN AND GEORGE RUDOLPH, 1602-1621

Two busts facing. Rev. Crowned arms.

7. 1 Ducat 1604-06 .... 35.00

Two busts facing each other. Rev. Crowned arms.

8. 2 Ducats 1608. Square 175.00
9. 2 Ducats 1609 ....*...... 75.00
10. 1 Ducat 1606-09 .... 35.00
11. ½ Ducat ND 60.00

Two busts facing each other. Rev. Arms with three helmets.

12.	10 Ducats 1609, 10, 17, 19	....	500.00
13.	7 Ducats 1610	....	400.00
14.	6 Ducats 1607, 17, 19, 21	....	350.00
15.	5 Ducats 1608-10, 19, 21	....	200.00
16.	4 Ducats 1605, 07, 09, 10	..................*	175.00
17.	3 Ducats 1610, 13	....	125.00
18.	1 Ducat 1620	....	100.00
19.	½ Ducat 1620	....	100.00

Half-length bust to right over two arms. Rev. Half-length bust to left of George Rudolph over two arms.

20.	10 Ducats 1609	....	750.00

Bust to right between two arms. Rev. Bust of George Rudolph to left between two arms.

21.	10 Ducats 1611	....	500.00
22.	6 Ducats 1611	....	350.00
23.	5 Ducats 1611, 17	....	200.00
24.	4 Ducats 1611	..................*	150.00
25.	4 Ducats 1610, 11. Square	....	300.00
26.	3 Ducats 1611, 17, 19	....	125.00
27.	3 Ducats 1610. Square	....	250.00
28.	2 Ducats 1609-11	....	80.00
29.	2 Ducats 1610. Square	....	175.00
30.	1 Ducat 1610, 11, 19	....	35.00

Crowned arms. Rev. Legend.

31.	1 Ducat 1610. Thick	....	150.00
32.	½ Ducat 1610. Legend in 6 lines	..............*	50.00
33.	½ Ducat 1610. Legend in 5 lines	....	75.00

Two busts facing each other. Rev. Crown over two arms.

34.	1 Ducat 1612	....	65.00

Two busts facing each other over two arms. Rev. Legend.

35.	1 Ducat 1619. Thick	....	150.00
36.	½ Ducat 1619	....	75.00
37.	½ Ducat 1619. Square	....	100.00

Crown over two arms. Rev. Legend.

38.	¼ Ducat 1619	....	100.00
39.	¼ Ducat 1619. Square	....	100.00

Bust to right between two arms. Rev. Bust of George Rudolph to left between two arms. Struck at Reichenstein.

40.	4 Ducats 1614	....	400.00
41.	2 Ducats 1614	....	300.00
42.	1 Ducat 1614	....	200.00

Two busts facing. Rev. Arms with three helmets. Struck at Reichenstein.

43.	10 Ducats 1617	....	650.00
44.	8 Ducats 1617	....	600.00
45.	6 Ducats 1615, 16	....	400.00
46.	5 Ducats 1615, 16	....	250.00

JOHN CHRISTIAN, DIED 1639

Bust. Rev. Arms with three helmets.

47.	7 Ducats 1621	....	400.00
48.	5 Ducats 1622. Kreuzberg	....	250.00
49.	4 Ducats 1622	....	350.00
50.	3 Ducats 1622	....	350.00
51.	3 Ducats 1622. Square	....	400.00

GEORGE RUDOLPH, DIED 1653

Bust. Rev. Crowned arms.

52.	5 Ducats 1621	....	250.00
53.	3 Ducats 1622	....	200.00
54.	2 Ducats 1622	....	150.00

Bust. Rev. Arms with three helmets.

55.	8 Ducats 1621	....	500.00
56.	7 Ducats 1621	....	450.00
57.	6 Ducats 1621	....	400.00
58.	1 Ducat 1621	....	75.00

Facing bust. Rev. Legend. On his death.

59.	2 Ducats 1653	....	150.00

GEORGE, LOUIS AND CHRISTIAN, 1639-1663

Three half-length busts. Rev. Arms with three helmets.

60.	5 Ducats 1656, 58, 59	....	250.00
61.	4 Ducats 1652, 58, 59	....	300.00
62.	3 Ducats 1651, 58, 60	....	200.00
63.	2 Ducats 1651, 53, 57-59	..................*	60.00
64.	1 Ducat 1651-62	....	30.00
65.	½ Ducat 1651, 52, 52/53, 52/54, 56	....	20.00

GEORGE III, 1639-1664

Crowned bust. Rev. Arms with three helmets.

66.	1 Ducat 1660	..................*	60.00
67.	1 Ducat 1664. Reichenstein	....	150.00

Facing bust. Rev. Legend. On his death.

68.	2 Ducats 1664	....	150.00

GERMANY-SILESIA-LIEGNITZ-BRIEG (cont'd)

LOUIS, 1653-1663

Crowned bust. Rev. Arms with three helmets.

69.	1 Ducat 1661 ....*......	60.00
70.	1 Ducat 1662. With DUCES	100.00

CHRISTIAN, 1639-1673

Crowned bust. Rev. Arms with three helmets.

71.	1 Ducat 1660. With DUCES ....*......	60.00
72.	1 Ducat 1661. Two different legends on Rev.	60.00

Bust. Rev. Eagle.

73.	10 Ducats 1666	750.00
74.	5 Ducats 1672	500.00
75.	3 Ducats 1666	350.00
76.	2 Ducats 1666, 70, 72 ....*......	100.00
77.	1 Ducat 1666, 70, 72	50.00

LOUISE OF ANHALT, DIED 1680

Facing bust. Rev. Two arms.

78.	¼ Ducat 1674	50.00

GEORGE WILLIAM, 1672-1675

Bust. Rev. Eagle.

79.	2 Ducats 1675	300.00
80.	1 Ducat 1674, 75 ....*......	60.00
81.	¼ Ducat 1675	40.00

Facing bust. Rev. Eagle.

82.	1 Ducat 1675. Thick	175.00
83.	½ Ducat 1675 ....*......	50.00

Bust. Rev. Legend. On his death.

84.	2 Ducats 1675	200.00

SILESIA-MUNSTERBERG

Duke of —

JOHN WEIKHARD OF AUERSPERG, 1654-1677
Facing bust. Rev. Arms.

1.	1 Ducat ND	150.00

SILESIA-MUNSTERBERG-OELS

Dukes of —

ALBERT AND CHARLES, 1498-1511

St. James standing. Rev. Arms on cross.

1.	1 Goldgulden ND	250.00

St. James standing. Rev. Cross and four arms.

2.	1 Goldgulden 1510, 11	150.00

CHARLES I, 1498-1536
Bust. Rev. Arms.

3.	2 Ducats 1528	400.00

St. James standing. Rev. Cross and four arms.

4.	1 Goldgulden 1512-19 ....*......	80.00
5.	1 Goldgulden 1515, 22, ND. With name on Rev.	100.00

Arms. Rev. St. Christopher.

6.	1 Ducat 1520-22, 26-36	60.00

JOAQUIM, HENRY II, JOHN AND GEORGE, 1536-1558

Arms. Rev. St. Christopher.

7.	1 Ducat 1537-53	50.00

JOAQUIM, HENRY III AND CHARLES II, 1552-1562

Arms. Rev. St. Christopher.

8.	1 Ducat 1553-58, 60-62	60.00

GERMANY-SILESIA-MUNSTERBERG-OELS (cont'd)

JOHN, DIED 1565

Bust. Rev. Arms.

9. 1 Ducat 1553-62 .... 70.00

Bust. Rev. Five shields.

10. 1 Ducat 1563, 64, 65 .... 80.00

HENRY III AND CHARLES II, 1562-1587

Five shields. Rev. St. Christopher.

11. 1 Ducat 1563-70 .... 70.00

Arms. Rev. St. Christopher.

12. 1 Ducat 1569 .... 70.00

CHARLES II, 1548-1617

Bust. Rev. Arms.

13. 2 Ducats 1593. Thick 250.00
14. 1 Ducat 1593 ....*...... 80.00

Bust. Rev. Arms with three helmets.

15. 10 Ducats 1612, 13, 16 .... 750.00
16. 9 Ducats 1612 .... 750.00
17. 6 Ducats 1611, 15, 16 .... 400.00
18. 5 Ducats 1611-13, 15, 16 ....*...... 300.00
19. 4 Ducats 1613, 15 .... 250.00
20. 3 Ducats 1613, 14 .... 200.00
21. 2 Ducats 1614, 15 .... 125.00

Bust. Rev. Five shields.

22. 4 Ducats 1612 .... 300.00
23. 3 Ducats 1612 .... 250.00

Bust. Rev. Crowned arms.

24. 2 Ducats 1612 .... 300.00
25. 1 Ducat 1611-16 .... 80.00

Eagle. Rev. Four shields.

26. ½ Ducat 1612 .... 50.00

Eagle. Rev. Crowned arms.

27. ½ Ducat 1616 .... 50.00

Bust over arms. Rev. Legend. On his death.

28. 12½ Ducats 1617 .... 800.00
29. 10 Ducats 1617 .... 750.00
30. 6 Ducats 1617 .... 400.00

Bust. Rev. Legend. On his death.

31. 2 Ducats 1617 .... 200.00

HENRY WENCESLAS AND CHARLES FREDERICK, 1617-1639

Two busts facing each other. Rev. Arms with three helmets.

32. 5 Ducats 1620, 21 .... 300.00
33. 4 Ducats 1619, 21 .... 250.00
34. 3 Ducats 1619, 21, 22 ....*...... 200.00

Half-length bust to right. Rev. Half-length bust of Charles Frederick to left. Five shields are on each side.

35. 6 Ducats 1619 .... 400.00
36. 4 Ducats 1620 .... 250.00
37. 3 Ducats 1620, 21 .... 200.00
38. 2 Ducats 1621 .... 150.00

Bust to right. Rev. Bust of Charles Frederick to left.

39. 1 Ducat 1619, 20, 21 .... 125.00

SILESIA-SCHWEIDNITZ

Dukes of —

BOLCO II, 1326-1368
Lily. Rev. St. John.

1. 1 Goldgulden ND 80.00

SILESIA-TESCHEN

Dukes of —

ADAM WENCESLAS, 1579-1617
Half-length bust. Rev. Helmeted eagle-shield supported by angels.

1. 5 Ducats 1611 .... 500.00

Half-length bust. Rev. Eagle.

2. 8 Ducats 1609 .... 750.00
3. 5 Ducats 1609 .... 600.00

Bust. Rev. Eagle.

4. 3 Ducats 1613. Square 400.00

ELISABETH LUCRETIA, 1625-1653
Facing bust. Rev. Arms.

5. 10 Ducats 1650 .... 1000.00
6. 5 Ducats 1650 .... 750.00

SILESIA-TROPPAU

Dukes of —

PRZEMISLAW, 1366-1433
Arms. Rev. Duke standing with flag and sword.

1. 1 Goldgulden ND 600.00

SILESIA-WURTTEMBERG-OELS

Counts of —

SYLVIUS FREDERICK, 1673-1697

Bust. Rev. Arms.

1. 2 Ducats 1677 .... 400.00
2. 1 Ducat 1674, 75, 76 ....* 150.00

Bust. Rev. Bust of Eleonore Charlotte. On their wedding.

3. 1 Ducat ND (1672) 100.00

CHRISTIAN ULRIC, 1673-1704
Bust. Rev. Helmeted arms.

4. 1 Ducat 1679, 98, 1701, 03 .... 350.00

Bust. Rev. Crowned arms.

5. 1 Ducat 1681, 83 .... 350.00
6. ½ Ducat 1683 .... 125.00
7. ¼ Ducat 1685 ....* 50.00

Bust. Rev. Five shields and four initials crossed.

8. 1 Ducat 1696 .... 200.00

Bust of Sybil Marie. Rev. Blank.

9. ½ Ducat ND. Square 50.00

Bust. Rev. Bust of Sophia of Mecklenburg. On his wedding.

10. 1 Ducat ND. (1700) Two different dies 75.00

CHARLES OF JULIUSBURG, 1684-1745
Bust. Rev. Arms.

11. 1 Ducat 1705 .... 350.00

CHARLES FREDERICK, 1704-1744
Bust. Rev. Arms.

12. 1 Ducat 1708, 11, 13, 14 .... 350.00

SINZENDORF

Counts of —

GEORGE LOUIS, 1632-1680
Bust with cap. Rev. Arms.

1. 1 Ducat 1676 .... 200.00

PHILIP LOUIS, 1687-1742
Bust. Rev. Arms.

2. 1 Ducat 1726 .... 75.00

JOHN WILLIAM, 1742-1766

Bust. Rev. Arms.

3. 1 Ducat 1753 .... 75.00

SOLMS-LAUBACH

Counts of —

CHRISTIAN AUGUST, 1738-1784
Bust. Rev. Arms and value.

1. 1 Ducat 1761 .... 100.00

SOLMS-LICH

Counts of —

ERNST I, EBERHARD AND HERMAN ADOLPH, 1588-1590
Arms. Rev. Double eagle. Name of Rudolph II.

1. 1 Goldgulden 1589 .... 350.00

HERMAN ADOLPH, GEORGE EBERHARD, ERNST II AND PHILIP, 1590-1610
Arms. Rev. Double eagle. Name of Rudolph II.

2. 1 Goldgulden 1601 .... 300.00

ERNST II, 1602-1619
Arms. Rev. Double eagle. Name of Matthias.

3. 1 Goldgulden 1615 .... 350.00

PHILIP, DIED 1631
Arms. Rev. Double eagle. Name of Matthias.

4. 1 Goldgulden 1616 .... 150.00

Arms. Rev. Double eagle. Name of Ferdinand II.

5. 1 Goldgulden 1623 .... 150.00

Arms. Rev. Emperor Matthias standing.

6. 1 Ducat 1613 .... 350.00

PHILIP REINHARD I, 1613-1635
Arms. Rev. Initials of Christian IV of Denmark.

7. 2 Ducats 1627 .... 500.00
8. 1 Ducat 1627 .... 350.00

SOLMS-ROEDELHEIM

Counts of —

JOHN AUGUST AND HIS BROTHERS, 1632-1665
Arms. Rev. Value in wreath.

1. 1 Ducat 1656 .... 300.00

JOHN AUGUST, 1665-1680
Bust. Rev. Arms.

2. 1 Ducat 1680 .... 350.00

SPEYER

Bishops of —

PHILIP CHRISTOPHER OF SOETERN, 1610-1652
Arms. Rev. Madonna.

1. 2 Goldgulden 1612 .... 750.00

LOTHAR FREDERICK OF METTERNICH, 1652-1675
Bust. Rev. Arms.

2. 1 Ducat 1665 .... 300.00

HENRY HARTARD OF ROLLINGEN, 1711-1719
Bust. Rev. Arms.

3. 2 Ducats 1711 .... 400.00

DAMIAN HUGO OF SCHOENBORN, 1719-1743

Arms. Rev. City view of Bruchsal.

4. 2 Ducats 1726 .... 250.00
5. 1 Ducat 1726 ....*...... 75.00

FRANCIS CHRISTOPHER OF HUTTEN, 1743-1770

Bust. Rev. Seated and kneeling figures.

6. 1 Ducat 1745 .... 60.00

AUGUST OF LIMBURG-STIRUM, 1770-1797

Three shields. Rev. Minerva with four genii.

7. 1 Ducat 1770 .... 40.00

STETTIN

Swedish Kings of —

Facing bust of Gustav Adolphe. Rev. Arms.

1. 1 Ducat 1632 .... 150.00

STOLBERG

Counts, and later, Princes of —
A. The Stolberg Line (Stolberg-Stolberg)

LOUIS II AND HIS BROTHERS, 1555-1571
Arms. Rev. Double eagle. Name of Charles V.

1. 1 Goldgulden ND 500.00

LOUIS II, 1535-1574
Arms. Rev. Double eagle. Name of Ferdinand I.

2. 1 Goldgulden 1560. Mint: Augsburg 350.00

Five shields in enclosure. Rev. Double eagle. Name of Maxmilian II.

3. 1 Goldgulden 1567. Mint: Frankfurt 400.00

Five shields. Rev. Orb. Name of Maximilian II.

4. 1 Goldgulden ND. Mint: Noerdlingen 400.00

JOHN AND HENRY XXII, 1607-1612
Stag. Rev. Arms.

5. 1 Goldgulden 1607, 09 .... 200.00

Stag and column. Rev. Arms.

6. 1 Goldgulden 1612 .... 200.00

JOHN, 1606-1512
Stag. Rev. Legend. On his death.

7. 1 Goldgulden 1612 .... 200.00

HENRY XXII AND WOLFGANG GEORGE, 1612-1615
Stag. Rev. Arms.

8. 1 Goldgulden 1613, 14, ND 125.00

WOLFGANG GEORGE, 1615-1631
Arms. Rev. Stag.

9. 1 Goldgulden 1619, 25, 26 .... 100.00

CHRISTOPHER II AND HENRY VOLRAD, 1618-1632
Stag. Rev. Double eagle. Name of Matthias.

10. 1 Goldgulden 1619 .... 300.00

JOHN MARTIN, 1638-1669
Stag and column. Rev. Value on tablet.

11. 1 Ducat 1647, 49, 53 .... 75.00

CHRISTOPHER FREDERICK AND JOST CHRISTIAN, 1704-1738
Stag and column. Rev. Arms.

12. 2 Ducats 1725 .... 80.00
13. 1 Ducat 1706, 23, 25, 34 .... 50.00
14. ¼ Ducat 1706 .... 30.00

Martin Luther at table. Rev. Legend. On the Reformation.

15. 1 Ducat 1717 .... 50.00

CHRISTOPHER FREDERICK, 1704-1738
Initials. Rev. Stag and column.

16. ½ Ducat 1715 .... 25.00
17. ¼ Ducat ND 15.00

JOST CHRISTIAN, 1704-1739
Initials. Rev. Stag and column.

18. ¼ Ducat ND 15.00
19. ⅛ Ducat ND 30.00

CHRISTIAN LOUIS II AND FREDERICK BOTHO, 1739-1761

Stag and column. Rev. Arms.

20. 4 Ducats 1743 .... 300.00
21. 2 Ducats 1743 .... 80.00
22. 1 Ducat 1740, 42, 43, 48, 50, 57 ....*...... 50.00
23. ½ Ducat 1745, 48, 50 .... 30.00
24. ¼ Ducat ND 20.00
25. ⅛ Ducat ND 15.00

CHRISTOPHER LOUIS II, 1738-1761
Initials. Rev. Stag and column.

26. ¼ Ducat ND 20.00
27. ⅛ Ducat ND 15.00
28. 1/16 Ducat ND 15.00
29. 1/32 Ducat ND 15.00

FREDERICK BOTHO AND CHARLES LOUIS, 1761-1768

Stag and column. Rev. Arms.

30. 2 Ducats 1764 .... 300.00
31. 1 Ducat 1762, 64, 66 ....*...... 60.00
32. ½ Ducat 1762, 66 .... 40.00

FREDERICK BOTHO, 1739-1768
Initials. Rev. Stag and column.

33. ¼ Ducat ND	....	20.00
34. ⅛ Ducat ND	....	15.00

CHARLES LOUIS AND HENRY CHRISTIAN FREDERICK, 1768-1810

Stag and column. Rev. Arms.

35. 1 Ducat 1768, 70, 88, 93, 96	.... *	60.00
36. ½ Ducat 1768. From the ducat die	....	150.00
37. ½ Ducat 1768 (very rare), 70	....	60.00

CHARLES LOUIS, 1796-1810
Bust. Rev. Arms.

38. 1 Ducat 1796	....	80.00

B. The Wernigerode Line

LOUIS GEORGE, DIED 1618
Arms. Rev. Stag and column. On the Reformation.

39. 1 Goldgulden 1617	....	150.00

HENRY ERNST, 1638-1672
Stag. Rev. Arms.

40. 1 Ducat 1661	....	250.00

ERNST, DIED 1710
Bust. Rev. Legend. On his death.

41. 1 Ducat 1710	....	125.00

FREDERICK CHARLES, 1710-1767
Head. Rev. Stag and column.

42. 1 Ducat 1719	....	200.00

CHRISTIAN ERNST, 1710-1771
Stag. Rev. Arms.

43. 1 Ducat 1742, 59	....	65.00

Bust. Rev. Stag.

44. 1 Ducat 1768	....	85.00

Bust. Rev. Arms.

45. 1 Ducat 1730	....	75.00

HENRY ERNST II, 1771-1778
Head. Rev. Stag.

46. 1 Ducat 1778	....	75.00

CHRISTIAN FREDERICK, 1778-1824
Stag. Rev. Value on tablet.

47. 1 Ducat 1784, 95	....	60.00

Stag. Rev. Value and date in wreath. On the golden wedding.

48. 1 Ducat 1818	....	70.00

HENRY XII, 1824-1854
Bust. Rev. Stag and value.

49. 1 Ducat 1824	....	70.00

STRALSUND

City emblem. Rev. Orb. Ferdinand II.

1. 1 Goldgulden 1628-31	....	100.00

City emblem. Rev. Double eagle. Ferdinand II.

2. 1 Ducat 1632, 33, 35, ND	....	100.00

City emblem. Rev. Double eagle. Ferdinand III.

3. 1 Ducat ND, 1638, 40, 41, 44, 55	....	100.00

City emblem. Rev. Double eagle. Leopold I.

4. 1 Ducat 1658, 62, 64, 66, 71, 77, 81	.... *	100.00

SUEBIAN LEAGUE

Arms. Rev. Two shields.

1. 1 Ducat 1737	....	150.00

TEUTONIC ORDER

Grand Masters of —

A. Coinage in Prussia

HENRY OF PLAUEN, 1410-1413
Arms on cross. Rev. Madonna.

1. 1 Ducat ND	....	750.00

Grand Master standing. Rev. Madonna standing.

2. 1 Ducat ND	....	750.00

ALBERT OF BRANDENBURG, 1511-1525
Arms on cross. Rev. Madonna with shield.

3. 2 Goldgulden 1521	....	1250.00

Arms on cross. Rev. Madonna over shield.

4. 1 Goldgulden ND	....	750.00

B. Coinage in Mergentheim

WALTER OF CRONBERG, 1526-1543
Three shields. Rev. Madonna.

5. 1 Goldgulden 1531	....	600.00

HENRY OF BOBENHAUSEN, 1572-1590
Three shields. Rev. Madonna.

6. 1 Ducat 1575	....	600.00

MAXIMILIAN OF AUSTRIA, 1590-1618
Grand Master standing. Rev. Arms.

7. 2 Ducats ND	....	250.00
8. 1 Ducat 1597, ND	....	60.00

CHARLES OF AUSTRIA, 1619-1624
Head. Rev. Arms between arms of Brixen and Breslau.

9. 1 Ducat ND	....	150.00

Armored bust. Rev. Arms.

10. 2 Ducats ND	....	250.00

JOHN EUSTACE OF WESTERNACH, 1624-1627
Three shields. Rev. Double eagle.

11. 1 Ducat 1626	....	125.00

JOHN CASPAR I OF STADION, 1627-1641
Madonna. Rev. Arms.

12. 1 Ducat ND	....	Rare

JOHN CASPAR II OF AMPRINGEN, 1664-1684
Armored bust. Rev. Madonna.

13. 1 Ducat 1673	....	175.00

Arms. Rev. Madonna.

14. 2 Ducats 1666	....	300.00
15. 1 Ducat 1666	....	80.00

FRANCIS LOUIS OF PALATINATE-NEUBURG, 1694-1732
Bust. Rev. Arms.

16. 1 Ducat 1696	....	200.00

GERMANY-TEUTONIC ORDER (cont'd)

Armored bust. Rev. Five shields.

17. 1 Ducat 1699, 1701 .... 175.00

CHARLES ALEXANDER OF LORRAINE, 1761-1780
Bust. Rev. Arms.

18. 1 Ducat 1765 .... 100.00

THURN AND TAXIS

Princes of —

ANSELM FRANCIS, 1714-1739
Bust. Rev. Arms and lions.

1. 1 Ducat 1734 .... 150.00

TRIER (TREVES)

Archbishops of —

BOEMUND OF WARSBERG, 1354-1362

Lily. Rev. St. John.

1. 1 Goldgulden ND 75.00

KUNO OF FALKENSTEIN, 1362-1388
A. Coinage of the Coblenz Mint.
Lily. Rev. St. John standing.

2. 1 Goldgulden ND 30.00

Arms in octofoil. Rev. St. John standing.

3. 1 Goldgulden ND 25.00

Arms in trefoil. Rev. St. John standing.

4. 1 Goldgulden ND 25.00

St. Peter on throne. Rev. Arms in octofoil.

5. 1 Goldgulden ND 30.00

St. Peter on throne over shield of Minzenberg. Rev. Arms in trefoil.

6. 1 Goldgulden ND 30.00

St. Peter on throne over shields of Minzenberg and Saarwerden. Rev. Arms in trefoil.

7. 1 Goldgulden ND 25.00
8. 1 Goldgulden ND. Arms in sexfoil 25.00

St. Peter on throne over shield of Minzenberg. Rev. Arms in sexfoil.

9. 1 Goldgulden ND 25.00

St. Peter on throne over shield of Minzenberg. Rev. Two shields in sexfoil.

10. 1 Goldgulden ND 25.00

St. Peter on throne over shields of Trier and Minzenberg. Rev. Arms in sexfoil.

11. 1 Goldgulden ND 25.00

St. John standing. Rev. Arms and three shields in trefoil.

12. 1 Goldgulden ND 25.00

B. Coinage of the Wesel Mint.
St. Peter standing under architecture. Rev. Arms in trefoil.

13. 1 Goldgulden ND 30.00

St. John standing. Rev. Arms and three shields in trefoil.

14. 1 Goldgulden ND 50.00

C. Coinage of the Trier Mint.
Arms with four shields in sexfoil. Rev. St. Peter on throne over crossed keys.

15. 1 Goldgulden ND 25.00

St. Peter on throne over crossed keys. Rev. Arms in sexfoil.

16. 1 Goldgulden ND 25.00

St. John standing. Rev. Arms and three shields in trefoil.

17. 1 Goldgulden ND 35.00

D. Coinage of the Deutz Mint.
Arms in sexfoil. Rev. Half-length bust of St. Peter under canopy over shield of Minzenberg.

18. 1 Goldgulden ND. With title as Coadjutor of Cologne 35.00
19. 1 Goldgulden ND. With title as Administrator 50.00
20. 1 Goldgulden ND. With title as Vicarius 40.00

St. Peter standing under architecture over shield of Minzenberg. Rev. Arms in sexfoil.

21. 1 Goldgulden ND. With title as Vicarius 50.00
22. 1 Goldgulden ND. With title as Administrator 50.00

WERNER OF FALKENSTEIN, 1388-1418
A. Coinage of the Coblenz Mint.
St. John standing. Rev. Arms and three shields in trefoil.

23. 1 Goldgulden ND 50.00
24. 1 Goldgulden ND. Eagle under St. John 25.00

St. John standing over eagle. Rev. Arms in trefoil.

25. 1 Goldgulden ND 25.00

St. John standing over cross. Rev. Five shields in quatrefoil.

26. 1 Goldgulden ND 25.00

Half-length bust of St. Peter over shield of Minzenberg under architecture. Rev. Arms in sexfoil.

27. 1 Goldgulden ND 60.00

Half-length bust of St. Peter over shield of Minzenberg under architecture. Rev. Arms in trefoil.

28. 1 Goldgulden ND 25.00
29. 1 Goldgulden ND. Without name of Werner 50.00

St. Peter standing under architecture. Rev. Arms in trefoil.

30. 1 Goldgulden ND 25.00

St. John standing. Rev. Angel over arms, two shields and ornament in trefoil.

31. 1 Goldgulden ND 30.00
32. 1 Goldgulden ND. Without angel 25.00

B. Coinage of the Wesel Mint.
St. John standing. Rev. Arms and three shield in trefoil.

33. 1 Goldgulden ND 25.00

St. John standing. Rev. Arms in trefoil.

34. 1 Goldgulden ND 25.00

St. John standing. Rev. Five shields in quatrefoil.

35. 1 Goldgulden ND 25.00

St. Peter standing and shield of Minzenberg under architecture. Rev. Arms in trefoil.

36. 1 Goldgulden ND 60.00

Half-length bust of St. Peter over shield of Minzenberg under architecture. Rev. Arms in trefoil.

37. 1 Goldgulden ND 25.00

St. Peter standing. Rev. Arms in trefoil.

38. 1 Goldgulden ND 30.00

St. John standing. Rev. Angel over arms and two shields (and sometimes ornament) in trefoil.

39. 1 Goldgulden ND 50.00
40. 1 Goldgulden ND. Without angel 25.00

C. Coinage of the Trier Mint.
Arms in sexfoil. Rev. St. Peter on throne over shield of Minzenberg.

41. 1 Goldgulden ND 30.00

Half-length bust of St. Peter over shield of Minzenberg under architecture. Rev. Arms in trefoil.

42. 1 Goldgulden ND 30.00

D. Coinage of the Offenbach Mint.
St. Peter standing under architecture. Rev. Arms in trefoil.

43. 1 Goldgulden ND 30.00

St. John standing. Rev. Arms, two shields and ornament in trefoil.

44. 1 Goldgulden ND **25.00**

OTTO OF ZIEGENHAIN, 1418-1430
A. Coinage of the Coblenz Mint.

Half-length bust of St. Peter over shield of Ziegenhain under architecture. Rev. Arms in trefoil.

45. 1 Goldgulden ND **30.00**

St. Peter standing behind shield of Ziegenhain. Rev. Arms and four shields in quatrefoil.

46. 1 Goldgulden ND **25.00**

Archbishop standing. Rev. Arms in trefoil.

47. 1 Goldgulden ND **25.00**

B. Coinage of the Wesel Mint.

Half-length bust of St. Peter over shield of Ziegenhain under architecture. Rev. Arms in trefoil.

48. 1 Goldgulden ND **30.00**

St. Peter standing behind shield of Ziegenhain. Rev. Arms and four shields in quatrefoil.

49. 1 Goldgulden ND **30.00**

C. Coinage of the Trier Mint.

St. Peter standing behind shield of Ziegenhain. Rev. Arms and four shields in quatrefoil.

50. 1 Goldgulden ND **25.00**
51. 1 Goldgulden ND. With three shields and rosette **25.00**

D. Coinage of the Offenbach Mint.

Archbishop standing. Rev. Arms in trefoil.

52. 1 Goldgulden ND **35.00**

ULRIC OF MANDERSCHEID, 1430-1436

Half-length bust of St. Peter over shield of Manderscheid. Rev. Arms in trefoil.

53. 1 Goldgulden ND. Mint: Coblenz **50.00**

RABAN OF HELMSTAEDT, 1436-1439

Arms on cross. Rev. Three shields.

54. 1 Goldgulden 1436, 37, 38, ND. Mint: Coblenz **35.00**

JAMES OF SIERK, 1439-1456

Arms on cross. Rev. Three shields.

55. 1 Goldgulden ND. Mint: Coblenz **25.00**

JOHN II OF BADEN, 1456-1503

Arms on cross. Rev. Three shields.

56. 1 Goldgulden ND. Mint: Coblenz **80.00**
57. 1 Goldgulden 1491, 1502. Mint: Wesel **80.00**

Christ on throne over shield of Baden. Rev. Cross and four shields.

58. 1 Goldgulden ND. Mint: Coblenz **75.00**

Arms and three shields in trefoil. Rev. Christ on throne over arms.

59. 1 Goldgulden 1491, 1502. Mint: Coblenz **150.00**

JAMES II OF BADEN, 1503-1511

Arms and three shields in trefoil. Rev. Christ on throne over arms.

60. 1 Goldgulden 1503, 04, 05 .... **350.00**

RICHARD GREIFFENKLAU OF VOLLRATHS, 1511-1531

Arms and three shields in trefoil. Rev. Christ on throne over arms.

61. 1 Goldgulden 1511 .... **350.00**

Christ standing. Rev. Arms and three shields in trefoil.

62. 1 Goldgulden ND **350.00**

Christ on throne. Rev. Arms and three shields in trefoil.

63. 1 Goldgulden 1518 .... **400.00**

JOHN III OF METZENHAUSEN, 1531-1540

Arms and three shields in trefoil. Rev. Christ on throne over arms.

64. 1 Goldgulden 1538 .... **400.00**

JOHN VI OF THE LEYEN, 1556-1567

Christ on throne over arms. Rev. Arms and three shields in trefoil.

65. 1 Goldgulden 1563, 64 .... **400.00**

JAMES III OF ELTZ, 1567-1581

Christ on throne over arms. Rev. Arms and three shields in trefoil.

66. 1 Goldgulden 1571 .... **400.00**

JOHN VII OF SCHOENENBERG, 1581-1599

Christ on throne. Rev. Arms and three shields in trefoil.

67. 1 Goldgulden 1587, 90, 93-95 .... **150.00**

LOTHAR OF METTERNICH, 1599-1623

Christ on throne over arms. Rev. Arms and three shields in trefoil.

68. 1 Goldgulden 1601, 05, 08, 09, 13, 17-19, ND. Mint: Coblenz **60.00**

Bust of St. Peter over arms. Rev. Arms and three shields in trefoil.

69. 1 Goldgulden 1619. Mint: Coblenz **75.00**
70. 1 Goldgulden 1622. Kipper **200.00**

St. Helen standing. Rev. Five shields in quatrefoil.

71. 1 Goldgulden 1608, 10, 11. Mint: Trier **75.00**

PHILIP CHRISTOPHER OF SOETERN, 1623-1652

Arms. Rev. Madonna.

72. 1 Goldgulden 1632. Phlippsburg **350.00**

CHARLES CASPAR OF THE LEYEN, 1652-1676

Facing bust. Rev. Arms.

73. 1 Ducat 1654, 56 .... **80.00**

JOHN HUGO OF ORSBECK, 1676-1711

Bust. Rev. Arms.

74. 2 Ducats 1703 .... **350.00**
75. 1 Ducat 1680, 84, 91, 92, 99 .... **250.00**
76. ½ Ducat ND **75.00**

Bust. Rev. Three shields.

77. 1 Ducat 1690 .... **275.00**

St. Peter and value. Rev. Three shields.

78. 1 Goldgulden 1684, 94, 1700, 01 .... **100.00**

FRANCIS LOUIS OF PALATINATE-NEUBURG, 1716-1729

Bust. Rev. Arms.

79. 1 Ducat 1720, 22 .... **175.00**

Bust. Rev. Lion.

80. 1 Ducat 1721 .... **65.00**

FRANCIS GEORGE OF SCHOENBORN, 1729-1756

Bust. Rev. Arms supported by lions.

81. 2 Ducats 1735, 45, 50, 52 .... **250.00**
82. 1 Ducat 1735, 50, 52 .... **40.00**

JOHN PHILIP OF WALDERDORF, 1756-1768

Bust. Rev. Arms supported by lions.

83. 1 Ducat 1759. With VNIONE MIRIFICA SPLENDESCO **400.00**
84. 1 Ducat 1760, 61, 62 .... **150.00**

CLEMENT WENCESLAS OF POLAND, 1768-1803

Bust. Rev. Arms.

85. 1 Ducat 1770 .... **60.00**

ULM

Arms. Rev. Book. On the Reformation.

1. 2 Ducats 1617 .... **150.00**

Tablet. Rev. Arms.

2. 1 Ducat 1635, 36, 38, ND **100.00**

Wreath. Rev. Arms.

3. 2 Ducats 1639 .... **400.00**
4. 1 Ducat 1639 .... **150.00**

Bust of Joseph I. Rev. Arms.

5. 1 Ducat 1705 .... **175.00**

Arms. Rev. Legend. Necessity coins.

6.	6 Goldgulden 1704. Square	....	800.00
7.	1 Goldgulden 1704	...........................*......	125.00

Arms. Rev. Legend. On the Reformation.

8.	1 Ducat 1717	....	80.00
9.	½ Ducat 1717		65.00

Arms. Rev. Book. On the Augsburg Confession.

10.	2 Ducats 1730. Rev. Altar	.....................*.....	150.00
11.	1 Ducat 1730. Rev. Book	....	75.00
12.	½ Ducat 1730. Rev. Book	....	50.00

Bust of Charles VII. Rev. Arms.

13.	1 Ducat 1742	....	150.00

WALDECK

Counts, and later, Princes of —

CHRISTIAN AND WOLRAD IV, 1588-1640

Arms. Rev. Double Eagle.

1.	1 Goldgulden 1615-17, 22, ND	....	250.00

GEORGE FREDERICK, JOHN AND HENRY WOLRAD, 1645-1664

Arms. Rev. Palm tree.

2.	1 Ducat 1654	....	250.00

CHARLES AUGUST FREDERICK, 1728-1763
Head. Rev. Arms.

3.	1 Ducat 1731, 32, 36, 42, 50	....	125.00
4.	½ Ducat 1736		100.00
5.	¼ Ducat 1741, 60, 61		25.00
6.	1 Carolin 1734. Head right		350.00
7.	1 Carolin 1750. Head left	....	350.00
8.	2 Ducats 1750. Head left		350.00

Bust left. Rev. Arms.

9.	1 Ducat 1762	....	125.00

Bust right. Rev. Arms.

10.	1 Ducat 1762	....	125.00

Head. Rev. Cross of initials.

11.	1 Carolin 1734	....	300.00

Head. Rev. Arms and initials.

12.	½ Carolin 1734	....	100.00

Bust. Rev. Cross of initials.

13.	½ Carolin 1735	....	350.00
14.	¼ Carolin 1735	....	100.00

FREDERICK, 1763-1812
Head. Rev. Arms.

15.	1 Ducat 1781	....	250.00

WALLENSTEIN

Mecklenburg Dukes of Friedland and Sagan

ALBERT WALLENSTEIN, 1625-1634
Facing bust. Rev. Arms with eagle.

1.	10 Ducats 1627, 29	....	2000.00
2.	5 Ducats 1627	....	1250.00
3.	2 Ducats 1627		500.00
4.	1 Ducat 1627, 28, 29		150.00
5.	1 Goldgulden 1627, 28		750.00

Bust right. Rev. Arms with eagle.

6.	10 Ducats 1628	....	2000.00
7.	5 Ducats 1628		1250.00
8.	1 Ducat 1628		300.00

Facing bust. Rev. Arms. With title as duke of Mecklenburg.

9.	10 Ducats 1630 (very rare), 31	...............*......	1000.00
10.	5 Ducats 1629-31, 33, 34	....	800.00
11.	2 Ducats 1631, 33, 34	....	600.00
12.	1 Ducat 1629-31, 33, 34	...............*......	150.00

WALMODEN-GIMBORN

Counts of —

.. LOUIS, DIED 1811

Initials. Rev. Value.

1.	1 Ducat 1802	....	125.00

WERDEN AND HELMSTAEDT

Abbots of —

HENRY IV DUECKER, 1646-1667

Arms. Rev. Value.

1.	1 Ducat 1647	....	150.00

WESTPHALIA

Kings of —

JEROME NAPOLEON, 1807-1813

Arms. Rev. Value.

1.	10 Taler 1810	100.00
2.	5 Taler 1810 ....*	75.00

Laureate head. Rev. Value.

3.	10 Taler 1811-13 ....*	85.00
4.	5 Taler 1811, 12	60.00

Laureate head. Rev. Value in wreath.

5.	40 Francs 1813	250.00
6.	20 Francs 1808-11	35.00
7.	10 Francs 1813	50.00
8.	5 Francs 1813	50.00

WIED

Counts of —

FREDERICK ALEXANDER, 1737-1791

Bust. Rev. Tree and all seeing eye.

1.	1 Ducat 1744	100.00

Bust. Rev. Peacock.

2.	1 Goldgulden 1751	125.00

Bust. Rev. City view of Neuwied.

3.	2 Ducats 1752	250.00
4.	1 Pistole 1752. Rev. Arms. ....*	200.00

WISMAR

St. Lawrence. Rev. City arms.

1.	1 Goldgulden 1558	250.00

St. Lawrence. Rev. Double eagle. Name of Rudolph II.

2.	1 Goldgulden 1587, 91, 97, 1604, ND	175.00

St. Lawrence. Rev. Double eagle. Name of Matthias.

3.	1 Goldgulden 1616	175.00

St. Lawrence. Rev. Double eagle. Name of Ferdinand II.

4.	1 Goldgulden 1626, 29, 32	175.00

Arms. Rev. Double eagle. Struck under Swedish rule.

5.	1 Ducat 1672, 76	500.00
6.	1 Ducat 1743 ....*	250.00

WORMS

A. City of —

Bust of Madonna over shield. Rev. Double eagle.

1.	1 Goldgulden 1510, ND	300.00

Dragon with shield. Rev. Double eagle.

2.	1½ Goldgulden 1571. Square	400.00
3.	1 Goldgulden ND (1519-56)	300.00
4.	1 Goldgulden 1614-22 ....*	75.00
5.	1 Ducat 1651, 55	250.00

B. Bishops of —

GEORGE OF SCHOENENBERG, 1580-1595

St. John. Rev. Lily.

6.	1 Goldgulden 1588-93	300.00

WURTTEMBERG

Dukes, and later, Kings of —

ULRIC, 1498-1550

Duke standing. Rev. Arms.

1.	2 Goldgulden ND	600.00
2.	1 Goldgulden ND ....*	60.00

Bust. Rev. Arms.

3.	2 Ducats 1513	500.00

Bust with hat. Rev. Arms.

4.	2 Ducats 1537	500.00
5.	1 Ducat 1537	75.00

AUSTRIAN OCCUPATION, 1519-1534
Bust of Charles V. Rev. Cross and four shields.

6.	2 Goldgulden 1520	600.00
7.	1 Goldgulden 1520	350.00

CHRISTOPHER, 1550-1568
Arms. Rev. Eagle. Charles V.

8.	1 Goldgulden 1554, 55	200.00

LOUIS, 1568-1593
Arms. Rev. Eagle. Maximilian II.

9.	2 Goldgulden 1575. Square	500.00
10.	1 Goldgulden 1575	175.00

Armored bust. Rev. Arms. Rudolph II.

11.	2 Goldgulden 1592. Bust right	500.00
12.	1 Goldgulden 1592. Bust right	400.00
13.	1 Goldgulden 1593. Bust left	350.00

FREDERICK, 1593-1608
Half length armored bust. Rev. Arms.

14.	2 Ducats 1597	500.00
15.	1 Ducat 1603, 05	300.00

Armored bust. Rev. Arms on cross.

16.	2 Goldgulden 1606	500.00
17.	1 Goldgulden 1597, 1606	300.00

JOHN FREDERICK, 1608-1628
Half length bust. Rev. Arms under eagle.

18.	2 Ducats 1609, 15	400.00

Half length bust. Rev. Arms on cross.

19.	1 Goldgulden 1609	300.00

Bust. Rev. Four shields around orb.

20.	1 Goldgulden 1614, 20, 21	300.00

Half length figure. Rev. Arms under eagle.

21.	2½ Ducats 1621	500.00

Half length figure. Rev. Arms.

22.	1 Ducat 1621	300.00

Duke on horse. Rev. Three wreaths.

23.	2 Ducats 1623, 24, 27	300.00

EBERHARD III, 1628-1674

Armored facing bust. Rev. Arms.

24.	2 Ducats 1640, 44, 48, 51	200.00

Bust right. Rev. Arms.

25.	1¼ Ducats 1631. Square	400.00
26.	1 Ducat 1639, 44, 51, 59, 68, 69	125.00
27.	½ Ducat 1659	75.00

Armored facing bust. Rev. Palm tree. On the peace.

28.	2 Ducats 1650	150.00

Three shields. Rev. Flag.

29.	½ Ducat ND	50.00

FREDERICK CHARLES, 1677-1693
Armored bust. Rev. Arms.

30.	2 Ducats 1681, 83	350.00
31.	1 Ducat 1681, 88	200.00

Head. Rev. Arms.

32.	½ Ducat 1688	175.00

EBERHARD LOUIS, 1693-1733
Bust. Rev. Arms.

33.	4 Ducats 1699, 1707	500.00
34.	3 Ducats 1699	400.00

Bust. Rev. Crowned arms.

35.	2 Ducats 1694, 1706	250.00
36.	1 Ducat 1694-97	75.00
37.	½ Ducat ND	125.00

Bust. Helmeted arms.

38.	2 Ducats 1699, 1707, ND . . . .* . . .	150.00
39.	1 Ducat 1732, 33, ND	75.00

Duke on horse. Rev. Arms.

40.	1 Goldgulden ND	80.00

Bust. Rev. Shield in chain of Order.

41.	1 Carolin 1731, 32, 33	75.00
42.	½ Carolin 1731, 32, 33	40.00
43.	¼ Carolin 1731, 32, 33	30.00

CHARLES ALEXANDER, 1733-1737
Bust. Rev. Five shields.

44.	1 Ducat 1736	80.00

Bust. Rev. Arms. Homage issue.

45.	2 Ducats 1733	100.00

Bust. Rev. Arms.

46.	1 Carolin 1734, 35, 36 . . . .* . . .	75.00
47.	½ Carolin 1734, 35, 36	40.00
48.	¼ Carolin 1734, 35, 36	30.00
49.	1 Ducat 1733. Helmeted arms	100.00
50.	1 Ducat 1735, ND	150.00
51.	½ Ducat ND	60.00

CHARLES RUDOLPH, 1737-1738
Bust. Rev. Arms.

52.	1 Ducat 1737	75.00
53.	½ Ducat ND	50.00
54.	¼ Ducat ND	30.00

CHARLES FREDERICK, 1738-1744

Bust. Rev. Arms.

55.	1 Ducat 1739, 42 . . . .* . . .	75.00
56.	½ Ducat ND	75.00
57.	¼ Ducat ND	30.00

CHARLES EUGENE, 1744-1793
Bust. Rev. Crowned arms.

58. 1 Ducat 1744, 47-50, 62, 90, 91, ND 60.00

Bust. Rev. Helmeted arms.

59. 1 Ducat 1746 .... 175.00

FC in shield. Rev. Altar. On his wedding.

60. 1 Ducat 1749 .... 40.00

LOUIS EUGENE, 1793-1795
Bust. Rev. Arms.

61. 1 Ducat 1794 .... 75.00

FREDERICK, 1795-1816
Bust. Rev. Legend. Struck in the presence of the king.

62. 1 Ducat 1803, 04 .... 200.00

Draped bust. Rev. Arms.

63. 1 Ducat 1804. Bust right 60.00
64. 1 Ducat 1808. Bust left 60.00

Head. Rev. Arms.

65. 1 Frederick d'or 1810 .... 85.00
66. 1 Ducat 1813 ....*...... 50.00

WILLIAM, 1816-1864

Head. Rev. Large supported arms without legend.

67. 1 Ducat 1818 .... 40.00

Head. Rev. Small supported arms with legend.

68. 1 Ducat 1840-48 .... 30.00

Head. Rev. Arms.

69. 10 Gulden 1824, 25 .... 60.00
70. 5 Gulden 1824, 25, 35, 36, 39 .... 40.00

Head. Rev. Date and four line legend. On the King's visit to the mint.

71. 10 Gulden 1825 .... 500.00

Head. Rev. Seated female and children. On the 25th year of reign.

72. 4 Ducats 1841 .... 85.00

Head. Rev. The Mint in Stuttgart. On the King's visit.

73. 4 Ducats 1844. The value is on the edge 350.00

WURZBURG

A. Bishops of —

GERHARD OF SCHWARZBURG, 1372-1400
Arms. Rev. St. John standing.

1. 1 Goldgulden ND 400.00

LAWRENCE OF BIBRA, 1495-1519

St. Kilian. Rev. Arms.

2. 2 Goldgulden 1506 .... 500.00
3. 1 Goldgulden 1506, 07, 08, 13, ND ....*...... 100.00

MELCHIOR ZOBEL OF GIEBELSTADT, 1544-1558
Three shields. Rev. Eagle.

4. 2 Goldgulden 1553 .... 500.00
5. 1 Goldgulden 1553 .... 300.00

FREDERICK OF WIRSBERG, 1558-1573
Three shields. Rev. Eagle.

6. 1 Goldgulden 1572 .... 300.00

JULIUS ECHTER OF MESPELBRUNN, 1573-1617

St. Kilian over arms. Rev. Madonna over eagle.

7. 4 Goldgulden ND 400.00
8. 2 Ducats ND 350.00
9. 1 Ducat ND ....*...... 85.00

Three shields. Rev. Legend. Homage issue.

10. 1 Goldgulden 1583 .... 150.00

St. Kilian standing. Rev. Date over arms. Name of Rudolph II.

11. 2 Goldgulden 1575, 78, 79 .... 250.00
12. 1 Goldgulden 1575 .... 150.00

St. Kilian standing. Rev. Arms with 3 helmets. Name of Rudolph II.

13. 2 Goldgulden 1581, 83, 85, 89, 90, 1608, 11, 13, ND .. **250.00**
14. 1 Goldgulden 1581, 83, 86, 89, 90, 92, 94,
       1601, 08, 11 ....* **125.00**
15. 1 Goldgulden 1613, 15. Name of Matthias II **125.00**

Arms with 3 helmets. Rev. Legend. On his death.

16. 2 Goldgulden 1617 .... **200.00**
17. 1 Goldgulden 1617 .... **100.00**

JOHN GODFREY OF ASCHHAUSEN, 1617-1622

Arms. Rev. Legend around shield.

18. 2 Goldgulden ND. Square. AUGUSTUM PATRIAE etc. * ... **350.00**
19. 1 Goldgulden ND. AUGUSTUM PATRIAE etc. **100.00**
20. 1 Goldgulden ND. ORE ET CORDE etc. **175.00**
21. 1 Goldgulden 1617, 18, 19 .... **175.00**

Arms with 4 helmets. Rev. Legend. On his death.

22. 1 Goldgulden 1622 .... **175.00**

PHILIP ADOLPH OF EHRENBERG, 1623-1631

St. Kilian. Rev. Arms.

23. 2 Goldgulden ND **400.00**
24. 1 Goldgulden 1626, ND ....* **175.00**

Arms. Rev. Legend. On his death.

25. 1 Goldgulden 1631 .... **175.00**

FRANCIS OF HATZFELD, 1631-1642
Arms. Rev. Wreath.

26. 1 Goldgulden 1631, ND **175.00**

Arms. Rev. Legend. On his death.

27. 1 Ducat 1642 .... **175.00**

JOHN PHILIP I OF SCHOENBORN, 1642-1673
Bust right over arms. Rev. Three mountain peaks.

28. 2 Ducats ND **125.00**
29. 1 Ducat ND **125.00**

Facing bust over arms. Rev. Three mountain peaks.

30. 2 Ducats ND **125.00**
31. 1½ Ducats ND ....* **125.00**
32. 1 Ducat ND **65.00**

Bust right over arms. Rev. Legend over shield.

33. 1 Goldgulden ND **100.00**

Facing bust over arms. Rev. Legend over shield.

34. 1 Goldgulden ND **75.00**

Arms. Rev. Legend over shield.

35. 1 Goldgulden ND **175.00**

JOHN HARTMANN OF ROSENBACH, 1673-1675
Bust over arms. Rev. Legend over shield.

36. 1 Goldgulden ND **175.00**

PETER PHILIP OF DERNBACH, 1675-1683
Bust. Rev. Legend over shield.

37. 1 Goldgulden ND **175.00**

CONRAD WILLIAM OF WARTENAU, 1683-1684
Bust. Rev. Arms.

38. 1 Ducat ND **125.00**

JOHN GODFREY II OF GUTTENBERG, 1684-1689
Facing bust. Rev. Legend over shield.

39. 1 Goldgulden ND **175.00**

Arms. Rev. Flag in cartouche.

40. 1 Goldgulden ND **175.00**

JOHN PHILIP II OF GREIFFENKLAU, 1699-1719
Bust. Rev. Three Saints.

41. 1 Ducat 1702 .... **60.00**

Bust. Rev. Arms with 3 helmets.

42. 2 Ducats 1705 .... **125.00**
43. 1 Ducat 1700 .... **85.00**

Bust. Rev. Mantling.

44. 2 Ducats 1705 .... **80.00**

Bust. Rev. Tree.

45. 1 Ducat 1703 .... **100,00**

Bust. Rev. Madonna over arms.

46. 3 Ducats 1707 .... **200.00**
47. 2 Ducats 1707 ....* **100.00**

Arms. Rev. Flag in shield.

48. 1 Goldgulden ND **40.00**

Arms supported by lions. Rev. Madonna over shield.

49. 1 Goldgulden ND **40.00**

JOHN PHILIP FRANCIS OF SCHOENBORN, 1719-1724
Bust. Rev. Lion with sword and scales before city view.

50. 2 Ducats ND **200.00**
51. 2 Ducats ND. Without the city view **225.00**

Bust. Rev. Arms.

52. 2 Ducats ND **200.00**
53. 2 Ducats 1719. On his election ....* **200.00**

Bust. Rev. Arms in cartouche.

54. 1 Ducat ND **65.00**

Bust. Rev. Altar with Wurzburg shield.

55. 1 Goldgulden ND **40.00**
56. 1 Goldgulden ND. With "QUIA TU ES" etc. **40.00**

CHRISTOPHER FRANCIS OF HUTTEN, 1724-1729
Arms. Rev. St. Christopher. With D.G.EL.EP.

57. 2 Ducats ND **70.00**
58. 1 Ducat ND **30.00**

Arms. Rev. Ship entering harbor. With D.G.EL.EP.

59. 1 Ducat ND **40.00**

Bust. Rev. St. Christopher. With D.G.EP.

60. 2 Ducats ND **70.00**

Arms. Rev. St. Christopher. With D.G.EP.

61. 1 Ducat ND **30.00**

Arms. Rev. Initials on mantle.

62. 1 Ducat 1725, 27, 28 .... **70.00**

Arms. Rev. Sword and stola.

63. ½ Ducat ND **25.00**

Arms. Rev. Mountain. "NON FULMEN" etc.

64. 1 Goldgulden ND **40.00**

Arms. Rev. Mountain and city view. "FELIX A DEO" etc.

65. 1 Goldgulden 1724. With flag-shield. **40.00**
66. 1 Goldgulden 1724. With flag and sceptre crossed **40.00**

FREDERICK CHARLES OF SCHOENBORN, 1729-1746

Bust. Rev. Arms.

67. 10 Gulden or 1 Carolin 1735, 36 ....* **100.00**
68. 5 Gulden or ½ Carolin 1735 .... **50.00**
69. 2½ Gulden or ¼ Carolin 1735, 36 .... **30.00**

Bust. Rev. Initials on mantle.

70. 10 Gulden or 1 Carolin 1735, 36 .... **100.00**
71. 5 Gulden or ½ Carolin 1735 .... **50.00**
72. 2½ Gulden or ¼ Carolin 1736 .... **30.00**

Bust. Rev. Arms supported by lions.

73. 2 Ducats 1729, 30, 31 .... **70.00**

Bust. Rev. Arms.

74. 1 Ducat 1731, 32, 33 .... **40.00**

Arms supported by lions. Rev. Initials on mantle.

75. 1 Ducat 1729, 30 .... **40.00**

Arms. Rev. Franconia standing and lion.

76. 2 Goldgulden 1729 .... **125.00**
77. 1 Goldgulden 1729 .... **50.00**

Bust. Rev. Flag shield.

78. 1 Goldgulden ND **35.00**
79. 1 Goldgulden ND. Shield with flowers ....* **70.00**

Arms. Rev. Initials on mantle.

80. ½ Ducat 1729 .... **35.00**

ANSELM FRANCIS OF INGELHEIM, 1746-1749
Arms. Rev. Hands over city shield.

81. 1 Goldgulden ND **35.00**

Angel and 3 lambs. Rev. Legend.

82. 1 Ducat 1747. On his consecration **90.00**

CHARLES PHILIP OF GREIFFENKLAU, 1749-1754
Bust over arms. Rev. Arms with 3 helmets.

83. 1 Goldgulden ND **35.00**

Arms with 3 helmets. Rev. Griffin.

84. 1 Goldgulden ND **50.00**

ADAM FREDERICK OF SEINSHEIM, 1755-1779
Bust. Rev. Arms and legend.

85. 1 Goldgulden 1755 .... **35.00**

Bust. Rev. Arms without legend.

86. 1 Ducat 1755-70 .... **40.00**

GERMANY-WURZBURG (cont'd)

Bust in square. Rev. Arms in square.

87. 1 Ducat 1772 .... **40.00**

Bust in square. Rev. Madonna in square.

88. 1 Ducat 1773-79 .... **35.00**

Bust and arms. Rev. Palm tree and shield.

89. 1 Goldgulden 1773, 74, 77, 78 .... **35.00**

Fame over arms. Rev. Three females.

90. 1 Goldgulden ND (1755). Homage issue **35.00**

Bust over arms. Rev. Franconia standing and dove. On the Peace of Hubertusburg.

91. 1 Goldgulden 1764 .... **35.00**

FRANCIS LOUIS OF ERTHAL, 1779-1795

Bust over arms. Rev. Palm tree and shield.

92. 1 Goldgulden 1779 .... **35.00**

Bust over arms. Rev. Arms.

93. 1 Goldgulden 1786, 91, 94 .... **35.00**

Bust. Rev. Three Saints over arms.

94. 1 Ducat 1785 .... **35.00**

Bust. Rev. St. Kilian standing and value.

95. 2 Goldgulden 1786 ....*...... **60.00**
96. 1 Goldgulden 1786 .... **35.00**

Bust. Rev. St. Burkhard standing and value.

97. 1 Goldgulden 1790 .... **75.00**

GEORGE CHARLES OF FECHENBACH, 1795-1803

Bust. Rev. Arms and value.

98. 1 Carolin 1795 .... **150.00**

Arms. Rev. Palm tree and shield.

99. 1 Goldgulden 1795 .... **40.00**

Bust. Rev. City view and value.

100. 1 Goldgulden 1798 .... **40.00**

FERDINAND, GRAND DUKE, 1806-1814

Bust. Rev. Palm tree and shield.

101. 1 Goldgulden 1807, 09 .... **70.00**

Head. Rev. Shield and value.

102. 1 Goldgulden 1812, 13 .... **80.00**

Head. Rev. Altar and shield.

103. 1 Goldgulden 1814 .... **100.00**

B. Swedish Rulers of —

Bust of Gustav Adolphe. Rev. Arms.

104. 1 Ducat 1631, 32 .... **75.00**

GREAT BRITAIN

Kings of —

OFFA, KING OF MERCIA, 757-796

Arabic legend. Rev. Arabic legend and "OFFA REX." Struck in the style of the contemporary Arabian Dinars.

1. 1 Dinar ND 4000.00

WIGMUND, ARCHBISHOP OF YORK, 837-854

Facing bust. Rev. Cross in wreath.

2. 1 Solidus ND 4000.00

AETHELRED II, 979-1016

Bust in helmet. Rev. Long cross.

3. 1 Gold Penny ND 4000.00

EDWARD THE CONFESSOR, 1042-1066
Diademed bust. Rev. Cross.

4. 1 Gold Penny ND 4000.00

HENRY III, 1216-1272

Ruler on throne. Rev. Long cross.

5. 1 Gold Penny ND 5000.00

EDWARD III, 1327-1377

Ruler on throne. Rev. Ornamental cross.

6. 1 Florin ND 6000.00

Crowned leopard with banner. Rev. Ornamental cross.

7. ½ Florin or Leopard ND 4500.00

Leopard on helm. Rev. Ornamental cross.

8. ¼ Florin or Helm ND 3000.00

Ruler in ship. Rev. Ornamental cross.

9. 1 Noble ND ....* 80.00
10. ½ Noble ND 60.00

Arms. Rev. Ornamental cross.

11. ¼ Noble ND 50.00

RICHARD II, 1377-1399

Ruler in ship. Rev. Ornamental cross.

12. 1 Noble ND 100.00
13. ½ Noble ND ....* 85.00

Arms. Rev. Ornamental cross.

14. ¼ Noble ND 50.00

HENRY IV, 1399-1413

Ruler in ship. Rev. Ornamental cross. The heavy Nobles weigh 120 grains, the light Nobles 108 grains. The smaller coins are in proportion.

15. 1 Noble ND. Heavy type 1000.00
16. 1 Noble ND. Light type ....* 250.00
17. ½ Noble ND. Heavy type 1500.00
18. ½ Noble ND. Light type 450.00

Arms. Rev. Ornamental cross.

19. ¼ Noble ND. Heavy type ....* 250.00
20. ¼ Noble ND. Light type 100.00

HENRY V, 1413-1422

Ruler in ship. Rev. Ornamental cross.

21.	1 Noble ND	85.00
22.	½ Noble ND ....*	85.00

Arms. Rev. Ornamental cross.

23.	¼ Noble ND	40.00

HENRY VI, 1422-1461 AND 1470-1471

Ruler in ship. Rev. Ornamental cross.

24.	1 Noble ND	75.00
25.	½ Noble ND ....*	40.00

Arms. Rev. Ornamental cross.

26.	¼ Noble ND	35.00

St. Michael slaying dragon. Rev. Cross and arms on ship. Restoration coinage.

27.	1 Angel ND ....*	150.00
28.	½ Angel (Angelet) ND	200.00

EDWARD IV, 1461-1470 AND 1471-1483

Ruler in ship. Rev. Ornamental cross.

29.	1 Noble ND. Heavy type	2500.00
30.	1 Noble ND. Light type	3500.00

Ruler in ship, rose at side. Rev. Radiate rose within royal emblems.

31.	1 Rose Noble or Ryal ND ....*	75.00
32.	½ Rose Noble or ½ Ryal ND	50.00

Arms. Rev. Radiate rose.

33.	¼ Ryal ND	50.00

St. Michael slaying dragon. Rev. Cross and arms on ship.

34.	1 Angel ND ....*	50.00
35.	½ Angel (Angelet) ND	75.00

EDWARD V, 1483

St. Michael slaying dragon. Rev. Cross and arms on ship.

36.	1 Angel ND. Mint mark boar's head ....*	1250.00
36a.	½ Angel ND	3000.00

RICHARD III, 1483-1485

St. Michael slaying dragon. Rev. Cross and arms on ship.

37.	1 Angel ND	175.00
38.	½ Angel ND ....*	500.00

HENRY VII, 1485-1509

Ruler on throne. Rev. Arms on large rose.

39.	2 Sovereigns ND	2000.00
40.	1 Sovereign ND ....*	650.00

Ruler in ship. Rev. Shield on large rose.

41.	1 Ryal ND	5000.00

GREAT BRITAIN (cont'd)

St. Michael slaying dragon. Rev. Cross and arms on ship.

42.	1 Angel ND	....................................*	50.00
43.	½ Angel ND	....	60.00

HENRY VIII, 1509-1547
Ruler on throne. Rev. Arms on large rose.

44.	1 Sovereian ND	....	450.00

Ruler on throne. Rev. Arms with supporters.

44a.	1 Sovereign ND	...........................*	500.00
45.	½ Sovereign ND	....	60.00

St. Michael slaying dragon. Rev. Cross and arms on ship.

46.	1 Angel ND	....	50.00
47.	½ Angel ND	...........................*	60.00
48.	¼ Angel ND	....	75.00

St. George on horse. Rev. Cross and rose on ship.

49.	1 George Noble ND	...........................*	600.00
50.	½ George Noble ND	....	Unique

Crowned arms. Rev. Rose, initials and floriated cross.

51.	1 Crown of the Rose ND	....	4000.00

Crown over double rose. Rev. Crowned arms.

52.	1 Crown ND	...........................*	50.00
53.	½ Crown ND	....	50.00

EDWARD VI, 1547-1553

Ruler on throne. Rev. Arms with supporters. With name and title of Henry VIII, although the figure is that of Edward VI.

54.	1 Sovereign ND	....	500.00
55.	½ Sovereign ND	...........................*	50.00

Ruler on throne. Rev. Arms on large rose. With his own name and title.

56.	2 Sovereigns ND	....	4500.00
57.	1 Sovereign ND	...........................*	1750.00

Ruler on throne. Rev. Arms with supporters. With his own name and title.

58.	1 Sovereign ND	....	350.00

Half length figure. Rev. Arms.

59.	1 Sovereign ND	...........................*	200.00
60.	½ Sovereign ND	....	100.00
61.	1 Crown ND	....	200.00
62.	½ Crown ND	....	250.00

Crowned child bust. Rev. Arms.

63.	½ Sovereign ND	...........................*	75.00

GREAT BRITAIN (cont'd)

64.	1 Crown ND	150.00
65.	½ Crown ND	150.00

Child bust without crown. Rev. Arms.

66.	½ Sovereign ND	75.00
67.	1 Crown ND ....*	175.00
68.	½ Crown ND	150.00

Crowned child bust on each side.

69.	½ Sovereign ND	450.00

Rose. Rev. Arms.

70.	1 Crown ND	1250.00
71.	½ Crown ND	400.00

Crown over double rose, with name of Henry VIII. Rev. Crowned arms.

72.	1 Crown ND	50.00
73.	½ Crown ND	40.00

St. Michael slaying dragon. Rev. Cross and arms on ship.

74.	1 Angel ND	1000.00
75.	½ Angel ND	1500.00

MARY, 1553-1554

Queen on throne. Rev. Arms on large rose.

76.	1 Sovereign 1553, 54, ND	400.00

Queen in ship. Rev. Radiate rose.

77.	1 Ryal 1553, ND	1500.00

St. Michael slaying dragon. Rev. Cross and arms on ship.

78.	1 Angel ND ....*	125.00
79.	½ Angel ND	500.00

PHILIP AND MARY, 1554-1558

St. Michael slaying dragon. Rev. Cross and arms on ship.

80.	1 Angel ND ....*	350.00
81.	½ Angel ND	750.00

ELIZABETH I, 1558-1603

Queen on throne. Rev. Arms on large rose.

82.	1 Sovereign ND	200.00

Queen in ship. Rev. Radiate rose.

83.	1 Ryal ND	500.00

St. Michael slaying dragon. Rev. Cross and arms on ship.

84.	1 Angel ND ....*	50.00
85.	½ Angel ND	60.00
86.	¼ Angel ND	50.00

Crowned bust. Rev. Crowned arms.

87.	1 Sovereign ND. Hammered coinage	125.00
88.	½ Sovereign ND. Hammered coinage	50.00
89.	½ Sovereign ND. Milled coinage ....*	125.00
90.	1 Crown ND. Hammered coinage	75.00
91.	1 Crown ND. Milled coinage	175.00
92.	½ Crown ND. Hammered coinage ....*	60.00
93.	½ Crown ND. Milled coinage	300.00

JAMES I, 1603-1625

Ruler on throne. Rev. Arms on large rose.

94. 1 Rose Ryal ND 150.00

Ruler on throne. Rev. XXX over arms.

95. 30 Shillings (Rose Ryal) ND 200.00

Ruler in ship. Rev. Radiate rose.

96. 1 Spur Ryal ND 500.00

Crowned bust. Rev. Crowned arms.

97. 1 Sovereign ND 150.00
98. ½ Sovereign ND .... * 300.00
99. 1 Unite (20 Shillings) ND 50.00
100. 2 Crowns ND 35.00
101. 1 Crown ND 25.00
102. ½ Crown ND .... * 25.00

Laureate bust. Rev. Crowned arms.

103. 1 Laurel (Unite) ND 50.00
104. ½ Laurel ND .... * 35.00
105. ¼ Laurel ND 25.00

St. Michael slaying dragon. Rev. Arms.

106. ¼ Angel ND 400.00

St. Michael slaying dragon. Rev. Large arms on ship.

107. 1 Angel ND .... * 250.00
108. ½ Angel ND 450.00

St. Michael slaying dragon. Rev. Large ship with three masts.

109. 1 Angel ND 300.00

Crowned facing lion over arms with XV. Rev. Radiate rose.

110. 15 Shillings (Spur Ryal) ND 450.00

Crowned rose. Rev. Crowned thistle.

111. 1 Thistle Crown or 4 Shillings ND 35.00

CHARLES I, 1625-1649

St. Michael with or without X for value in field. Rev. Three masted ship.

112. 10 Shillings (1 Angel) ND .... * 250.00
113. 10 Shillings ND. Smaller size and finer style.
     By Nicholas Briot 1500.00

Crowned bust. Rev. Scroll type legend (The Declaration). The
20 and 10 Shilling values are indicated by Roman numerals
on the Obv.

114. 3 Pounds (Triple Unite) 1642-44. Oxford Mint ... * 450.00

GREAT BRITAIN (cont'd)

115.	3 Pounds 1642. Shrewsbury Mint	Unique
116.	20 Shillings (1 Unite) 1642-46. Oxford Mint	100.00
117.	20 Shillings 1645. Bristol Mint	1000.00
118.	10 Shillings (½ Unite) 1642-44. Oxford Mint	150.00
119.	10 Shillings 1645. Bristol Mint	1000.00

Crowned bust and Roman numerals for value. Rev. Arms.

120.	20 Shillings ND. Tower Mint		50.00
121.	20 Shillings ND. Briot's coinage		200.00
122.	20 Shillings ND. Aberystwyth Mint		Unique
123.	20 Shillings ND. Truro Mint		1750.00
124.	20 Shillings ND. Weymouth Mint		1750.00
125.	20 Shillings ND. Salisbury Mint		Unique
126.	10 Shillings ND. Tower Mint . . . . *		35.00
127.	10 Shillings ND. Tower Mint. Briot's coinage		150.00
128.	5 Shillings ND. Tower Mint		30.00
129.	5 Shillings ND. Tower Mint. Briot's coinage . . . *		1500.00

CIVIL WAR
Siege of Colchester

Castle, date and value. Rev. Blank.

130.	10 Shillings 1648	2000.00

Siege of Pontefract

Crown over CR. Rev. Castle. Octagonal shaped.

131.	1 Unite 1648	2500.00

Crown over legend. Rev. Castle in circle, with name of Charles II.

132.	1 Unite 1648	1500.00

THE COMMONWEALTH OF ENGLAND, 1649-1660

Shield of St. George. Rev. Shields of St. George and Ireland. With Roman numerals for value.

133.	20 Shillings 1649-60	75.00
134.	10 Shillings 1649-60 . . . . *	60.00
135.	5 Shillings 1649-60	50.00

OLIVER CROMWELL, 1656-1660

Laureate head. Rev. Arms.

136.	50 Shillings 1656	1500.00
137.	1 Broad 1656	175.00
138.	½ Broad 1656 . . . . *	350.00

CHARLES II, 1660-1685

Crowned bust with or without value as indicated. Rev. Arms.

139.	20 Shillings ND. Without value . . . . *		75.00
140.	20 Shillings ND. With value		60.00
141.	10 Shillings ND. Without value		125.00
142.	10 Shillings ND. With value . . . . *		125.00
143.	5 Shillings ND. Without value		100.00
144.	5 Shillings ND. With value		100.00

Laureate head. Rev. Cross of four shields. With or without the various symbols below the head as indicated.

5 Guineas

145.	1668-84. No symbol	200.00
146.	1668, 69, 75. Elephant	250.00
147.	1675-84. Elephant and castle	250.00

2 Guineas

148.	1664-84. No symbol	100.00
149.	1664, 78. Elephant	100.00
150.	1676-84. Elephant and castle	150.00

1 Guinea

151.	1663-84. No symbol	40.00
152.	1663-78. Elephant . . . . *	85.00
153.	1674-84. Elephant and castle	75.00

½ Guinea

154.	1669-84. No symbol	40.00
155.	1676-84. Elephant and castle	70.00

JAMES II, 1685-1688

Laureate head. Rev. Cross of four shields. With or without the various symbols below the head as indicated.

GREAT BRITAIN (cont'd)

5 Guineas

156.	1686, 87, 88. No symbol ....*.....	225.00
157.	1687, 88. Elephant and castle	300.00

2 Guineas

158.	1687, 88. No symbol	160.00

1 Guinea

159.	1685-88. No symbol	50.00
160.	1685-88. Elephant and castle	65.00

½ Guinea

161.	1686, 87, 88. No symbol	40.00
162.	1686. Elephant and castle	100.00

WILLIAM AND MARY, 1688-1694

Conjoined heads. Rev. Crowned arms. With or without the various symbols below the heads as indicated.

5 Guineas

163.	1691-94. No symbol	225.00
164.	1691-94. Elephant and castle	250.00

2 Guineas

165.	1693, 94. No symbol	150.00
166.	1691, 93, 94. Elephant and castle	175.00

1 Guinea

167.	1689-94. No symbol	50.00
168.	1692. Elephant	125.00
169.	1689-94. Elephant and castle	100.00

½ Guinea

170.	1689-94. No symbol	40.00
171.	1691, 92. Elephant and castle ....*.....	50.00

WILLIAM III, 1694-1702

Laureate head. Rev. Cross of four shields. With or without the various symbols below the head as indicated.

5 Guineas

172.	1699, 1700, 01. No symbol	250.00
173.	1699. Elephant and castle	350.00

2 Guineas

174.	1701. No symbol ....*.....	200.00

1 Guinea

175.	1695-1701. No symbol	45.00
176.	1695-1701. Elephant and castle	125.00

½ Guinea

177.	1695-1701. No symbol	30.00
178.	1695, 96, 98. Elephant and castle	40.00

ANNE, 1702-1714

Draped bust. Rev. Cross of four shields. With or without the various symbols below the bust as indicated.

5 Guineas

179.	1705-14. No symbol	300.00
180.	1703. Vigo	2000.00

2 Guineas

181.	1709-14. No symbol	125.00

1 Guinea

182.	1702-14. No symbol	35.00
183.	1703. Vigo ....*.....	400.00
184.	1707, 08, 09. Elephant and castle	100.00

½ Guinea

185.	1702-14. No symbol	30.00
186.	1703. Vigo	300.00

GEORGE I, 1714-1727

Laureate head. Rev. Cross of four shields. With or without the symbol below the head as indicated.

5 Guineas

187.	1716, 17, 20, 26. No symbol	400.00

2 Guineas

188.	1717, 20, 26. No symbol	150.00

1 Guinea

189.	1714-27. No symbol	50.00
190.	1721, 22, 26. Elephant and castle ....*.....	100.00

½ Guinea

191.	1715-27. No symbol	30.00
192.	1721. Elephant and castle	450.00

¼ Guinea

193.	1718. No symbol	17.50

GEORGE II, 1727-1760

Laureate head. Rev. Crowned arms. With or without "E.I.C." or "Lima" below the head as indicated.

5 Guineas

194.	1729-41. Young head, plain	225.00
195.	1729. Young head, E.I.C.	225.00
196.	1748, 53. Old head, plain	250.00
197.	1746. Old head, Lima	275.00

2 Guineas

198.	1734-39. Young head, plain	60.00
199.	1739, 40. Middle aged head, plain	65.00
200.	1748, 53. Old head, plain	80.00

1 Guinea

201.	1727-38. Young head, plain ....*.....	35.00
202.	1729, 31, 32. Young head, E.I.C.	60.00
203.	1739-46. Middle aged head, plain	40.00
204.	1739. Middle aged head, E.I.C. ....*.....	65.00
205.	1745. Middle aged head, Lima	75.00
206.	1747-60. Old head, plain ....*.....	35.00

½ Guinea

207.	1728-39. Young head, plain	30.00
208.	1729-39. Young head, E.I.C.	60.00
209.	1740-46. Middle aged head, plain	35.00
210.	1745. Middle aged head, Lima	85.00
211.	1747-60. Old head, plain	25.00

GEORGE III, 1760-1820

Laureate head. Rev. Arms. The 5 and 2 Guinea pieces were not placed in circulation.

212.	5 Guineas 1770, 73, 77	2000.00
213.	2 Guineas 1768, 73, 77	450.00
214.	1 Guinea 1761-86 ....*	30.00
215.	½ Guinea 1762-86	20.00
216.	¼ Guinea 1762 ....*	17.50

Laureate head. Rev. Spade shaped arms.

217.	1 Guinea 1787-99. "Spade Guinea." ....*	27.50
218.	½ Guinea 1787-1800	17.50

Laureate head. Rev. Arms within the Order of the Garter.

219.	1 Guinea 1813. "Military Guinea." ....*	50.00
220.	½ Guinea 1801-13	15.00

Laureate head. Rev. Crown.

221.	⅓ Guinea 1797-1800. Date within legend	15.00
222.	⅓ Guinea 1801-13. Date below crown	12.50

Laureate head. Rev. St. George slaying dragon. The 5 and 2 Pound pieces were not placed in circulation.

223.	5 Pounds 1820. Lettered edge	1250.00
224.	5 Pounds 1820. Plain edge	Unique
225.	2 Pounds 1820. Lettered edge	350.00
226.	2 Pounds 1820. Plain edge	500.00
227.	1 Pound 1817, 18, 20 ....*	25.00

Laureate head. Rev. Arms.

228.	½ Pound 1817, 18, 20	15.00

GEORGE IV, 1820-1830

Head. Rev. Arms. The 5 and 2 Pound pieces were not placed in circulation.

229.	5 Pounds 1826	375.00
230.	2 Pounds 1825, 26	150.00
231.	1 Pound 1825-30 ....*	27.50
232.	½ Pound 1821-25. Laureate head	20.00
233.	½ Pound 1826, 27, 28. Plain head ....*	20.00

Head. Rev. St. George slaying dragon.

234.	2 Pounds 1823 ....*	65.00
235.	1 Pound 1821-25	27.50

WILLIAM IV, 1830-1837

Head. Rev. Arms. The 5 and 2 Pound pieces were not placed in circulation.

236.	5 Pounds 1831	3000.00
237.	2 Pounds 1831 ....*	175.00
238.	1 Pound 1831-37	32.50
239.	½ Pound 1834-37	22.50

VICTORIA, 1837-1901

Young head. Rev. Una and the lion. This coin was not placed in circulation.

240.	5 Pounds 1839. Lettered edge	600.00
241.	5 Pounds 1839. Plain edge	900.00

Young head. Rev. Arms.

242.	1 Pound 1837-74 ....*	22.50
243.	½ Pound 1838-86	15.00

Young head. Rev. St. George slaying dragon.

244.	1 Pound 1871-86	22.50

Jubilee bust. Rev. St. George slaying dragon.

245.	5 Pounds 1887	....	125.00
246.	2 Pounds 1887	....	50.00
247.	1 Pound 1887-92	..............................*	17.50
248.	½ Pound 1887-93. Rev. Arms	....	12.50

Old veiled bust. Rev. St. George slaying dragon.

249.	5 Pounds 1893	..............................*	150.00
250.	2 Pounds 1893	....	65.00
251.	1 Pound 1893-1901	....	17.50
252.	½ Pound 1893-1901	....	12.50

EDWARD VII, 1901-1910

Head. Rev. St. George slaying dragon.

253.	5 Pounds 1902	....	125.00
254.	2 Pounds 1902	....	60.00
255.	1 Pound 1902-10	..............................*	16.00
256.	½ Pound 1902-10	....	10.00

GEORGE V, 1910-1936

Head. Rev. St. George slaying dragon.

257.	5 Pounds 1911	....	150.00
258.	2 Pounds 1911	....	75.00
259.	1 Pound 1911-25	..............................*	16.00
260.	½ Pound 1911-15	....	10.00

GEORGE VI, 1936-1952

Head. Rev. St. George slaying dragon.

261.	5 Pounds 1937. Proof	.......................*	160.00
262.	2 Pounds 1937. Proof	....	75.00
263.	1 Pound 1937. Proof	....	50.00
264.	½ Pound 1937. Proof	....	40.00

ELIZABETH II, 1952-

Head. Rev. St. George slaying dragon. A few sets were struck in 1953 for presentation and to maintain the series. None was made available and all are now in official custody. The 1 Pound pieces of 1957 were struck in larger quantities and placed in circulation.

265.	5 Pounds 1953	....	—
266.	2 Pounds 1953	.............................*	—
267.	1 Pound 1953	....	—
268.	1 Pound 1957 1958	.....................*	22.50
269.	½ Pound 1953	....	—

GREECE

A. Kings of —

OTTO, 1831-1863

Young head. Rev. Arms.

1.	20 Drachmae 1833	....	35.00

Head with moustache. Rev. Arms. Not placed in circulation.

2.	40 Drachmae 1852	...........................*	Rare
3.	20 Drachmae 1852	....	Rare

GEORGE I, 1863-1913

Young head. Rev. Arms. Coins dated 1875 are Essais.

4.	100 Drachmae 1876	....	750.00
5.	50 Drachmae 1876	.........................*	250.00
6.	20 Drachmae 1876	....	30.00

Young head. Rev. Value and date.

7.	10 Drachmae 1876	....	30.00
8.	5 Drachmae 1876	....	35.00

GREECE (cont'd)

Old head. Rev. Arms.

9. 20 Drachmae 1884 .... 25.00

GEORGE II, 1935-1947

Head. Rev. Value. On the re-establishment of the Kingdom. Not placed in circulation.

10. 100 Drachmae 1935 ....*...... 300.00
11. 20 Drachmae 1935 .... 75.00

B. Cities and Islands of —

CHIOS

A. Genoese Doges of —

MARTIN AND BENEDICT II ZACCHARIA, 1319-1324

Shield. Rev. Cross.

1. ¼ Zecchino ND 400.00

Cross. Rev. Christ on throne.

2. ¼ Zecchino ND 400.00

THE CAMPOFREGOSI, 1415-1421 AND 1436-1458

Ruler kneeling before St. Lawrence. Rev. Christ.

3. 1 Zecchino ND 150.00

B. Milanese Dukes of —

PHILIP MARIA, 1421-1436

Ruler kneeling before St. Peter. Rev. Christ.

4. 1 Zecchino ND. S mm for Chios 200.00
5. 1 Zecchino ND. P mm for Pera ....*... 300.00

C. French Kings of —

CHARLES VII, 1458-1461

Ruler kneeling before St. Lawrence. Rev. Christ.

6. 1 Zecchino ND 300.00

D. Venetian Coinage for —

LEONARDO LOREDANO, 1501-1521

Ruler kneeling before St. Mark, legend completely around. Rev. Christ.

7. 1 Zecchino ND 125.00

FOKIA (PHOCAEA)

Mytilene Lords of —

DORINO GATTILUSIO, 1400-1449

Ruler kneeling before Saint. Rev. Christ.

1. 1 Zecchino ND 400.00

MYTILENE

Lords of —

THE GATTILUSI, 1376-1462

Ruler kneeling before Saint. Rev. Christ.

1. 1 Zecchino ND 250.00

HOLY ROMAN EMPIRE

(See under General Introduction and under Austria, Bohemia and Hungary).

HUNGARY

A. Kings of —

CHARLES ROBERT, 1308-1342
St. John. Rev. Lily.

1. 1 Goldgulden ND 60.00

LOUIS I, 1342-1382

St. John. Rev. Lily.

2. 1 Goldgulden ND 40.00

HUNGARY (cont'd)

St. John. Rev. Arms.

3. 1 Goldgulden ND 40.00

St. Ladislas. Rev. Arms.

4. 1 Ducat ND 40.00

MARIA, 1382-1387
St. Ladislas. Rev. Arms.

5. 1 Ducat ND 50.00

SIGISMUND, 1387-1437

St. Ladislas. Rev. Quartered arms.

6. 1 Ducat ND 50.00

ALBERT OF AUSTRIA, 1438-1439
St. Ladislas. Rev. Quartered arms.

7. 1 Ducat ND 60.00

LADISLAS OF POLAND, 1440-1449
St. Ladislas. Rev. Quartered arms.

8. 1 Ducat ND 60.00

JOHN HUNYAD, 1446-1452
St. Ladislas. Rev. Quartered arms.

9. 1 Ducat ND 60.00

LADISLAS V, 1452-1457
St. Ladislas. Rev. Quartered arms.

10. 1 Ducat ND 60.00

MATTHIAS CORVINUS, 1458-1490

St. Ladislas. Rev. Quartered arms.

11. 1 Ducat ND 40.00

St. Ladislas. Rev. Madonna seated.

12. 1 Ducat ND 50.00

LADISLAS II, 1495-1516

St. Ladislas. Rev. Madonna seated.

13. 1 Ducat 1507, ND 50.00

St. Ladislas. Rev. Madonna standing.

14. 1 Ducat 1510-16 . . . . 50.00

St. Ladislas on horseback. Rev. Arms.

15. 10 Ducats 1506 . . . . Rare
16. 8 Ducats 1506 . . . . Rare

LOUIS II, 1516-1526
Ruler on horse. Rev. Madonna seated.

17. 2 Ducats 1525 . . . . 250.00

St. Ladislas. Rev. Madonna standing.

18. 1 Ducat 1518-23 . . . . 40.00

Youthful King seated. Rev. Legend.

19. 5 Ducats 1544 . . . .* 200.00
20. 3 Ducats 1544 . . . . 125.00
21. 2 Ducats 1544 . . . . 75.00

JOHN ZAPOLYA, 1526-1540
Madonna seated. Rev. Arms.

22. 1 Ducat 1539 . . . . 50.00

St. Ladislas. Rev. Arms.

23. 1 Ducat 1540 . . . . 50.00

St. Ladislas. Rev. Madonna standing.

24. 1 Ducat 1527-40 . . . . 50.00

FERDINAND I, 1521-1564
St. Ladislas. Rev. Madonna standing.

25. 2 Ducats 1535-60 . . . . 100.00
26. 1 Ducat 1521-64 . . . . 50.00
27. 1 Ducat 1565. Posthumous 75.00

St. Ladislas. Rev. Arms.

28. 1 Ducat 1545-58 . . . . 40.00

MAXIMILIAN II, 1564-1576
St. Ladislas. Rev. Madonna standing.

29. 2 Ducats 1567, 72 . . . . 100.00
30. 1 Ducat 1564-76 . . . . 50.00
31. 1 Ducat 1577, 78. Posthumous 100.00

Ruler standing. Rev. St. Ladislas.

32. 1 Ducat 1564-76 . . . . 75.00

RUDOLPH II, 1576-1612
St. Ladislas. Rev. Madonna standing.

33. 3 Ducats 1580 . . . . 150.00
34. 1 Ducat 1578-1608 . . . . 40.00

MATTHIAS II, 1612-1619

Ruler standing. Rev. Madonna.

35. 5 Ducats 1614 . . . .* 200.00
36. 2 Ducats 1612-19 . . . . 100.00
37. 1 Ducat 1612-19 . . . . 35.00
38. ¼ Ducat 1615 . . . . 20.00

Bust. Rev. Double eagle between K-B or N-B.

39. 15 Ducats 1617 . . . . 500.00
40. 5 Ducats 1617 . . . . 150.00

FERDINAND II, 1618-1637

Ruler standing. Rev. Madonna.

40a. 5 Ducats 1632 . . . . 200.00
41. 2 Ducats 1622-37 . . . . 85.00

42.	1 Ducat 1620-37 ....*	35.00
43.	¼ Ducat 1630-35	30.00

Bust. Rev. Double eagle between K-B or N-B.

44.	10 Ducats 1626-35 ....*	300.00
45.	5 Ducats 1632-37	150.00

FERDINAND III, 1627-1657
Ruler standing. Rev. Madonna.

46.	2 Ducats 1637-57	100.00
47.	1 Ducat 1637-57	40.00
48.	1 Ducat 1658, 59. Posthumous	75.00

Bust. Rev. Double eagle between K-B or N-B.

49.	10 Ducats 1629-57	300.00

LEOPOLD I, (THE HOGMOUTH), 1658-1705

Ruler standing. Rev. Madonna.

50.	1 Ducat 1658-1704	35.00

Laureate bust. Rev. Madonna on crescent.

51.	10 Ducats 1687	500.00
52.	8 Ducats 1695	400.00
53.	5 Ducats 1675, 87	250.00
54.	4 Ducats 1687, 95	250.00
55.	3 Ducats 1695	175.00
56.	2 Ducats 1695	125.00

Laureate bust. Rev. Madonna seated, two shields below.

57.	1 Ducat 1675	75.00

Bust and value. Rev. Madonna.

58.	¼ Ducat 1684-99 ....*	15.00
59.	⅙ Ducat 1673-98	15.00
60.	1/12 Ducat ND. With blank Rev.	12.50

REBELLION OF THE MALCONTENTS, 1703-1707
Arms and date. Rev. Value in cartouche.

61.	5 Ducats 1704	450.00

Arms. Rev. Madonna.

62.	1 Ducat 1704-07 ....*	50.00
63.	1 Ducat 1705. Square	125.00

JOSEPH I, 1705-1711

Ruler standing. Rev. Madonna.

64.	1 Ducat 1705-11	35.00

CHARLES VI, 1711-1740

Ruler standing. Rev. Madonna.

65.	1 Ducat 1712-40 ....* ...	35.00
66.	½ Ducat 1740	35.00
67.	¼ Ducat 1712-40	25.00

Bust. Rev. Madonna.

67a.	1 Ducat 1736-40	40.00
68.	⅙ Ducat 1712-40	15.00
69.	⅛ Ducat 1739	15.00
70.	1/12 Ducat 1739	15.00

MARIA THERESA, 1740-1780

Ruler standing. Rev. Madonna.

71.	2 Ducats 1763-65 ....*	75.00
72.	1 Ducat 1741-64	35.00

Bust. Rev. Madonna.

73.	1 Ducat 1753-65	30.00

Old veiled bust. Rev. Madonna.

74.	1 Ducat 1765-80	30.00

JOSEPH II, 1765-1790
Ruler standing. Rev. Madonna.

75.	2 Ducats 1781-85	75.00
76.	1 Ducat 1781-85	35.00

LEOPOLD II, 1790-1792
Ruler standing. Rev. Madonna.

77.	1 Ducat 1790-92	50.00

FRANCIS II, 1792-1835
Ruler standing. Rev. Madonna.

78.	1 Ducat 1792-1835	30.00

FERDINAND I, 1835-1848
Ruler standing. Rev. Madonna.

79.	1 Ducat 1837-48. Latin legends	30.00
80.	1 Ducat 1848. Magyar legends	50.00

FRANZ JOSEPH, 1848-1916
Ruler standing. Rev. Arms supported by angels.

81.	1 Ducat 1868-70. KB mm.	40.00
82.	1 Ducat 1868, 69. GYF mm.	35.00

HUNGARY (cont'd)

Laureate head. Rev. Crowned arms.

83. 1 Ducat 1877-81 .... 40.00

Laureate head. Rev. Arms and two values.

84. 8 Florins-20 Francs 1870-92. KB mm. ....* 22.50
85. 8 Florins-20 Francs 1870, 71. GYF mm. 30.00
86. 4 Florins-10 Francs 1870-92. KB mm. ....* 17.50
87. 4 Florins-10 Francs 1870. GYF mm. 25.00

Ruler standing. Rev. Arms.

88. 100 Korona. 1907, 08 .... 175.00
89. 20 Korona 1892-1916 ....* 22.50
90. 20 Korona 1916. Slight change in arms 75.00
91. 10 Korona 1892-1915 ....* 15.00

Head. Rev. Coronation scene. On the 40th year of his reign.

92. 100 Korona 1907 .... 125.00

Crowned bust. Rev. Madonna and child. On the 1000th year of the Hungarian Kingdom.

93. 10 Ducats 1896 .... 300.00

St. John. Rev. Lily. On the 1000th year of the Hungarian Kingdom.

94. 1 Goldgulden 1896 .... 65.00

B. Cities of —

BATTHYANI

Princes of —

CHARLES, 1764-1772

Bust. Rev. Arms.

1. 10 Ducats 1764 .... 600.00
2. 5 Ducats 1764 .... 300.00
3. 1 Ducat 1764, 65 ....* 100.00

LOUIS, 1787-1806
Bust. Rev. Arms.

4. 10 Ducats 1788 .... 500.00
5. 5 Ducats 1789 .... 200.00
6. 1 Ducat 1791 .... 75.00

ESTERHAZY

Princes of —

NICHOLAS, 1762-1790
Bust. Rev. Arms.

1. 1 Ducat 1770 .... 75.00

KREMNITZ

St. George slaying dragon. Rev. Christ in boat. Struck during the period 1600-1800.

1. 10 Ducats ND ....* 300.00
2. 6 Ducats ND 200.00
3. 5 Ducats ND 200.00
4. 3 Ducats ND 125.00
5. 2 Ducats ND 75.00
6. 1 Ducat ND 40.00

TRANSYLVANIA (SIEBENBURGEN)

Voivodes (Princes) of —

JOHN I ZAPOLYA, 1538-1540
Ruler standing. Rev. Madonna.

1. 1 Ducat 1540 .... 100.00

St. Ladislas standing. Rev. Madonna.

2. 1 Ducat 1539, 40 .... 100.00

HUNGARY-TRANSYLVANIA (cont'd)

Madonna. Rev. Arms.

3.	1 Ducat 1539	75.00

ISABELLA AND JOHN SIGISMUND, 1556-1559

Madonna. Rev. Arms.

4.	5 Ducats 1557	500.00
5.	1 Ducat 1556-60	65.00
6.	½ Ducat 1558, 59	60.00
7.	¼ Ducat 1559	50.00

St. Ladislas. Rev. Arms.

8.	1 Ducat 1556	125.00

Arms. Rev. Legend.

9.	10 Ducats 1557	1000.00
10.	10 Ducats 1557. Square	1250.00
11.	5 Ducats 1557	500.00

JOHN SIGISMUND, 1559-1571

Madonna. Rev. Arms.

12.	4 Ducats 1577. Thick flan.	500.00
13.	2 Ducats 1562	150.00
14.	1 Ducat 1560-72 ....*....	100.00

St. Ladislas standing. Rev. Arms.

15.	1 Ducat 1556-59	75.00

Arms and ISRV. Rev. Blank.

16.	10 Ducats 1562, 65	750.00

STEPHAN BATHORI, 1571-1575

Madonna. Rev. St. Ladislas.

17.	1 Ducat 1572-79	100.00

CHRISTOPHER BATHORI, 1576-1581

Arms. Rev. Legend.

18.	10 Ducats 1577, 83 ....*....	750.00
19.	5 Ducats 1577, 83	400.00
20.	4 Ducats 1577	300.00
21.	2 Ducats 1577	175.00
22.	1½ Ducats 1577	150.00

Madonna. Rev. Arms.

23.	1 Ducat 1579	100.00

Madonna. Rev. St. Ladislas.

24.	1 Ducat 1577-80	100.00

ELIZABETH BOCSKAI, 1577

Lion seated. Rev. Legend.

25.	10 Ducats 1577 ....*....	750.00
26.	5 Ducats 1577	400.00
27.	3 Ducats 1577	250.00
28.	2 Ducats 1577	175.00

SIGISMUND BATHORI, 1581-1602

Bust. Rev. Eagle.

29.	10 Ducats 1598	750.00
30.	9 Ducats 1598	750.00

Bust. Rev. Arms supported by angels.

31.	10 Ducats 1590	750.00

Madonna. Rev. St. Ladislas.

32.	5 Ducats 1590. Thick flan.	400.00
33.	1 Ducat 1581-97 ....*....	100.00

St. Ladislas. Rev. Eagle.

34.	1 Ducat 1598	100.00

Arms. Rev. Legend.

35.	10 Ducats 1583	750.00

MOSES SZEKELY, 1602-1603

Two lions with sword. Rev. Legend.

36.	10 Ducats 1603	Rare

STEPHAN BOCSKAI, 1604-1606

Bust. Rev. Arm with sword.

37.	10 Ducats 1605	750.00

Bust. Rev. Arms.

38.	10 Ducats 1606	750.00
39.	5 Ducats 1606	350.00

Bust. Rev. Crossed swords.

40.	1 Ducat 1606	125.00

Head with fur cap. Rev. Arms.

41.	2 Ducats 1606	200.00
42.	1 Ducat 1606 ....*....	125.00

HUNGARY-TRANSYLVANIA (cont'd)

Madonna. Rev. St. Ladislas.

43. 1 Ducat 1605, 06, 07, ND 85.00

Madonna. Rev. Arms.

44. ½ Ducat 1606 .... 50.00
45. ¼ Ducat 1606 .... 35.00

SIGISMUND RAKOCZI, 1607-1608

Bust. Rev. Legend.

46. 10 Ducats 1607 .... 850.00

Bust. Rev. Eagle on castles.

47. 1 Ducat 1607, 08 .... 150.00

Madonna. Rev. Arms.

48. ¼ Ducat 1608 .... 40.00

GABRIEL BATHORI, 1608-1613
Bust. Rev. Three shields.

49. 10 Ducats 1609 .... 600.00

Bust. Rev. Eagle.

50. 6 Ducats 1613. Thick flan 500.00
51. 1 Ducat 1611, 12, 13 ....*...... 100.00

Bust. Rev. Arms.

52. 2 Ducats 1610, 12 .... 150.00
53. 1 Ducat 1609-12, ND 85.00

Head with cap. Rev. Arms.

54. 1 Ducat 1613 .... 125.00

Bust. Rev. Crossed swords.

55. 1 Ducat 1613 .... 125.00

Madonna. Rev. St. Ladislas.

56. 1 Ducat 1609 .... 75.00

Three shields. Rev. Legend.

57. 10 Ducats 1611, 12, 13 .... 500.00
58. 8 Ducats 1612 .... 450.00

Madonna. Rev. Arms.

59. ½ Ducat 1612, 13 .... 35.00
60. ¼ Ducat 1610, 12, 13 .... 25.00

MICHAEL WEISS (1613)

Legend on each side.

---

61. 10 Ducats 1612 ....*...... 750.00
62. 1 Ducat 1612, 13 .... 150.00

GABRIEL BETHLEN, 1613-1629
Bust with cap. Rev. Arms.

63. 2 Ducats 1613 .... 150.00
64. 1 Ducat 1613-18 .... 85.00

Bust with cap. Rev. Arm with sword.

65. 10 Ducats 1616 .... 750.00

Bust. Rev. Elaborate arms.

66. 1 Ducat 1618 .... 100.00

Bust. Rev. Three shields.

67. 10 Ducats 1619 .... 750.00
68. 1 Ducat 1619 .... 85.00

Bust. Rev. Arms.

69. 10 Ducats 1620, 21, 22, 28, ND 500.00
70. 5 Ducats 1622 .... 350.00
71. 3 Ducats 1627 .... 250.00
72. 1 Ducat 1620, 22, ND ....*...... 75.00

Bust. Rev. Madonna.

73. 1 Ducat 1620-27 .... 75.00

Bust. Rev. Madonna in flames.

74. 2 Ducats 1628 .... 200.00
75. 1 Ducat 1627, 28, 29 .... 100.00

Madonna. Rev. Arms.

76. 1 Ducat 1627 .... 75.00
77. ¼ Ducat 1619-27 .... 25.00

CATHERINE BETHLEN, 1629-1630
Bust. Rev. Madonna.

78. 1 Ducat 1630 .... 250.00

Bust. Rev. Arms.

79. 1 Ducat 1630 .... 250.00

STEPHAN BETHLEN, 1630

Bust. Rev. Arms.

80. 1 Ducat 1630 .... 250.00

GEORGE RAKOCZI I, 1630-1648

Bust. Rev. Legend.

81.	20 Ducats 1637, 39			Rare
82.	10 Ducats 1631, 36, 37, 39	................*		500.00
83.	5 Ducats 1631, 36, 37, 39	....		300.00

Bust. Rev. Arms.

84.	10 Ducats 1645, 47		600.00
85.	6 Ducats 1647	....	400.00

Bust. Rev. Eagle and castles.

86.	2 Ducats 1632	....	200.00
87.	1 Ducat 1631-39	....	85.00

Bust with fur cap. Rev. Arms.

88.	10 Ducats 1646, 48	....	600.00

Bust with fur cap. Rev. Eagle on castles.

89.	1 Ducat 1646	....	100.00

Bust with cap. Rev. Madonna.

90.	1 Ducat 1646, 48	....	85.00

Bust. Rev. Madonna.

91.	1 Ducat 1645, 48	....	85.00

Madonna. Rev. Arms.

92.	¼ Ducat 1642, 47	....	30.00

GEORGE RAKOCZI II, 1648-1660

Bust with fur cap. Rev. Arms.

93.	13 Ducats 1657. Square	....		Rare
94.	12 Ducats 1657. Square	....		Rare
95.	10 Ducats 1652, 57, 60. Square or hexagonal	..*		750.00
96.	10 Ducats 1648-60. Round	....		450.00
97.	7 Ducats 1654			450.00

Bust with fur cap. Rev. Madonna.

98.	1 Ducat 1648-57	....	75.00

Bust with fur cap. Rev. Eagle and castles.

99.	1 Ducat 1657	....	100.00
100.	1 Ducat 1657. Square	....	150.00

Madonna. Rev. Arms.

101.	¼ Ducat 1650, 53	....	30.00

ACHATIUS BARCSAI, 1658-1660

Bust. Rev. Arms.

102.	10 Ducats 1659, 60			650.00
103.	10 Ducats 1659. Square or hexagonal	....		800.00
104.	2 Ducats 1659			200.00
105.	1 Ducat 1659	....................*		125.00

Arms. Rev. Legend.

106.	10 Ducats 1660	....	750.00
107.	10 Ducats 1660. Square	....	850.00
108.	9 Ducats 1660. Square	....	750.00
109.	7 Ducats 1660. Square	....	600.00
110.	5 Ducats 1660. Square	....	500.00
111.	5 Ducats 1660	....	400.00
112.	1 Ducat 1660	....	125.00

Arms on each side.

113.	10 Ducats 1660	....	750.00

JOHN KEMENY, 1661-1662

Bust with fur cap. Rev. Arms.

114.	10 Ducats 1661	...................*		750.00
115.	5 Ducats 1661	....		450.00
116.	3 Ducats 1661	....		350.00
117.	2 Ducats 1661	....		250.00
118.	2 Ducats 1661. Square	....		300.00
119.	1 Ducat 1661	....		125.00

MICHAEL APAFI, 1661-1690

Bust with fur cap. Rev. Arms.

ROUND COINS

120.	100 Ducats 1677	....	Rare
121.	30 Ducats 1677, 83	....	Rare
122.	10 Ducats 1662-74	....	500.00
123.	5 Ducats 1662-73	....	300.00
124.	4 Ducats 1665	....	275.00
125.	1 Ducat 1662	....	100.00

SQUARE OR HEXAGONAL COINS

126.	10 Ducats 1662, 63, 75, 81	...............*		650.00

HUNGARY-TRANSYLVANIA (cont'd)

127.	6	Ducats 1668	375.00
128.	4½	Ducats 1668	350.00
129.	3	Ducats 1663	300.00
130.	2	Ducats 1662, 68	200.00
131.	1	Ducat 1663, 68	125.00

Bust. Rev. Arms.

ROUND COINS

132.	10	Ducats 1672-89	450.00
133.	5	Ducats 1677, 87	350.00
134.	4	Ducats 1677, 89	250.00
135.	1	Ducat 1673-90	75.00

SQUARE OR HEXAGONAL COINS

136.	25	Ducats 1687	Rare
137.	10	Ducats 1684, 89	600.00
138.	6	Ducats 1686	500.00
139.	5	Ducats 1689	350.00
140.	4	Ducats 1678	300.00
141.	3	Ducats 1684	250.00
142.	2	Ducats 1689	200.00
143.	1	Ducat 1678-89	100.00

*Bust in center within circle of ten other busts. Rev. Arms in
center within circle of ten other arms.*

144.	100	Ducats 1674, 75	Rare

EMERIC TOKOLY, 1682-1690

Bust with fur cap. Rev. Arm with sword.

145.	10	Ducats 1683	500.00
146.	8	Ducats 1683	400.00
147.	4	Ducats 1683	250.00

Bust with fur cap. Rev. Arms.

148.	1	Ducat 1690	150.00

FRANZ RAKOCZI II, 1704-1711

Arms. Rev. Palm tree.

149.	1	Ducat 1705	125.00

CHARLES VI, 1711-1740
Head. Rev. Arms.

150.	¼	Ducat ND	25.00

Arms. Rev. Globe.

151.	¼	Ducat ND	25.00

MARIA THERESA, 1740-1780
Arms. Rev. Value.

152.	¼	Ducat 1749	25.00
153.	⅛	Ducat 1778	25.00
154.	¹⁄₁₆	Ducat 1778	25.00

ITALY

A. Republic of —, 1797-1805

Head of Napoleon as founder and president. Rev. Value in wreath or circle.

1.	1 Doppia 1803 (year 2) ....*	750.00
2.	½ Doppia 1803 (year 2)	600.00

Head of Napoleon. Rev. Scales.

3.	20 Lire 1804	750.00

B. Kings of —, 1805-1814 and 1861-1945

NAPOLEON 1805-1814

Head. Rev. Arms. Milan Mint with M mm.

4.	40 Lire 1806-14 ....*......	60.00
4a.	40 Lire 1808. Without M mm.	750.00
5.	20 Lire 1806-14	25.00

(For the French type coins struck at the Italian Mints, see under France).

VICTOR EMANUELE II, 1861-1878
(For the earlier coins of this ruler, see under Sardinia and Emilia).

Head. Rev. Arms.

6.	100 Lire 1864. T & BN mm.	150.00
7.	100 Lire 1872, 78. R mm.	200.00
8.	50 Lire 1864. T & BN mm.	1000.00
9.	20 Lire 1861-70. T & BN mm.	16.00
10.	20 Lire 1870-78. R mm.	16.00
11.	20 Lire 1872-75. M & BN mm. ....* ..	20.00
12.	10 Lire 1861-65. T & BN mm. ....* ..	15.00
13.	5 Lire 1863, 65. T & BN mm.	20.00

HUMBERT I, 1878-1900

Head. Rev. Arms.

14.	100 Lire 1880-91	100.00
15.	50 Lire 1884, 88, 91	60.00
16.	20 Lire 1879-97 ....* ..	17.50

VICTOR EMANUELE III, 1900-1944

Head. Rev. Eagle. All coins of 1902 are rare.

17.	100 Lire 1903, 05	125.00
18.	20 Lire 1902, 03, 05 ....* ..	30.00
19.	20 Lire 1902. With small anchor at bottom of Obv. indicating gold from Eritrea	200.00

Head. Rev. Allegorical scene. On the 50th year of the Kingdom.

20.	50 Lire 1911	75.00

ITALY (cont'd)

Uniformed bust. Rev. Agricultural scene. The 1926, 1927 issues are rare.

21. 100 Lire 1912, 26, 27 .... 125.00
22. 50 Lire 1912, 26, 27 .... 75.00
23. 20 Lire 1912, 26, 27 ....* 30.00
24. 10 Lire 1912, 26, 27 .... 100.00

Head. Rev. Fasces. On the first year of the Fascist march on Rome.

25. 100 Lire 1923 .... 100.00
26. 20 Lire 1923 ....* 30.00

Small head. Rev. Naked male holding winged Victory. On the 25th year of reign and on the 10th year of entry into World War I.

27. 100 Lire 1925 .... 125.00

Head. Rev. Italia on prow of ship.

28. 100 Lire 1931, 32, 33 .... 40.00

Head. Rev. Figure holding Fasces.

29. 50 Lire 1931, 32, 33 .... 22.50

Head right. Rev. Figure holding Fasces. After the conquest of Ethiopia, with the title of Emperor added to that of King.

30. 100 Lire 1936 ....* 100.00
31. 100 Lire 1937. Size reduced 175.00

Head left. Rev. Eagle over two medallions.

32. 50 Lire 1936 .... 50.00

C. States and Cities of —

ACHAIA

Princes of —

ROBERT OF ANJOU, 1346-1364

St. John standing. Rev. Lily.

1. 1 Florin ND 750.00

AMADEUS VI OF SAVOY, 1367-1383
St. John. Rev. Helmeted arms.

2. 1 Florin ND 750.00

Arms. Rev. Cross.

3. 1 Scudo d'oro ND 750.00

LOUIS OF SAVOY, 1402-1418
Ruler on horse. Rev. Helmet.

4. 1 Florin ND 250.00

AMALFI

Rulers of —

PRINCE GUAIMARIO V AND MANSONE IV, 1042
Cufic legend on each side.

1. 1 Tari ND 75.00

AUTONOMOUS, 1050-1100
Cufic legend on each side.

2. 1 Tari ND 25.00

DUKE ROGER BORSA, 1085-1111
Cufic legend on each side.

3. 1 Tari ND 35.00

DUKE WILLIAM I, 1111-1127
W. Rev. Cross.

4. 1 Tari ND 40.00

COUNT ROGER II, 1105-1154

R. Rev. Cross.

5. 1 Tari ND 40.00

KING WILLIAM II, 1162-1189

W. Rev. Rex.

6. 1 Tari ND 40.00

KING TANCRED, 1189-1194
ACD Monogram. Rev. Rex.

7. 1 Tari ND 50.00

KING TANCRED AND WILLIAM, 1193
Rex and TCD Monogram. Rev. W.

8. 1 Tari ND 85.00

ITALY-AMALFI (cont'd)

KING HENRY VI, 1194-1197
Bust. Rev. Cross.

9. 1 Tari ND 200.00

KING CONSTANCE AND FREDERICK II, 1197-1198
Palm Tree. Rev. Cross.

10. 1 Tari ND 100.00

KING FREDERICK II, 1198-1250
FRE. Rev. Star.

11. 1 Tari ND 40.00

F. Rev. Rex.

12. 1 Tari ND 50.00

IMP. Rev. Cross Potent.

13. 1 Tari ND 50.00

ANCONA

Anonymous Rulers of —

Knight standing. Rev. St. Quiriacus standing.

1. 2 Ducats ND (1500-1600) 500.00
2. 1 Ducat ND (1500-1600) 200.00

(For additional coins of Ancona, see under Vatican-Ancona).

ANTIGNATE

Lords of —

JOHN BENTIVOGLIO II, 1494-1509
Bust with cap. Rev. Legend.

1. 4 Ducats 1494 .... 1000.00
2. ½ Ducat 1494 .... 200.00

Bust with cap. Rev. Arms.

3. 2 Ducats ND 250.00
4. 1 Ducat ND ....*...... 350.00

ARQUATA

Marcheses of —

JULIUS SPINOLA, 1681-1691
Bust. Rev. Arms.

1. ½ Doppia 1681 .... 500.00

GERARD SPINOLA, 1682-1694
Bust. Rev. Arms.

2. 1 Doppia 1682 .... 500.00

ASTI

A. Kings of —

LOUIS XII OF FRANCE, 1498-1513
Crowned bust. Rev. Crowned arms.

1. 2 Ducats ND 2000.00
2. 1 Ducat ND 1250.00

Porcupine. Rev. Crowned arms.

3. 1 Ducat ND 1250.00

B. Lords of —

CHARLES OF ORLEANS, 1408-1465
Arms. Rev. Cross.

4. 1 Scudo d'oro ND 300.00

LOUIS OF ORLEANS, 1465-1498
Ruler on horse. Rev. Arms.

5. 1 Ducat ND 300.00

Arms. Rev. Cross.

6. 1 Scudo d'oro ND 300.00

EMANUEL FILIBERT, 1542-1553
Arms. Rev. Cross.

7. 1 Scudo d'oro ND 300.00

BARDI

Marcheses of —

FREDERICK LANDI, 1590-1627
Bust. Rev. St. Francis kneeling.

1. 5 Doppia 1622 .... 750.00

Bust. Rev. St. John standing.

2. 2 Doppia 1623 .... 400.00

Bust. Rev. Double eagle in shield.

3. 2 Doppia ND 600.00
4. 1 Doppia ND ....*...... 400.00

Bust. Rev. St. Theresa.

5. 1 Doppia ND 1000.00

BARLETTA

Dukes of —

CHARLES I, 1266-1278

Bust. Rev. Arms.

1. 1 Real ND ....*...... 400.00
2. ½ Real ND .... Unique

K. Rev. Arms.

3. 1 Tari ND 65.00

BELGIOIOSO

Princes of —

ANTONY BARBIANO

Bust. Rev. Arms.

1. 1 Zecchino 1769 .... 200.00

ITALY (cont'd)

BELMONTE

Princes of —

ANTONY PIGNATELLI

Bust. Rev. Arms.

1. 1 Zecchino 1733 .... 350.00

BENEVELLO

Counts of —

JOHN ANTONY FALLETTI, 1520-1544
Arms on cross. Rev. Eagle.

1. 1 Scudo d'oro ND 300.00

BENEVENTUM

Dukes, and later, Princes of —

ANONYMOUS, 569-706
Bust. Rev. Cross.

1. 1 Solidus ND 75.00
2. ⅓ Solidus ND 35.00

ROMUALD II, 706-731

Bust. Rev. Cross.

3. 1 Solidus ND ....* 100.00
4. ⅓ Solidus ND 40.00

AUDELAO, 731
Bust. Rev. Cross.

5. 1 Solidus ND 500.00
6. ⅓ Solidus ND 300.00

GREGORY, 732-739
Bust. Rev. Cross.

7. 1 Solidus ND 60.00
8. ⅓ Solidus ND 40.00

GODESCALCO, 739-742

Bust. Rev. Cross.

9. 1 Solidus ND ....* 125.00
10. ⅓ Solidus ND 60.00

GISULF II, 742-751

Bust. Rev. Cross.

11. 1 Solidus ND ....* 100.00
12. ⅓ Solidus ND 40.00

LUITPRAND AND SCAUNIPERGA, 751-755

Bust. Rev. Cross.

13. 1 Solidus ND ....* 300.00
14. ⅓ Solidus ND 100.00

LUITPRAND, 755-758
Bust. Rev. Cross.

15. 1 Solidus ND 150.00
16. ⅓ Solidus ND 60.00

INTERREGNUM, 758
Bust. Rev. Cross.

17. 1 Solidus ND 150.00
18. ⅓ Solidus ND 60.00

ARICHIS II, 758-774

Bust. Rev. Cross.

19. 1 Solidus ND ....* 75.00
20. ⅓ Solidus ND 30.00

ARICHI II, 774-787
Bust. Rev. Cross.

21. 1 Solidus ND 250.00
22. ⅓ Solidus ND 80.00

GRIMOALD III, 788-806
Bust. Rev. Cross.

23. 1 Solidus ND 75.00
24. ⅓ Solidus ND 30.00

SICO, 817-832
Bust. Rev. St. Michael.

25. 1 Solidus ND 125.00

Bust. Rev. Cross.

26. ⅓ Solidus ND 40.00

SICARDO, 832-839
Bust. Rev. Cross.

27. 1 Solidus ND 75.00
28. ⅓ Solidus ND 30.00

RADELCHIS, 839-851
Bust. Rev. Cross.

29. 1 Solidus ND 75.00

BERGAMO

CHARLEMAGNE, 773-800
Cross Potent. Rev. Cross and four globes.

1. ⅓ Solidus ND 500.00

BOLOGNA

(For additional coins struck at Bologna, see under Cispadane Republic, Emilia and Vatican).

A. Republic of —, 1376-1500

St. Peter. Rev. Lion.

ITALY-BOLOGNA (cont'd)

1. 2 Bolognino d'oro ND 125.00
2. 1 Bolognino d'oro ND ....* 60.00

B. Governors of —

JOHN I BENTIVOGLIO, 1401-1402
St. Peter. Rev. Lion.

3. 1 Bolognino d'oro ND 150.00

PHILIP MARIA VISCONTI, 1438-1443
St. Peter. Rev. Lion.

4. 1 Florin ND 500.00

JOHN II BENTIVOGLIO, 1463-1506

St. Peter. Rev. Lion.

5. 2 Bolognino d'oro ND 75.00
6. 1 Bolognino d'oro ND ....* 40.00

St. Petronius seated. Rev. Lion.

7. 2 Bolognino d'oro ND 150.00
8. 1 Bolognino d'oro ND ....* 75.00

CHARLES V OF SPAIN
Head. Rev. Pillars of Hercules.

9. 1 Imperial or 2½ Ducats 1530 .... 1000.00

BOZZOLO

Princes of —

JULIUS CAESAR GONZAGA, 1593-1609
Bust. Rev. Chameleon.

1. 5 Doppia (Gold Piastre) ND 2000.00
2. 1 Doppia ND 500.00

Bust. Rev. Arms.

3. 1 Doppia ND 500.00

Soldier. Rev. Arms.

4. 1 Ducat ND 250.00

SCIPIO GONZAGA, 1609-1670
Crowned female. Rev. Arms.

5. 1 Doppia 1618 .... 400.00

Bust. Rev. St. Peter kneeling before Christ.

6. 6 Doppia 1639 .... 2000.00
7. 4 Doppia 1639 .... 1000.00

Bust. Rev. Arms.

8. 5 Doppia ND 1000.00
9. 1 Doppia ND 400.00

Bust. Rev. Two shields.

10. 1 Doppia ND 400.00

Soldier. Rev. Tablet.

11. 1 Ducat ND 200.00

BRESCELLO

Lords of —

ALFONSO II D'ESTE, 1570-1595
Arms. Rev. Cross.

1. 1 Scudo d'oro ND 250.00

BRINDISI

Kings of —

FREDERICK II, 1197-1250

Bust. Rev. Eagle:

1. 1 Augustalis ND 150.00
2. ½ Augustalis ND 125.00

Eagle in circle. Rev. Legend divided by cross.

3. 10 Tari ND 350.00
4. 6 Tari ND ....* 100.00

CHARLES I OF ANJOU, 1266-1278
Bust. Rev. Arms.

5. 1 Real ND 500.00

Ruler on horse. Rev. Cross.

6. 5 Tari ND 150.00
7. 1 Tari ND 50.00

K. Rev. Cross.

7a. Multiple Tari ND 75.00

K. Rev. Arms.

8. 1 Tari ND 50.00

Name. Rev. Cross.

9. Multiple Tari ND 75.00

CAGLIARI

Spanish Kings of —

CHARLES V
Arms. Rev. Cross.

1. 1 Scudo d'oro ND (1517-56) 400.00

PHILIP V

Arms. Rev. Cross.

2. 1 Scudo d'oro 1701, 02, 03 .... 50.00

CHARLES III
Arms. Rev. Cross.

3. 1 Scudo d'oro 1710, 11, 12 .... 50.00

CAMERINO

Dukes of —

JOHN MARIA VARANO, 1511-1527

Bust. Rev. Arms.

1. 1 Ducat ND 400.00

JULIA VARANO, 1527-1534
Head. Rev. Arms.

2. 1 Scudo d'oro ND 500.00

Arms. Rev. Cross.

3. 1 Scudo d'oro ND 50.00

JULIA VARANO AND GUIDOBALD II DELLA ROVERE, 1534-1539

Arms. Rev. Cross.

4. 1 Scudo d'oro ND 50.00

CAMPI

Marcheses of —

CHARLES CENTURIONI, 1654-1663
Bust. Rev. Eagle.

1. 1 Doppia 1661 .... 600.00

JOHN BAPTIST CENTURIONI, 1663-1715
Bust. Rev. Arms.

2. ½ Doppia 1668 .... 400.00

Busts of John and his wife, Julia. Rev. Arms.

3. 1 Doppia 1668 .... 800.00

CARMAGNOLA

Marcheses of —

LOUIS II DI SALUZZO, 1475-1504

Bust with cap. Rev. Arms.

1. 1 Doppia ND ....*...... 300.00
2. 1 Ducat ND 200.00

Bust with cap. Rev. Helmet.

3. 1 Ducat ND 250.00

Busts of Louis and Margaret. Rev. Eagle.

4. 10 Scudi d'oro 1503 .... 1000.00

MICHAEL ANTHONY DI SALUZZO, 1504-1528

St. Constantine on horse. Rev. Cross.

5. 1 Scudo d'oro ND 150.00

St. Constantine. Rev. Helmet.

6. 1 Scudo d'oro ND 200.00

Eagle. Rev. Cross.

7. 1 Scudo d'oro ND 200.00

FRANCIS DI SALUZZO, 1529-1537
Arms. Rev. Cross.

8. 1 Scudo del sole ND 200.00

Marcheses of —

GABRIEL DI SALUZZO, 1537-1548
Saint Constantine on horse. Rev. Helmeted shield.

9. 10 Scudi d'oro ND 1000.00

CASALE

WILLIAM I PALEOLOGO, 1464-1483
St. Theodore. Rev. Helmeted shield.

1. 1 Ducat ND 200.00

WILLIAM II PALEOLOGO, 1494-1518
Bust with cap. Rev. Stag.

2. 4 Ducats ND 750.00

Bust with cap. Rev. Arms.

3. 2 Ducats ND 500.00

Bust. Rev. Plant.

4. 2 Ducats ND 500.00

Arms. Rev. Cross.

5. 1 Scudo d'oro ND 200.00

Double eagle. Rev. Cross.

6. 1 Scudo d'oro ND 75.00

BONIFACE II PALEOLOGO, 1518-1530
Bust with cap. Rev. Saint on horse.

7. 1 Ducat ND 250.00

Double eagle. Rev. Cross.

8. 1 Scudo d'oro ND 75.00

JOHN GEORGE PALEOLOGO, 1530-1533
Double eagle. Rev. Cross.

9. 1 Scudo d'oro ND 200.00

ITALY-CASALE (cont'd)

Arms. Rev. Cross.

10. 1 Scudo d'oro ND 200.00

ANONYMOUS, 1500-1600
Double eagle. Rev. Cross.

11. 1 Scudo d'oro ND 150.00

CHARLES V OF SPAIN, 1533-1536
Arms. Rev. Cross.

12. 1 Scudo d'oro ND 300.00

FREDERICK II GONZAGA AND MARGARET PALEOLOGO, 1536-1540
Arms. Rev. Cross and initials.

13. 1 Scudo d'oro ND 400.00

FRANCIS III GONZAGA AND MARGARET PALEOLOGO, 1540-1550

Arms. Rev. Cross and initials.

14. 1 Scudo d'oro ND 150.00

WILLIAM GONZAGA AND MARGARET PALEOLOGO, 1550-1566

Arms. Rev. Cross and initials.

15. 1 Scudo d'oro 1563-67, ND 150.00

WILLIAM III GONZAGA, 1566-1587

Arms. Rev. Cross and initials.

16. 1 Scudo d'oro 1578, ND 75.00

Bust right or left. Rev. Arms.

17. 2 Doppia 1578-86, ND 250.00
18. 1 Doppia 1578, ND ....*...... 500.00

Bust. Rev. Cross.

19. 1 Scudo d'oro 1578-82 .... 200.00

VINCENT I GONZAGA, 1587-1612

Bust. Rev. Arms.

---

20. 2 Doppia 1588-1601 ....*.....200.00
21. 4 Scudi d'oro 1600 .... 500.00

Arms. Rev. Cross.

22. 1 Scudo d'oro ND 200.00

Ruler standing. Rev. Eagle.

23. 1 Ducat ND 200.00

FRANCIS IV GONZAGA, 1612-1613

Busts of Francis and Margaret. Rev. Flower.

24. 1 Doppia 1612 .... 1000.00

Cross. Rev. Arms on Mt. Olympus.

25. 1 Doppia 1612 .... 500.00

FERDINAND GONZAGA, 1613-1626

Bust. Rev. Arms.

26. 2 Doppia 1617, 21, ND 250.00
27. 1 Doppia 1617, ND ....*....... 250.00

Bust. Rev. Stag.

28. 5 Doppia ND 1500.00

VINCENT II GONZAGA, 1626-1627
Bust. Rev. Arms.

29. 2 Doppia 1627 .... 500.00
30. 1 Doppia ND 300.00

CHARLES I GONZAGA, 1627-1637
Bust. Rev. Arms.

31. 2 Doppia 1629, 31, 36 .... 200.00
32. 1 Doppia 1632 .... 200.00

CHARLES II GONZAGA, 1637-1655
Busts of Charles and Maria. Rev. Arms.

33. 2 Doppia ND 500.00
34. 1 Doppia ND 200.00

FERDINAND CHARLES GONZAGA, 1665-1708
Bust. Rev. Arms.

35. 2 Doppia ND 500.00

CASTEL SEPRIO

DESIDERIUS, 757-773
Cross potent. Rev. Star.

1. ⅓ Solidus ND 300.00

CHARLEMAGNE, 773-800
Cross potent. Rev. Cross and four globes.

2. ⅓ Solidus ND 400.00

CASTIGLIONE DELLE STIVIERE

Princes of —

FRANCIS GONZAGA, 1593-1616
Bust. Rev. Arms.

1. 5 Doppia 1614 .... 1000.00
2. ½ Doppia ND 300.00
3. ⅛ Doppia ND 50.00

FERDINAND GONZAGA, 1616-1678
Soldier. Rev. Eagle.

4. 1 Florin 1639 .... 250.00

St. Nazarius. Rev. Value.

5. 1 Florin ND 250.00

St. Ferdinandus. Rev. Value.

6. 1 Florin ND 250.00

Madonna. Rev. Value.

7. 1 Florin ND 250.00

Lion. Rev. Value.

8. 1 Florin ND 250.00

CASTIGLIONE DEI GATTI

Counts of —

HERCULES AND CORNELIUS PEPOLI, 1700

Tablet. Rev. Double eagle.

1. 1 Ducat ND 200.00

ALEXANDER AND SICINIUS PEPOLI, 1703-1713
Tablet. Rev. Double eagle.

2. 1 Ducat ND 200.00

CASTRO

Dukes of —

PETER LUIGI FARNESE, 1545-1547

Arms. Rev. Cross.

1. 1 Scudo d'oro ND 50.00

CHIVASSO

Marcheses of —

THEODORE I PALEOLOGO, 1307-1338
St. John. Rev. Lily.

1. 1 Florin ND 250.00

CISPADANE REPUBLIC

Madonna. Rev. Trophies. Struck at Bologna.

1. 20 Lire or 1 Doppia 1797 .... 800.00

CISTERNA

Princes of —

JAMES DAL POZZO, 1667-1677
Bust. Rev. Arms.

1. 10 Scudi d'oro 1677 .... 1500.00
2. 2 Doppia 1677 .... 1000.00

CORREGGIO

Princes of —

GIBERT, CAMILLO, AND FABRIZIO, 1569-1597
Madonna. Rev. Eagle and arms.

1. 1 Doppia ND 500.00
2. 1 Scudo d'oro ND 200.00

St. Quirinus. Rev. Eagle and arms.

3. 1 Scudo d'oro ND 100.00

St. Quirinus. Rev. Double eagle.

4. 1 Scudo d'oro ND 100.00

Young St. Quirinus in oval. Rev. Arms.

5. 1 Scudo d'oro ND 200.00

Soldier standing. Rev. Madonna.

6. 1 Ducat ND 100.00

CAMILLO AND FABRIZIO, 1580-1597
Bust of St. Quirinus. Rev. Arms.

7. 144 Soldi (Scudo d'oro) ND 300.00

CAMILLO, 1597-1605

Ruler standing. Rev. Arms.

8. 1 Ducat 1599, ND 75.00

Ruler standing. Rev. Double eagle.

9. 1 Ducat ND 75.00

Ruler standing. Rev. Madonna.

10. 1 Ducat ND 100.00

SIRUS, 1605-1630
Soldier. Rev. Tablet.

11. 1 Ducat ND 100.00

CORTONA

LOMBARDIC PERIOD, 600-800
Cross. Rev. Legend.

1. ⅓ Solidus ND 300.00

CREMONA

Lords of —

FRANCIS II SFORZA, 1521-1535
Saint standing. Rev. Serpent.

1. 1 Scudo d'oro ND 1000.00

CUNEO

SIEGE OF 1641
Column and flag. Rev. Arms.

1. 5 Doppia 1641 .... 1500.00
2. 1 Doppia 1641 .... 1500.00

DESANA

Counts of —

LOUIS TIZZONE II, 1510-1525
Bust. Rev. Arms.

1. 2 Ducats ND 1000.00

St. Peter seated. Rev. Arms.

2. 2 Scudi d'oro ND 1000.00
3. 1 Scudo d'oro ND 500.00

Arms. Rev. Cross.

4. 1 Scudo d'oro ND 300.00

PETER BERARD, 1516-1529
Bust. Rev. Arms.

5. 1 Scudo d'oro ND 1000.00

Arms on cross. Rev. Cross.

6. 1 Scudo d'oro ND 500.00

AUGUSTIN TIZZONE, 1559-1582
Bust. Rev. Arms.

7. 1 Doppia 1581 .... 1000.00

DELFINO TIZZONE, 1583-1598
St. Lawrence. Rev. Arms.

8. 1 Scudo d'oro ND 200.00

ANTHONY MARIA TIZZONE, 1598-1641
Bust. Rev. Arms.

9. 2 Doppia ND 400.00
10. 1 Doppia ND 400.00
11. 1 Florin ND 200.00

Bearded bust. Rev. Arms.

12. 2 Doppia ND 400.00
13. 1 Doppia ND 300.00

Head. Rev. Female at column.

14. 2 Doppia ND 400.00

Head. Rev. St. Dorothea standing.

15. 1 Doppia ND 400.00

Bust. Rev. Double eagle.

16. 1 Florin ND 200.00

St. Peter. Rev. Bust.

17. 1 Florin ND 200.00

Double eagle. Rev. Arms.

18. 1 Florin ND 200.00
19. 1 Ducat ND 200.00

Arms. Rev. Cross.

20. 1 Scudo d'oro ND 200.00

Soldier standing. Rev. Tablet.

21. 1 Ducat 1603 .... 250.00

Ruler standing. Rev. Tablet.

22. 1 Ducat ND 100.00

St. Catherine seated. Rev. Arms.

23. 1 Ducat ND 200.00

St. Lawrence. Rev. Eagle.

24. 1 Ducat ND 200.00

St. Louis standing. Rev. Double eagle.

25. 1 Ducat ND 200.00

CHARLES JOSEPH FRANCIS TIZZONE, 1641-1676
Ruler standing. Rev. Tablet.

26. 1 Ducat ND 200.00

Soldier standing. Rev. Tablet.

27. 1 Ducat ND 200.00

EMILIA

VICTOR EMANUELE II, KING ELECT, 1859-1861

Head. Rev. Value in wreath. Bologna Mint with B mm.

1. 20 Lire 1860 .... 250.00
2. 10 Lire 1860 ....* 60.00

FERRARA

Dukes of —

LIONEL D'ESTE, 1441-1450
Christ. Rev. Sail on mast.

1. 1 Ducat ND 300.00

Pillow and helmet. Rev. Arms.

2. ½ Ducat ND 300.00

BORSO D'ESTE, 1450-1471
Christ. Rev. Arms.

3. 1 Ducat ND 200.00

Bust. Rev. Christ.

4. 1 Ducat ND 1500.00

HERCULES I D'ESTE, 1471-1475
Duke kneeling before saint. Rev. Christ.

5. 1 Doppia ND 1000.00

Head. Rev. Hercules and bull.

6. 1 Doppia ND 600.00

ITALY-FERRARA (cont'd)

Head. Rev. Hercules and lion.

7. 1 Doppia ND 600.00

Bust. Rev. Christ.

8. 1 Ducat ND 200.00

Duke standing. Rev. St. Maurelius seated.

9. ½ Ducat ND 125.00

Eagle. Rev. Animal.

10. ½ Ducat ND 75.00

ALFONSO I D'ESTE, 1505-1534

Plain or bearded bust. Rev. Christ and the Pharisee.

11. 2 Zecchini ND 500.00

Arms. Rev. Calvary cross.

12. 1 Scudo d'oro ND 40.00

HERCULES II D'ESTE, 1534-1559

Mary Magdalene at cross. Rev. Arms.

13. 1 Scudo d'oro 1534, ND 50.00

Bust. Rev. Hercules with lion skin.

14. 10 Scudi d'oro 1546 .... 1000.00

ALFONSO II D'ESTE, 1559-1597

Arms. Rev. Cross.

15. 1 Scudo d'oro 1576, ND 60.00

Duke standing. Rev. Arms.

16. 1 Ducat 1596, 97, ND 75.00

Bust. Rev. Eagle.

17. ½ Ducat ND 300.00

FLORENCE

A. Republic of —, 1189-1531

St. John. Rev. Lily.

1. 1 Florin ND (1252-1422) ....*...... 35.00
2. 1 Florin ND. Broad type. (1422-1531) 35.00
3. ¼ Florin ND (1252-1422) 100.00

St. John baptizing Christ. Rev. Lily.

4. 2 Florins ND (1504-31) 1750.00

Arms. Rev. Cross. Struck during the Siege of Florence, 1530.

5. 1 Scudo d'oro ND 2000.00

B. Tuscan Grand Dukes of —
ALEXANDER, 1531-1536

Arms. Rev. Cross.

6. 1 Scudo d'oro ND 50.00

COSIMO I, 1536-1574
Bust. Rev. Cross.

7. 1 Gold Piastre ND 2000.00

Bust. Rev. St. John standing.

8. 1 Gold Piastre 1571, 72 .... 2000.00
9. 1 Ducat ND ....*...... 200.00

Bust. Rev. St. John preaching to disciples.

10. ½ Gold Piastre 1571, 72 .... 1500.00

Arms. Rev. Cross.

11.	1 Gold Piastre ND	....	2000.00
12.	1 Scudo d'oro ND	.... *	50.00
13.	½ Scudo d'oro ND	....	60.00

Bust of St. John. Rev. Arms.

14.	¼ Scudo d'oro ND	....	200.00

FRANCIS I, 1574-1587
Bust. Rev. St. John standing.

15.	1 Gold Piastre (5 Doppia) 1574-84	....	2000.00

Head. Rev. The Annunciation.

16.	1 Doppia 1580, 82	....	500.00

Arms. Rev. Cross.

17.	1 Scudo d'oro ND	....	40.00

FERDINAND I, 1587-1608
Bust. Rev. Bees in flight.

18.	14 Scudi d'oro 1587	....	2500.00

Bust. Rev. The Annunciation.

19.	2 Doppia 1591	....	750.00
20.	1 Doppia 1587, 89, 91	....	250.00
21.	½ Doppia 1587, 93	....	300.00

Bust. Rev. Cross of St. Stephan.

22.	½ Doppia 1587	....	300.00

Bust. Rev. Cross.

23.	¼ Doppia ND	.... *	60.00
24.	⅛ Doppia ND	....	30.00

Bust. Rev. St. John baptizing Christ.

25.	1 Gold Piastre 1589, 92, 96	....	2000.00

St. John standing. Rev. Lily.

26.	2 Ducats 1595	....	350.00
27.	1 Ducat 1595, 96, 97, 1608	.... *	40.00

Arms. Rev. Ornate cross.

28.	1 Doppia 1607	....	350.00

Arms. Rev. Floriated cross.

29.	1 Scudo d'oro ND	....	50.00
30.	¼ Doppia ND	....	40.00

Bust of St. John. Rev. Arms.

31.	⅛ Doppia ND	....	40.00

Arms. Rev. Cross of St. Stephan.

32.	⅛ Doppia ND	....	50.00

Arms. Rev. The Annunciation.

33.	1 Doppia 1588	....	125.00

St. John seated. Rev. Arms.

34.	1 Ducat 1588	....	100.00

St. John standing. Rev. Cross of St. Stephan.

35.	1 Ducat 1588	....	75.00

COSIMO II, 1609-1621
Bust. Rev. St. John baptizing Christ.

36.	1 Gold Piastre 1610	....	2500.00

Bust. Rev. Cross.

37.	¼ Doppia 1609	....	100.00

Arms. Rev. Cross.

38.	1 Doppia 1608, ND	....	150.00
38a.	1 Scudo d'oro ND	.... *	200.00

St. John standing. Rev. Lily.

39.	1 Florin 1608, 10, 11, 14	....	40.00

FERDINAND II, 1621-1670
Bust. Rev. St. John standing.

40.	1 Gold Piastre 1628	....	2500.00

Arms. Rev. Cross.

41.	1 Doppia ND	....	75.00
42.	½ Doppia ND	....	40.00
43.	⅛ Doppia ND	....	25.00

St. John standing. Rev. Lily.

44.	1 Zecchino 1655, ND	....	40.00

ITALY-FLORENCE (cont'd)

Bust of St. John. Rev. Arms.

45.	¼ Doppia 1663, 68	.................................*	......	50.00
46.	⅛ Doppia ND	....		30.00

COSIMO III, 1670-1723

Arms. Rev. Cross.

47.	2 Doppia 1676	....		125.00
48.	1 Doppia 1711, 16	....		60.00
49.	½ Doppia ND	...............................*	......	35.00

St. John seated. Rev. Lily.

50.	1 Ruspone 1719	....		250.00
51.	1 Florin 1712-23	..........................*	......	65.00

JOHN GASTON, 1723-1737

St. John seated. Rev. Lily.

52.	1 Ruspone 1724	........................*	......	300.00
53.	1 Zecchino 1723-36	....		30.00
54.	½ Zecchino 1726	....		50.00

Bust of St. John. Rev. Lily.

55.	½ Zecchino 1726	....	60.00

FRANCIS II, 1737-1765
St. John seated. Rev. Lily.

56.	1 Ruspone 1743-64	....	60.00
57.	1 Zecchino 1737-43	....	35.00

Head. Rev. Arms.

58.	1 Ducat 1738, 41	....	500.00

PETER LEOPOLD, 1765-1790

St. John seated. Rev. Lily.

59.	1 Ruspone 1765-90	....		60.00
60.	1 Zecchino 1779-89	........................*	......	25.00

FERDINAND III, 1791-1801
St. John seated. Rev. Lily.

61.	1 Ruspone 1791-1801	....	60.00
62.	1 Zecchino 1791, 92	....	40.00

LOUIS I, 1801-1803
St. John seated. Rev. Lily.

63.	1 Ruspone 1801, 03	....	125.00

CHARLES LOUIS AND MARIE LOUISE, 1803-1807

St. John seated. Rev. Lily.

64.	1 Ruspone 1803-07	....	125.00

St. John standing. Rev. St. Zanobius kneeling before Christ. Struck for the Levant.

65.	1 Zecchino ND	....	275.00

FERDINAND III, 1814-1824
St. John seated. Rev. Lily.

66.	1 Ruspone 1815-23	....	100.00
67.	1 Zecchino 1816, 21	....	75.00

LEOPOLD II, 1824-1859

Lily. Rev. Arms.

68.	80 Florins or 200 Paoli 1827, 28	....	200.00

St. John seated. Rev. Lily.

69.	1 Ruspone 1824-36	....	60.00
70.	1 Zecchino 1824-53	....	40.00

(For the last coin of this type, see under Tuscany).

FORLI

Lords of —

HIERONYMUS RIARIO, 1480-1488
St. Mercurialus standing. Rev. Double eagle.

1.	1 Ducat 1480	....	1000.00

232

FRINCO

Arms. Rev. Cross. Anonymous Princely coinage.

1. 1 Scudo d'oro ND (1581-1601) 500.00

GAETA

Dukes of —

ALFONSO I, 1436-1458

Ruler on horse. Rev. Arms.

1. 1 Ducatone d'oro ND (5.23 grams) .... * 250.00
2. 1 Ducat ND 150.00

GAZZOLDO

Counts of —

HANNIBAL DEGLI IPPOLITI, 1632-1666

Bust. Rev. St. Hippolitus.

1. 2 Doppia 1662 .... 650.00

GENOA

A. Doges of —

The following coins are all of the same type and show a castle on the Obv. and a cross on the Rev. All are without dates.

ANONYMOUS DOGES, 1200-1350

1. 1 Genovino .... * 40.00
2. 1 Quarterola 40.00
3. 1 Soldo .... * 100.00

SIMON BOCCANEGRA, 1339-1344 AND 1356-1363

4. 1 Genovino .... * 40.00
5. ⅓ Genovino 40.00
6. ¼ Genovino 30.00

GABRIEL ADORNO, 1363-1370

7. 1 Genovino 50.00

DOMINIC DI CAMPOFREGOSO, 1370-1378

8. 1 Genovino 200.00

ANTONIOTTO ADORNO, 1378

9. 1 Genovino 300.00

NICHOLAS GUARCO, 1378-1383

10. 1 Genovino 75.00

LEONARD DI MONTALDO, 1383-1384

11. 1 Genovino 100.00

GEORGE ADORNO, 1413-1415

12. 1 Genovino 100.00

BARNABAS DI GOANO, 1415

13. 1 Genovino 150.00

THOMAS DI CAMPOFREGOSO, 1415-1421 (FIRST RULE)

14. 1 Ducat 75.00

PHILIP MARIA OF MILAN, 1421-1425

15. 1 Ducat 75.00

THOMAS DI CAMPOFREGOSO, 1436-1442 (SECOND RULE)

16. 1 Ducat. With "Dux XX." 200.00
17. 1 Ducat. With "Dux XXI." 40.00

THE EIGHT CAPTAINS OF LIBERTY, 1442-1443

18. 1 Ducat 300.00

RAFFAEL ADORNO, 1443-1447

19. 1 Ducat. With "Dux XXII." 100.00
20. 1 Ducat. With "Dux XXIII." 500.00
21. ½ Ducat 200.00
22. ¼ Ducat 200.00

JOHN CAMPOFREGOSO, 1447

23. 1 Ducat 500.00
24. ½ Ducat 500.00

LOUIS CAMPOFREGOSO, 1447-1450 AND 1461-1462

25. 1 Ducat 100.00

PETER CAMPOFREGOSO, 1450-1458

26. 1 Ducat 60.00

PROSPERO ADORNO, 1461

27. 1 Ducat 500.00

PAUL CAMPOFREGOSO, 1463-1464

28. 1 Ducat 350.00
29. ½ Ducat 75.00

FRANCIS I OF MILAN, 1464-1466

30. 1 Ducat .... * 100.00
31. ½ Ducat 60.00

GALEAZZO MARIA OF MILAN, 1466-1476

32. 1 Ducat 75.00
33. ½ Ducat 200.00
34. ¼ Ducat 200.00

PROSPERO ADORNO AND TWELVE CAPTAINS, 1478

35. 1 Ducat 300.00

BAPTIST CAMPOFREGOSO, 1478-1483

36. 1 Ducat 75.00

PAUL CAMPOFREGOSO, 1483-1488

37. 1 Ducat. As Governor 500.00
38. 1 Ducat. As Doge 75.00
39. ½ Ducat 400.00

AUGUSTIN ADORNO, 1488-1489

40. 1 Ducat 75.00

JOHN GALEAZZO OF MILAN, 1489-1494

41. 3 Ducats 800.00
42. 2 Ducats 800.00
43. 1 Ducat 75.00

LOUIS MARIA OF MILAN, 1494-1499

44. 1 Ducat 75.00

ANTONIOTTO ADORNO, 1522-1527

45.	1	Ducat	100.00
46.	½	Ducat	200.00
47.	2	Scudi d'oro	400.00
48.	1	Scudo d'oro ....*	75.00
49.	½	Scudo d'oro	200.00

B. French Kings of —

(Same type as above).

CHARLES VI, 1396-1409

50.	1	Genovino	200.00
51.	⅓	Genovino	400.00

CHARLES VII, 1458-1461

52.	1	Ducat	350.00

LOUIS XII, 1499-1513

53.	1	Ducat	200.00

Crowned arms of France with name of Genoa in title. Rev.
Floriated cross.

54.	1	Ecu d'or ND	75.00

FRANCIS I, 1515-1528

Castle flanked by F and lis. Rev. Floriated cross.

55.	1	Ecu d'or ND	600.00
56.	½	Ecu d'or ND	600.00
57.	¼	Ecu d'or ND	600.00

*Castle flanked by F and lis. Rev. Two F's and two lis in angles
of floriated cross.*

58.	1	Ecu d'or ND	450.00
59.	½	Ecu d'or ND	400.00

C. The Biennial Doges of —, 1521-1797

Castle. Rev. Cross.

60.	10	Scudi d'oro 1633	500.00
61.	1	Scudo d'oro 1541-55, ND	60.00
62.	½	Scudo d'oro 1541-55, ND	35.00
63.	25	Doppia 1636	2500.00
64.	12½	Doppia 1632, 34, 36, 37	1250.00
65.	5	Doppia 1600-20	450.00
66.	2½	Doppia 1596	250.00
67.	2	Doppia 1592-1638 ....*	150.00
68.	1	Doppia 1557-1638	75.00
69.	½	Doppia 1557-1638	40.00
70.	¼	Doppia 1623-38	30.00
71.	⅛	Doppia 1623-38	25.00

Madonna. Rev. Cross.

72.	25	Doppia 1638-1714	2000.00
73.	20	Doppia 1645	1750.00
74.	12½	Doppia 1638-1711	1250.00
75.	10	Doppia 1641-94	1000.00
76.	5	Doppia 1640-97	500.00
77.	4	Doppia 1720	500.00
78.	2½	Doppia 1697	250.00
79.	2	Doppia 1638-1722 ....*	150.00
80.	1	Doppia 1640-1748	50.00
81.	½	Doppia 1639-1749	35.00
82.	¼	Doppia 1641	35.00
83.	⅛	Doppia 1641	35.00

Doge kneeling before St. John. Rev. Christ.

84.	1	Zecchino ND	100.00

St. George on horse. Rev. Arms.

85.	1	Zecchino 1718-23	75.00
86.	½	Zecchino 1723	50.00

St. John standing. Rev. Arms.

87.	1	Zecchino 1724-39 ....*	60.00
88.	½	Zecchino 1724-36	35.00

*Madonna. Rev. Arms supported by griffins. The denominations do
not appear on the first four pieces.*

89.	100	Lire 1758-67	300.00
90.	50	Lire 1758-67 ....*	200.00
91.	25	Lire 1758-67	125.00
92.	12½	Lire 1758-67	75.00
93.	96	Lire 1792-97	125.00
94.	48	Lire 1792-97 ....*	75.00
95.	24	Lire 1792-95	75.00
96.	12	Lire 1793-95	75.00

D. The Republic (Ligurian) of —

Liguria seated. Rev. Fasces.

97.	96	Lire 1798-1805 ....*	125.00
98.	48	Lire 1798, 1801, 04	75.00
99.	24	Lire 1798	250.00
100.	12	Lire 1798	150.00

GORIZIA

Counts of —

HENRY II, 1304-1323
St. John. Rev. Lily.

1. 1 Florin ND 300.00

ALBERT IV, 1338-1374
St. John. Rev. Lily.

2. 1 Florin ND 300.00

HENRY III, 1338-1364
St. John.. Rev. Lily.

3. 1 Florin ND 300.00

MAINHARD, 1364-1385
St. John. Rev. Lily.

4. 1 Florin ND 300.00

St. John. Rev. Arms.

5. 1 Florin ND 300.00

GUASTALLA

Dukes of —

CAESAR I GONZAGA, 1557-1575
Arms. Rev. Cross.

1. 1 Scudo d'oro ND 300.00

FERDINAND II GONZAGA, 1575-1630
Bust. Rev. The Annunciation.

2. 10 Doppia 1610 .... 1500.00

Ruler standing. Rev. Arms.

3. 1 Ducat ND 200.00

Arms. Rev. Cross.

4. 1 Scudo d'oro ND 100.00

GUBBIO

Lords of —

FRANCIS MARIA I DELLA ROVERE, 1508-1538
St. Ubaldus seated. Rev. Arms.

1. 1 Scudo d'oro ND 300.00

FRANCIS MARIA II DELLA ROVERE, 1574-1634

Bust. Rev. Arms.

2. 1 Scudo d'oro ND 300.00

LEGHORN (LIVORNO)

Tuscan Grand Dukes of —

FERDINAND II, 1621-1670

Head. Rev. View of the Port of Leghorn.

1. 1 Ducat 1655, ND 350.00

COSIMO III, 1670-1723

Ruler standing. Rev. Legend in tablet.

2. 1 Ducat 1674, 75, 76, 91 .... 100.00

Arms. Rev. Rose bush. These coins are also referred to as "Pezza d'oro della rosa".

3. 2 Doppia or Rosine 1718 .... 400.00
4. 1 Doppia or Rosina 1717, 18, 21 ....* 100.00
5. ½ Doppia or Rosina 1718, 20 .... 65.00

Bust. Rev. View of the Port of Leghorn.

6. 1 Ducat ND 350.00

Ruler standing. Rev. Fame over globe.

7. 1 Ducat ND 100.00

LOANO

Princes of —

JOHN ANDREW II, 1622-1640
Bust. Rev. Eagle.

1. 2 Doppia 1639 .... 2000.00
2. 1 Doppia 1639 .... 1000.00

Madonna. Rev. Tablet.

3. 1 Ducat ND 250.00

JOHN ANDREW III, 1654-1737
Bust. Rev. Arms and cross.

4. 1 Doppia 1665 .... 1000.00

LOMBARDY

Provisional Government of —

Italia standing. Rev. Value. Struck at Milan.

1. 40 Lire 1848 ....* 65.00
2. 20 Lire 1848 .... 35.00

LUCCA

A. Dukes of —

ANONYMOUS, 650-749
Monogram. Rev. Cross.

1. ⅓ Solidus ND **65.00**

Rose. Rev. Cross.

2. ⅓ Solidus ND **65.00**

ASTOLF, 749-756
Rose. Rev. Cross.

3. ⅓ Solidus ND **150.00**

Star. Rev. Cross.

4. ⅓ Solidus ND **150.00**

DESIDERIUS, 757-773
Star. Rev. Cross.

5. ⅓ Solidus ND **125.00**

CHARLEMAGNE, 773-814
Bust. Rev. Star.

6. ⅓ Solidus ND **500.00**

Star. Rev. Cross.

7. ⅓ Solidus ND **125.00**

FREDERICK II, 1190-1250

Bust facing or left of St. Vultus. Rev. Monogram and name of Otto IV.
8. 1 Grosso d'oro ND **500.00**

ANONYMOUS, 1300-1350

Bust of St. Vultus. Rev. St. Martin on horse.
9. 1 Florin ND **200.00**

B. Republic of —,1369-1799
Bust of St. Vultus. Rev. St. Peter.
10. 1 Florin ND (1387-1400) **750.00**

Bust of St. Vultus. Rev. St. Martin on horse.
11. 1 Ducat ND (1400-1500) ....* **60.00**
12. 1 Zecchino 1572, ND **50.00**

Bust of St. Vultus. Rev. Arms.
13. 4 Scudi d'oro 1748 ....* **150.00**
14. 2 Scudi d'oro 1749, 50 .... **50.00**
15. 1 Scudo d'oro 1552-1749, ND **40.00**
16. ½ Scudo d'oro 1551, 52, ND **30.00**

Head of St. Vultus. Rev. Four letters crossed.
17. ½ Scudo d'oro ND **50.00**

St. Paulinus seated. Rev. Arms.
18. 1 Doppia 1758 .... **300.00**

MACCAGNO

Counts of —

GIACOMO III MANDELLI, 1618-1645
Soldier. Rev. Arms.

1. 1 Ducat 1622, 23 .... **250.00**

Saint with shield. Rev. Eagle.
2. 1 Ducat 1622 .... **250.00**

Saint with shield. Rev. Orb.
3. 1 Ducat ND **250.00**

St. Stephan kneeling. Rev. Arms.
4. 1 Ducat 1622 .... **250.00**

Arms. Rev. Eagle.
5. 1 Ducat 1622, ND **250.00**

Arms. Rev. Orb.
6. 1 Ducat 1622 .... **250.00***

Ruler standing. Rev. Arms.
7. 1 Doppia ND **750.00**
8. 1 Ducat 1622, ND ....* **250.00**

Ruler standing. Rev. Eagle.
9. 1 Ducat ND **250.00**

Soldier. Rev. Tablet.
10. 1 Ducat 1623, ND **250.00**

Madonna. Rev. Tablet.
11. 1 Ducat ND **250.00**

Bust of Saint. Rev. Eagle.
12. 1 Ducat ND **250.00**

Bust. Rev. Arms.
13. 1 Doppia 1625, ND **750.00**

Bust. Rev. Eagle.
14. 1 Ducat ND **250.00**

Bust. Rev. Orb.
15. 1 Ducat ND **250.00**

MANFREDONIA

MANFRED, 1258-1266

Eagle. Rev. Legend.

1. 10 Tari ND 100.00
2. 8 Tari ND 80.00
3. 6 Tari ND 60.00
4. 4 Tari ND ....*...... 40.00
5. 3 Tari ND 25.00

MANTUA

Marcheses, and later, Dukes of —

LOUIS II GONZAGA, 1445-1478

Bust. Rev. Sacred vessel.

1. 1 Ducat ND 1000.00

Ruler standing. Rev. St. George on horse.

2. 1 Ducat ND 300.00

Sun. Rev. Sacred vessel.

3. ⅓ Ducat ND 200.00

FREDERICK I GONZAGA, 1478-1484

Bust. Rev. Sacred vessel.

4. 1 Ducat ND 1000.00

FRANCIS II GONZAGA, 1484-1519

Bust. Rev. Arms.

5. 2 Ducats ND 750.00

Bust. Rev. Crucible in flames.

6. 2 Ducats ND 1000.00
7. 1 Ducat ND ....*...... 300.00

Bust with hat. Rev. Sacred vessel.

8. 1 Ducat ND 350.00

Madonna. Rev. Altar.

9. ½ Ducat ND 400.00

FREDERICK II GONZAGA, 1519-1540

Head. Rev. Ruler on horse.

10. 3 Ducats ND 1000.00
11. 2 Ducats ND 450.00

Head. Rev. St. Catherine.

12. 1 Ducat ND 200.00

Head. Rev. Mt. Olympus.

13. 2 Ducats ND ....*...... 250.00
14. 1 Ducat ND 200.00

Christ and cross. Rev. Arms.

15. 1 Scudo d'oro ND 35.00

Madonna seated. Rev. Mt. Olympus.

16. ½ Ducat ND 150.00

FRANCIS III GONZAGA, 1540-1550

Christ and cross. Rev. Arms.

17. 1 Scudo d'oro ND 75.00

WILLIAM GONZAGA, 1550-1587

Christ and cross. Rev. Arms.

18. 1 Scudo d'oro ND 100.00

ITALY-MANTUA (cont'd)

Seated female. Rev. Arms.

19. 1 Scudo d'oro ND 100.00

Standing female. Rev. Arms.

20. 1 Ducat ND 100.00

Arms. Rev. Cross and initials.

21. 1 Scudo d'oro ND 50.00

VINCENT I GONZAGA, 1587-1612

Bust. Rev. Arms.

22. 7 Doppia 1589 .... 3000.00
23. 4 Doppia 1590 .... 1000.00
24. 2 Doppia 1590, ND .... * 500.00

Bust. Rev. Tree.

25. 2 Doppia 1590 .... 750.00

Bust. Rev. St. George on horse.

26. 10 Doppia ND 2500.00

Bust. Rev. Arms on cross.

27. 2 Zecchini ND 750.00

Ruler standing. Rev. Arms.

28. 1 Ducat ND 100.00

Soldier standing. Rev. Arms.

29. 1 Ducat ND 50.00

Bust of Virgil. Rev. Half moon.

30. ⅛ Scudo d'oro ND 100.00

Eagle. Rev. Compass and clock.

31. ¼ Ducat 1596 .... 50.00

Eagle. Rev. Crescent and legend.

32. ¼ Ducat 1596 .... 100.00
33. ⅛ Ducat 1596 .... * 50.00

FRANCIS IV GONZAGA, 1612

St. Andrew and St. Longinus. Rev. Arms.

34. 5 Doppia 1612 .... 2000.00

Bust. Rev. Arms.

35. 2 Doppia 1612 .... 1000.00
36. 1 Doppia 1612 .... 1000.00

FERDINAND VI GONZAGA, 1612-1626

Bust. Rev. Sun.

37. 12 Zecchini 1617 .... 2000.00
38. 6 Doppia 1613, 14, 15 .... 1250.00
39. 4 Doppia ND .... * 1000.00

Bust. Rev. Two angels.

40. 2 Doppia 1613, 14, 15 .... * 250.00
41. 1 Doppia 1614, 16 .... 400.00

Bust. Rev. St. Andrew and St. Longinus.

42. 1 Doppia 1613 .... 450.00

Bust. Rev. St. Longinus.

43. 1 Doppia 1616, ND 450.00

Bust. Rev. Madonna.

44. 12 Doppia 1614 .... Unique
44a. 6 Doppia 1614 .... 1000.00

Bust right or left. Rev. Arms.

45. 6 Doppia 1616 .... 1000.00
46. 2 Doppia 1621, ND .... * 250.00
47. 1 Doppia ND 200.00
48. ½ Zecchino ND 400.00

St. Andrew and St. Longinus. Rev. Arms.

49. 2 Doppia 1613 .... 750.00

Arms on each side.

50. 6 Doppia 1620 .... 1250.00

238

Cardinal standing. Rev. Madonna.

51. 1 Scudo d'oro 1613, ND 750.00

Madonna. Rev. Rose.

52. 1 Zecchino ND 100.00

VINCENT II GONZAGA, 1626-1627

Bust. Rev. Arms.

53. 2 Doppia 1627 .... 750.00

Ship. Rev. Legend.

54. 1 Scudo d'oro ND 750.00

CHARLES I GONZAGA, 1627-1637
Bust. Rev. Sun in zodiac.

55. 8 Doppia 1628 .... 1500.00
56. 6 Doppia 1628, 32 .... 1500.00
57. 5 Doppia 1636 .... 1000.00

Bust. Rev. Arms.

58. 2 Doppia 1629, 31, 36 ....*...... 400.00
59. 1 Doppia ND 1000.00

CHARLES II GONZAGA, 1637-1665
Busts of Charles and Maria. Rev. Madonna.

60. 12 Scudi d'oro ND 2500.00
61. 8 Doppia ND 2000.00
62. 5 Doppia ND 1000.00
63. 4 Doppia ND 1000.00

Busts of Charles and Maria. Rev. Arms.

64. 2 Doppia ND 300.00

Bust. Rev. Sun in shield.

65. 12 Scudi d'oro 1649 .... 1500.00
66. 10 Zecchini 1649 ....*..... 1500.00
67. 6 Doppia 1649 .... 750.00

Bust. Rev. Arms.

68. 2 Doppia ND 750.00
69. 1 Doppia ND 750.00

FERDINAND CHARLES GONZAGA, 1665-1707

Busts of Ferdinand and Isabella Clara. Rev. Sun.

70. 6 Doppia 1666 .... 2500.00
71. 2 Doppia 1666 ....*..... 1000.00

Busts of Ferdinand and Isabella Clara. Rev. Madonna.

72. 6 Doppia 1666 .... 1500.00
73. 5 Doppia 1666 .... 1000.00
74. 4 Doppia 1666 .... 1000.00
75. 2 Doppia 1666 .... 750.00

Bust. Rev. Sun and rock.

76. 8 Doppia 1679 .... 2000.00

Bust. Rev. Arms.

77. 2 Doppia ND 600.00

MASSA DI LUNIGIANA

Dukes of —

ALBERIC CYBO MALUSPINA, 1559-1623

Bust. Rev. Arms.

1. 2 Doppia 1582, 88, 89, ND ....*...... 250.00
2. 1 Doppia 1588 .... 150.00

Bust. Rev. Temple.

3. 2 Doppia 1588, ND 300.00

Bust. Rev. Fire.

4. 1 Doppia ND 150.00

Bust. Rev. Arms and eagle.

5. 2 Doppia 1593, 98, ND 250.00
6. 1 Doppia 1593 .... 150.00

Arms. Rev. Eagle.

7. 1 Doppia ND 150.00

Arms. Rev. Anvil.

8. 1 Scudo d'oro ND 100.00

St. Peter. Rev. Arms.

9. 1 Scudo d'oro ND 100.00

Arms. Rev. Cross.

10. 1 Scudo d'oro ND 100.00

Arms. Rev. Pyramid.

11. ½ Scudo d'oro ND 100.00

Arms. Rev. Rose Bush.

12. ½ Scudo d'oro ND 100.00

CHARLES I CYBO MALUSPINA, 1623-1662
Bust. Rev. Arms.

13. 5 Doppia ND 1000.00

MASSA-LOMBARDY

Marcheses of —

FRANCIS D'ESTE, 1562-1578
Bust. Rev. Eagle.

1. 1 Scudo d'oro ND 150.00

Eagle. Rev. Cross.

2. 1 Scudo d'oro ND 100.00

MESSERANO

Princes of —

ANONYMOUS, 1492-1521
Emperor. Rev. Madonna.

1. 1 Ducat ND 200.00

Eagle. Rev. Cross.

2. 1 Scudo d'oro ND 400.00

LOUIS II AND PETER LUCAS II, 1521-1528
Arms. Rev. Cross.

3. 1 Scudo d'oro ND 300.00

LOUIS II, 1528-1532
Bust. Rev. Horse.

4. 1 Doppia ND 750.00

Head. Rev. Arms.

5. 1 Ducat ND 500.00

Head. Rev. St. Theonestus seated.

6. 1 Ducat ND 300.00

Eagle. Rev. Cross.

7. 1 Scudo d'oro ND 200.00

PETER LUCAS II, 1528-1548
Eagle. Rev. Cross.

8. 1 Scudo d'oro ND 300.00

FILIBERT FERRERO, 1532-1559
Arms. Rev. Cross.

9. 1 Scudo d'oro ND 300.00

BESSO FERRERO, 1559-1584
Bust. Rev. Arms.

10. 1 Doppia 1582 .... 750.00

Arms. Rev. Cross.

11. 1 Scudo d'oro ND 200.00

FRANCIS FILIBERT FERRERO, 1584-1629
Bust. Rev. Arms.

12. 1 Doppia 1594, ND 500.00

Bust. Rev. The Annunciation.

13. 2 Doppia ND 1000.00
14. 1 Doppia ND 500.00

Ruler standing. Rev. Eagle.

15. 1 Ducat 1596, 98 .... 200.00

Soldier. Rev. Arms on eagle.

16. 1 Ducat ND 200.00

PAUL BESSO FERRERO, 1629-1667
Bust. Rev. Arms.

17. 5 Doppia 1638 .... 2750.00
18. 1 Scudo d'oro 1640 .... 300.00

Soldier. Rev. Tablet.

19. 1 Ducat ND 300.00

Tablet. Rev. Eagle.

20. 1 Ducat ND 300.00

FRANCIS LOUIS FERRERO, 1667-1685
Bust. Rev. Arms.

21. 1 Doppia 1667 .... 750.00

Bust. Rev. Four shields crossed.

22. 5 Doppia 1672 .... 2750.00

CHARLES BESSO FERRERO, 1685-1690
Bust. Rev. Arms.

23. 1 Doppia 1689 .... 750.00

MESSINA

A. Norman Kings of —

ROGER II, 1102-1154
Cufic legend on each side.

1. 3 Tari ND 35.00
2. 2 Tari ND 25.00
3. 1 Tari ND 12.50

WILLIAM I, 1154-1166
Cufic legend on each side.

4. 2 Tari ND 25.00
5. 1 Tari ND 12.50

WILLIAM II, 1166-1189
Six globes. Rev. Cross.

6. 1 Tari ND 12.50

W. Rev. Star.

7. 1 Tari ND 12.50

Star. Rev. Cufic legend.

8. 3 Tari ND .... * 35.00
9. 2 Tari ND 20.00
10. ½ Tari ND 12.50

TANCRED, 1190-1194
Globe. Rev. Cross.

11. 2 Tari ND 20.00
12. 1 Tari ND 12.50

B. German and Anjou Kings of —

HENRY VI OF HOHENSTAUFEN, 1194-1197
Bust. Rev. Cross and four globes.

13. 1 Tari ND 200.00

E. Rev. Cross.

14. 1 Tari ND 12.50

ITALY-MESSINA (cont'd)

HENRY VI AND FREDERICK II OF HOHENSTAUFEN, 1195
FE. Rev. Cross.

15.	3 Tari ND	60.00
16.	2 Tari ND	50.00
17.	1 Tari ND	12.50

Five globes. Rev. Cross.

18. 3 Tari ND 50.00

FREDERICK II OF HOHENSTAUFEN, 1198-1250
FRE. Rev. Cross.

19. 1 Tari ND 25.00

Cross on hill. Rev. Cross.

20. 1 Tari ND 25.00

Eagle. Rev. Cross.

21.	2 Tari ND ....*	25.00
22.	1 Tari ND	12.50

Five globes. Rev. Cross.

23. 1 Tari ND 20.00

CHARLES I OF ANJOU, 1266-1282
Bust. Rev. Arms.

24. 1 Real ND 350.00

C. Spanish Kings of —

COSTANZA SVEVA AND PETER III OF ARAGON, 1282-1285

Arms. Rev. Eagle.

25. 1 Ducat or Oncia ND 200.00

JOHN, 1458-1479

Ruler seated. Rev. Eagle.

26. 1 Real ND 350.00

FERDINAND II, 1479-1516
Ruler on throne. Rev. Eagle.

27.	1 Ducat ND	75.00
28.	½ Ducat ND	200.00

CHARLES V, 1516-1566
Bust. Rev. Eagle.

29.	2 Ducats ND	750.00
30.	½ Ducat ND	400.00

Cross of St. Andrew. Rev. Shield.

31.	1 Scudo d'oro 1541-44	100.00
32.	½ Scudo d'oro 1541-43	100.00

Cross of St. Andrew. Rev. Eagle.

33.	1 Scudo d'oro 1544-54 ....*	100.00
34.	½ Scudo d'oro 1544-51	100.00

PHILIP II, 1556-1598
Bust. Rev. Eagle.

35. 1 Scudo d'oro 1557 .... 750.00

MILAN

A. Dukes of —

DESIDERIUS, 757-773
Cross. Rev. Star.

1. ⅓ Solidus ND 750.00

CHARLEMAGNE, 774-814
Cross potent. Rev. Cross.

2. ⅓ Solidus ND 750.00

Cross. Rev. Star.

3. ⅓ Solidus ND 750.00

FIRST REPUBLIC, 1250-1310
Saints Protaxius and Gervasius standing. Rev. St. Ambrose standing.

4. 1 Florin ND 1200.00

Bust of St. Ambrose. Rev. M.

5. ½ Florin ND 40.00

LUCHINUS AND JOHN VISCONTI, 1339-1349
St. Ambrose seated. Rev. Dragon with shield.

6. 1 Florin ND 500.00

GALEAZZO II AND BARNABAS VISCONTI, 1354-1378

Helmeted arms on each side.

7. 1 Florin ND 125.00

GALEAZZO II VISCONTI, 1354-1378

Ruler on horse. Rev. Helmeted arms.

8. 1 Florin ND 75.00

BARNABAS VISCONTI, 1354-1385

Helmeted arms. Rev. Serpent and initials.

9. 1 Florin ND 75.00

JOHN GALEAZZO VISCONTI, 1385-1402
Ruler on horse. Rev. Helmeted arms.

10. 1 Florin ND 75.00

Bust. Rev. Serpent.

11. 10 Florins ND 2000.00

JOHN MARIA VISCONTI, 1402-1412
Ruler on horse. Rev. Helmeted arms.

12. 1 Florin ND 400.00

PHILIP MARIA VISCONTI, 1412-1447

Ruler on horse. Rev. Helmeted arms.

13. 1 Florin ND 50.00

SECOND REPUBLIC, 1447-1450
St. Ambrose standing. Rev. M.

14. 1 Florin ND 450.00

Bust of St. Ambrose. Rev. M.

14a. ½ Florin ND 40.00

FRANCIS I SFORZA, 1450-1466

Bust. Rev. Ruler on horse.

15. 1 Ducat ND 100.00

Ruler on horse. Rev. Helmeted arms.

16. 1 Ducat ND 250.00

GALEAZZO MARIA SFORZA, 1466-1476
Bust. Rev. Arms.

17. 10 Ducats ND 2500.00

Bust. Rev. Helmeted arms.

18. 2 Ducats ND 750.00
19. 1 Ducat ND ....*...... 100.00

Bust. Rev. Lion.

20. 2 Ducats ND 450.00

BONA DI SAVOIA AND JOHN GALEAZZO MARIA SFORZA, 1476-1481
Bust on each side.

21. 2 Zecchini ND 1250.00

JOHN GALEAZZO MARIA SFORZA, 1481

Bust. Rev. Arms.

22. 2 Ducats ND 500.00

JOHN GALEAZZO MARIA AND LOUIS MARIA SFORZA, 1481-1494
Bust on each side.

23. 2 Ducats ND 750.00

Bust of John. Rev. Arms.

24. 1 Ducat ND 400.00

LOUIS MARIA SFORZA, 1494-1500

Bust. Rev. Ruler on horse.

25. 10 Ducats ND 2500.00
26. 2 Gold Testones ND ....*...... 400.00

FRANCIS II SFORZA, 1522-1535
Bust. Rev. Bust of St. Ambrosius.

27. 6 Scudi d'oro ND 1500.00

Ruler on horse. Rev. Arms.

28. 2 Scudi d'oro ND 400.00

Arms. Rev. Cross.

29. 1 Scudo d'oro ND 100.00

B. French Rulers of —

LOUIS XII, 1500-1513
Bust. Rev. Arms.

30. 10 Ducats ND 3000.00

Crowned bust. Rev. St. Ambrosius on horse.

31. 2 Ducats ND 1500.00

FRANCIS I, 1515-1522
Armored bust. Rev. Crowned arms.

32. 2 Ducats ND 3000.00

Crowned arms with small head of St. Ambrosius above. Rev. Floriated cross.

33. 1 Scudo d'oro ND 150.00

C. Spanish Rulers of —

CHARLES V, 1534-1556
Bust. Rev. The Pillars of Hercules.

34. 2 Scudo d'oro ND 500.00

PHILIP II, 1556-1598
Bust. Rev. Arms.

35. 3 Doppia 1555, 79, 82 .... 750.00
36. 2 Doppia ND 750.00
37. 1 Doppia ND 500.00

Bust. Rev. St. Ambrosius on horse.

38. 2 Doppia 1562 .... 750.00

Bust. Rev. Bust of St. Ambrosius.

39. 3 Doppia 1591 .... 1000.00

Bust. Rev. The Crucifixion.

40. 4 Doppia ND 2000.00

Radiate head right or left. Rev. Arms.

41. 2   Doppia 1562, 88, 95 .... 750.00
42. 1   Doppia 1578-98, ND .... * ... 100.00
43. 1½ Scudi d'oro ND 750.00
44. 1   Scudo d'oro ND 75.00

Arms. Rev. Cross.

45. 1 Scudo d'oro ND 125.00

PHILIP III, 1598-1621

Bust. Rev. Arms.

46. 2 Doppia 1610, 17, ND .... * ... 100.00
47. 1 Doppia 1617, ND 200.00

PHILIP IV, 1621-1665
Bust. Rev. City view.

48. 4½ Doppia 1630 .... 2000.00

Bust. Rev. Arms.

49. 20 Zecchini 1643 .... 2500.00
50. 2 Doppia 1630, ND .... * ... 200.00
51. 1 Doppia 1630, ND 175.00

CHARLES II, 1665-1700

Busts of Charles and Maria Anna. Rev. Arms.

---

52. 2 Doppia 1666 .... 500.00

Young bust. Rev. Arms.

53. 1 Doppia 1676 .... 500.00

Old bust. Rev. Arms.

54. 1 Doppia 1698 .... 500.00

D. Austrian Rulers of —

(For Austrian type coins struck at Milan with "M" mm, see under Austria. Italian type coins are listed here).

CHARLES VI, 1711-1740
Head. Rev. Arms.

55. 2 Scudi d'oro 1720, 24 .... 400.00

Head. Rev. Double eagle.

56. 1 Scudo d'oro 1723, 24 .... 400.00

Bust. Rev. Arms.

57. 12 Scudi d'oro ND 1750.00

MARIA THERESA, 1740-1780
Bust. Rev. St. Ambrosius standing.

58. 1 Zecchino ND 500.00

Bust. Rev. Arms.

59. 2 Doppia 1778, 79 .... 125.00
60. 1 Doppia 1778, 79, 80 .... 85.00
61. 1 Zecchino 1778, 79, 80 .... * ... 35.00

JOSEPH II, 1780-1790

Bust. Rev. Legend. On his Inauguration.

62. 1 Doppia 1781 .... 150.00
63. 1 Zecchino 1781 .... * ... 50.00

Bust. Rev. Arms.

64. 1 Doppia 1781-85 .... * ... 85.00
65. 1 Zecchino 1781-88 .... 50.00

FRANCIS II, 1792-1797

Bust. Rev. Legend. On his Inauguration.

66. 1 Doppia 1792 .... * ... 150.00
67. 1 Zecchino 1792 .... 50.00

MIRANDOLA

Dukes of —

JOHN FRANCIS PICO, 1499-1533
Book. Rev. The Resurrection.

1. 3 Zecchini ND 600.00

Bust. Rev. The Resurrection.

2. 1 Doppia ND 500.00

Plain bust right. Rev. St. Francis kneeling.

3. 1 Doppia ND 500.00

Bust with hat to left. Rev. St. Francis kneeling.

4. 1 Doppia ND 300.00

Bust with hat. Rev. Arms.

5. 1 Zecchino ND 200.00

Head. Rev. Arms.

6. 1 Zecchino ND 200.00

Head. Rev. Two Apostles standing.

7. 1 Zecchino ND 200.00

Arms. Rev. Legend.

8. 1 Zecchino ND 100.00

GALEOTTO PICO II, 1533-1550
Arms. Rev. Cross.

8a. 1 Scudo d'oro ND 200.00

LOUIS PICO II, 1550-1568

Arms. Rev. Cross.

9. 1 Scudo d'oro ND . . . . * 50.00
10. ½ Scudo d'oro ND 60.00

GALEOTTO PICO III, 1568-1590
Arms. Rev. Cross.

11. 1 Scudo d'oro ND 200.00

ALEXANDER PICO, 1602-1637
Bust. Rev. Arms.

12. 24 Scudi d'oro 1618 . . . . 2500.00

MODENA
Dukes of —

HERCULES I D'ESTE, 1471-1505
Head. Rev. St. Geminianus seated.

1. 1 Ducat ND 350.00

Head with cap. Rev. St. Geminianus seated.

2. 1 Ducat ND 350.00

MAXIMILIAN I D'ESTE, 1513-1514
Bust. Rev. St. Geminianus seated.

3. 1 Ducat ND 600.00

ALFONSO I D'ESTE, 1505-1534
Bust. Rev. St. Geminianus seated.

4. 1 Ducat ND 500.00

Cross. Rev. St. Geminianus seated.

5. 1 Scudo d'oro ND 200.00

HERCULES II D'ESTE, 1534-1559

Cross. Rev. St. Geminianus seated.

6. 1 Scudo d'oro ND 50.00

ALFONSO II D'ESTE, 1559-1597
Cross. Rev. St. Geminianus seated.

7. 1 Scudo d'oro ND 100.00

CAESAR D'ESTE, 1598-1628

Ruler standing. Rev. Arms.

8. 1 Ducat 1598, 1600, ND . . . . * 50.00
9. ¼ Ducat ND 50.00

Head. Rev. Patience standing.

10. 1 Doppia 1605, 09 . . . . 100.00

Bust. Rev. Female standing.

11. 2 Doppia 1608 . . . . 250.00

Bust. Rev. Soldier seated.

12. 4 Doppia 1612 . . . . 500.00

Bust. Rev. Eagle.

13. 2 Doppia ND 300.00

Arms. Rev. Cross.

14. 1 Scudo d'oro ND 60.00

FRANCIS I D'ESTE, 1629-1658

Bust. Rev. Ship.

15. 24 Scudi d'oro 1631, ND 2500.00

ITALY-MODENA (cont'd)

16. 20 Scudi d'oro ND 2000.00
17. 16 Scudi d'oro 1631, ND 1250.00
18. 12 Scudi d'oro 1633, 46, ND 1000.00
19. 10 Scudi d'oro ND 1000.00
20. 8 Scudi d'oro 1631, 33, ND .... * .. 1000.00
21. 6 Scudi d'oro ND 500.00

Bust. Rev. Madonna.

22. 8 Scudi d'oro 1631 .... 1000.00
23. 4 Scudi d'oro 1632, 34, ND .... * .. 150.00
24. 2 Scudi d'oro 1631 .... 250.00

Bust. Rev. Arms.

25. 1 Doppia 1651 .... 250.00
26. ½ Doppia 1651 .... 200.00

Bust. Rev. Eagle.

27. 4 Scudi d'oro ND 250.00
28. 2 Scudi d'oro ND 125.00
29. 1 Scudo d'oro ND 75.00
30. ½ Scudo d'oro ND 50.00

Ruler standing. Rev. Tablet.

31. 1 Ducat 1649 .... 100.00

Ruler standing. Rev. Eagle.

32. 1 Doppia 1633 .... 125.00
33. 1 Ducat 1649 .... * 100.00

Ruler standing. Rev. Eagle with shield.

34. 1 Ducat 1649 .... 100.00

Legend. Rev. Eagle.

35. 5 Lire or ⅓ Scudo d'oro ND 35.00
36. 103 Soldi or ⅓ Scudo d'oro ND ..... * ... 25.00

ALFONSO IV D'ESTE, 1658-1662
Bust. Rev. Sword.

37. 12 Scudi d'oro 1659 .... 1250.00

Bust. Rev. Eagle.

38. 2 Doppia 1660 .... 400.00
39. 1 Doppia 1660, ND 200.00

FRANCIS II D'ESTE, 1662-1694

Ruler standing. Rev. Eagle.

40. 1 Ducat ND 40.00

MONTALCINO

SIENESE RULE, 1555-1559
Madonna. Rev. She-Wolf.

1. 4 Scudi d'oro 1556 .... 800.00

She-Wolf. Rev. Arms.

2. 1 Scudo d'oro 1556, 57, 58, 59 .... 300.00

S. Rev. Arms.

3. ½ Scudo d'oro ND 200.00

MONTANARO

Abbots of —
BONIFACE FERRERO, 1529-1543
Arms. Rev. Cross.

1. 1 Scudo d'oro ND 500.00

Eagle. Rev. Cross.

2. 1 Scudo d'oro ND 500.00

SEBASTIAN FERRERO, 1546-1547
Bust. Rev. Arms.

3. 3 Scudi d'oro ND 1000.00

Arms. Rev. Cross.

4. 1 Scudo d'oro ND 500.00

JOHN BAPTIST, 1581-1582
Soldier standing. Rev. Arms.

5. 2 Doppia ND 1500.00
6. 1 Doppia ND 1000.00

Arms. Rev. Cross.

7. 1 Scudo d'oro ND 500.00

MUSSO

Marcheses of —
JOHN JAMES OF MEDICI, 1528-1530
Arms. Rev. Cross.

1. 1 Scudo d'oro ND 1000.00

Bust. Rev. Reclining figure.

2. 1 Zecchino ND 1000.00

NAPLES

(NAPLES AND SICILY)

A. Anjou Rulers of —
CHARLES I, 1266-1278

The Annunciation. Rev. Arms.

1. 1 Salut d'or ND .... * 150.00
2. ½ Salut d'or ND 500.00

CHARLES II, 1285-1309
The Annunciation. Rev. Arms.

3. 1 Salut d'or ND 150.00

JOANNA I, 1343-1347
Ruler seated. Rev. Cross.

4. 1 Ducat ND 200.00

St. John. Rev. Arms.

5. 1 Florin ND 100.00

JOANNA AND LOUIS, 1352-1362
St. John. Rev. Lily.

6. 1 Florin ND 75.00

LOUIS, 1382-1384
St. John. Rev. Arms.

7. 1 Florin ND 100.00

B. Aragon Rulers of —

ALFONSO I, 1442-1458

Ruler on horse. Rev. Arms.

8. 1 Ducatone ND (31 Millimetres) 175.00
9. 1 Ducat ND (27 Millimetres) ....*...... 100.00

FERDINAND I, 1458-1494
Crowned bust. Rev. Victory in chariot.

10. 5 Ducats ND 1000.00

Crowned bust. Rev. Arms.

11. 2 Ducats ND 1000.00
12. 1 Ducat ND ....*...... 100.00

ALFONSO II, 1494-1495

Crowned bust. Rev. Arms.

13. 1 Ducat ND 100.00

FERDINAND II, 1495-1496

Crowned bust. Rev. Arms.

14. 1 Ducat ND 125.00

FREDERICK III, 1496-1501

Crowned bust. Rev. Animal over shield.

15. 1 Ducat ND 150.00

C. French Rulers of —

CHARLES VIII, 1495
Arms. Rev. Cross of Jerusalem.

16. 1 Scudo d'oro ND 400.00

Arms between initials. Rev. Cross of Jerusalem in quadrilobe.

17. 2 Scudi d'oro ND 1000.00
18. 1 Scudo d'oro ND ....*...... 500.00

LOUIS XII, 1501-1503

Crowned bust. Rev. Arms.

19. 1 Ducat ND 600.00

D. Spanish Rulers of —

FERDINAND AND ISABELLA, 1504

Crowned busts facing each other. Rev. Arms.

20. 1 Zecchino ND 500.00

FERDINAND THE CATHOLIC, 1504-1516

Crowned bust. Rev. Arms.

21. 1 Ducat ND 150.00

CHARLES AND JOANNA, 1516-1519

Arms. Rev. Cross.

22. 1 Ducat ND 125.00

CHARLES V, 1519-1556

Bust. Rev. Peace standing.

23. 4 Scudi d'oro ND 1000.00
24. 2 Scudi d'oro ND .... * 200.00

Bust. Rev. Pallas seated.

25. 2 Scudi d'oro ND 600.00

Crowned bust. Rev. Arms.

26. 1 Ducat ND 250.00

Laureate head. Rev. Arms.

27. 1 Ducat ND 75.00

Arms. Rev. Cross.

28. 1 Scudo d'oro ND 65.00

PHILIP II, 1556-1598

Head. Rev. Arms.

29. 1 Scudo d'oro 1582, 97, ND 100.00

PHILIP III, 1598-1621

Radiate bust. Rev. Eagle.

30. 1 Scudo d'oro ND 750.00

PHILIP IV, 1621-1665

Plain head right. Rev. Arms.

31. 2 Scudi d'oro 1626 .... 1000.00
32. 1 Scudo d'oro 1622-36 .... * 125.00

Armored bust left. Rev. Arms.

33. 1 Scudo d'oro 1642, 47 .... 250.00

CHARLES II, 1667-1700

Bust. Rev. Arms.

34. 1 Ducat 1665 .... 750.00

Bust. Rev. Eagle.

35. 1 Scudo d'oro 1697 .... Unknown

E. Bourbon Rulers of —

CHARLES, 1734-1759

Bust. Rev. Arms and value.

36. 6 Ducati 1749-55 .... * 60.00
37. 4 Ducati 1749-59 .... 40.00
38. 2 Ducati 1749-54 .... 30.00

FERDINAND IV (I), 1759-1825
(Ferdinand IV from 1759-1816 and Ferdinand I from 1817-1825).

Youthful bust. Rev. Arms.

39. 6 Ducati 1759-67 .... 50.00
40. 4 Ducati 1760-67 .... * 40.00
41. 2 Ducati 1762 .... 40.00

Older bust. Rev. Arms.

42. 6 Ducati 1768-82 .... * 60.00
43. 4 Ducati 1768-82 .... 40.00
44. 2 Ducati 1771 .... 40.00

Oldest bust. Rev. Arms.

45. 6 Ducati 1783, 84, 85 .... 75.00

Bust of Queen Maria Caroline. Rev. Two figures at altar.

46. 2 Ducati 1768 .... 100.00

Bust. Rev. Legend.

47. 2 Ducati 1772 .... 100.00

ITALY-NAPLES (cont'd)

Crowned bust. Rev. Male standing at column.

48.	30 Ducati 1818	............................*......	250.00
49.	15 Ducati 1818	....	100.00
50.	3 Ducati 1818	............................*......	30.00

JOACHIM MURAT, 1808-1815
(Napoleonic Dynasty)

Head. Rev. Value.

51.	40 Franchi 1810	....	1000.00
52.	40 Lire 1813	....	75.00
53.	20 Lire 1813	.....................*......	50.00
53a.	20 Lire 1813. N mm.	....	200.00

FRANCIS I, 1825-1830

Head. Rev. Male standing at column.

54.	30 Ducati 1825, 26	....	250.00
55.	15 Ducati 1825	....	1000.00
56.	6 Ducati 1826	...........................*......	85.00
57.	3 Ducati 1826	...........................*......	85.00

FERDINAND II, 1830-1859

Head with or without beard. Rev. Male standing at column with or without wings.

58.	30 Ducati 1833-56	.........................*......	175.00
59.	15 Ducati 1831-56	.........................*......	100.00
60.	6 Ducati 1831-56	.........................*......	40.00
61.	3 Ducati 1831-56	....	30.00

NOVARA

Marcheses of —

PETER LUIGI FARNESE, 1538-1547

Arms. Rev. Cross.

1.	1 Scudo d'oro ND	....	500.00

PADUA

FRANCIS I, 1355-1388
St. Prosdocimus. Rev. Arms.

1.	1 Ducat ND	....	500.00

PALERMO

A. Fatimid Caliphs of —

AL QAYM, 934-945
Cufic legend on each side.

1.	1 Tari ND	....	35.00

EL HAKEM BIAMR ILAH, 996-1020

Cufic legend on each side.

2.	1 Tari ND	....	35.00

DHAER LEAZIZ DIN ILAH, 1020-1036
Cufic legend on each side.

3.	1 Tari ND	....	30.00

ANONYMOUS
ERTINA. Rev. Si Mirio.

4.	1 Tari ND (1020)	....	75.00

B. Kings of —

ROGER II, 1105-1154
Cufic legend on each side.

5.	2 Tari ND	....	75.00
6.	1 Tari ND	....	35.00

T. Rev. Cufic legend.

7.	1 Tari ND	....	40.00

WILLIAM II, 1166-1189
Cufic legend. Rev. Cross.

8.	1 Tari ND	....	35.00

FREDERICK II, 1198-1250
Eagle. Rev. Cross.

9.	2 Tari ND	....	75.00

CHARLES II, 1665-1700

Shield on breast of eagle. Rev. Small head in border under palms.

10.	1 Scudo Riccio 1697	....	200.00

CHARLES III, 1711-1734

Head. Rev. Phoenix.

11.	1 Oncia 1714-34	....	60.00

ITALY-PALERMO (cont'd)

CHARLES BOURBON, 1734-1759

Bust. Rev. Bourbon shield on eagle.

12. 2 Oncia 1734-54 .... 50.00

Bare head. Rev. Phoenix.

13. 1 Oncia 1734-59 .... 30.00

FERDINAND IV (III OF SICILY), 1759-1815

Radiate head. Rev. Triskelis.

14. 2 Oncia 1814 .... 250.00

PARMA AND PIACENZA

(For the Papal coinage of Parma, see under Vatican-Parma).

A. Republic of —, 1448-1449

Christ and Madonna. Rev. St. John and St. Hillary standing.

1. 1 Ducat ND 500.00

B. Dukes of —

(Unless otherwise stated, all coins are for Parma. Those coins struck for Piacenza are so indicated at the end of the description).

OCTAVIUS FARNESE, 1547-1586

Arms. Rev. Security seated.

2. 1 Scudo d'oro 1552-57, ND ....*...... 50.00
3. 1 Scudo d'oro 1552. For Piacenza 125.00

Pallas seated. Rev. Arms.

4. ½ Scudo d'oro 1552, ND 100.00

Head. Rev. She-wolf. For Piacenza.

5. 2 Doppia 1582, 86, 87, ND ....*...... 200.00
6. 1 Doppia 1582, 85, 86, 89, ND 175.00

ALEXANDER FARNESE, 1586-1591

Bust. Rev. The three Graces standing.

7. 7 Scudi d'oro 1588 .... 1750.00
8. 4 Doppia 1588 .... 750.00

Bust. Rev. Arms.

9. 2 Doppia ND 250.00

Bust. Rev. Security standing.

10. 1 Doppia ND 250.00

Bust. Rev. She-wolf. For Piacenza.

11. 2 Doppia 1590-99, ND 125.00

RANUCCIO FARNESE I, 1592-1622

Bust of Alexander Farnese. Rev. The three Graces standing.

12. 8 Scudi d'oro 1594 .... 1250.00

Ruler standing. Rev. Arms.

13. 1 Ducat 1602, 03 .... 60.00

Ruler standing. Rev. Madonna.

14. 1 Ducat ND 60.00

Bust. Rev. Ship. For Piacenza.

15. 2 Doppia 1592 .... 200.00

Bust. Rev. Wind blowing. For Piacenza.

16. 4 Doppia 1601 .... 600.00
17. 2 Doppia 1595, 1612, 13 .... 175.00
18. 1 Doppia 1595-1612 ....*...... 125.00

Bust. Rev. She-wolf. For Piacenza.

19. 2 Doppia 1599-1622 .... 150.00

249

Ruler standing. Rev. Tablet.

20. 1 Ducat 1601 .... **60.00**

ODOARDO FARNESE, 1622-1646

Bust. Rev. Madonna.

21. 8 Doppia 1639 .... **1250.00**
22. 6 Doppia ND **850.00**
23. 2 Doppia 1625, 39, ND ....*...... **125.00**
24. 1 Doppia ND **175.00**

Bust. Rev. Mars and Pallas standing.

25. 8 Doppia 1629 .... **1500.00**

Bust. Rev. The three Graces standing.

26. 3 Doppia 1633 .... **400.00**

Bust. Rev. Lily. For Piacenza.

27. 2 Doppia 1623, 24 .... **175.00**

Bust. Rev. St. Anthony on horse. For Piacenza.

28. 6 Doppia 1626, 29 .... **1000.00**

Bust. Rev. She-wolf. For Piacenza.

29. 2 Doppia 1626, 31 ....*...... **175.00**
30. 1 Doppia 1626 .... **100.00**

RANUCCIO FARNESE II, 1646-1694
Bust. Rev. Madonna.

31. 2 Doppia 1658, ND **250.00**

Head. Rev. Wind blowing.

32. 1 Doppia 1692 .... **200.00**

Bust. Rev. Mars and Pallas standing.

33. 10 Doppia 1673 .... **2000.00**
34. 8 Doppia 1660, 79 .... **1750.00**

Bust. Rev. St. Anthony on horse. For Piacenza.

35. 10 Doppia 1676 .... **1500.00**

FRANCIS FARNESE I, 1694-1727

Head. Rev. Arms.

36. 1 Doppia 1695 .... **275.00**

FERDINAND, 1765-1802

Head. Rev. Arms.

37. 8 Doppia 1786-96 .... **350.00**
38. 6 Doppia 1786 .... **350.00**
39. 4 Doppia 1784-96 .... **150.00**
40. 3 Doppia 1786 .... **150.00**
41. 1 Doppia 1784-96 ....*.... **45.00**
42. ½ Doppia 1785 .... **40.00**
43. 1 Zecchino 1784 .... **40.00**

MARIE LOUISE, 1815-1847

Head. Rev. Arms.

44. 40 Lire 1815, 21 ....*...... **75.00**
45. 20 Lire 1815, 32 .... **40.00**

PASSERANO

Eagle. Rev. Cross.

1. 10 Scudi d'oro 1582 .... **1500.00**

Arms. Rev. Cross.

2. 2 Scudi d'oro 1597 .... **750.00**

PAVIA

Kings of —

ROTARI, 636-652
Bust. Rev. Victory standing.

1. ⅓ Solidus ND **150.00**

CUNIBERT, 686-700
Bust. Rev. St. Michael standing.

2. ⅓ Solidus ND **150.00**

Bust. Rev. Victory standing.

3. ⅓ Solidus ND **100.00**

LUITBERT, 700-701

Bust. Rev. St. Michael standing.

4. ⅓ Solidus ND **200.00**

ARIBERT, 701-712
Bust. Rev. St. Michael standing.

5. ⅓ Solidus ND **200.00**

ITALY-PAVIA (cont'd)

LUITBRAND, 712-744
Bust. Rev. St. Michael standing.

6. ⅓ Solidus ND 100.00

RACHIS, 744-749
Bust. Rev. St. Michael standing.

7. ⅓ Solidus ND 300.00

ASTOLF, 749-756
St. Michael standing. Rev. Christogram.

8. ⅓ Solidus ND 300.00

DESIDERIUS, 756-774
Cross. Rev. Star.

9. ⅓ Solidus ND 300.00

CHARLEMAGNE, 774-800
Cross. Rev. Star.

10. ⅓ Solidus ND 300.00

PHILIP MARIA, 1402-1412
Horseman. Rev. Arms.

11. 1 Florin ND 500.00

FRANCIS I, 1447-1450
Ruler on horse. Rev. Crowned serpent.

12. 1 Ducat ND 300.00

SIEGE OF PAVIA, 1524-1525
Legend. Rev. Legend incused. Square shape.

13. 1 Ducat 1524 .... 800.00

PERUGIA

(Roman Republic, 1799).
Eagle facing, and below "Perugia." Rev. Value in wreath.

1. 1 Gold Scudo. Year VII (1799) 1000.00

(For additional coins of Perugia, see under Vatican).

PESARO

Dukes of —

JOHN SFORZA, 1489-1510
Bust. Rev. St. Paul standing.

1. 1 Zecchino ND 600.00

CONSTANCE II SFORZA, 1510-1512
St. Paul standing. Rev. Arms.

2. 1 Scudo d'oro ND 400.00

FRANCIS MARIA DELLA ROVERE, 1513-1538
St. Francis standing. Rev. Plan of fortress.

3. 1 Scudo d'oro ND 400.00

GUIDOBALD II DELLA ROVERE, 1538-1574

Three pyramids. Rev. Legend.

4. 1 Ducat ND 300.00
5. ½ Ducat ND ....* 200.00

PIOMBINO

Princes of —

NICHOLAS LUDOVISI, 1634-1665
Madonna. Rev. Arms.

1. 2 Doppia 1651 .... 600.00

JOHN BAPTIST LUDOVISI, 1665-1699

Bust. Rev. Arms.

2. 1 Doppia 1695 .... 500.00
3. 1 Zecchino 1695, 96 ....* 250.00

PISA

A. Kings of —

ANONYMOUS, 650-749
Cross. Rev. Star.

1. ⅓ Solidus ND 200.00

Rose. Rev. Cross.

2. ⅓ Solidus ND 200.00

ASTOLF, 749-756
Cross. Rev. Star.

3. ⅓ Solidus ND 300.00

DESIDERIUS, 757-778
Cross. Rev. Star.

4. ⅓ Solidus ND 300.00

CHARLEMAGNE, 774-800
Cross. Rev. Star.

5. ⅓ Solidus ND 300.00

B. Republic of —

Madonna. Rev. Eagle.

6. 1 Zecchino ND (1313-1494) 300.00

Madonna. Rev. Cross.

7. 1 Zecchino ND (1495-1509) 300.00

C. French Rulers of —

CHARLES VIII, 1494-1495
Madonna and child. Rev. Crowned arms.

8. 1 Zecchino ND 350.00

D. Tuscan Grand Dukes of —

FERDINAND I, 1587-1609
Madonna in clouds. Rev. Cross of Pisa.

9. 2 Doppia 1595 .... 500.00
10. 1 Doppia 1595 .... 300.00

FERDINAND II, 1621-1670

Madonna in clouds. Rev. Cross of Pisa.

11. 2 Doppia ND 500.00
12. 1 Doppia 1641-55, ND ....* 100.00
13. ½ Doppia 1643, ND 75.00

COSIMO III, 1670-1723

Madonna in clouds. Rev. Cross of Pisa.

14. 1 Doppia ND 300.00

PISTOIA

Rose. Rev. Cross.

1. ⅓ Solidus ND (700-800) 300.00

POMPONESCO

Marcheses of —

JULIUS CAESAR GONZAGA, 1583-1593
Arms. Rev. Cross.

1. 1 Scudo d'oro ND 500.00

PORCIA

Princes of —

HANNIBAL ALFONSO EMANUEL, 1704
Bust. Rev. Arms.

1. 1 Ducat 1704 .... 500.00

RAVENNA

Kings of —

ASTOLF, 749-756
Bust. Rev. Cross.

1. 1 Solidus ND 250.00
2. ⅓ Solidus ND 75.00

REGGIO-EMILIA

Dukes of —

HERCULES I D'ESTE, 1471-1505
Hercules lifting Antaeus. Rev. St. Prospero standing.

1. 1 Ducat ND 400.00

ALFONSO I D'ESTE, 1505-1534

Bust. Rev. St. Prospero seated.

2. 1 Ducat ND 350.00

HERCULES II D'ESTE, 1534-1559

Christ with cross. Rev. Arms.

---

3. 1 Scudo d'oro 1550-58, ND 40.00

ALFONSO II D'ESTE, 1559-1597
Christ with cross. Rev. Arms.

4. 1 Scudo d'oro 1560-72 .... 40.00

Bust. Rev. Nude male with shield.

5. 2 Doppia 1567 .... 500.00

Bust. Rev. Eagle.

6. 10 Scudi d'oro 1572 .... 1000.00

RETEGNO

Barons of —

ANTHONY THEODORE TRIVULZIO, 1676-1678
Ruler on horse. Rev. Bundle of corn ears.

1. 1 Zecchino 1676 .... 300.00

Bust. Rev. Arms.

2. 10 Zecchini 1677 .... 1000.00

Soldier standing. Rev. Tablet.

3. 2 Ducats 1677 .... 600.00
4. 1 Ducat 1677 .... 300.00

ANTHONY CAIETAN TRIVULZIO, 1679-1705

Bust. Rev. Arms.

5. 10 Zecchini 1686 .... 1000.00

Soldier standing. Rev. Legend.

6. 2 Doppia ND 600.00

Soldier standing. Rev. Tablet.

7. 2 Ducats 1686, ND .... * 300.00
8. 1 Ducat 1686, ND 200.00

ANTHONY PTOLEMY TRIVULZIO, 1708-1767

Bust. Rev. Arms.

9. 1 Ducat 1724, 26 .... 200.00

RIFREDI

PISAN RULE, 1363
Madonna. Rev. Eagle.

1. 1 Zecchino ND 300.00

ITALY (cont'd)

ROME

(See Vatican).

RONCO

Marcheses of —

NAPOLEON SPINOLA, 1647-1672

Bust. Rev. Eagle.

1.	4 Ducats 1647	800.00
2.	1 Ducat 1668	500.00

CHARLES SPINOLA

Bust. Rev. Eagle on arms.

3.	1 Doppia ND (1699)	600.00

SABBIONETA

Dukes of —

VESPASIAN GONZAGA, 1562-1565
Arms. Rev. Cross.

1.	1 Scudo d'oro ND	400.00

Head. Rev. Madonna.

2.	½ Scudo d'oro ND	300.00

Three shields. Rev. Cross.

3.	1 Scudo d'oro ND	400.00

LUIGI CARAFA AND ISABELLA GONZAGA, 1591-1637
Madonna. Rev. Arms on eagle.

4.	1 Ducat ND	400.00

SALERNO

Princes of —

GISULF I, 935-974

Cufic legend on each side.

1.	1 Tari ND	50.00

GUAIMARIO IV, 999-1015
Cufic legend on each side.

2.	1 Tari ND	50.00

ABU TAMIM MUSTANSIR, 1250

Cufic legend on each side.

3.	1 Tari ND	100.00

GISULF II, 1052-1075
Cufic legend on each side.

4.	1 Tari ND	50.00

ROBERT, 1059-1085

Cufic legend on each side.

5.	1 Tari ND	100.00

ROGER II, 1127-1130
Cufic legend on each side.

6.	1 Tari ND	50.00

WILLIAM II, 1166-1189

W. Rev. Star and Cufic legend.

7.	1 Tari ND	75.00

TANCRED, 1189-1194
ACD REX. Rev. Cufic legend.

8.	1 Tari ND	75.00

SAN GIORGIO

Marcheses of —

JOHN DOMINIC MILANO, 1732
Bust. Rev. Arms.

1.	2 Zecchini 1732	1000.00
2.	1 Zecchino 1732	400.00

SAN JACOPO AL SERCHIO

FLORENTINE RULE, 1256
St. John standing, trefoil mm. Rev. Lily.

1.	1 Florin ND	50.00

SARDINIA

(HOUSE OF SAVOY)

Counts, and later, Kings of —

AMADEUS VI, 1343-1383
St. John. Rev. Lily.

1.	1 Florin ND	750.00

AMADEUS VII, 1383-1391

St. John. Rev. Arms.

2.	1 Florin ND	750.00

Ruler on throne. Rev. Arms.

3.	1 Florin ND	1500.00

Helmeted shield. Rev. Cross.

4.	1 Scudo d'oro ND	750.00

ITALY-SARDINIA (cont'd)

AMADEUS VIII (DUKE), 1391-1439

Ruler kneeling before St. Maurice. Rev. Helmeted shield.

5. 1 Ducat ND **500.00**

LOUIS I, 1434-1465

Ruler on horse. Rev. Arms.

6. 1 Ducat ND **300.00**

Arms and "Fert". Rev. Cross.

7. 1 Scudo d'oro ND ....* **300.00**
8. ½ Scudo d'oro ND **750.00**

Arms in enclosure. Rev. Cross.

9. 1 Scudo d'oro ND **100.00**

AMADEUS IX, 1465-1472
Ruler on horse. Rev. Arms.

10. 1 Ducat ND **750.00**

Arms in enclosure. Rev. Cross.

11. 1 Scudo d'oro ND **700.00**

FILIBERT I, 1472-1482
Ruler on horse. Rev. Arms.

12. 1 Ducat ND **450.00**

CHARLES I, 1482-1490

Ruler on horse. Rev. Arms.

13. 1 Ducat ND **350.00**

Bust with cap. Rev. Helmeted shield.

14. 1 Ducat ND **450.00**

Bust with cap. Rev. Arms and "Fert".

15. 1 Ducat ND **350.00**

PHILIP II, 1496-1497
Ruler on horse. Rev. Arms.

16. 1 Ducat ND **800.00**

FILIBERT II, 1497-1504

Bust with cap. Rev. Arms and "Fert".

17. 2 Ducats ND **2750.00**
18. 1 Ducat ND ....* **750.00**

CHARLES II, 1504-1553
Armored bust. Rev. Arms.

19. 10 Ducats 1546 .... **2500.00**

Crowned bust. Rev. Arms between two K's.

20. 1 Ducat ND **500.00**

Bust with cap. Rev. Arms and "Fert".

21. 1 Ducat ND **500.00**

Ruler on horse. Rev. Arms.

22. 1 Scudo d'oro ND **500.00**

Arms and "Fert". Rev. Cross.

23. 1 Scudo d'oro ND **275.00**

Arms. Rev. Ornate cross.

24. 1 Scudo d'oro ND **275.00**

St. Maurice on horse. Rev. Arms.

25. 1 Scudo d'oro ND **500.00**

EMANUEL FILIBERT, 1553-1580

Oval shield. Rev. Cross.

26. 1 Scudo d'oro 1555-71 .... **60.00**

Arms. Rev. Small cross on large cross.

27. 1 Doppia 1576-80 .... **250.00**
28. 1 Scudo d'oro 1570-80 ....* **100.00**

ITALY-SARDINIA (cont'd)

Bust. Rev. Arms.

29.	1 Doppia 1570-76	300.00

Armored bust. Rev. Elephant.

30.	9 Lire ND	1750.00

Busts of the Royal couple. Rev. Serpent.

31.	3 Filibertos ND	2500.00

CHARLES EMANUEL I, 1580-1630

Armored bust. Rev. Arms.

32.	10 Ducats 1619-28	2000.00
33.	10 Scudi d'oro 1623	2000.00
34.	4 Scudi d'oro 1586, 87	800.00
35.	2 Doppia 1595, 98, 1601, ND	400.00
36.	1 Doppia 1580-1611, ND ....*	125.00

Bust. Rev. Cross.

37.	1 Scudo d'oro 1627	700.00
38.	½ Scudo d'oro 1627	400.00

Bust. Rev. Legend.

39.	1 Scudo d'oro 1630	700.00

Bust. Rev. Compass.

40.	10 Scudi d'oro 1630	2500.00

Arms. Rev. Cross.

41.	1 Doppia 1581	125.00
42.	1 Scudo d'oro 1580	75.00

Madonna. Rev. Arms.

43.	1 Ducat 1601, 02	75.00

VICTOR AMADEUS I, 1630-1637
Bust. Rev. Three flags.

44.	10 Scudi d'oro 1633	2750.00
45.	4 Scudi d'oro 1633, 34	700.00
46.	2 Doppia 1632	700.00

Bust. Rev. Arms.

47.	30 Scudi d'oro 1635	3500.00
48.	20 Scudi d'oro 1635	2500.00
49.	10 Scudi d'oro 1633, 34, 35, 36 ....*	1600.00
50.	4 Scudi d'oro 1634, ND	700.00
51.	1 Doppia ND	600.00

Bust. Rev. Cross.

52.	10 Scudi d'oro 1635	2500.00

FRANCIS HYACINT, 1637-1638

Busts of Francis and his mother, Christina. Rev. Madonna.

53.	8 Scudi d'oro ND	850.00
54.	4 Scudi d'oro ND ....*	500.00

CHARLES EMANUEL II, 1638-1675

Youthful bust. Rev. Arms.

55.	10 Scudi d'oro 1639	2000.00
56.	4 Scudi d'oro 1639, 40 ....*	750.00

Mature bust. Rev. Arms.

57.	40 Scudi d'oro 1656	6000.00
58.	30 Scudi d'oro 1656	6000.00
59.	20 Scudi d'oro 1649-71	4000.00
60.	10 Scudi d'oro 1649-71	3000.00
61.	4 Scudi d'oro 1649-54	750.00
62.	1 Doppia 1650-70	100.00
63.	1 Scudo d'oro 1670	750.00
64.	½ Scudo d'oro 1649	400.00

Head. Rev. Arms.

65.	1 Doppia 1675	125.00

Head. Rev. Cross.

66.	1 Scudo d'oro ND	750.00

Busts of Charles and Christina to right or left. Rev. Arms.

67.	20 Scudi d'oro 1641	3000.00
68.	10 Scudi d'oro 1641, 48	1600.00
69.	8 Scudi d'oro 1641, ND	1400.00
70.	4 Scudi d'oro 1639, 41, 48 ....*	125.00
71.	2 Doppia 1640, 48	250.00
72.	1 Doppia 1640, 41	200.00

Busts of Charles and Christina. Rev. Madonna.

73. 8 Scudi d'oro ND 1500.00

Busts of Charles and Christina. Rev. Crossed initials.

74. ½ Scudo d'oro ND 350.00

Arms. Rev. Cross.

75. 1 Scudo d'oro ND 350.00

VICTOR AMADEUS II, 1675-1730
Youthful bust. Rev. Arms.

76. ½ Doppia 1679 .... 350.00

Older bust. Rev. Arms.

77. 2 Doppia 1680 .... 1000.00
78. 1 Doppia 1680-1690 .... 300.00
79. ½ Doppia 1680-1706 .... 300.00
80. 1 Scudo d'oro 1709 .... 350.00

Bust. Rev. Arms and lions.

81. 10 Scudi d'oro 1680 .... 2750.00

Head. Rev. Arms.

82. 1 Doppia 1713-22 .... 200.00

Ruler on horse. Rev. Justice standing.

83. 5 Doppia 1694 .... 2500.00

Busts of Victor and Maria Joan. Rev. Arms.

84. 5 Doppia 1675, 78 .... 1250.00
85. 1 Doppia 1675-80 ....*...... 125.00
86. ½ Doppia 1675-79 .... 100.00

Busts of Victor and Maria Joan. Rev. Seated female and cherub.

87. 2 Doppia 1675-77 .... 750.00

CHARLES EMANUEL III, 1730-1773
Bust. Rev. Arms.

88. 1 Doppia 1733-41 .... 350.00
89. ½ Doppia 1733-42 .... 350.00

Head. Rev. Arms.

90. 5 Doppia 1755-68 .... 350.00
91. 2½ Doppia 1755, 56, 57 .... 200.00
92. 1 Doppia 1755-69 .... 60.00
93. ½ Doppia 1755-70 ....*...... 40.00
94. ¼ Doppia 1755-58 .... 75.00

Bust. Rev. Oval shield of Sardinia.

95. 5 Doppia 1768, 69 .... 500.00
96. 2½ Doppia 1768-71 .... 125.00
97. 1 Doppia 1768-72 ....*...... 50.00

Eagle. Rev. The Annunciation.

98. 4 Zecchini 1745, 46 ....*...... 150.00
99. 1 Zecchino 1743-46 .... 40.00
100. ½ Zecchino 1744-46 .... 30.00

Madonna. Rev. Angel.

101. ⅙ Zecchino ND 350.00

VICTOR AMADEUS III, 1773-1796
Head. Rev. Arms.

102. 1 Doppia 1773-78 .... 100.00
103. ½ Doppia 1773-78 .... 40.00
104. ¼ Doppia 1773-82 .... 25.00

Head. Rev. Eagle.

105. 5 Doppia 1786 .... 300.00
106. 2½ Doppia 1786 .... 125.00
107. 1 Doppia 1786-96 .... 50.00
108. ½ Doppia 1786-96 ....*...... 30.00
109. ¼ Doppia 1786 ....*...... 30.00

Bust. Rev. Oval shield of Sardinia.

110. 5 Doppia 1773-84 .... 300.00
111. 2½ Doppia 1773-84 .... 125.00
112. 1 Doppia 1773-86 ....*...... 50.00

CHARLES EMANUEL IV, 1796-1802

Head. Rev. Eagle.

113. 1 Doppia 1797-1800 ....*...... 75.00
114. ½ Doppia 1797, 98 .... 50.00

VICTOR EMANUEL I, 1802-1821

Head. Rev. Eagle.

115. 1 Doppia 1814, 15 .... 100.00

ITALY-SARDINIA (cont'd)

Head. Rev. Square shield in circle.

116. 20 Lire 1816-20 .... 30.00

Head. Rev. Oval shield within branches.

117. 80 Lire 1821 ....* 250.00
117a. 20 Lire 1821 .... 75.00

CHARLES FELIX, 1821-1831

Head. Rev. Arms.

118. 80 Lire 1823-31. Eagle's head mm. 85.00
119. 80 Lire 1824-31. Anchor mm. ....* 85.00
120. 40 Lire 1822-31. Eagle's head mm. 60.00
121. 40 Lire 1825, 26. Anchor mm. 75.00
122. 20 Lire 1821-31. Eagle's head mm. 20.00
123. 20 Lire 1824-31. Anchor mm. 25.00

CHARLES ALBERT, 1831-1849

Head. Rev. Arms.

124. 100 Lire 1832-44. Eagle's head mm. 85.00
125. 100 Lire 1832-45. Anchor mm. ....* 85.00
126. 50 Lire 1832-43. Eagle's head mm. 50.00
127. 50 Lire 1833, 35, 41. Anchor mm. 60.00
128. 20 Lire 1831-49. Eagle's head mm. 20.00
129. 20 Lire 1831-49. Anchor mm. 20.00
130. 10 Lire 1832-47. Eagle's head mm. 22.50
131. 10 Lire 1833-47. Anchor mm. ....* 25.00

VICTOR EMANUEL II, 1849-1861

Head. Rev. Arms.

132. 20 Lire 1850-61. Eagle's head mm. 20.00
133. 20 Lire 1850-60. Anchor mm. ....* 20.00
134. 20 Lire 1860. M mm. 35.00
135. 10 Lire 1850-60. Eagle's head mm. 20.00
136. 10 Lire 1850. Anchor mm. 100.00

(For the later coins of Victor Emanuel II, as King of all Italy, see under Italy, Kings of ——).

SAVONA

St. John. Rev. Lily.

1. 1 Florin ND (1350-96) 60.00

Madonna and child flanked by two lis. Rev. Eagle. Struck under Louis XII of France.

2. 2 Ducats ND (1499-1510) 1000.00
3. 1 Ducat ND (1499-1510) 400.00

SAVOY, HOUSE OF

(See Sardinia).

SICILY

(See Messina and Palermo).

SIENA

A. Republic of —

S. Rev. Cross.

1. 1 Florin ND (1340-1450) 85.00
2. 1 Sanese d'oro ND (1375-90) ....* 75.00
3. 1 Ducat ND (1450-1550) 65.00
4. ½ Ducat 1553-55, ND 40.00
5. ½ Scudo d'oro 1549-53 .... 40.00

Madonna. Rev. Victory standing.

6. 2 Ducats ND 150.00

She-wolf in shield. Rev. Cross.

7. 1 Scudo d'oro ND (1533-48) 60.00

ITALY-SIENA (cont'd)

She-wolf. Rev. Cross.

8. 1 Scudo d'oro 1548-54, ND **50.00**

Madonna. Rev. Cross.

9. 1 Scudo d'oro 1549 . . . . **75.00**

Madonna. Rev. St. Victorius standing.

10. 3 Doppia 1550 . . . . **750.00**

B. Rulers of —

JOHN GALEAZZO, 1390-1404

S. Rev. Cross.

11. 1 Sanese d'oro ND **60.00**

COSIMO I, 1557-1574
Arms. Rev. Cross.

12. 1 Scudo d'oro ND **50.00**

HENRY II OF FRANCE, 1547-1559
Madonna and child. Rev. She-wolf.

13. 4 Ecu d'or 1556 . . . . **1500.00**

She-wolf. Rev. Band across oval shield.

14. 1 Ecu d'or 1557 . . . . **750.00**

S. Rev. Band across oval shield.

15. ½ Ecu d'or ND **300.00**

SOLFERINO

Marcheses of —

CHARLES GONZAGA, 1643-1678
Bust. Rev. Arms.

1. 2 Florins ND **200.00**

Ruler standing. Rev. Arms.

2. 1 Ducat ND **125.00**

SORAGNA

Princes of —

NICHOLAS MELI-LUPI, 1731-1741

Arms. Rev. Eagle.

1. 1 Scudo d'oro 1731 . . . . **500.00**

SUB-ALPINE REPUBLIC

Helmeted female head. Rev. Value and date. On the Victory of Marengo. Struck at Turin.

1. 20 Francs. Years 9 and 10 (1800, 01) **60.00**

TASSAROLO

Counts of —

AUGUSTIN SPINOLA, 1604-1616
Bust. Rev. Arms.

1. 5 Doppia 1604 . . . . **1000.00**
2. 2 Doppia 1604 . . . . **500.00**

Bust of Rudolph II. Rev. Eagle.

3. 1 Ducat 1604 . . . . **175.00**

Soldier standing. Rev. Tablet.

4. 1 Ducat 1611, 12 . . . . **100.00**

Soldier standing. Rev. Eagle.

5. 1 Ducat ND **100.00**

Soldier standing. Rev. Arms.

6. 1 Ducat ND **100.00**

Madonna. Rev. Arms.

7. 1 Ducat 1614 . . . . **100.00**

St. Nicholas. Rev. Eagle.

8. 1 Doppia ND **250.00**

PHILIP SPINOLA, 1616-1688

Bust. Rev. Arms.

9. 2 Doppia 1629 . . . .*. **500.00**
10. 1 Doppia 1630 . . . . **250.00**

Bust. Rev. St. Charles in fire.

11. 2 Doppia 1640 . . . . **500.00**
12. 1 Doppia 1640 . . . . **250.00**

ITALY-TASSAROLO (cont'd)

Soldier standing. Rev. Eagle.

13. 1 Ducat 1637 .... 100.00

Soldier standing. Rev. Tablet.

14. 1 Ducat ND 100.00

Rose. Rev. Tablet.

15. 1 Ducat ND 100.00

St. Nicholas. Rev. Eagle.

16. 2 Doppia ND 450.00

TRENTO

Bishops of —

PETER VIGILIO, 1776-1796
Bust. Rev. Arms and eagle.

1. 1 Ducat 1776 .... 200.00

TRESANA

Marcheses of —

WILLIAM II, 1613-1651
St. Ladislas standing. Rev. Madonna.

1. 1 Ducat 1620 .... 100.00

St. Louis standing. Rev. Eagle.

2. 1 Ducat ND 100.00

Soldier standing. Rev. Tablet.

3. 1 Ducat 1619 .... 125.00

Arab legend on each side. Struck for use in the Levant.

4. 1 Dinar ND 125.00

TREVISO

DESIDERIUS, 757-773
Cross. Rev. Star.

1. ⅓ Solidus ND 60.00

TUSCANY

(For the coins of the Grand Dukes of Tuscany, see under Florence, Leghorn and Pisa).

Government of —

St. John seated. Rev. Lily. Struck at Florence.

1. 1 Ruspone 1859 .... 125.00

URBINO

Dukes of —

GUIDOBALD I, 1482-1508

Bust. Rev. Eagle and shield.

1. 1 Ducat ND 200.00

FRANCIS MARIA I, 1508-1538
Bust. Rev. Palm tree.

2. 1 Doppia ND 200.00

Bust. Rev. Eagle and shield.

3. 1 Ducat ND 125.00

LORENZO, 1516-1519
Bust. Rev. Arms.

4. 1 Ducat ND 300.00

GUIDOBALD II, 1538-1574
Head. Rev. Arms.

5. 4 Scudi d'oro ND 250.00

Bust. Rev. Legend.

6. 1 Ducat ND 125.00

Arms. Rev. The Annunciation.

7. 1 Ducat ND 75.00

St. Helen and cross. Rev. Arms.

8. 1 Ducat ND 75.00

Plant. Rev. Winged thunderbolt.

9. ¼ Ducat ND 50.00

FRANCIS MARIA II, 1574-1624

Bust. Rev. Arms.

10. 20 Scudi d'oro 1604 .... 2500.00
11. 10 Scudi d'oro 1603, 21 .... 1000.00
12. 1 Scudo d'oro ND ....* 100.00

Arms. Rev. City view.

13. 4 Scudi d'oro ND 350.00
14. 1 Scudo d'oro ND ....* 150.00

ITALY-URBINO (cont'd)

St. Michael standing. Rev. Arms.

15. 1 Scudo d'oro ND 65.00

St. Francis standing. Rev. Fortress.

16. 1 Scudo d'oro ND 85.00

VASTO

Marcheses of —

CAESAR D'AVALOS, 1704-1729

Bust. Rev. Arms.

1. 20 Zecchini 1706 .... 4000.00
2. 1 Zecchino 1706 .... 750.00
3. ½ Zecchino 1707 ....* 700.00

VENICE

Doges of —

TYPE I

Doge kneeling before standing figure of St. Mark. Rev. Christ standing within stars. The following coins are undated.

JOHN DANDOLO, 1280-1289

1. 1 Ducat 50.00

PETER GRADENIGO, 1289-1311

2. 1 Ducat 25.00

MARINO ZORZI, 1311-1312

3. 1 Ducat 200.00

JOHN SORANZO, 1312-1328

4. 1 Ducat 40.00

FRANCIS DANDOLO, 1329-1339

5. 1 Ducat 25.00

BARTHOLOMEW GRADENIGO, 1339-1342

6. 1 Ducat 30.00

ANDREW DANDOLO, 1343-1354

7. 1 Ducat 25.00

MARINO FALIER, 1354-1355

8. 1 Ducat 250.00

JOHN GRADENIGO, 1355-1356

9. 1 Ducat 50.00

JOHN DELFINO, 1356-1361

10. 1 Ducat 25.00

LORENZO CELSI, 1361-1365

11. 1 Ducat 25.00

MARCO CORNER, 1365-1368

12. 1 Ducat 25.00

ANDREW CONTARINI, 1368-1382

13. 1 Ducat 25.00

MICHAEL MOROSINI, 1382

14. 1 Ducat 100.00

ANTHONY VENIER, 1382-1400

15. 1 Ducat 25.00

MICHAEL STENO, 1400-1413

16. 1 Ducat 25.00

THOMAS MOCENIGO, 1414-1423

17. 1 Ducat 25.00

FRANCIS FOSCARI, 1423-1457

18. 1 Ducat 25.00

PASQUALE MALIPIERO, 1457-1462

19. 1 Ducat 30.00

CHRISTOPHER MORO, 1462-1471

20. 1 Ducat 30.00

NICHOLAS TRONO, 1471-1474

21. 1 Ducat 100.00

NICHOLAS MARCELLO, 1473-1474

22. 1 Ducat ....* 200.00

PETER MOCENIGO, 1474-1476

23. 1 Ducat 200.00

ANDREW VENDRAMIN, 1476-1478

24. 1 Ducat 40.00

JOHN MOCENIGO, 1478-1485

25. 1 Ducat 30.00

MARCO BARBARIGO, 1485-1486

26. 1 Ducat 300.00

AUGUSTIN BARBARIGO, 1486-1501

27. 1 Ducat 25.00

LEONARDO LOREDANO, 1501-1521

28. 1 Ducat 25.00
29. ½ Ducat 100.00

ANTHONY GRIMANI, 1521-1523

30. 1 Ducat 600.00
31. ½ Ducat 100.00

ANDREW GRITTI, 1523-1539

32. 1 Ducat 25.00
33. ½ Ducat 100.00

PETER LANDO, 1539-1545

34. 1 Ducat 30.00
35. ½ Ducat 100.00

FRANCIS DONA, 1545-1553

36. 1 Zecchino 30.00

MARC ANTHONY TREVISANI, 1553-1554

37.	1 Zecchino	75.00
38.	½ Zecchino	100.00

FRANCIS VENIER, 1554-1556

39.	1 Zecchino	25.00
40.	½ Zecchino	100.00

LORENZO PRIULI, 1556-1559

41.	1 Zecchino	30.00
42	½ Zecchino	100.00

GIROLAMO PRIULI, 1559-1567

43.	1 Zecchino	25.00
44.	½ Zecchino	100.00

PETER LOREDANO, 1567-1570

45.	1 Zecchino	25.00
46.	½ Zecchino	100.00
47.	¼ Zecchino	25.00

ALOIS MOCENIGO I, 1570-1577

48.	2 Zecchini	500.00
49.	1 Zecchino	25.00
50.	½ Zecchino	100.00

SEBASTIAN VENIER, 1577-1578

51.	1 Zecchino	100.00
52.	½ Zecchino	100.00
53.	¼ Zecchino	100.00

NICHOLAS DAPONTE, 1578-1585

54.	1 Zecchino	25.00
55.	½ Zecchino	100.00
56.	¼ Zecchino	100.00

PASQUALE CICOGNA, 1585-1595

57.	1 Zecchino	25.00
58.	½ Zecchino	100.00
59.	¼ Zecchino	100.00

MARINO GRIMANI, 1595-1605

60.	10 Zecchini	1000.00
61.	1 Zecchino	25.00
62.	½ Zecchino	25.00
63.	¼ Zecchino	20.00

LEONARDO DONA, 1605-1612

64.	1 Zecchino	25.00
65.	½ Zecchino	40.00
66.	¼ Zecchino	30.00

MARC ANTHONY MEMMO, 1612-1615

67.	1 Zecchino	50.00
68.	½ Zecchino	40.00
69.	¼ Zecchino	60.00

JOHN BEMBO, 1615-1618

70.	1 Zecchino	80.00
71.	½ Zecchino	100.00
72.	¼ Zecchino	100.00

NICHOLAS DONA, 1618

73.	1 Zecchino	150.00
74.	¼ Zecchino	100.00

ANTHONY PRIULI, 1618-1623

75.	5 Zecchini	800.00
76.	2 Zecchini	300.00
77.	1 Zecchino	25.00
78.	½ Zecchino	20.00
79.	¼ Zecchino	15.00

FRANCIS CONTARINI, 1623-1624

80.	1 Zecchino	300.00
81.	½ Zecchino	100.00
82.	¼ Zecchino	100.00

JOHN CORNER I, 1625-1629

83.	1 Zecchino	500.00
84.	½ Zecchino	100.00
85.	¼ Zecchino	100.00

NICHOLAS CONTARINI, 1630-1631

86.	25 Zecchini	1750.00

87.	20 Zecchini	700.00
88.	15 Zecchini	500.00
89.	10 Zecchini	500.00
90.	5 Zecchini	300.00
91.	3 Zecchini	300.00
92.	2 Zecchini	300.00
93.	1 Zecchino	200.00
94.	½ Zecchino	100.00
95.	¼ Zecchino	100.00

FRANCIS ERIZZO, 1631-1646

96.	1 Zecchino	27.50
97.	½ Zecchino	20.00
98.	¼ Zecchino	15.00

FRANCIS MOLIN, 1646-1655

99.	20 Zecchini	1250.00
100.	15 Zecchini	1000.00
101.	12 Zecchini	750.00
102.	10 Zecchini	500.00
103.	7 Zecchini	300.00
104.	1 Zecchino	22.50
105.	½ Zecchino	80.00
106.	¼ Zecchino	50.00

CHARLES CONTARINI, 1655-1656

107.	1 Zecchino	22.50
108.	½ Zecchino	100.00
109.	¼ Zecchino	100.00

FRANCIS CORNER, 1656

110.	1 Zecchino	200.00
111.	½ Zecchino	100.00

BURTUCCIO VALIER, 1656-1658

112.	1 Zecchino	22.50
113.	½ Zecchino	100.00
114.	¼ Zecchino	100.00

JOHN PESARO, 1658-1659

115.	1 Zecchino	60.00
116.	½ Zecchino	100.00
117.	¼ Zecchino	80.00

DOMINIC CONTARINI, 1659-1674

118.	1 Zecchino	25.00
119.	½ Zecchino	50.00
120.	¼ Zecchino	50.00

NICHOLAS SAGREDO, 1675-1676

121.	1 Zecchino	50.00
122.	½ Zecchino	100.00
123.	¼ Zecchino	100.00

ALOIS CONTARINI, 1676-1684

124.	1 Zecchino	22.50
125.	½ Zecchino	100.00
126.	¼ Zecchino	40.00

MARC ANTHONY GIUSTIMANI, 1684-1688

127.	1 Zecchino	22.50
128.	½ Zecchino	80.00
129.	¼ Zecchino	80.00

FRANCIS MOROSINI, 1688-1694

130.	10 Zecchini	350.00
131.	8 Zecchini	250.00
132.	6 Zecchini	200.00
133.	1 Zecchino	25.00
134.	½ Zecchino	50.00
135.	¼ Zecchino	50.00

SILVESTER VALIER, 1694-1700

135a.	25 Zecchini	1750.00
136.	15 Zecchini	500.00
137.	12 Zecchini	350.00
138.	10 Zecchini	300.00
139.	1 Zecchino	25.00
140.	½ Zecchino	80.00
141.	¼ Zecchino	80.00

ALOIS MOCENIGO II, 1700-1709

142.	10 Zecchini	300.00
143.	1 Zecchino	22.50
144.	½ Zecchino	40.00
145.	¼ Zecchino	40.00

JOHN CORNER II, 1709-1722

146.	36 Zecchini	2000.00
147.	33 Zecchini	1250.00
148.	25 Zecchini	850.00
149.	20 Zecchini	750.00
150.	16 Zecchini	500.00
151.	15 Zecchini	450.00
152.	12 Zecchini	350.00
153.	10 Zecchini	300.00
154.	8 Zecchini	250.00
155.	2 Zecchini	150.00
156.	1 Zecchino	25.00
157.	½ Zecchino	100.00
158.	¼ Zecchino	80.00

ALOIS MOCENIGO III, 1722-1732

159.	50 Zecchini	2500.00
160.	10 Zecchini	300.00
161.	4 Zecchini	500.00
162.	1 Zecchino	22.50
163.	½ Zecchino	20.00
164.	¼ Zecchino	15.00

CHARLES RUZZINI, 1732-1735

165.	10 Zecchini	400.00
166.	3 Zecchini	125.00
167.	1 Zecchino	25.00
168.	½ Zecchino	20.00
169.	¼ Zecchino	15.00

ALOIS PISANI, 1735-1741

170.	40 Zecchini	1750.00
171.	30 Zecchini	1250.00
172.	10 Zecchini	300.00
173.	1 Zecchino	25.00
174.	½ Zecchino	20.00
175.	¼ Zecchino	15.00

PETER GRIMANI, 1741-1752

176.	50 Zecchini	2500.00
177.	28 Zecchini	1250.00
178.	22 Zecchini	850.00
179.	15 Zecchini	450.00
180.	10 Zecchini	300.00
181.	2 Zecchini	75.00
182.	1 Zecchino	25.00
183.	½ Zecchino	20.00
184.	¼ Zecchino	15.00

FRANCIS LOREDANO, 1752-1762

185.	2 Zecchini	75.00
186.	1 Zecchino	25.00
187.	½ Zecchino	20.00
188.	¼ Zecchino	15.00

MARCO FOSCARINI, 1762-1763

189.	1 Zecchino	35.00
190.	½ Zecchino	30.00
191.	¼ Zecchino	25.00

ALOIS MOCENIGO IV, 1763-1778

192.	100 Zecchini	7500.00
193.	60 Zecchini	3000.00
194.	50 Zecchini	2500.00
195.	30 Zecchini	1250.00
196.	25 Zecchini	850.00
197.	20 Zecchini	750.00
198.	18 Zecchini	600.00
199.	12 Zecchini	350.00
200.	10 Zecchini	300.00
201.	8 Zecchini	275.00
202.	1 Zecchino	22.50
203.	½ Zecchino	20.00
204.	¼ Zecchino	15.00

PAUL RAINIER, 1779-1789

205.	50 Zecchini	2500.00
206.	40 Zecchini	2000.00
207.	30 Zecchini	1250.00
208.	24 Zecchini	850.00
209.	18 Zecchini	600.00
210.	12 Zecchini	350.00
211.	10 Zecchini	300.00
212.	8 Zecchini	275.00

213.	4 Zecchini	175.00
214.	1 Zecchino	22.50
215.	½ Zecchino	20.00
216.	¼ Zecchino	15.00

LOUIS MANIN, 1789-1797

217.	105 Zecchini		7500.00
218.	50 Zecchini		2500.00
219.	10 Zecchini	*	300.00
220.	9 Zecchini		300.00
221.	8 Zecchini		275.00
222.	6 Zecchini		200.00
223.	5 Zecchini		175.00
224.	2 Zecchini		75.00
225.	1 Zecchino		22.50
226.	½ Zecchino		20.00
227.	¼ Zecchino		15.00

(For Austrian type coins struck at Venice and bearing the "V" mint mark, see under Austria.)

TYPE II

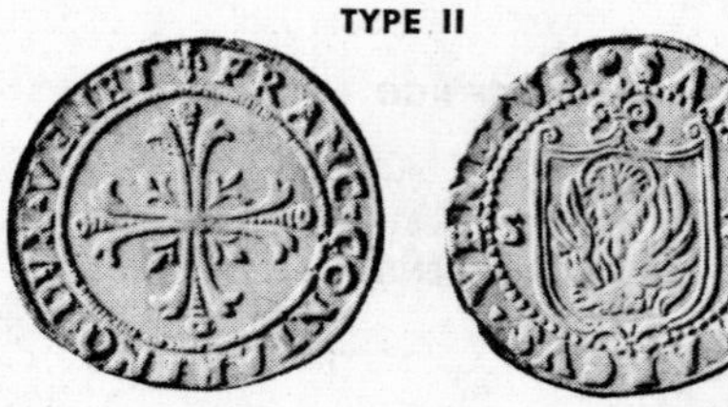

Cross. Rev. Lion in shield. The following coins are undated.

ANDREW GRITTI, 1523-1539

228.	1 Scudo d'oro	25.00
229.	½ Scudo d'oro	30.00

PETER LANDO, 1539-1545

230.	1 Scudo d'oro	40.00
231.	½ Scudo d'oro	100.00

FRANCIS DONA, 1545-1553

232.	1 Scudo d'oro	100.00
233.	½ Scudo d'oro	150.00

FRANCIS VENIER, 1554-1556

234.	1 Scudo d'oro	100.00
235.	½ Scudo d'oro	100.00

ANTHONY PRIULI, 1618-1623

236.	2 Scudi d'oro	350.00
237.	1 Scudo d'oro	400.00

FRANCIS CONTARINI, 1623-1624

238.	2 Scudi d'oro	*	150.00
239.	1 Scudo d'oro		200.00

JOHN CORNER I, 1625-1629

240.	2 Scudi d'oro	100.00
241.	1 Scudo, d'oro	100.00

NICHOLAS CONTARINI, 1630-1631

242.	2 Scudi d'oro	400.00
243.	1 Scudo d'oro	400.00

FRANCIS ERIZZO, 1631-1646

244.	2 Scudi d'oro	400.00
245.	1 Scudo d'oro	400.00

FRANCIS CORNER, 1656

246.	1 Scudo d'oro	400.00

BERTUCCIO VALIER, 1656-1658

247.	2 Scudi d'oro	400.00

NICHOLAS SAGREDO, 1675-1676

248.	2 Scudi d'oro	400.00

SILVESTER VALIER, 1694-1700

249.	2 Scudi d'oro	400.00
250.	1 Scudo d'oro	400.00

JOHN CORNER II, 1709-1722

251.	1 Scudo d'oro	400.00

ALOIS MOCENIGO III, 1722-1732

252.	½ Scudo d'oro	400.00

ITALY-VENICE (cont'd)

CHARLES RUZZINI, 1732-1735
253.	½ Scudo d'oro	400.00

ALOIS PISANI, 1735-1741
254.	2 Scudi d'oro	400.00
255.	½ Scudo d'oro	400.00

PETER GRIMANI, 1741-1752
256.	1 Scudo d'oro	400.00

FRANCIS LOREDANO, 1752-1762
257.	2 Scudi d'oro	400.00
258.	1 Scudo d'oro	400.00
259.	½ Scudo d'oro	300.00

MARCO FOSCARINÍ, 1762-1763
260.	2 Scudi d'oro	500.00
261.	1 Scudo d'oro	400.00
262.	½ Scudo d'oro	300.00

ALOIS MOCENIGO IV, 1763-1778
263.	2 Scudi d'oro	500.00
264.	1 Scudo d'oro	400.00
265.	½ Scudo d'oro	400.00

PAUL RAINIER, 1779-1789
266.	2 Scudi d'oro	400.00
267.	1 Scudo d'oro	400.00
268.	½ Scudo d'oro	400.00

LOUIS MANIN, 1789-1797
269.	2 Scudi d'oro	100.00
270.	1 Scudo d'oro	100.00
271.	½ Scudo d'oro	100.00

TYPE III

Doge kneeling before St. Mark seated. Rev. Lion. The following coins are undated.

LEONARDO DONA, 1605-1612
272.	2 Ducats	100.00
273.	1 Ducat ....*	60.00
274.	½ Ducat	35.00

NICHOLAS DONA, 1618
275.	1 Ducat	200.00

ANTHONY PRIULI, 1618-1623
276.	1 Ducat	60.00

JOHN CORNER I, 1625-1629
277.	1 Ducat	60.00

DOMINIC CONTARINI, 1659-1674
278.	10 Ducats	600.00

TYPE IV
Doge kneeling and lion. Rev. St. Justina standing.

LEONARDO DONA, 1605-1612
279.	1 Ducat ND	100.00

TYPE V
Doge kneeling before St. Mark. Rev. Christ on pedestal.

LEONARDO DONA, 1605-1612
280.	1 Ducat ND	75.00

TYPE VI
Cross. Rev. Arms.

ANDREW GRITTI, 1523-1539
281.	1 Scudo d'oro ND	75.00

PETER LANDO, 1539-1545
282.	1 Scudo d'oro ND	75.00

TYPE VII
Bust of Christ. Rev. St. Mark standing.

LEONARDO LOREDANO, 1501-1521
283.	¼ Ducat ND	50.00

TYPE VIII

Lion on pedestal. Rev. Value. Struck under the Provisional Government of Venice.

284.	20 Lire 1848	60.00

VENTIMIGLIA

Head of John VI. Rev. Arms.
1.	2 Zecchini 1725	2500.00

VERCELLI

Bust of Charles Emanuel of Sardinia. Rev. Legend. Siege Issue.
1.	4 Scudi d'oro 1617	500.00

Arms. Rev. Legend. Siege Issue.
2.	1 Doppia 1638	250.00

VERONA

HENRY II, 1013-1024
Cross on each side.
1.	1 Gold Denarius ND	2500.00

MAXIMILIAN I, 1509-1516

Bust. Rev. St. Zeno seated.
2.	1 Ducat ND	750.00

LATVIA (RIGA)

A. Archbishops of —
WILLIAM, 1554-1563
Bust. Rev. Arms.
1.	1 Ducat 1559	500.00

B. Polish Kings of —
STEPHAN BATHORI, 1576-1586

Bust. Rev. Riga City arms.

LATVIA (RIGA) (cont'd)

2. 10 Ducats 1586 ....* 2500.00
3. 5 Ducats 1586 .... 1000.00
4. 1 Ducat 1584, 85 .... 400.00

SIGISMUND III, 1587-1632

Bust. Rev. Riga City arms.

5. 1 Ducat 1588, 94, 97, 99, 1619 .... 250.00

C. Swedish Kings of —

GUSTAV ADOLPHE II, 1611-1632

Bust. Rev. Riga City arms.

6. 1 Ducat 1623 .... 2000.00

CHRISTINA, 1632-1654
Facing bust. Rev. Riga City arms.

7. 6 Ducats 1644 .... 1000.00
8. 5 Ducats 1644, 45 .... 1000.00
9. 3 Ducats 1643 .... 750.00

Bust left. Rev. Riga City arms.

10. 1 Ducat 1644 .... 250.00

Bust right. Rev. Riga City arms.

11. 4 Ducats 1646 .... 1250.00
12. 3 Ducats 1646 .... 1250.00
13. 2 Ducats 1646 ....* .. 500.00
14. 1 Ducat 1646 .... 200.00

CHARLES X, 1654-1660

Bust. Rev. City view of Riga.

15. 6 Ducats 1654 .... 1000.00
16. 5 Ducats 1654 ....* ... 1000.00

CHARLES XI, 1660-1697

Bust. Rev. Riga City arms.

17. 2 Ducats 1667 .... 300.00
18. 1 Ducat 1664, 73 ....* 175.00

CHARLES XII, 1697-1718

Bust. Rev. Riga City arms.

19. 1 Ducat 1701, 07 .... 250.00

LIECHTENSTEIN

Princes of —

CHARLES, 1614-1627
Bust. Rev. Arms.

1. 10 Ducats 1616 .... 1000.00
2. 6 Ducats 1617 .... 500.00
3. 5 Ducats 1615 .... 500.00
4. 4 Ducats 1618 .... 450.00
5. 3 Ducats 1614, 18 .... 300.00
6. 2 Ducats 1614, 16 .... 200.00
7. 1 Ducat 1614, 17, 18 .... 150.00

JOSEPH JOHN ADAM, 1721-1732
Bust. Rev. Arms.

8. 10 Ducats 1728 .... 1000.00
9. 1 Ducat 1728, 29 .... 150.00

JOSEPH WENZEL, 1748-1772

Armored bust. Rev. Arms.

10. 1 Ducat 1758 .... 150.00

FRANZ JOSEPH I, 1772-1781

Bust. Rev. Arms.

11. 1 Ducat 1778 .... 150.00

JOHN II, 1858-1929

Head. Rev. Arms.

12. 20 Kronen 1898, 1900 ....* ... 65.00
13. 10 Kronen 1898, 1900 .... 40.00

LIECHTENSTEIN (cont'd)

FRANZ I, 1929-1938

Head. Rev. Arms.

14.	20 Franken 1930	....	50.00
15.	10 Franken 1930	....	35.00

FRANZ JOSEPH II, 1938-

Head. Rev. Arms.

16.	20 Franken 1946	....	27.50
17.	10 Franken 1946	....	17.50

Conjoined heads of the Prince and Princess. Rev. Arms.

18.	100 Franken 1952	....	100.00
19.	50 Franken 1956	..........................*......	40.00
20.	25 Franken 1956	....	25.00

LITHUANIA

Polish Kings of —

SIGISMUND II, 1544-1572
Bust. Rev. Horseman.

1.	10 Ducats 1562	....	2000.00
2.	1 Ducat 1548-69	....	200.00

STEPHAN BATHORI, 1576-1586
Bust. Rev. Arms.

3.	1 Ducat 1586	....	600.00

SIGISMUND III, 1587-1632

Bust. Rev. Arms.

4.	10 Ducats 1604-22	....	500.00
5.	8 Ducats 1592	....	500.00
6.	5 Ducats 1618-22	..........................*......	350.00
7.	1 Ducat 1589, 90	....	250.00

LADISLAS IV, 1632-1648
Bust. Rev. Arms.

8.	10 Ducats 1639	....	Rare

JOHN CASIMIR, 1648-1668

Bust. Rev. Horseman.

9.	1 Ducat 1666	....	300.00
10.	½ Ducat 1664, 65	....	175.00

LIVONIA

A. Army Masters of —

WALTER, 1495-1535
Ruler standing. Rev. Madonna.

1.	10 Ducats 1525	....	1000.00

Ruler standing. Rev. Castle.

2.	2 Ducats 1528	....	350.00

Madonna. Rev. Castle.

3.	1 Ducat 1528	....	200.00

Arms. Rev. Crossed keys.

4.	½ Ducat 1533	....	125.00

HERMANN, 1535-1549
Madonna. Rev. Arms.

5.	1 Florin 1535	....	250.00

WILLIAM, 1557-1559
Madonna. Rev. Arms.

6.	1⅓ Ducats 1558, 59	....	350.00

GOTTHARD, 1559-1561

Armored bust. Rev. Christ over arms.

7.	2⅜ Ducats ND	..........................*......	500.00
8.	1⅜ Ducats ND	....	200.00

B. Swedish Rulers of —

CHRISTINA, 1632-1654

Facing bust. Rev. Arms.

9.	10 Ducats 1645	....	3000.00
10.	2 Ducats 1646	..........................*......	300.00
11.	1 Ducat 1645, 47, 48	..........................*......	150.00

LIVONIA (cont'd)

Bust right. Rev. Arms.

12. 1 Ducat 1648 .... **350.00**

LUXEMBOURG

Grand Dukes of —

HENRY II, 1246-1281
Lamb. Rev. Cross.

1. 1 Mouton d'or ND **200.00**

JOHN THE BLIND, 1310-1346
St. John. Rev. Lily.

2. 1 Florin ND **75.00**

Ruler standing. Rev. Cross.

3. 1 Franc à Pied ND **500.00**

Ruler on throne. Rev. Cross.

4. 1 Chaise d'or ND **150.00**

CHARLES IV, 1346-1354

Ruler on throne. Rev. Cross.

5. 1 Chaise d'or ND **150.00**

St. John. Rev. Lily.

6. 1 Florin ND **75.00**

WENCESLAS, 1354-1383

St. John. Rev. Lily.

7. 1 Florin ND **75.00**

Ruler under dais. Rev. Arms.

8. 1 Florin ND **125.00**

St. John. Rev. Eagle.

9. 1 Florin ND **100.00**

ELIZABETH, 1424-1444
St. Elizabeth. Rev. Two shields.

10. 1 Florin ND **200.00**

PHILIP OF BURGUNDY, 1444-1467
St. Philip and arms. Rev. Arms on cross.

11. 1 Ecu d'or 1502 .... **200.00**

PHILIP OF AUSTRIA, 1482-1506
Double eagle. Rev. Arms on cross.

12. 1 Couronne d'or 1502 .... **150.00**

PHILIP IV OF SPAIN, 1621-1665
Shield and cross. Rev. Arms.

13. 1 Couronne d'or 1632 .... **100.00**

CHARLOTTE, 1919-

Conjoined heads of Prince Jean of Luxembourg and Princess Josephine Charlotte of Belgium. Rev. Arms; on their marriage. Although without a mark of value, this coin has the same specifications as the standard 20 Franc piece of the Latin Monetary Union.

14. (20 Francs) 1953 .... **22.50**

MOLDAVIA

Princes of —

JOHN HERACLIDES
Crowned head. Rev. Arms.

1. 1 Ducat 1563 .... **500.00**

MONACO

Princes of —

LUCIANO, 1505-1523
Crowned arms. Rev. Cross.

1. 1 Scudo d'oro ND **1500.00**

HONORE II, 1604-1662

Bust. Rev. Cross of initials.

2. 2 Doppia 1649, 50 .... **800.00**
3. 1 Doppia 1648-60 ....*..... **600.00**
4. ½ Doppia 1650 .... **500.00**

Bust. Rev. Crowned initial.

5. 2 Doppia 1656 .... **1000.00**
6. 1 Doppia 1656, 61 .... **600.00**

Bust. Rev. Arms.

7. 5 Doppia 1649 .... **2000.00**

LOUIS I, 1662-1701
Bust. Rev. Two L's.

8. 4 Ducats 1663, 64 .... **1000.00**

HONORE V, 1819-1841

Head. Rev. Arms with supporters. These coins were not placed in circulation.

9. 40 Francs 1838 .... **350.00**
10. 20 Francs 1838 ....*...... **300.00**

CHARLES III, 1856-1889

Head. Rev. Arms.

11.	100 Francs 1882, 84, 86	....	100.00
12.	20 Francs 1878, 79	......................*	35.00

ALBERT, 1889-1922

Head. Rev. Arms. The 20 Franc piece was not placed in circulation.

13.	100 Francs 1891-1904	..........................*	100.00
14.	20 Francs 1892	....	300.00

LOUIS II, 1922-1949

(Souvenir gold coins struck from dies also used for minor coins).
Large bust. Rev. Arms.

15.	20 Francs 1947. Normal thickness	....	200.00
16.	20 Francs 1947. Double thickness	....	250.00
17.	10 Francs 1946. Normal thickness	....	150.00
18.	10 Francs 1946. Double thickness	....	200.00

Head. Rev. Arms.

19.	5 Francs 1945. Normal thickness	....	200.00
20.	5 Francs 1945. Double thickness	....	250.00
21.	2 Francs ND (1943)	....	125.00
22.	1 Franc ND (1943)	....	125.00

RAINIER III, 1949-

(Souvenir gold coins struck from dies also used for minor coins).

Head. Rev. Horseman.

23.	100 Francs 1950. Normal thickness	..............*	175.00
24.	100 Francs 1950. Double thickness	....	250.00
25.	50 Francs 1950. Normal thickness	....	150.00
26.	50 Francs 1950. Double thickness	....	175.00

Head. Rev. Arms.

27.	20 Francs 1950. Normal thickness	..............*	125.00
28.	20 Francs 1950. Double thickness	....	150.00
29.	10 Francs 1950. Normal thickness	..............*	100.00
30.	10 Francs 1950. Double thickness	....	125.00

New type head. Rev. Arms. Of smaller size than previous issues of this value.

31.	100 Francs 1956	....	85.00

MONTENEGRO

Kings of —

NICHOLAS I, 1860-1918

Plain head to right. Rev. Arms.

1.	100 Perpera 1910	....	400.00
2.	20 Perpera 1910	........................*	50.00
3.	10 Perpera 1910	........................*	30.00

Laureate head to left. Rev. Arms. On the 50th year of both his reign and marriage.

4.	100 Perpera 1910	....	600.00
5.	20 Perpera 1910	..........................*	50.00
6.	10 Perpera 1910	..........................*	30.00

NETHERLANDS

A. Kings of —

NAPOLEON, 1810-1814

(For French type coins struck in the Netherlands, see under France).

LOUIS NAPOLEON, 1806-1810

Head. Rev. Arms.

1.	20 Guilders 1808, 10	....	400.00
2.	10 Guilders 1808, 10	.........................*	225.00
3.	1 Ducat 1809, 10	.........................*	40.00

Head. Rev. Knight standing.

4.	1 Ducat 1808, 09	....	40.00

NETHERLANDS (cont'd)

Knight standing. Rev. Square tablet.

5. 2 Ducats 1806, 07, 08 ....* 75.00
6. 1 Ducat 1806, 07, 08 .... 35.00

WILLIAM I, 1813-1840

Head. Rev. Arms.

7. 10 Guilders 1818-40. Torch or lis mm. ....* 30.00
8. 10 Guilders 1824-29. B mm. 35.00
9. 5 Guilders 1827. Torch mm. 27.50
10. 5 Guilders 1826, 27. B mm. 22.50

WILLIAM II, 1840-1849

Head. Rev. Arms flanked by value.

11. 10 Guilders 1842 .... 150.00
12. 5 Guilders 1843 .... 50.00

*Head. Rev. Arms in wreath. Trade coins called "Negotiepenning".
The denomination is expressed by the weight of the coin in
grams and may be found on the Rev.*

13. 20 Guilders or 13.458 Grams 1848 .... 250.00
14. 10 Guilders or 6.729 Grams 1848 ....* 150.00
15. 5 Guilders or 3.3645 Grams 1848 .... 75.00

WILLIAM III, 1849-1890

Head. Rev. Arms in wreath. Trade coins or "Negotiepenning".

16. 20 Guilders or 13.458 Grams 1850, 51, 53 .....* 200.00
17. 10 Guilders or 6.729 Grams 1850, 51 .... 75.00
18. 5 Guilders or 3.3645 Grams 1850, 51 .... 50.00

Head. Rev. Arms flanked by value.

19. 10 Guilders 1875-89 .... 20.00

WILHELMINA, 1890-1948

*Girl head with long flowing hair. Rev. Arms. The first two dates
are rare.*

20. 10 Guilders 1892, 95, 97 .... 25.00

Large youthful head with coronet. Rev. Arms.

21. 10 Guilders 1898 .... 35.00

Small older head with coronet. Rev. Arms.

22. 10 Guilders 1911-17 .... 20.00
23. 5 Guilders 1912 .... 15.00

Mature head. Rev. Arms.

24. 10 Guilders 1925-33 .... 17.50

B. United Provinces of —, 1576-1806

*(The Issues of the United Provinces were succeeded by those of
the Batavian Republic, which see).*

*Heads of Ferdinand and Isabella of Spain. Rev. Arms on eagle.
The coins were struck about 1600 and are undated.*

25. CAMPEN.   2 Ducats 125.00
26.   1 Ducat 50.00
27. GELDERLAND. 2 Ducats 125.00
28. OVERYSSEL.   2 Ducats 100.00
29.   1 Ducat 50.00
30. WESTFRISIA. 2 Ducats 100.00
31. ZEELAND.   2 Ducats ....* 100.00
32.   1 Ducat 50.00
33. ZWOLLE.   2 Ducats 100.00
34.   1 Ducat 50.00

*Bust of Philip II of Spain. Rev. Arms. The coins were struck
about 1590 and are undated.*

NETHERLANDS (cont'd)

35.	BATENBURG.	1 Real d'Or	....	500.00
36.	GELDERLAND.	1 Real d'Or	.............*	75.00
37.		½ Real d'Or	....	40.00
38.		½ Real d'Or. "England" in title	....	125.00
39.	HOLLAND.	1 Real d'Or	....	75.00
40.		½ Real d'Or. Bust left	....	35.00
41.		½ Real d'Or. Bust right	....	150.00
42.	OVERYSSEL.	½ Real d'Or	....	60.00

Royal figure in ship. Rev. Rose in center of crowns.

43.	CAMPEN.	1 Noble ND (1600)	....	150.00
44.		½ Noble ND (1600)	....	75.00
45.		¼ Noble ND (1600)	....	100.00
46.	FRISIA.	1 Noble ND (1600)	....	250.00
47.		½ Noble ND (1600)	....	75.00
48.	GELDERLAND.	1 Noble 1579, ND	....	150.00
49.		½ Noble 1579, ND	....	75.00
50.	OVERYSSEL.	1 Noble 1583, ND	..........*	100.00
51.		¼ Noble 1585, ND	....	85.00
52.	UTRECHT.	1 Noble 1579	....	500.00
53.		½ Noble 1579	....	300.00
54.		¼ Noble 1579	....	150.00
55.	ZEELAND.	1 Noble 1583, 84, 85, ND	....	125.00
56.		½ Noble 1587, 94, 95, ND	....	100.00

Royal figure in ship. Rev. Sun.

57.	UTRECHT.	1 Noble ND (1600)	....	100.00
58.		½ Noble ND (1600)	....	50.00

Knight in ship holding seven shields. Rev. Rose and bundle of arrows.

59.	ZEELAND.	1 Noble 1586	....	500.00
60.		½ Noble 1586, 93, 95	....	250.00

Royal figure seated. Rev. Rose.

61.	CAMPEN.	2 Nobles or 1 Souverain d'or ND (1600)..		600.00
61a.		8 Nobles or 4 Souverain d'or ND (1600)..		Rare

Arms. Rev. Cross.

62.	BATENBURG.	1 Cruzado ND	....	250.00
63.	HOLLAND.	1 Couronne d'Or 1576, 80, ND	....	125.00
64.	UTRECHT.	1 Couronne d'Or 1573-80, ND	....	125.00
65.		2 Florins 1577		300.00

Eagle. Rev. Arms.

66.	DEVENTER.	1 Florin ND (1576-1612)	....	30.00
67.	ZWOLLE.	1 Florin ND (1576-1612)	....	30.00

Double eagle, Rev. Five shields.

68.	FRISIA.	1 Florin 1617, 18, 19	....	65.00

Orb. Rev. Three shields.

69.	CAMPEN.	1 Florin ND (1612-19)	....	40.00

Royal figure standing. Rev. Legend (plain or in tablet).

70.	CAMPEN.	2 Ducats 1650-58	..............*	100.00
71.		1 Ducat 1596-1676, ND	....	40.00
72.	DEVENTER.	1 Ducat 1603-66	....	75.00
73.	ZWOLLE.	2 Ducats 1655, 56, 62	....	75.00
74.		1 Ducat 1630-76	..............*	40.00

Royal figure standing. Rev. Three shields.

75.	CAMPEN.	1 Florin 1597	....	50.00

Royal figure standing. Rev. Arms.

76.	WESTFRISIA.	1 Ducat 1587-1606	....	40.00

Royal figure standing. Rev. Madonna.

77.	OVERYSSEL.	1 Ducat ND (1579)	....	40.00
78.	UTRECHT.	1 Ducat 1591. Figure between V-D	......	300.00
79.	ZWOLLE.	1 Ducat ND (1600)	....	40.00

William the Silent standing. Rev. Legend.

79a.	HOLLAND.	1 Ducat 1583	....	300.00

Knight standing with shield. Rev. Tablet.

80.	FRISIA.	1 Ducat 1604, 05	....	50.00

Knight standing. Rev. Tablet.

81.	FRISIA.	2 Ducats 1612, 61	....	100.00
82.		1 Ducat 1586-1676	....	40.00
83.	GELDERLAND.	2 Ducats 1656-1761	....	75.00
84.		1 Ducat 1586-1792	....	30.00
85.	HOLLAND.	2 Ducats 1646-1793	....	50.00
86.		1 Ducat 1586-1791	..............*	25.00
87.	OVERYSSEL.	1 Ducat 1593-1733	....	35.00
88.	UTRECHT.	2 Ducats 1652-1794	..............*	50.00
89.		1 Ducat 1587-1794	....	20.00
90.	WESTFRISIA.	2 Ducats 1662-1779	....	75.00
91.		1 Ducat 1607-1780	....	25.00
92.	ZEELAND.	2 Ducats 1646-84	....	60.00
93.		1 Ducat 1586-1763	....	30.00

Knight standing. Rev. Circle of shields.

94.	ZEELAND.	30 Guilders 1683, 84, 87	....	400.00

NETHERLANDS (cont'd)

Knight standing. Rev. Arms.

95. ZEELAND.   10 Ducats 1682-87 .... 500.00

Knight standing between F-D. Rev. Shield.

96. FRISIA.   1 Ducat ND (1600) 300.00

Horseman. Rev. Arms. Early style.

97. FRISIA.	2 Cavaliers 1583. Small type	150.00
98.	1 Cavalier 1582-99. Small type	75.00
99.	1 Cavalier 1607-20. Large type	75.00
100.	½ Cavalier 1585. Small type	125.00
101.	½ Cavalier 1620-44. Large type	75.00
102. GELDERLAND.	1 Cavalier 1582, ND. Small type	150.00
103.	1 Cavalier 1607-28. Large type	100.00
104.	½ Cavalier 1607-44	50.00
105. HOLLAND.	1 Cavalier 1607-32 ....*	125.00
106.	½ Cavalier 1607-45	65.00
107. OVERYSSEL.	1 Cavalier ND. Small type	300.00
108.	1 Cavalier 1607-20. Large type	125.00
109.	½ Cavalier 1606-16	65.00
110. UTRECHT.	1 Cavalier 1606-25	100.00
111.	½ Cavalier 1607-44 ....*	50.00
112. WESTFRISIA.	1 Cavalier 1621, 23	125.00
113.	½ Cavalier 1632-44	65.00
114. ZEELAND.	1 Cavalier 1606-44	125.00
115.	½ Cavalier 1610-48	60.00
116. ZWOLLE.	½ Cavalier 1644	60.00

Horseman. Rev. Arms. Modern style.

117. GELDERLAND.	14 Guilders 1750-62	60.00
118.	7 Guilders 1750-62 ....*	35.00
119. GRONINGEN.	14 Guilders 1761	60.00
120.	7 Guilders 1761	35.00
121. HOLLAND.	14 Guilders 1749-63	60.00
122.	7 Guilders 1749-63	35.00
123. OVERYSSEL.	14 Guilders 1760-63	65.00
124.	7 Guilders 1760-63	40.00
125. UTRECHT.	14 Guilders 1749-63 ....*	60.00
126.	7 Guilders 1749-63	35.00
127. WESTFRISIA.	14 Guilders 1749-63	60.00
128.	7 Guilders 1749-63	35.00
129. ZEELAND.	14 Guilders 1760-64	60.00
130.	7 Guilders 1760-64	35.00

C. Cities and States of —

Knight standing. Rev. Tablet and city shield.

1.	5 Ducats 1673	300.00
2.	4 Ducats 1673	250.00
3.	3 Ducats 1673	250.00
4.	1 Ducat 1673	60.00

BATAVIAN REPUBLIC

Knight standing. Rev. Tablet. This type was continued under the Kings of the Netherlands.

1.	2 Ducats 1795-1805 ....*......	75.00
2.	1 Ducat 1795-1805	30.00

BATENBURG

Barons of —

ANONYMOUS, 1400-1500
St. John. Rev. Orb.

1. 1 Florin ND 250.00

THIERRY II, 1432-1456
St. Peter. Rev. Floriated cross.

2. 1 Peter d'or ND 750.00

WILLIAM, 1556-1573
St. Stephen. Rev. Eagle shield.

3.	2 Ducats ND	150.00
4.	1 Ducat ND	100.00

St. Victor standing. Rev. Madonna.

5. 1 Ducat ND 75.00

Bust of Ferdinand. Rev. Madonna.

6. 1 Ducat ND 75.00

St. Michael. Rev. Ship.

7. 1 Angel 1561, 62 .... 100.00

Serpent on cross. Rev. Floriated cross.

8. 1 Couronne d'or ND 250.00

Arms. Rev. Cross. Portuguese style.

9. 1 Cruzado ND 175.00

NETHERLANDS-BATENBURG (cont'd)

HERMAN THIERRY, 1573-1612

Ruler standing. Rev. Arms.

10. 1 Ducat 1577, 78, 79 .... 100.00

Arms. Rev. Cross.

11. 1 Couronne d'or ND 150.00

Knight standing. Rev. Madonna.

12. 1 Ducat ND 75.00

Knight. Rev. Lion.

13. 1 Ducat ND 150.00

CAMPEN

St. John. Rev. Arms.

1. 1 Florin ND (1550) 60.00

DEVENTER

St. Lebuin. Rev. Orb.

1. 1 Florin 1488 .... 125.00
2. 1 Florin ND (1493-1519) 75.00

Double eagle. Rev. Orb.

3. 1 Florin 1523 .... 60.00

DEVENTER-CAMPEN-ZWOLLE

Orb. Rev. Three or four shields.

1. 1 Florin 1546, ND 65.00

Double eagle. Rev. Three helmeted shields.

2. 1 Florin 1566, 78 .... 125.00

Royal figure standing. Rev. Three shields and orb.

3. 1 Florin 1557 .... 200.00

DUURSTEDE

Head of Madelinus. Rev. Cross.

1. 1 Triens ND (650-750 A.D.) 125.00

FRANEKER

St. John. Rev. Orb.

1. 1 Florin 1491, 92, ND 100.00

GELDERLAND

Dukes of —

EDWARD, 1361-1371
Lamb. Rev. Cross.

1. 2 Mouton d'or 500.00

MARIE, 1361-1399
Bust under dais. Rev. Arms.

2. 1 Florin ND 75.00

Arms. Rev. Cross.

3. 1 Couronne d'or ND 250.00

WILLIAM I, 1377-1402
Bust under dais. Rev. Arms.

4. 1 Florin ND 40.00

Ruler on throne. Rev. Cross.

5. 1 Chaise d'or ND 500.00

REINALD IV, 1402-1423
St. John. Rev. Arms.

6. 1 Florin ND 40.00

Angel. Rev. Madonna.

7. 1 Florin ND 250.00

Madonna. Rev. Saint.

8. ½ Florin ND 200.00

ARNOLD, 1423-1473
Ruler standing. Rev. Four shields.

9. 1 Florin ND 125.00

St. John. Rev. Arms.

10. 1 Florin ND 40.00

St. John. Rev. Five shields.

11. 1 Florin ND 40.00

Horseman. Rev. Arms.

12. 1 Florin ND 40.00

CHARLES I, 1473-1477
St. Andrew. Rev. Arms.

13. 1 Florin ND 50.00

CHARLES II (MINORITY), 1477-1492
St. John. Rev. Arms.

14. 1 Florin ND. Struck in Roermond 150.00

CHARLES II, 1492-1538
St. John. Rev. Arms.

15. 1 Florin ND 40.00

Horseman. Rev. Arms.

16. 1 Florin ND 40.00

Christ. Rev. Three shields.

17. 1 Florin ND 250.00

NETHERLANDS-GELDERLAND (cont'd)

CHARLES V OF SPAIN, 1543-1555
Bust with sword and sceptre. Rev. Arms on eagle.

18.	1 Real d'or ND	125.00
19.	1 Florin ND	75.00

Arms. Rev. Cross.

20.	1 Couronne d'or 1544, 45, ND	100.00

PHILIP II OF SPAIN, 1555-1598
St. Andrew. Rev. Arms.

21.	1 Florin 1568	100.00

Arms between P-P. Rev. Cross.

22.	1 Couronne d'or 1572	250.00

GRONINGEN

St. John. Rev. Orb.

1.	1 Florin 1488, ND	100.00

St. John. Rev. Double eagle.

2.	1 Florin 1591	100.00

St. Martin. Rev. Orb.

3.	1 Florin ND	50.00
4.	½ Florin ND	50.00

'S-HEERENBERG

Counts of —

WILLIAM III, 1506-1511 OR OSWALD, 1511-1546

St. John. Rev. Four shields.

1.	1 Florin ND	175.00

WILLIAM IV, 1546-1586

St. Michael. Rev. Ship.

2.	1 Angel ND	125.00

Bust of St. Oswald. Rev. Madonna.

3.	1 Florin ND	175.00

St. Oswald standing. Rev. Arms.

4.	1 Florin ND	175.00
5.	1 Ducat 1577	175.00

FREDERICK, 1577-1580
Horse carriage. Rev. Cross.

6.	1 Florin 1579	150.00

St. Pancras standing. Rev. Madonna.

7.	1 Florin 1578, 79	150.00

HERMAN FREDERICK, 1627-1631
Bust. Rev. Four shields.

8.	1 Florin ND	150.00

St. Stephen. Rev. Arms.

9.	1 Florin ND	50.00

HOLLAND

Counts of —

WILLIAM V, 1346-1359
Lamb. Rev. Cross.

1.	2 Mouton d'or ND	250.00
2.	1 Mouton d'or ND	200.00

Ruler on throne. Rev. Cross.

3.	1 Chaise d'or ND *	50.00
4.	⅓ Chaise d'or ND	40.00

Ruler standing. Rev. Arms.

5.	1 Florin ND	50.00

Horseman. Rev. Cross.

6.	1 Rider ND	250.00

ALBERT, 1359-1404
Ruler on throne. Rev. Cross.

7.	1 Chaise d'or ND	75.00

Ruler standing. Rev. Arms.

8.	1 Florin ND	75.00

Arms. Rev. Cross.

9.	1 Couronne d'or ND	300.00

JOHN OF BRABANT, 1418-1427
Ruler on throne. Rev. Cross.

10.	1 Chaise d'or ND	100.00

JOHN OF BAVARIA, 1421-1425
Ruler on throne. Rev. Cross.

11.	1 Chaise d'or ND	100.00

St. John. Rev. Five shields.

12.	1 Florin ND	45.00

PHILIP THE GOOD, 1425-1467 (AS HEIR)
Ruler on throne. Rev. Cross.

13.	1 Chaise d'or ND	75.00
14.	½ Chaise d'or ND	50.00

PHILIP THE GOOD AND JACQUELINE, 1428-1433
Ruler on throne. Rev. Cross.

15.	1 Chaise d'or ND	100.00
16.	½ Chaise d'or ND	60.00

NETHERLANDS-HOLLAND (cont'd)

PHILIP THE GOOD, 1433-1467 (AS COUNT)

Lion. Rev. Arms.

17.	1 Lion d'or ND	60.00
18.	⅔ Lion d'or ND ....*	150.00

St. Andrew. Rev. Arms.

19.	1 Florin ND	200.00

Knight on horse. Rev. Arms on cross.

20.	1 Rider ND ....*	75.00
21.	½ Rider ND	75.00

MAXIMILIAN AND PHILIP, 1482-1494
Ruler on throne. Rev. Crowned arms.

22.	1 Real d'or ND	450.00

Ruler in ship. Rev. Arms on cross.

23.	1 Noble ND ....*	225.00
24.	½ Noble 1488	125.00

PHILIP THE FAIR, 1496-1506
Bust of St. Philip. Rev. Cross.

25.	1 Florin ND	35.00
26.	½ Florin ND	50.00

Full length figure. Rev. Arms on cross.

27.	1 Florin ND	75.00

CHARLES V OF SPAIN, 1515-1555
St. Philip. Rev. Cross.

28.	1 Florin ND	40.00

Bust with sword and orb. Rev. Arms on eagle.

29.	1 Real d'or ND ....*	75.00
30.	½ Real d'or ND	40.00
31.	1 Florin ND	30.00

Arms. Rev. Eagle in shield.

32.	½ Real d'or ND	50.00

Cross. Rev. Arms.

33.	1 Couronne d'or 1541-45, ND	65.00

PHILIP II OF SPAIN, 1555-1581
St. Andrew standing. Rev. Arms.

34.	1 Florin 1567, 68, 69	175.00

MIDDELBURG

Legend in circle. Rev. Blank. Square siege coins.

1.	4 Ducats 1573	400.00
2.	2 Ducats 1573	200.00
3.	1 Ducat 1573, 74 ....*	100.00

NYMEGEN

St. Stephen standing. Rev. Arms.

1.	2 Ducats ND (1500-56) ....*	125.00
2.	1 Florin ND (1499-1525)	50.00
3.	½ Florin ND (1500-26)	50.00

Type as above but with title of Charles V of Spain.

4.	1 Florin ND	250.00

St. Stephen seated. Rev. Arms.

5.	1 Florin 1557, 69	200.00

Arms. Rev. Double eagle.

6.	1 Florin 1620	150.00

UTRECHT

Bishops of —

FLORIS, 1379-1393

Bust in dais. Rev. Two shields.

1.	1 Florin ND	125.00

Bust in dais. Rev. Eagle on shield.

2.	1 Florin ND	125.00

NETHERLANDS-UTRECHT (cont'd)

Ruler seated. Rev. Cross.

3. 1 Chaise d'or ND 400.00

FREDERICK, 1394-1423
St. Peter. Rev. Arms.

4. 1 Florin ND 250.00

St. John. Rev. Arms.

5. 1 Florin ND 30.00

ZWEDER, 1425-1426
St. John. Rev. Five shields.

6. 1 Florin ND 500.00

RUDOLPH, 1426-1455
St. Martin. Rev. Arms.

7. 1 Florin ND 25.00

DAVID, 1455-1496
St. Martin. Rev. Arms.

8. 1 Florin ND 30.00

King David behind shield. Rev. Ornate floriated cross.

9. 2 Harpe d'or ND 100.00

Half length bust with harp. Rev. Arms.

10. 1 Harpe d'or 1492 .... 250.00

King David seated. Rev. Arms.

11. 1 Florin 1492 .... 125.00

Christ seated. Rev. Four shields.

12. 1 Florin ND 125.00

ENGELBERT, 1481-1483
St. Martin. Rev. Arms.

13. 1 Florin ND 200.00

FREDERICK, 1496-1516
St. John. Rev. Five shields.

14. 1 Florin ND 50.00

Christ seated. Rev. Four shields.

15. 1 Florin ND 250.00

PHILIP, 1517-1524
Seated figure. Rev. Arms.

16. 1 Florin ND 125.00

PHILIP II OF SPAIN, 1555-1579
St. Andrew. Rev. Arms.

17. 1 Florin 1568 .... 200.00

VIANEN

Lords of —

HENRY, 1556-1568
St. Michael. Rev. Arms on ship.

1. 1 Angel ND 100.00

Arms on each side.

2. 1 Courrone d'or ND 500.00

Bust of St. Henry. Rev. Madonna.

3. 1 Ducat ND 100.00

ZWOLLE

St. Michael. Rev. Orb.

1. 1 Florin ND (1488-1519) 60.00

NORWAY

A. Danish Kings of —

FREDERICK III, 1648-1670

Crowned bust facing. Rev. Lion.

1. 1 Ducat 1660 .... 250.00

Laureate bust. Rev. Lion.

2. 1 Portugaloser 1665, 68, 69 .... 2000.00
3. 2 Ducats 1665 ....*..... 250.00
4. 1 Ducat 1665, 68, 69 .... 175.00
5. ½ Ducat 1666, ND 100.00

CHRISTIAN V, 1670-1699

Laureate bust. Rev. Lion.

6. 4 Ducats 1671 .... 500.00
7. 3 Ducats 1671, 73, 77 .... 400.00

NORWAY (cont'd)

8. 2 Ducats 1673, ND ....* 250.00
9. 1 Ducat 1673, ND 150.00
10. ½ Ducat ND 100.00

Laureate head. Rev. Lion. Thick flan.

11. 2 Ducats ND 250.00

Ruler on horse. Rev. Lion.

12. 3 Ducats 1673 .... 400.00

Crowned C5 and lion. Rev. Long cross.

13. 1 Louis d'or 1673, 84, 85 ....* 500.00
14. ½ Louis d'or 1684, 85 .... 350.00

B. Swedish Kings of —

OSCAR II, 1872-1907

Head. Rev. Lion shield and two values.

15. 5 Species-20 Kronor 1874, 75 .... 50.00
16. 2½ Species-10 Kronor 1874 .... 50.00

Head. Rev. Lion shield.

17. 20 Kronor 1876-1902 .... 40.00
18. 10 Kronor 1877-1902 .... 30.00

C. Independent Kings of —

HAAKON VII, 1905-1957

Crowned head. Rev. St. Olaf standing.

19. 20 Kronor 1910 .... 40.00
20. 10 Kronor 1910 .... 25.00

POLAND

A. Kings of —

LADISLAS LOKIETEK, 1306-1333
King on throne. Rev. St. Stanislas.

1. 1 Ducat ND .... Rare

SIGISMUND I, 1506-1548
Bust. Rev. Arms.

2. 1 Ducat 1528-48 .... 150.00

STEPHAN BATHORI, 1576-1586
Bust. Rev. Arms.

3. 1 Ducat 1586 .... 500.00

SIGISMUND III, 1587-1632

Bust. Rev. Arms.

4. 100 Ducats 1621 .... 9000.00
5. 90 Ducats 1621 .... 5000.00
6. 60 Ducats 1621 .... 2500.00
7. 20 Ducats 1614, 17 .... 850.00
8. 10 Ducats 1588-1628, ND 450.00
9. 5 Ducats 1596-1623 ....* 250.00
10. 4 Ducats 1611, 12 .... 250.00
11. 3 Ducats 1612 .... 175.00
12. 2 Ducats 1610 .... 125.00
13. 1 Ducat 1588-1630, ND ....* 75.00

LADISLAS IV, 1632-1648

Bust. Rev. Arms.

14. 10 Ducats 1635, 36 .... 600.00
15. 5 Ducats 1642, 45, 47 .... 350.00
16. 1 Ducat 1639-44 ....* 75.00

JOHN CASIMIR, 1648-1668

Bust. Rev. Arms.

17. 10 Ducats 1661 .... 600.00
18. 5 Ducats 1649-52, ND 250.00
19. 2 Ducats 1650-67 ....* 125.00
20. 1 Ducat 1649-62 ....* 75.00
21. ½ Ducat 1653-62, ND 35.00

Bust. Rev. Eagle.

22. 2 Ducats 1650 .... 175.00

Ruler standing. Rev. Arms.

23. 1 Ducat 1649 .... 125.00

POLAND (cont'd)

MICHAEL KORYBUT, 1669-1673

Bust. Rev. Arms.

24. 2 Ducats 1671 .... 300.00

JOHN III SOBIESKI, 1674-1696

Bust. Rev. Arms.

25. 2 Ducats ND 200.00
26. 1 Ducat 1682, 83 ....* 200.00

AUGUST II AND AUGUST III, 1697-1763

(See under Germany-Saxony).

STANISLAS AUGUST, 1764-1795

Head. Rev. Arms.

27. 3 Ducats 1794 ....* 200.00
28. 1½ Ducats 1794 .... 125.00
29. 1 Ducat 1765. Armored bust 200.00

Initials on star. Rev. Arms.

30. 1 Ducat 1766 .... 150.00

Head. Rev. Value in square.

30a. 1 Ducat 1766-79 .... 65.00

Ruler standing. Rev. Value in square.

31. 1 Ducat 1766, 67, 70, 71, 72 .... 85.00

Head. Rev. Legend.

31a. 1 Ducat 1780-95 .... 60.00

B. Russian Czars of —

ALEXANDER I

Plain head. Rev. Eagle.

32. 50 Zloty 1817-19. Oblique milling ....* 85.00
33. 25 Zloty 1817-19. Oblique milling 50.00
34. 50 Zloty 1820-23. Straight milling 85.00
35. 25 Zloty 1820-25. Straight milling ....* 50.00

Laureate head. Rev. Value and date in wreath.

36. 50 Zloty 1827-29 .... 125.00
37. 25 Zloty 1828-33 .... 75.00

NICHOLAS I

Eagle. Rev. Two values as indicated.

38. 20 Zloty-3 Roubles 1834-40 .... 30.00

C. Revolution 1830-1831

Knight standing. Rev. Tablet. Dutch type coin counterstamped with a small eagle.

39. 1 Ducat 1831 .... 40.00

D. Republic of —

Crowned head of Boleslaus. Rev. Eagle. On the 900th Anniversary of Poland.

40. 20 Zloty 1925 .... 50.00
41. 10 Zloty 1925 .... 30.00

E. Cities of —

GNESEN

Bishops of —

STANISLAUS SZEMBEK, 1706-1721

Bust. Rev. Arms.

1. 1 Ducat 1721 .... 250.00

KRAKAU

Bishops of —

CAJETAN SOLTYK, 1759-1782

Bust. Rev. Legend.

1. 1 Ducat 1762 .... 250.00

THORN

Polish Kings of —

SIGISMUND III, 1587-1632

Bust. Rev. Arms.

1. 1 Ducat 1630 .... 85.00

City view. Rev. Legend.

2. 5 Ducats 1629 .... 300.00

LADISLAS IV, 1632-1648

Bust. Rev. Arms.

3. 1 Ducat 1633-48 .... 75.00

JOHN CASIMIR, 1648-1668

Bust. Rev. Arms.

4. 2 Ducats 1660-68 ....* 125.00
5. 1 Ducat 1649-67 .... 75.00

Bust. Rev. City view.

6. 5 Ducats 1655, 59 ....* 300.00
7. 4 Ducats 1655 .... 300.00
8. 3 Ducats 1655 .... 250.00

MICHAEL KORYBUT, 1669-1673

Bust. Rev. Arms.

9. 2 Ducats 1671 .... 300.00

Bust. Rev. City view.

10. 2 Ducats 1670, ND 150.00

AUGUST II OF SAXONY, 1697-1733

Bust. Rev. Arms.

11. 1 Ducat 1702 .... 150.00

WARSAW

Saxon Grand Dukes of —

FREDERICK AUGUST

Head. Rev. Arms.

1. 1 Ducat 1812, 13 .... 50.00

PORTUGAL

Kings of —

SANCHO I, 1185-1211

Ruler on horse. Rev. Cross of five shields with a star in each angle.

1. 1 Morabitino ND 250.00

ALFONSO II, 1211-1223
Ruler on horse. Rev. Cross of five shields with three stars and a cross in angles.

2. 1 Morabitino ND 3000.00

SANCHO II, 1223-1248
Ruler on horse. Rev. Cross of five shields.

3. 1 Morabitino ND 2000.00

ALFONSO III, 1248-1279
Ruler on horse. Rev. Cross of five shields.

4. 1 Morabitino ND 750.00

PEDRO I, 1357-1367
(Dobras and Half Dobras are mentioned in contemporary documents as existing, but no specimen of either coin has yet been discovered.)

PORTUGAL (cont'd)

FERDINAND, 1367-1383
Ruler standing. Rev. Ornate floriated cross in quadrilobe.

5. 1 Dobra ND 750.00

Ruler standing. Rev. Cross of five shields in circle.

6. 1 Dobra ND ....* 500.00
7. ½ Dobra ND 3000.00

DUARTE, 1433-1438
Crowned E in octolobe. Rev. Crowned shield.

8. 1 Escudo ND .... Unique

ALFONSO V, 1438-1481

Arms. Rev. Cross in ornamental frame.

9. 1 Cruzado ND 100.00

Crown over ALFQ. Rev. Shield.

10. 1 Escudo ND 1500.00

Crowned shield. Rev. Castle. Struck for Ceuta.

11. ½ Escudo ND .... Unique

Crowned shield. Rev. Quartered arms. Struck for Toro.

12. 1 Escudo ND .... Unique

JOHN II, 1481-1495

Ruler on throne. Rev. Shield.

13. 1 Justo ND 600.00

Ruler standing. Rev. Shield.

14. 1 Justo ND 1500.00

Hand holding sword. Rev. Arms.

15. ½ Justo ND 175.00

Arms. Rev. Cross in ornamental frame.

16. 1 Cruzado ND 60.00

MANUEL I, 1495-1521

Arms. Rev. Cross.

17. 1 Portuguez (10 Ducats) ND 1000.00
18. 1 Cruzado ND ....* 60.00
19. ¼ Cruzado ND 1500.00

JOHN III, 1521-1557
Arms. Rev. Cross.

20. 1 Portuguez ND 1000.00
21. 1 Cruzado ND 75.00

Arms. Rev. Cross of Calvary.

22. 1 Calvario ND 75.00

St. Vincent standing. Rev. Arms.

23. 1 San Vicente ND ....* 175.00
24. ½ San Vicente ND 150.00

SEBASTIAN, 1557-1578

St. Vincent standing. Rev. Arms.

25. 1 San Vicente ND 175.00
26. ½ San Vicente ND ....* 200.00

Arms. Rev. Cross of Jerusalem.

27. 1 Engenhoso 1562, 63, 65, ND. (Long cross) ...* 200.00
28. ½ Engenhoso ND. (Long cross) 1500.00
29. 500 Reis (1 Cruzado) ND. (Short cross) ....* 40.00

HENRY I, 1578-1580

Arms. Rev. Cross of Jerusalem.

30. 500 Reis ND. (1 Cruzado) 500.00

THE GOVERNORS, 1580

Arms. Rev. Cross of Jerusalem.

31. 1 Cruzado ND 750.00

ANTONIO I, 1580-1583
Arms. Rev. Cross of Jerusalem.

32. 500 Reis ND. (1 Cruzado) 2500.00

Arms. Rev. Floriated cross. Struck for the Azores.

33. 2000 Reis ND 1500.00
34. 1000 Reis ND 600.00

Arms. Rev. Cross of St. George. Struck for the Azores.

35. 1000 Reis ND 2500.00

PHILIP I OF SPAIN, 1580-1598
Arms. Rev. Cross of St. George.

36. 4 Cruzados ND 1000.00
37. 2 Cruzados ND 500.00
38. 1 Cruzado ND 500.00

Arms. Rev. Cross of Jerusalem.

39. 500 Reis ND 1500.00

PHILIP II OF SPAIN, 1598-1621

Arms. Rev. Cross of St. George.

40. 4 Cruzados ND 300.00
41. 2 Cruzados ND 500.00
42. 1 Cruzado ND ....*...... 500.00

PHILIP III OF SPAIN, 1621-1640

Arms. Rev. Cross of St. George.

43. 4 Cruzados ND ....*...... 250.00
44. 2 Cruzados ND 500.00
45. 1 Cruzado ND 500.00

JOHN IV, 1640-1656

Arms. Rev. Cross of St. George.

46. 4 Cruzados 1642-52 ....*...... 275.00
47. 2 Cruzados 1642, 46, 47 .... 250.00
48. 1 Cruzado 1642, 47 .... 300.00

Laureate bust. Rev. Arms on cross. This coin was not placed in circulation.

49. 4 Cruzados 1650 ....Unknown

ALFONSO VI, 1656-1683
(4 and 2 Cruzado pieces were struck, but all known specimens are counterstamped. They are listed under Brazil).

Arms. Rev. Cross of Jerusalem. 1000 Reis pieces were also struck, but all known pieces are counterstamped. They are listed under Brazil.

50. 4000 Reis 1663 .... 600.00
51. 2000 Reis 1663 .... 500.00

PETER, PRINCE REGENT, 1667-1683

Arms. Rev. Cross in quadrilobe.

52. 4400 Reis 1668-74 ....*...... 250.00
53. 2200 Reis 1668, 69, 74 .... 300.00
54. 1100 Reis 1668, 71 .... 400.00

Arms. Rev. Cross.

55. 4000 Reis 1677-82 .... 100.00
56. 2000 Reis 1677-81 .... 75.00
57. 1000 Reis 1677-81 ....*...... 100.00

PETER II, 1683-1706
Arms. Rev. Cross.

58. 4000 Reis 1688-1706 .... 75.00
59. 2000 Reis 1683-1704 .... 60.00
60. 1000 Reis 1683-1706 .... 30.00

JOHN V, 1706-1750

Bust. Rev. Arms. The 24 and 16 Escudo pieces were not placed in circulation.

61. 24 Escudos 1731 .... Rare
62. 16 Escudos 1731 .... Rare
63.   8 Escudos 1717-32 .... 175.00
64.   4 Escudos 1722. L mm. 175.00
65.   4 Escudos 1723-50. No mm. ....*...... 60.00

66.	2 Escudos 1722. L mm.	....	150.00
67.	2 Escudos 1723-50. No mm.	....	50.00
68.	1 Escudo 1722. L mm.	....	75.00
69.	1 Escudo 1723-49. No mm.	....	25.00
70.	½ Escudo 1722. L mm.	....	20.00
71.	½ Escudo 1723-50. No mm.	....	12.50

Arms. Rev. Cross. The 8000 Reis piece was not placed in circulation.

72.	8000 Reis 1711	....	Rare
73.	4000 Reis 1707-22. No mm.	....	50.00
73a.	4000 Reis 1712, 13, 14. P mm.	....	100.00
73b.	2000 Reis 1707-25. No mm.	....	30.00
73c.	2000 Reis 1713, 14. P mm.	............*	100.00
74.	1000 Reis 1707-47. No mm.	....	20.00
75.	1000 Reis 1713. P mm.	....	175.00

Cross. Rev. crown over name.

76.	400 Reis 1717-48	....	12.50

JOSEPH I, 1750-1777

Bust. Rev. Arms.

77.	4 Escudos 1750-76		60.00
78.	2 Escudos 1751-76	.........................*	75.00
79.	1 Escudo 1751-76	....	30.00
80.	½ Escudo 1751-76	....	15.00

Arms. Rev. Cross.

81.	1000 Reis 1749-69	....	17.50

Cross. Rev. Crown over name.

82.	400 Reis 1752-76	....	12.50

MARY I AND PETER III, 1777-1786

Conjoined busts. Rev. Arms.

83.	4 Escudos 1778-85	.........................*	60.00
84.	2 Escudos 1778, 84	....	60.00
85.	1 Escudo 1777-85	....	30.00
86.	½ Escudo 1777-84	....	22.50

Arms. Rev. Cross.

87.	1000 Reis 1777-84	....	20.00

Cross. Rev. Crown over name.

88.	400 Reis 1777-85	....	15.00

MARY I, 1786-1816

Bust with widow's veil. Rev. Arms.

89.	4 Escudos 1786, 87	....	80.00
90.	1 Escudo 1787	....	100.00
91.	½ Escudo 1787, 88	....................*	100.00

Bust with ornamental headdress. Rev. Arms.

92.	4 Escudos 1789-99	.......................*	60.00
93.	2 Escudos 1789	....	75.00
94.	1 Escudo 1789-96	....	30.00
95.	½ Escudo 1789-96	....	20.00

Arms. Rev. Cross.

96.	1000 Reis 1787, 89, 92		20.00

Cross. Rev. Crown over name.

97.	400 Reis 1787-96	....	15.00

JOHN, PRINCE REGENT, 1799-1816

Bust. Rev. Plain arms.

98.	4 Escudos 1802	....	125.00

Bust. Rev. Ornamental arms.

99.	4 Escudos 1804-17	....	60.00
100.	2 Escudos 1805, 07	....	60.00
101.	1 Escudo 1807	........................*	50.00
102.	½ Escudo 1805, 06, 07	....	30.00

Cross. Rev. Crown over name.

103.	400 Reis 1807	....	50.00

JOHN VI, 1816-1826

Bust. Rev. Arms.

PORTUGAL (cont'd)

104.	4 Escudos 1819-24	....	60.00
105.	2 Escudos 1818-22	............................*	40.00
106.	1 Escudo 1818, 19, 21	....	60.00
107.	½ Escudo 1818-21	....	30.00

Arms. Rev. Cross.

| 108. | 1000 Reis 1818, 19, 21 | .... | 60.00 |

Cross. Rev. Crown over name.

| 109. | 400 Reis 1818-21 | .... | 40.00 |

PETER IV, 1826-1828

Laureate head. Rev. Arms.

| 110. | 4 Escudos 1826-28 | .... | 100.00 |
| 111. | 2 Escudos 1827 | ....* | 85.00 |

MICHAEL I, 1828-1834

Small laureate bust. Rev. Arms in clinging palms.

| 112. | 4 Escudos 1828 | ....* | 100.00 |
| 113. | 2 Escudos 1828 | .... | 85.00 |

Large laureate bust with collar. Rev. Arms in spreading palms.

| 114. | 4 Escudos 1830, 31, 32 | ....* | 80.00 |
| 115. | 2 Escudos 1830, 31 | .... | 75.00 |

MARY II, 1834-1853

Head with upswept hair. Rev. Arms.

| 116. | 4 Escudos 1833 | .... | 200.00 |

Draped bust with diadem. Rev. Arms.

| 117. | 4 Escudos 1833, 34, 35 | .... | 80.00 |

Head. Rev. Arms.

118.	5000 Reis 1836-51	........................*	35.00
119.	2500 Reis 1836-53	....	25.00
120.	1000 Reis 1851	....	17.50

During this reign, the Brazilian 20,000 Reis pieces of the Minas Mint, 1724-27, were counterstamped with the arms of Portugal, giving these coins a decreed legal value of 30,000 Reis.

| 121. | 20,000 Reis 1724-27. Counterstamped | .... | 350.00 |

PETER V, 1853-1861

Head. Rev. Arms. The 10,000 Reis piece was not placed in circulation.

122.	10000 Reis 1861	....	Rare
123.	5000 Reis 1860, 61	........................*	35.00
124.	2000 Reis 1856-60	....	25.00
125.	1000 Reis 1855	....	17.50

LOUIS I, 1861-1889

Young head. Rev. Small arms in palms.

| 126. | 5000 Reis 1862, 63 | ....* | 40.00 |
| 127. | 2000 Reis 1864, 65, 66 | .... | 25.00 |

Older head. Rev. Large draped arms.

128.	10000 Reis 1878-89	........................*	75.00
129.	5000 Reis 1867-89	........................*	35.00
130.	2000 Reis 1868-88	....	17.50

Head. Rev. Value.

| 131. | 1000 Reis 1879 | .... | 75.00 |

CARLOS I, 1889-1908

Head. Rev. Arms. This coin was not placed in circulation.

| 132. | 5000 Reis 1895 | .... | Rare |

PORTUGAL (cont'd)

Republic, 1910-1926

Seated female. Rev. Arms. This coin was not placed in circulation.

133. 5 Escudos 1920 .... **Rare**

ROUMANIA

Kings of —

CAROL I, 1866-1914

Young head with side whiskers. Rev. Value.

1. 20 Lei 1867, 68 .... 250.00

Older head with whiskers. Rev. Value.

2. 20 Lei 1870 .... 35.00

Head. Rev. Arms.

3. 20 Lei 1883-90 .... 22.50

Old head of 1906. Rev. Young head of 1867. On the 40th year of reign.

4. 100 Lei 1906 ....*...... 200.00
5. 20 Lei 1906 .... 35.00

Uniformed bust. Rev. Ruler on horse. On the 40th year of reign.

6. 50 Lei 1906 .... 85.00

Uniformed bust. Rev. Eagle. On the 40th year of reign.

7. 25 Lei 1906 ....*...... 40.00
8. 12½ Lei 1906 ....*...... 22.50

FERDINAND I, 1914-1927

Head. Rev. Arms. On his Coronation.

9. 100 Lei 1922 ....*...... 250.00
10. 20 Lei 1922 .... 50.00

Crowned bust. Rev. Crowned bust of Marie. On his Coronation.

11. 50 Lei 1922 .... 125.00
12. 25 Lei 1922 ....*...... 60.00

CAROL II, 1930-1940

Commemorative Coins on the Centennial of Birth of Carol I.

Head. Rev. Large arms.

13. 100 Lei 1939 .... 300.00
14. 20 Lei 1939 ....*...... 100.00

Head. Rev. Angel over shield.

15. 100 Lei 1939 .... 300.00

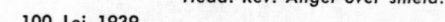

Head. Rev. Eagle over shield.

16. 20 Lei 1939 .... 100.00

Commemorative Coins on the 10th year of his Reign.

Head and legena within ornamental circle. Rev. Small crown over large monogram.

17. 100 Lei 1940 .... 325.00
18. 20 Lei 1940 ....*...... 100.00

ROUMANIA (cont'd)

Head and legend only. Rev. Large crown over small monogram.

19.	100 Lei 1940	300.00
20.	20 Lei 1940	100.00

Special Issue of 1944

Conjoined heads of three Roumanian Kings, with dates 1601, 1918, 1944. Rev. Eagle within circle of shields. Although without the mark of value, this coin has the same specifications as the standard 20 Lei coin.

21.	(20 Lei) 1944	22.50

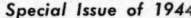

RUSSIA

Czars of —

IVAN IV, THE TERRIBLE, 1533-1584
Eagle on each side.

1.	5 Ducats ND	Rare

Eagle. Rev. Legend.

2.	4 Gold Grivnas ND	1000.00
3.	2 Gold Grivnas ND	750.00
4.	1 Gold Grivna ND	500.00
5.	½ Gold Grivna ND	350.00

THEODORE, 1584-1598
Eagle. Rev. Legend.

6.	1 Ducat ND	500.00

Ruler on horse. Rev. Legend.

7.	1 Ducat ND	500.00
8.	⅔ Ducat ND	350.00

BORIS GODUNOV, 1598-1605
Bust with sceptre. Rev. Eagle.

9.	1 Ducat ND	1500.00

DEMETRIUS (PRETENDER), 1604-1606
Bust with sceptre. Rev. Eagle.

10.	12 Ducats ND	Rare

Eagle on each side.

11.	10 Ducats ND	Rare
12.	1½ Ducats ND	500.00

Ruler on horse. Rev. Legend.

13.	1 Gold Grivna ND	300.00
14.	½ Gold Grivna ND	300.00

BASIL SHUISKY, 1606-1610
St. George. Rev. Eagle.

15.	5 Ducats ND	Rare
16.	1 Ducat ND	750.00

Eagle. Rev. Legend.

17.	1 Gold Grivna ND	300.00

Ruler on horse. Rev. Legend.

18.	1 Gold Grivna ND	...........................*	250.00
19.	½ Gold Grivna ND	....	200.00

LADISLAS, 1610-1612

Ruler on horse. Rev. Legend.

20.	1 Gold Grivna ND	250.00

MICHAEL, 1613-1645

Eagle on each side.

21.	3 Ducats ND	...........................*	500.00
22.	2 Ducats ND	....	350.00
23.	1 Ducat ND	....	200.00
24.	⅔ Ducat ND	....	200.00

Eagle. Rev. Legend.

25.	1½ Gold Grivnas ND	250.00

Ruler on horse. Rev. Legend.

26.	1 Gold Grivna ND	...........................*	250.00
27.	½ Gold Grivna ND	....	200.00

ALEXIUS, 1645-1676
Eagle on each side.

28.	10 Ducats ND	Rare
29.	3 Ducats ND	1000.00
30.	2 Ducats ND	1000.00
31.	1 Ducat ND	750.00

Bust with sceptre. Rev. Bust of Christ.

32.	4 Ducats ND	Rare
33.	2 Ducats ND	Rare

Eagle. Rev. Legend.

34.	⅔ Ducat ND	....	300.00
35.	½ Ducat ND	....	300.00
36.	⅓ Ducat ND	....	200.00
37.	1 Gold Grivna 1654, ND	..................*	250.00
38.	½ Gold Grivna ND	....	150.00

THEODORE ALEXEIVITCH, 1676-1682

Eagle on each side.

39.	1 Ducat ND	300.00

RUSSIA (cont'd)

SOPHIA, REGENT FOR PETER I, 1682-1689

Bust of Sophia. Rev. Busts of Peter I and Ivan V.

40.	5 Ducats ND	2500.00
41.	3 Ducats ND	1000.00
42.	2 Ducats ND	500.00
43.	1 Ducat ND ....*	350.00
44.	⅔ Ducat ND	300.00
45.	½ Ducat ND	200.00
46.	1 Gold Grivna ND ....*	200.00

Eagle. Rev. Legend.

47.	4 Ducats ND	500.00

Eagle on each side.

48.	2 Ducats ND	250.00
49.	1½ Ducats ND	250.00
50.	1 Ducat ND	200.00

IVAN V, REGENT FOR PETER I, 1682-1689
Eagle on each side.

51.	9 Ducats ND	Rare
52.	6 Ducats ND	Rare

Ruler on horse. Rev. Legend.

53.	½ Gold Grivna ND	150.00

PETER I, THE GREAT, 1682-1725

Bust. Rev. Eagle.

54.	12 Ducats 1702. Dated March 1	2000.00
55.	10 Ducats 1702. Dated March 1	1500.00
56.	8 Ducats 1702. Dated February 1	1250.00
57.	8 Ducats 1702. Dated March 1	1500.00
58.	6 Ducats 1702. Dated February 1	800.00
59.	5 Ducats 1702. Dated February 1	750.00
59a.	4 Ducats 1714 ....*	500.00
60.	3 Ducats 1702. Dated February 1	500.00
61.	2 Ducats 1701, 14	500.00
62.	1 Ducat 1701-07. Date in Slavic numerals	200.00
63.	1 Ducat 1710-16. Date in Cardinal numerals ...*	150.00

Bust. Rev. St. Andrew.

64.	2 Roubles 1718-25	75.00

Bust. Rev. Ruler on horse.

65.	1 Ducat 1708	250.00

Crown on cushion. Rev. Crown and legend. On his Coronation.

66.	1 Ducat 1724	100.00

CATHERINE I, 1725-1727

Bust. Rev. St. Andrew.

67.	2 Roubles 1726, 27	150.00

PETER II, 1727-1730

Bust. Rev. Eagle.

68.	1 Ducat 1729	150.00

Crown on pedestal. Rev. Crown over legend. On his Coronation.

69.	1 Ducat 1728	100.00

Bust. Rev. St. Andrew.

70.	2 Roubles 1727, 28	75.00

ANNE, 1730-1740

Bust. Rev. Eagle.

71.	1 Ducat 1730, 38, 39	125.00

Crown. Rev. Legend. On her Coronation.

72.	1 Ducat 1730	100.00

Crowned bust. Rev. Eagle and trophies. On the Peace with Turkey.

73.	1 Ducat 1739	150.00

Crowned bust. Rev. Legend. On her death.

74.	1 Ducat 1740	150.00

ELIZABETH, 1741-1762

Bust. Rev. St. Andrew.

75.	2 Ducats 1749, 51 ....*	150.00
76.	1 Ducat 1749-53	75.00

Bust. Rev. Eagle.

77.	2 Ducats 1747-51	125.00
78.	1 Ducat 1742-57 ....*	75.00
79.	5 Roubles 1755	175.00
80.	2 Roubles 1756-58	60.00
81.	1 Rouble 1756-58	40.00

RUSSIA (cont'd)

Bust. Rev. Crowned initials.

82. ½ Rouble or Poltina 1755, 56 .... 30.00

Bust. Rev. Eagle to left on clouds. This issue was not placed in circulation.

83. 2 Roubles 1756 .... 200.00
84. 1 Rouble 1756 .... 150.00

Bust. Rev. Cross of four shields.

85. 20 Roubles 1755 .... 2000.00
86. 10 Roubles 1755-59 ....*...... 150.00
87. 10 Roubles 1757. Larger bust 250.00
88. 5 Roubles 1755-59 .... 100.00

Tomb. Rev. Crown over legend. On her death.

89. 1 Ducat 1761 .... 100.00

PETER III, 1762

Bust. Rev. Cross of four shields.

90. 10 Roubles 1762 .... 250.00
91. 5 Roubles 1762 ....*...... 175.00

Bust. Rev. Eagle.

92. 1 Ducat 1762 .... 150.00

CATHERINE II, THE GREAT, 1762-1796

Bust. Rev. Cross of four shields.

93. 10 Roubles 1762-96 ....*...... 100.00
94. 5 Roubles 1762-96 .... 75.00

Bust. Rev. Eagle.

95. 10 Ducats 1762 .... 1500.00
96. 2 Ducats 1796 .... 200.00
97. 1 Ducat 1762-96 .... 60.00
98. 2 Roubles 1766-86 ....*...... 50.00
99. 1 Rouble 1779 .... 50.00

Bust. Rev. Crowned initials.

100. ½ Rouble or Poltina 1777, 78 .... 25.00

Crown. Rev. Legend. On her Coronation.

101. 1 Ducat 1762 .... 75.00

Bust. Rev. Flying eagle.

102. 1 Ducat 1766 .... 75.00

Ceres seated. Rev. Caduceus. On the Peace with Turkey.

103. 1 Ducat 1774 .... 75.00

Olive Branch. Rev. Legend. On the Peace with Sweden.

104. 1 Ducat 1790 .... 75.00

PAUL I, 1796-1801

Cross of four crowned initials. Rev. Tablet.

105. 5 Roubles 1798-1801 ....*..... 75.00
106. 1 Ducat 1797 .... 75.00

Eagle. Rev. Tablet.

107. 1 Ducat 1796 .... 75.00

ALEXANDER I, 1801-1825

Cross of four shields. Rev. Legend.

108. 10 Roubles 1802-05, 09 ....*...... 150.00
109. 5 Roubles 1802-05 .... 100.00

Eagle. Rev. Legend in wreath.

110. 5 Roubles 1817-25 .... 50.00

NICHOLAS I, 1825-1855

Conjoined busts of the Czar and Czarina. Rev. As indicated. These coins were not placed in circulation.

111. 10 Roubles 1836. Rev. Initials 450.00
112. 10 Roubles 1836. Rev. Value and date ....*...... 500.00

Eagle. Rev. Legend in four lines.

113. 5 Roubles 1826-31 .... 50.00

Eagle. Rev. Value and date.

114. 5 Roubles 1832-55 .... 40.00

Eagle. Rev. Value and date. With additional legend indicating gold from the Kolywan Mines.

115. 5 Roubles 1832 .... 150.00

Eagle. Rev. Value and date.

116. Platinum 12 Roubles 1830-45 .... 750.00
117. Platinum 6 Roubles 1829-45 .... 300.00
118. Platinum 3 Roubles 1828-45 .... * 100.00

ALEXANDER II, 1855-1881

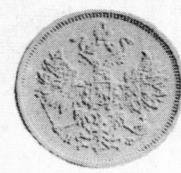

Eagle. Rev. Value. The 25 Rouble piece was not placed in circulation.

119. 25 Roubles 1876 .... 850.00
120. 5 Roubles 1855-81 .... * 25.00
121. 3 Roubles 1869-81 .... 25.00

ALEXANDER III, 1881-1894

Eagle. Rev. Value.

122. 5 Roubles 1881-85 .... * 25.00
123. 3 Roubles 1881-85 .... 25.00

Head. Rev. Eagle.

---

124. 10 Roubles 1886-94 .... 60.00
125. 5 Roubles 1886-94 .... * 25.00

NICHOLAS II 1894-1917

Head. Rev. Eagle in circle, legend around. These coins were not placed in circulation.

126. 37½ Roubles or 100 Francs 1902 .... * 1000.00
127. 25 Roubles or 2½ Imperials 1896, 1908 .... 750.00
128. 10 Roubles or 1 Imperial 1895-97 .... 300.00
129. 5 Roubles or ½ Imperial 1895-97 .... * 200.00

Head. Rev. Eagle.

130. 15 Roubles 1897 .... 40.00
131. 7½ Roubles 1897 .... 27.50
132. 10 Roubles 1898-1911 .... 20.00
133. 5 Roubles 1897-1910 .... * 12.50

SOVIET UNION

Sower scattering seed. Rev. Hammer and Sickle.

134. 10 Roubles or 1 Chervonetz 1923 .... 150.00

SAN MARINO

St. Marinus standing. Rev. Three towers.

1. 20 Lire 1925 .... 65.00
2. 10 Lire 1925 .... 50.00

SCOTLAND

Kings of —

DAVID II, 1329-1371
Ruler in ship. Rev. Ornate cross.

1. 1 Noble ND 3500.00

ROBERT III, 1390-1406

Crowned shield. Rev. St. Andrew with long cross.

SCOTLAND (cont'd)

2. 1 Lion ND ....* 85.00
3. ½ Lion or Demy ND 75.00

Crowned shield. Rev. St. Andrew with short cross.

4. 1 Lion ND 100.00

Crowned shield within border. Rev. St. Andrew with long cross.

5. ½ Lion or Demy ND 250.00

Crowned shield. Rev. Cross of St. Andrew.

6. 1 Lion ND 85.00
7. ½ Lion or Demy ND ....* 75.00

JAMES I, 1406-1437

Lion in square. Rev. Cross of St. Andrew in border.

8. 1 Demy ND 60.00
9. ½ Demy ND ....* 75.00

JAMES II, 1437-1460

Lion in square. Rev. Cross of St. Andrew in border.

10. 1 Demy ND 65.00

Crowned shield. Rev. St. Andrew with cross.

11. 1 Lion ND ....* 100.00
12. ½ Lion ND 100.00

JAMES III, 1460-1488

Ruler on horse. Rev. Shield on long cross.

13. 1 Rider ND ....* 100.00
14. ½ Rider ND ....* 125.00
15. ¼ Rider ND 250.00

Unicorn. Rev. Star with wavy rays.

16. 1 Unicorn ND ....* 100.00
17. ½ Unicorn ND 75.00

JAMES IV, 1488-1513

Unicorn. Rev. Star with wavy rays.

18. 1 Unicorn ND 85.00
19. ½ Unicorn ND ....* 90.00

Crowned shield. Rev. St. Andrew with cross.

20. 1 Lion ND ....* 200.00
21. ½ Lion ND 250.00

JAMES V, 1514-1542

Unicorn. Rev. Star.

22. 1 Unicorn ND ....* 100.00
23. ½ Unicorn ND 150.00

Shield and value. Rev. Cross with thistles in angles.

24. 20 Shillings or 1 Crown. ND 60.00

Bust with hat. Rev. Arms.

25. 1 Bonnet Piece ND ....* 225.00
26. ⅔ Bonnet Piece ND 150.00
27. ⅓ Bonnet Piece ND 175.00

MARY, 1542-1567

Crowned shield. Rev. Floriated cross.

28. 1 Abbey Crown or 20 Shillings ND 200.00

SCOTLAND (cont'd)

Crowned shield. Rev. Crown over MR or Maria monogram.

29.	20 Shillings 1543 ....*	200.00
30.	1 Lion or 44 Shillings 1553	150.00
31.	½ Lion or 22 Shillings 1553 ....*	150.00

Crowned shield between M and R. Rev. Crown over Maria monogram.

32.	1 Lion 1557	450.00

Bust. Rev. Crowned shield.

33.	3 Pounds or 1 Ryal 1555-58 ....*	500.00
34.	1½ Pounds or ½ Ryal 1555-58	500.00

Busts of Mary and Francis of France facing each other. Rev. Floriated cross.

35.	1 Ducat or 60 Shillings 1558	4000.00

Shield. Rev. Cross of four crowned M's.

36.	1 Crown 1561-65	2000.00

JAMES VI, 1567-1625

Half length figure. Rev. Shield.

37.	20 Pounds 1575, 76	1250.00

Youthful bust. Rev. Shield between divided date.

38.	1 Ducat (4 Pounds or Noble) 1580	600.00

Lion holding sword and sceptre. Rev. Cross of four IR's.

39.	1 Lion Noble 1582-89	600.00
40.	⅔ Lion Noble 1582-89 ....*	750.00
41.	⅓ Lion Noble 1582-89	700.00

Shield on ship. Rev. Cross in embellished border.

42.	1 Thistle Noble 1588, 89	150.00

Bust with high hat. Rev. Seated lion.

43.	1 Hat Piece 1591-94	300.00

Ruler on horse. Rev. Crowned shield.

44.	1 Rider 1593-1601 ....*	65.00
45.	½ Rider 1593-1601	85.00

Sword and sceptre. Rev. Crowned shield.

46.	1 Sword and Sceptre Piece 1601-04 ....*	50.00
47.	½ Sword and Sceptre Piece 1601-04	40.00

Crowned bust with orb and sceptre. Rev. Arms.

48.	1 Unite (20 Shillings or 1 Sceptre) ND	100.00

SCOTLAND (cont'd)

Crowned bust. Rev. Arms.

49.	2 Crowns or ½ Unite ND	85.00
50.	1 Britain Crown ND ....*	75.00
51.	½ Crown ND ....*	50.00

Crowned thistle. Rev. Crowned rose.

52.	1 Thistle Crown ND	50.00

CHARLES I, 1625-1649

Bust of James with orb and sceptre but with name and initials of Charles. Rev. Arms.

53.	1 Unite ND	85.00

Crowned bust of James. Rev. Arms. With name and initials of Charles.

54.	2 Crowns or ½ Unite ND ....*	450.00
55.	1 Britain Crown ND	65.00

Bust of Charles with orb and sceptre. Rev. Arms. Briot's coinage.

56.	1 Unite ND	65.00

Bust of Charles. Rev. Arms. Briot's coinage.

57.	2 Crowns or ½ Unite ND ....*	85.00

58.	1 Britain Crown ND	100.00
59.	½ Crown ND	60.00

WILLIAM II (III OF ENGLAND), 1694-1702

Bust with small rising sun below. Rev. Arms.

60.	1 Pistole 1701 ....*	175.00
61.	½ Pistole 1701	200.00

SERBIA

Kings of —

STEPHAN UROSH, 1346-1370
Ruler on horse. Rev. Helmet and insignia.

1.	1 Solidus or Ducat ND	750.00

MILAN OBRENOVICH IV, 1868-1889

Head by Tasset with full title in legend. Rev. Value.

2.	20 Dinars 1879	35.00

New head by Scharff with short title. Rev. Value.

3.	20 Dinars 1882	30.00
4.	10 Dinars 1882	17.50

SPAIN

(The Houses of Castile and Leon)

A. Kings of —

ALFONSO VIII, 1158-1214

Arab legend on each side with the addition of "ALF" on Obv. Struck in the style of the Arab Dinars of the period.

1.	1 Maravedi ND	100.00

ALFONSO X, 1252-1284

Castle. Rev. Lion.

2.	1 Dobla ND	125.00

ALFONSO XI, 1312-1350
Castle. Rev. Lion.

2a. 1 Dobla ND 300.00

PETER I, 1350-1369

Crowned bust. Rev. Arms.

3. 10 Doblas ND 2000.00
4. 1 Dobla ND ....* 150.00
5. 20 Maravedis ND 125.00

Castle. Rev. Lion.

6. 1 Dobla ND 100.00
7. 20 Maravedis ND 75.00

HENRY II, 1368-1379

Ruler on horse. Rev. Arms.

8. 1 Dobla ND 200.00

JOHN II, 1406-1454

Shield. Rev. Arms.

9. 1 Dobla de la Banda ND 75.00

HENRY IV, 1454-1474
Castle. Rev. Lion.

10. 1 Dobla ND 75.00
10a. ½ Dobla ND 200.00

Ruler on throne. Rev. Arms.

10b. 5 Enriques or 5 Doblas ND .... Rare
11. 1 Enrique or Dobla ND ....* 125.00
12. ½ Enrique or ½ Dobla ND 100.00

Shield. Rev. Arms.

12a. 1 Dobla de la Banda ND 175.00

ALFONSO DE AVILA, 1465-1468
Ruler on horse. Rev. Arms.

13. 1 Dobla ND 200.00
14. ½ Dobla ND 125.00

FERDINAND V AND ISABELLA I, 1476-1516

Crowned busts facing each other. Rev. Arms on eagle.

15. 20 Excelentes ND. S mm. .... Rare
16. 10 Excelentes ND. S or G mm. .... Rare
17. 4 Excelentes ND. B mm. ....* 200.00
18. 4 Excelentes ND. Aqueduct mm. 250.00
19. 2 Excelentes ND. B mm. 100.00
20. 2 Excelentes ND. G mm. 75.00
21. 2 Excelentes ND. S mm. 75.00
22. 2 Excelentes ND. T mm. ....* 75.00
23. 2 Excelentes ND. Aqueduct mm. 100.00
24. 2 Ducats ND. S mm. 75.00

Crowned busts facing each other. Rev. Arms without eagle.

25. 1 Excelente ND. C mm. (Cuenca) 125.00
26. 1 Excelente ND. G mm. 75.00
27. 1 Excelente ND. S mm. ....* 65.00
28. 1 Excelente ND. T mm. 75.00
29. 1 Castellano ND. S mm. 75.00
30. 1 Castellano ND. T mm. 75.00
31. ½ Castellano ND. S mm. 65.00
32. ½ Castellano ND. T mm. 65.00
33. 1 Ducat ND. S mm. 75.00

Crowned figures seated on thrones. Rev. Two shields on eagle.

33a. 4 Ducats ND. S mm. 750.00

Crowned F. Rev. Crowned Y.

34. ½ Excelente ND. B mm. 75.00
35. ½ Excelente ND. S mm. 50.00

CHARLES I AND JOHANNA, 1516-1556

Crowned arms. Rev. Cross.

36. 1 Escudo ND. S mm. ....* 30.00
37. 1 Escudo ND. Aqueduct mm. 50.00

PHILIP II, 1556-1598

Crowned arms. Rev. Cross. With or without poorly showing dates.

38. 4 Escudos ND. S mm. ....* 125.00
38a. 4 Escudos 1591. M mm. 200.00
38b. 4 Escudos 1597. BA mm. 200.00
38c. 2 Escudos ND. B mm. 125.00
38d. 2 Escudos ND. M mm. 125.00

SPAIN (cont'd)

39.	2 Escudos ND. G mm.	75.00
40.	2 Escudos ND. S mm.	60.00
41.	2 Escudos ND. T mm.	75.00
41a.	1 Escudo ND. G mm.	75.00
42.	1 Escudo ND. S mm.	40.00

PHILIP III, 1598-1621

Arms. Rev. Cross. The cobs with or without poorly showing dates.

42a.	100 Escudos 1618	Rare
43.	8 Escudos ND. MD mm. Cob type	150.00
44.	8 Escudos 1614. Aqueduct mm. Modern style	350.00
45.	4 Escudos 1607, 11. Aqueduct mm. Modern style	350.00
46.	2 Escudos 1611. S mm. Cob type	75.00
47.	2 Escudos 1610. Aqueduct mm. Modern style	250.00
47a.	2 Escudos 1616. MD mm.	150.00
48.	1 Escudo 1607, 08. Aqueduct mm. Modern style *	100.00

Crowned arms. Rev. Cross with castles and lions in the angles.
Struck from dies used for the silver 50 Real coin.

49.	Gold 50 Reales 1620	Rare

PHILIP IV, 1621-1665

Arms. Rev. Cross. The cobs with or without poorly showing dates.

50.	100 Escudos 1633	Rare
51.	8 Escudos 1631, 32. MD mm. Cob type	150.00
52.	8 Escudos 1631-59. S mm. Cob type	125.00
53.	8 Escudos 1627-55. Aqueduct mm. Modern style *	275.00
54.	4 Escudos 1638-44. MD mm. Cob type	125.00
55.	4 Escudos 1631-59. S mm. Cob type	100.00
55a.	4 Escudos 1655. Aqueduct mm. Modern style	300.00
55b.	2 Escudos 1640-61. S mm. Cob type	75.00
55c.	2 Escudos ND. B mm. Cob type	125.00
55d.	2 Escudos 1652. Aqueduct mm. Modern style	250.00
56.	1 Escudo 1646. MD mm. Cob type	50.00
57.	1 Escudo 1639. Aqueduct mm. Cob type	50.00

Crowned arms. Rev. Cross with castles and lions in the angles.
Struck from dies used for the silver 50 Real coin.

58.	Gold 50 Reales 1626	Rare

CHARLES II, 1665-1700

Arms. Rev. Cross. The cobs with or without poorly showing dates.

59.	8 Escudos 1697. B mm. Cob type	200.00
60.	8 Escudos 1668. MD mm. Cob type	200.00
61.	8 Escudos. Poorly dated. S mm. Cob type	175.00
62.	8 Escudos 1699, 1700. S mm. Modern style	225.00
63.	8 Escudos 1687. Aqueduct mm. Modern style .... *	250.00

64.	4 Escudos. Poorly dated. MD mm. Cob type	100.00
65.	4 Escudos 1699, 1700. S mm. Modern style	175.00
66.	4 Escudos 1687. Aqueduct mm. Modern style	250.00
67.	2 Escudos 1699. S mm.	125.00
67a.	2 Escudos 1683. Aqueduct mm. Modern style	200.00
67b.	1 Escudo 1689. MD mm. Cob type	75.00
68.	1 Escudo 1672-1700. S mm. Cob type	40.00
69.	1 Escudo 1683. Aqueduct mm. Modern style	100.00

PHILIP V, 1700-1746

Bust with long hair. Rev. Arms.

70.	8 Escudos 1729, 30. M mm.	200.00
71.	8 Escudos 1729-38. S mm. .... *	175.00
72.	4 Escudos 1732-34. M mm.	150.00
73.	4 Escudos 1729, 30, 33. S mm.	125.00
74.	2 Escudos 1729-34. M mm.	50.00
75.	2 Escudos 1730-42. S mm. .... *	50.00
76.	1 Escudo 1729-42. M mm.	35.00
77.	1 Escudo 1729, 31, 33. S mm.	50.00
78.	½ Escudo 1738-46. M mm.	20.00
79.	½ Escudo 1738-45. S mm.	20.00

Arms. Rev. Cross. The cobs with or without poorly showing dates.

80.	8 Escudos 1719-27. M mm.	175.00
81.	8 Escudos 1717, 21, 23. Aqueduct mm.	200.00
82.	8 Escudos 1701-29. S mm. .... *	150.00
83.	8 Escudos 1746. S mm. Cob type	125.00
84.	4 Escudos 1710, 19. M mm.	150.00
85.	4 Escudos 1701-29. S mm.	100.00
85a.	4 Escudos 1740. S mm. Cob type	200.00
85b.	4 Escudos 1707. V mm.	400.00
85c.	2 Escudos 1707. V mm.	250.00
85d.	2 Escudos 1721. M mm.	125.00
86.	2 Escudos 1701-26. S mm.	65.00
87.	2 Escudos 1719. S mm. Cob type	50.00
88.	1 Escudo 1723. M mm.	60.00
89.	1 Escudo 1701-21. S mm.	50.00
90.	1 Escudo 1736. S mm. Cob type	40.00

LOUIS I, 1724

Arms. Rev. Cross.

91.	8 Escudos 1724. Aqueduct mm.	2000.00
92.	4 Escudos 1724. Aqueduct mm. .... *	1000.00
93.	2 Escudos 1724. S mm. Cob type	200.00
93a.	2 Escudos 1724. S mm. Modern style	600.00

SPAIN (cont'd)

FERDINAND VI, 1746-1760

Bust. Rev. Arms.

93b.	8 Escudos 1748. S mm.	300.00
94.	8 Escudos 1747, 49, 50. M mm.	175.00
94a.	4 Escudos 1748. M mm. ....*......	300.00
94b.	2 Escudos 1749. M mm.	175.00

Plain head. Rev. Arms.

95.	2 Escudos 1749. S mm.	100.00
96.	½ Escudo 1746-59. M mm.	15.00
97.	½ Escudo 1746-58. S mm. ....*......	15.00

Arms. Rev. Cross. Cob type.

98.	8 Escudos 1752, 55. S mm.	175.00
99.	2 Escudos 1751, 54. S mm.	60.00

CHARLES III, 1759-1788

Plain head. Rev. Arms.

100.	½ Escudo 1759-71. M mm. ....*......	17.50
101.	½ Escudo 1759-71. S mm.	20.00

Young bust. Rev. Arms.

101a.	8 Escudos 1760. M mm.	250.00
101b.	4 Escudos 1761. M mm.	250.00

Older bust. Rev. Arms.

102.	8 Escudos 1772-88. M mm.	125.00
103.	8 Escudos 1772-88. S mm. ....*......	125.00
104.	4 Escudos 1773-88. M mm.	100.00
105.	4 Escudos 1772-85. S mm.	125.00
106.	2 Escudos 1773-88. M mm.	30.00
107.	2 Escudos 1776, 79, 87. S mm.	65.00
108.	1 Escudo 1779-88. M mm.	15.00
109.	1 Escudo 1773-87. S mm.	20.00
110.	½ Escudo 1772-88. M mm.	12.50
111.	½ Escudo 1773-88. S mm.	15.00

CHARLES IV, 1788-1808

Bust. Rev. Arms.

112.	8 Escudos 1788-1808. M mm.	100.00
113.	4 Escudos 1791-1803. M mm. ....*......	75.00
114.	2 Escudos 1789-1808. M mm.	25.00
115.	2 Escudos 1791-1807. S mm.	35.00
116.	1 Escudo 1789-1801. M mm.	15.00
117.	½ Escudo 1788-96. M mm.	12.50

JOSEPH NAPOLEON BONAPARTE, 1808-1814

Head. Rev. Arms. All with M mm.

118.	320 Reales 1810, 12. Laureate head ....*......	200.00
119.	80 Reales 1809, 10. Plain head	50.00
120.	80 Reales 1811, 12, 13. Laureate head	40.00

FERDINAND VII, 1808-1833

Broad draped bust. Rev. Arms.

121.	2 Escudos 1808, 09. S mm.	50.00

Draped laureate bust. Rev. Arms.

122.	8 Escudos 1811. C mm.	200.00
123.	2 Escudos 1811. C mm. ....*......	75.00
124.	2 Escudos 1813. M mm.	75.00
124a.	2 Escudos 1809. S mm.	85.00

Laureate bust with high collar. Rev. Arms.

125.	2 Escudos 1812. M mm.	75.00

Plain laureate head. Rev. Arms. The large C mm. is for Catalonia. The small C mm. is for Cadiz and is crowned.

126.	8 Escudos 1813, 14. Large C mm.	500.00
127.	8 Escudos 1814-20. M mm.	125.00
128.	4 Escudos 1814-20. M mm. ....*......	60.00
129.	2 Escudos 1811-14. Small C mm.	35.00
130.	2 Escudos 1811, 12, 13, 14. Large C mm.	150.00
131.	2 Escudos 1813-33. M mm.	25.00
132.	2 Escudos 1815-33. S mm.	25.00
133.	1 Escudo 1817. M mm.	40.00
134.	½ Escudo 1817. M mm.	20.00

SPAIN (cont'd)

Plain older head. Rev. Arms.

135.	320 Reals 1822, 23. M mm.	....	200.00
136.	160 Reals 1822. M mm.	.......................*	125.00
137.	80 Reals 1822, 23. M mm.	....	40.00
138.	80 Reals 1823. B mm.	....	50.00
139.	80 Reals 1823. S mm.	....	50.00

ISABELLA II, 1833-1868

Head right with hair combed up. Rev. Arms.

140.	80 Reals 1836-47. B mm.	..................*	25.00
141.	80 Reals 1834-44. M mm.	....	25.00
142.	80 Reals 1836, 38, 41, 48. S mm.	....	35.00

Head left with hair combed down. Rev. Arms.

143.	1 Doblon or 100 Reals 1850. M mm.	.......*	50.00
143a.	1 Doblon or 100 Reals 1850. B mm.	......	80.00

Head left with hair combed down. Rev. Arms in palms.

144.	100 Reals 1854, 55	....	30.00

Draped laureate bust. Rev. Arms in palms.

145.	100 Reals 1856-62	...................*	25.00
146.	40 Reals 1861, 62, 63	....	20.00
147.	20 Reals 1861, 62, 63	....	15.00

Draped laureate bust. Rev. Draped arms. The 10 Escudos value is equal in size and weight to the 100 Reals value.

148.	100 Reals 1863, 64	....	30.00
149.	40 Reals 1864	....	30.00
150.	10 Escudos 1865-68	...............*	25.00
151.	4 Escudos 1865-68	................*	17.50
152.	2 Escudos 1865	....	17.50

PROVISIONAL GOVERNMENT, 1870

Hispania standing. Rev. Arms.

153.	100 Pesetas 1870	....	3000.00

AMADEO I, 1871-1873

Head. Rev. Arms.

154.	100 Pesetas 1871	...............*	1750.00
155.	25 Pesetas 1871	....	1000.00

ALFONSO XII, 1875-1886

Young head. Rev. Arms.

156.	25 Pesetas 1876-80	....	25.00
157.	10 Pesetas 1878	....	20.00

Older bearded head. Rev. Arms.

158.	25 Pesetas 1881-85	....	25.00

ALFONSO XIII, 1886-1931

Large baby head. Rev. Arms.

159.	20 Pesetas 1889, 90	....	22.50

Child head with curly hair. Rev. Arms.

160.	20 Pesetas 1892	....	30.00

Juvenile head. Rev. Arms.

161. 100 Pesetas 1897 .... 125.00
162. 20 Pesetas 1899 ....*...... 22.50

Uniformed bust. Rev. Arms.

163. 20 Pesetas 1904 .... 75.00

B. Cities and Kingdoms of —

ARAGON

Kings of —

PETER IV, 1336-1387

St. John standing. Rev. Lily.

1. 1 Florin ND ....*...... 75.00
2. ½ Florin ND 150.00
3. ¼ Florin ND 150.00

JOHN I, 1387-1396
St. John standing. Rev. Lily.

4. 1 Florin ND 75.00
5. ½ Florin ND 150.00

MARTIN, 1396-1410
St. John standing. Rev. Lily.

6. 1 Florin ND 75.00
7. ½ Florin ND 75.00

FERDINAND I, 1412-1416
St. John standing. Rev. Lily.

8. 1 Florin ND 150.00
9. ½ Florin ND 150.00

ALFONSO V, 1416-1458
St. John standing. Rev. Lily.

10. 1 Florin ND 75.00
11. ½ Florin ND 65.00

JOHN II, 1458-1479
Crowned bust. Rev. Shield and dragon.

12. 1 Timbre ND 750.00

Crowned bust. Rev. Crowned arms.

13. 1 Florin ND 150.00
14. ¼ Florin ND 200.00

FERDINAND II, 1479-1516

Crowned bust. Rev. Crowned arms.

15. 4 Ducats ND. Bust left 500.00
16. 2 Ducats ND. Bust left 400.00
17. 1 Ducat ND. Bust right ....*...... 150.00

CHARLES AND JOHANNA, 1516-1555

Crowned busts facing each other. Rev. Arms.

18. 50 Ducats 1520 .... Rare
19. 20 Ducats 1520, ND................................ Rare
20. 2 Ducats ND ....*...... 250.00

BARCELONA

Arms. Rev. Value. Siege coin of the Napoleonic Wars.

1. 20 Pesetas 1812, 13, 14 .... 35.00

CATALONIA

Barcelona Mint

Princes of —

BERENGUER RAMON I, 1018-1035
Arab legend in circle within Latin legend. Rev. Arab legend.

1. 1 Mancuso ND 300.00

PEDRO OF PORTUGAL, 1464-1466
Crowned bust facing. Rev. Arms.

2. 1 Pacifico or Ducat ND 350.00
3. ½ Pacifico or ½ Ducat ND 300.00

RENE OF ANJOU, 1466-1472

Crowned bust facing. Rev. Arms.

4. 1 Pacifico or Ducat ND ....*...... 175.00
5. ½ Pacifico or ½ Ducat ND 250.00
6. ¼ Pacifico or ¼ Ducat ND 75.00

FERDINAND II, 1479-1516

Crowned bust. Rev. Arms.

7. 4 Principats or 4 Ducats ND 500.00
8. 2 Principats or 2 Ducats ND 400.00
9. 1 Principat or Ducat ND ....*...... 150.00
10. ½ Principat or ½ Ducat ND 100.00

CHARLES AND JOHANNA, 1516-1558

Crowned busts facing each other. Rev. Arms.

11. 2 Principats 1542, ND **300.00**

Initials I and C in circle. Rev. Arms.

12. ½ Principat ND **50.00**

PHILIP III, 1598-1621

Bust. Rev. Arms.

13. ⅓ Trentin 1618 .... **150.00**

PHILIP IV, 1621-1665
Bust. Rev. Arms.

14. ⅓ Trentin 1625 .... **200.00**

Busts of Ferdinand and Isabella facing each other. Rev. Arms.

15. 1 Trentin 1622-32, ND **150.00**
16. ½ Trentin 1626, 30, ND .... * **125.00**

PRIVATE ISSUE, 1900

Empty throne. Rev. St. George slaying dragon. Private contribution coins without denomination but corresponding to the contemporary Spanish gold coins.

17. (100 Pesetas) 1900 .... **200.00**
18. (20 Pesetas) 1900 .... **50.00**

LEON

Kings of —

FERDINAND II, 1157-1188
Crowned bust. Rev. Lion and globe.

1. 1 Maravedi ND **400.00**

ALFONSO IX, 1188-1230

Crowned bust. Rev. Lion walking.

2. 1 Maravedi Alfonsi ND **175.00**

MAJORCA

Kings of —

PETER IV, 1343-1387

Ruler on throne. Rev. Cross potent.

1. 1 Gold Real ND ....* **200.00**
2. ½ Gold Real ND **150.00**
3. ¼ Gold Real ND **100.00**
4. ⅛ Gold Real ND **75.00**

FERDINAND II, 1479-1516

Bust. Rev. Arms.

5. 1 Ducat ND **200.00**

CHARLES I, 1516-1556

Bust. Rev. Arms.

6. 1 Ducat ND **200.00**

PHILIP III, 1598-1621

Arms. Rev. Square shield.

7. 4 Escudos ND **200.00**
8. 2 Escudos ND ....* **125.00**
9. 1 Escudo ND **200.00**

PHILIP IV, 1621-1665
Arms. Rev. Square shield.

10. 4 Escudos 1648, ND **250.00**

Crowned bust. Rev. Arms.

11. 2 Ducats ND **500.00**

CHARLES II, 1665-1700

Arms. Rev. Square shield.

12. 4 Escudos 1698 ....* **200.00**
13. 2 Escudos ND **125.00**
14. 1 Escudo 1698 .... **150.00**
15. ½ Escudo 1695 .... **125.00**

PHILIP V, 1700-1746

Bust. Rev. Arms.

16. 2 Escudos 1723, 26 .... **150.00**

Arms. Rev. Square shield.

17.	4 Escudos 1704	300.00
18.	2 Escudos 1704	200.00

VALENCIA

Kings of —

ALFONSO V OF ARAGON, 1416-1458

Dragon over shield. Rev. Square shield.

1.	1 Timbre or ⅔ Ducat ND ....*......	100.00
2.	½ Timbre ND	100.00

JOHN II, 1458-1479

Bust facing. Rev. Arms.

3.	1 Ducat ND	150.00

FERDINAND AND ISABELLA, 1479-1504

Crowned heads facing each other. Rev. Arms.

4.	4 Ducats ND	500.00
5.	2 Ducats ND	350.00
6.	1 Ducat ND ....*......	125.00

Initials F and I crowned. Rev. Arms.

7.	½ Ducat ND	60.00

FERDINAND II, 1504-1516

Bust right or left. Rev. Square shield.

8.	4 Ducats ND	250.00
9.	2 Ducats ND ....*......	150.00
10.	1 Ducat ND	100.00
11.	½ Ducat ND	75.00

Initial F. Rev. Arms.

12.	½ Ducat ND	50.00

CHARLES I, 1517-1556

Bust. Rev. Square shield.

13.	4 Ducats ND	600.00
14.	2 Ducats ND ....*......	150.00
15.	1 Ducat ND	250.00

Cross of Jerusalem. Rev. Square shield.

16.	4 Corona or 4 Ducats ND	200.00
17.	2 Corona or 2 Ducats ND	250.00
18.	1 Corona or Ducat ND ....*......	100.00

PHILIP II, 1556-1598

Cross of Jerusalem. Rev. Square shield.

19.	4 Escudos ND	400.00

PHILIP IV, 1621-1665

Cross of Jerusalem. Rev. Square shield.

20.	1 Escudo ND or poorly dated	200.00

CHARLES II, 1665-1700

Cross of Jerusalem. Rev. Square shield.

21.	1 Escudo 1695	100.00

Dragon over shield. Rev. Square shield.

22.	1 Escudo ND	50.00

SWEDEN

Kings of —

ERIC XIV, 1560-1568

Head. Rev. Jehova in Hebrew characters over Sceptre.

1.	1 Goldgulden 1568	1500.00

JOHN III, 1568-1592

Bust in circle. Rev. Heart shaped shield within inscribed circle.

2.	20 Ducats or 2 Portugalosers ND	Unique
3.	10 Ducats or 1 Portugaloser ND	2000.00
4.	5 Ducats or ½ Portugaloser or 2 Rosenobles ND .*......	1750.00

SWEDEN (cont'd)

Bust in circle. Rev. Christ over shield.

5. 5 Ducats or ½ Portugaloser or 2 Rosenobles 1576 .... **3500.00**

Crowned sheaf with value and date. Rev. Arms in circle.

6. 48 Marks 1590 .... **Rare**
7. 24 Marks 1590 .... **Rare**
8. 12 Marks 1590 .... **Rare**

Crowned sheaf and value. Rev. Three crowns and date.

9. 6 Marks 1590, 91 .... **750.00**

Rampant lion in circle. Rev. Three crowns and value.

10. 3 Marks 1590 .... **500.00**

Crowned bust. Rev. Quartered arms.

11. 1 Hungarian Gulden 1569, 73 .... **850.00**

Crowned bust. Rev. Shield with three crowns.

12. 1 Crown Gulden 1569, 70 .... **800.00**

Crowned sheaf between I and R. Rev. Legend and three crowns.

13. 2 Ducats ND. Square .... **Unique**

CHARLES IX, 1560-1611
Bust. Rev. Value.

14. 8 Marks 1587-1603. Square **750.00**

Laureate or crowned bust. Rev. Arms.

15. 16 Marks 1606-11 .... **750.00**

Bust. Rev. Crown over three shields.

16. 6 Marks 1609, 10 .... **350.00**

Sheaf. Rev. Hebrew "Jehova."

---

17. 10 Marks 1610. Square **1000.00**
18. 5 Marks 1610, 11. Square **300.00**

Arms superimposed on bust holding sword. Rev. Lion shield and three crowns in circle.

19. 6 Ducats 1606-09 .... **1250.00**

GUSTAV ADOLPHE II, 1611-1632
Bust. Rev. Arms.

20. 16 Marks 1615, 24 .... **2000.00**

Sheaf. Rev. Hebrew "Jehova."

21. 10 Marks 1616, 26. Square .... *...... **1500.00**
22. 5 Marks 1612. Square **1250.00**

Bust. Rev. Arms supported by lions.

23. 10 Ducats 1617 .... **2500.00**
24. 6 Ducats 1620 .... **2000.00**
25. 5 Ducats 1617, 20 .... *...... **1500.00**

Bust. Rev. Carnation in vase, and large crown.

26. 1½ Ducats 1617 .... **150.00**

CHRISTINA, 1632-1654
Bust. Rev. Arms.

27. 5 Ducats 1649 .... **4000.00**

CHARLES X, 1654-1660

Bust. Rev. Arms.

28. 10 Ducats 1654 .... **4000.00**
29. 1 Ducat 1654-60, ND .... *...... **1000.00**

CHARLES XI, 1660-1697

Bust. right. Rev. Arms.

30. 1 Ducat 1662-65 .... **350.00**

SWEDEN (cont'd)

Bust or head left. Rev. Cross of arms.

31. 1 Ducat 1666-69 .... **300.00**

Laureate bust left. Rev. Crown over linked C's.

32. 1 Ducat 1670-76, ND **300.00**

Plain bust left. Rev. Crown over linked C's.

33. 1 Ducat 1677 .... **300.00**

Plain bust right. Rev. Crown over linked C's.

34. 1 Ducat 1677-95 ....*...... **250.00**
35. ¼ Ducat 1692 .... **50.00**

Head right. Rev. Legend. From gold of the Dalarna Mines.

36. 1 Ducat 1695 .... **350.00**

CHARLES XII, 1697-1718

Bust with long hair. Rev. Crown over linked C's.

37. 2 Ducats 1702, 04, 17 ....*...... **500.00**
38. 1 Ducat 1697-1704 .... **150.00**
39. ½ Ducat 1701 .... **125.00**
40. ¼ Ducat 1700 .... **100.00**

Bust with short hair. Rev. Crown over linked C's.

41. 1 Ducat 1707-18 .... **125.00**

Bust with short hair. Rev. Six line legend.

42. 1 "Alchemy" Ducat 1706 .... **250.00**

ULRICA ELEONORA, 1719-1720

Bust. Rev. Arms.

43. 2 Ducats 1719 .... **200.00**

Bust. Rev. Crown over linked UE.

44. 1 Ducat 1719, 20 .... **150.00**

FREDERICK I, 1720-1751

Bust. Rev. Crown over linked FR or FF.

45. 1 Ducat 1720-28 .... **125.00**

Bust. Rev. Cross of four F's.

46. 1 Ducat 1728, 29, 32 .... **125.00**
47. ¼ Ducat 1730, 33, 40 .... **30.00**

Bust. Rev. Crowned shield.

48. 1 Ducat 1734-50 .... **125.00**
49. ½ Ducat 1735, 38 .... **60.00**

Bust. Rev. Crowned shield with sun rising from bottom left. From gold mined in the East Indies.

50. 1 Ducat 1738-50 .... **150.00**

298

SWEDEN (cont'd)

Bust. Rev. Crowned shield, and below, the small arms of Smaland, indicating gold from the Adelfors Mines.

51. 1 Ducat 1741-50	....	250.00
52. ½ Ducat 1741, 46, 47	....	100.00

ADOLPHE FREDERICK, 1751-1771

Head. Rev. Crowned shield.

53. 1 Ducat 1751-71	...................................*	125.00
54. ½ Ducat 1754, 55	....	60.00
55. ¼ Ducat 1754, 55	....	35.00

Head. Rev. Crowned shield and legend indicating gold from the Dalarna Mines.

56. 1 Ducat 1751, 54	....	250.00

Head. Rev. Crowned shield, and below, the small arms of Smaland, indicating gold from the Adelfors Mines.

57. 1 Ducat 1752-70	....	200.00

GUSTAV III, 1771-1792

Head. Rev. Crowned shield.

58. 1 Ducat 1771-92	....	75.00

Head. Rev. Crowned shield, and below, the small arms of Smaland indicating gold from the Adelfors Mines.

59. 1 Ducat 1771-86	....	200.00

GUSTAV ADOLPHE IV, 1792-1809

Head. Rev. Crowned shield.

60. 1 Ducat 1793-98	....	100.00

Armored bust. Rev. Crowned shield.

61. 1 Ducat 1799-1809	....	60.00

Head. Rev. Crowned shield, and below, the small arms of Smaland, indicating gold from the Adelfors Mines.

62. 1 Ducat 1796	....	175.00

Armored bust. Rev. Similar to above.

63. 1 Ducat 1801	....	175.00

Armored bust. Rev. Crowned shield, and below, the small arms of Dalarna, indicating gold from the Dalarna Mines.

64. 1 Ducat 1804	....	150.00

CHARLES XIII, 1809-1818

Head with title as King of Sweden. Rev. Crowned shield.

65. 1 Ducat 1810-14	....	65.00

Head with title as King of Sweden and Norway. Rev. Crowned shield.

66. 1 Ducat 1815, 16, 17	....	65.00

Head. Rev. Crowned shield, and below, the small arms of Dalarna, indicating gold from the Dalarna Mines.

67. 1 Ducat 1810	....	150.00

SWEDEN (cont'd)

CHARLES XIV, 1818-1844

Head. Rev. Crowned shield.

68. 1 Ducat 1818-29 .... 60.00

Head. Rev. Arms.

69. 4 Ducats 1837-43 ....*...... 200.00
70. 2 Ducats 1836-43 .... 125.00
71. 1 Ducat 1830-43 .... 40.00

OSCAR I, 1844-1859

Head. Rev. Arms.

72. 4 Ducats 1846, 50 .... 250.00
73. 2 Ducats 1850, 52, 57 ....*...... 150.00
74. 1 Ducat 1844-59 .... 35.00

CHARLES XV, 1859-1872

Head. Rev. Arms.

75. 1 Ducat 1860-68 .... 40.00

Head. Rev. Crowned shield. With two values as indicated.

76. 1 Carolin-10 Francs 1868-72 .... 30.00

OSCAR II, 1872-1907

Head. Rev. Arms.

77. 20 Kronor 1873-1902 ....*...... 32.50
78. 10 Kronor 1873-1901 .... 17.50

Head. Rev. Value.

79. 5 Kronor 1881-1901 .... 10.00

GUSTAV V, 1907-1950

Head. Rev. Arms.

80. 20 Kronor 1925 .... 50.00

Head. Rev. Value.

81. 5 Kronor 1920 .... 10.00

SWITZERLAND

A. Confederation of —

Cross on shield. Rev. Value. Not placed in circulation.

1. 20 Francs 1871 .... 100.00

Head of Helvetia. Rev. Cross on shield. Not placed in circulation.

2. 20 Francs 1871 .... 225.00

Helvetia seated. Rev. Value and date. Not placed in circulation.

3. 20 Francs 1873 .... 75.00

Head of Helvetia. Rev. Arms and value.

4. 20 Francs 1883-96 .... 25.00

Girl head against Alps background. Rev. Value and date.

5. 100 Francs 1925 .... 350.00

SWITZERLAND (cont'd)

Girl head against Alps background. Rev. Shield.

6. 20 Francs 1897-1947 ....*...... 15.00
7. 10 Francs 1911-22 .... 10.00

Rifleman standing. Rev. Oval shield. On the Fribourg Shooting Match.

8. 100 Francs 1934 .... 125.00

Rifleman kneeling. Rev. Legend over shield. On the Luzerne Shooting Match.

9. 100 Francs 1939 .... 75.00

Three standing figures depicting the Oath on the Rutli. Rev. Value.

10. 50 Francs 1955 .... —

William Tell with bow and arrow. Rev. Value.

11. 25 Francs 1955 .... —

(Note: As of April 1958, the above two coins have not been placed in circulation.)

B. Cantons and Cities of —

APPENZELL

St. Mauritius standing. Rev. Legend in cartouche.

1. 1 Ducat 1737, 39 .... 400.00

BASEL

Coinage as a mint of the Holy Roman Empire.

Madonna standing. Rev. Orb. With the name of Sigismund.

1. 1 Goldgulden ND. (1410-33). As King 35.00
2. 1 Goldgulden ND. (1410-37). As Emperor 35.00
3. 1 Goldgulden ND. Without his name ....*...... 200.00

Madonna standing. Rev. Orb. With the name of Albert II.

4. 1 Goldgulden ND. (1437-39) 100.00

Madonna standing. Rev. Orb. With the name of Frederick III.

5. 1 Goldgulden ND. (1440-51). As King 35.00
6. 1 Goldgulden ND. (1451-93). As Emperor 30.00
7. 1 Goldgulden ND. With Weinsberg shield 32.50
8. 1 Goldgulden 1491, 92, 93 .... 350.00

Madonna standing. Rev. Orb. With the name of Maximilian.

9. 1 Goldgulden 1503. With Weinsberg shield 250.00
10. 1 Goldgulden 1505, 06, 07, 08, 09. With Minzenberg
    shield ....*...... 175.00

Coinage as a City or Canton.

Madonna standing, Basel arms at feet. Rev. Orb. With the name of Pope Julius II.

11. 1 Goldgulden 1512 .... 500.00

Madonna standing. Rev. Arms on cross. With the name of Pope Julius II.

12. 1 Goldgulden 1513 .... 300.00

Madonna standing. Rev. Arms on cross. With the name of Maximilian.

13. 1 Goldgulden 1516 .... 175.00

Madonna standing. Rev. Arms on cross. With the name of the City of Basel.

14. 1 Goldgulden 1520-39 .... 350.00

City arms. Rev. Orb.

15. 2 Goldgulden ND. (1600-1700) 150.00
16. 1 Goldgulden ND. (1600-1700) 60.00

Basilisk and shield. Rev. Orb.

17. 2 Goldgulden ND. (1600-1700) 200.00

Basilisk and shield. Rev. Double eagle.

18. 2 Goldgulden ND. (1600-1700) 275.00

Arms on cartouche. Rev. Liberty cap on pole.

19.	2 Goldgulden ND. (1700-1800)	. . . .	135.00
20.	1 Goldgulden ND. (1700-1800)	. . . .	50.00

Basilisk and arms within eight shields. Rev. Northern view of the city.

21.	25 Ducats ND. (1695-1710)	. . . .	1500.00
22.	15 Ducats ND. (1695-1710)	. . . .	1000.00

Basilisk holding shield. Rev. A different northern view of the city.

23.	10 Ducats ND. (1700-10)	. . . .	750.00

Arms within eight shields. Rev. Northern view of the city.

24.	8 Ducats ND. (1700-10)	. . . .	600.00
25.	6 Ducats ND. (1700-10)	. . . .	500.00
26.	4 Ducats ND. (1700-10)	. . . .	375.00
27.	3 Ducats ND. (1700-10)	. . . .	300.00

Arms. Rev. Double eagle.

28.	4 Ducats ND. (1565-80)	. . . .	1000.00

Legend on cartouche. Rev. Basilisk with shield.

29.	2 Ducats ND. (1650-1700)	. . . .	200.00
30.	1 Ducat ND. (1650-1780)	. . . . *	75.00
31.	½ Ducat ND. (1700-50)	. . . .	75.00

City emblem on cartouche. Rev. Double eagle.

32.	1 Ducat ND. (1620-40)	. . . .	75.00

Legend in rectangular cartouche. Rev. City emblem in cartouche.

33.	1 Ducat ND. (1650-1700)	. . . .	75.00

Basilisk and oval shield. Rev. Value and name.

34.	½ Ducat ND. (1750-80)	. . . .	60.00
35.	¼ Ducat ND. (1750-80)	. . . .	45.00

Arms on cross. Rev. Double eagle.

36.	1 Goldgulden 1621, 22, 23	. . . .	150.00

Arms on cartouche. Rev. Double eagle.

37.	1 Ducat 1640	. . . .	125.00

Legend on cartouche. Rev. Basilisk with arms.

38.	1 Ducat 1653	. . . .	100.00

Eastern view of the city. Rev. Basilisk with shield.

39.	20 Ducats 1741	. . . .	1000.00
40.	12 Ducats 1741	. . . .	800.00
41.	8 Ducats 1741	. . . .	650.00
42.	6 Ducats 1741	. . . .	550.00
43.	5 Ducats 1740	. . . . *	375.00
44.	4 Ducats 1740	. . . .	300.00
45.	3 Ducats 1740	. . . .	275.00

Northern view of the city. Rev. Basilisk with arms, shields below.

46.	2 Ducats 1743	. . . .	275.00
47.	1 Ducat 1743	. . . . * . . .	225.00

Basilisk with city emblem. Rev. Value on drapery, liberty cap above.

48.	2 Ducats 1795, ND	. . . .	250.00

Arms. Rev. Tripod.

49.	1 Duplone 1795	. . . .	150.00

Arms. Rev. Legend in wreath.

50.	1 Duplone 1795, 96	. . . .	75.00

"Show Pieces" of Basel

Plancus standing. Rev. City emblem within eight shields.

51. 12 Ducats ND. (1620-40) 900.00
52. 10 Ducats ND. (1620-40) ....*...... 800.00
53. 6 Ducats ND. (1620-40) 600.00

Plancus standing. Rev. Northern view of the city.

54. 3 Ducats ND. (1620-40) 300.00

Plancus standing. Rev. Double eagle.

55. 1 Ducat ND. (1620-40) 100.00

Western view of the city. Rev. Hen.

56. 12 Ducats ND. (1630-70) 900.00
57. 10 Ducats ND. (1630-70) 800.00
58. 8 Ducats ND. (1630-70) 600.00
59. 3 Ducats ND. (1630-70) ....*...... 300.00
60. 2 Ducats ND. (1630-70) 200.00

Northern view of the city. Rev. Hen.

61. 3 Ducats ND. (1630-70) 200.00
62. 2 Ducats ND. (1630-70) 175.00

Northern view of the city. Rev. The Adoration by the shepherds.

63. 3 Christmas Ducats ND. (1600-1700) 100.00
64. 2 Christmas Ducats ND. (1600-1700) 75.00

Northern view of the city. Rev. The Adoration by the three Magi.

65. 3 Christmas Ducats ND. (1600-1700) 100.00
66. 2 Christmas Ducats ND. (1600-1700) ....*...... 75.00

The Adoration by the three Magi. Rev. The Adoration by the shepherds.

67. 3 Christmas Ducats ND. (1600-1700) 125.00
68. 2 Christmas Ducats ND. (1600-1700) 100.00

BERNE

Eagle over arms. Rev. St. Vincent standing.

1.   4 Goldgulden 1492 .... 1000.00
2.   3 Goldgulden 1492 .... 800.00
3.   2 Goldgulden 1492 .... 600.00
4.   2 Ducats 1600 ....*...... 300.00
5.   1 Ducat 1600 ....*...... 150.00
6. ½ Ducat 1600, 01 .... 125.00

Bear walking left within circle of 27 shields. Rev. St. Vincent standing.

7. 10 Ducats 1501 .... 2000.00
8.   9 Ducats 1501 .... 1800.00
9.   5 Ducats 1501 .... 1600.00

Arms. Rev. St. Peter standing.

10. 1 Goldgulden ND. (1470-1500) 400.00

Arms. Rev. Bust of St. Vincent.

11. 1 Goldgulden ND. (1500-30) 400.00

Arms. Rev. Orb with name of Frederick II.

12. 1 Goldgulden ND. (1530-50) 350.00
13. 1 Goldgulden 1590, 94 .... 300.00

Eagle over arms. Rev. Cross.

14. 2 Goldgulden ND. (1500-50) 1200.00
15. 1 Goldgulden ND. (1500-50) 350.00
16. ½ Goldgulden ND. (1500-50) 325.00
17. ½ Goldgulden 1554, 56, 90 .... 400.00

Arms. Rev. Name of Frederick II and with eagle as indicated.

18. 1 Goldgulden 1537, 39. Single head eagle ......*...... 500.00
19. 1 Goldgulden 1566. Double eagle 600.00

Bear. Rev. Cross.

20. 3 Ducats or Florins ND. (1500-1600) 500.00

Bear. Rev. Legend as indicated.

21. 3 Ducats or Florins ND. (1500-1600). Legend in circle 500.00
21a. 3 Ducats or Florins ND. (1500-1600). Legend in seven lines 500.00

Arms. Rev. Double eagle.

22. 4 Ducats 1659 .... 650.00
23. 3 Ducats 1659 .... 400.00
24. 2 Ducats 1658, ND 275.00
25. 1 Ducat 1658 ....*...... 100.00

Bear and lion with arms. Rev. Shield supported by bears.

26. 4 Ducats ND. (1500-1600) 400.00

*Lion and bear holding shield. Rev. Legend and value in cartouche
with floral wreath.*

27.	12 Ducats 1681	2000.00
28.	10 Ducats 1681	1500.00
29.	4 Ducats 1680, 84. Without floral wreath on Rev. *	400.00

Two crowned shields and value. Rev. Male and female holding drapery.

30.	3 Ducats 1680, 84, 97, 99, 1707	375.00

Arms. Rev. Male and female holding drapery.

31.	3 Ducats 1699	450.00
32.	2 Ducats 1698 *	250.00
33.	1 Ducat 1697, 1718 *	125.00

Two crowned shields and value. Rev. Legend on cartouche.

34.	3 Ducats 1734	450.00

Arms supported by bears. Rev. View of the city.

35.	10 Ducats ND. (1650-1700)	2000.00

Arms. Rev. Legend in cartouche or floral wreath.

36.	10 Ducats ND. (1650-1750)	900.00
37.	8 Ducats ND. (1650-1750)	700.00
38.	6 Ducats ND. (1650-1750) *	600.00
39.	5 Ducats ND. (1650-1750)	500.00
40.	4 Ducats ND. (1650-1750)	400.00

Arms supported by lion and bear. Rev. Male and female at altar.

41.	10 Ducats ND. (1700)	900.00
42.	8 Ducats ND. (1700)	700.00
43.	7 Ducats ND. (1700)	700.00
44.	6 Ducats ND. (1700)	600.00
45.	5 Ducats ND. (1700)	500.00
46.	4 Ducats ND. (1700) *	400.00

Crowned arms. Rev. Male and female at altar.

47.	6 Ducats ND. (1700)	650.00
48.	5 Ducats ND. (1700)	550.00
49.	4 Ducats ND. (1700)	450.00

Bear in circle of shields. Rev. Male and female at altar.

50.	5 Ducats ND. (1700)	550.00
51.	4 Ducats ND. (1700)	450.00

Bear in cartouche. Rev. Angel with shield.

52.	1 Ducat 1696	175.00

Arms supported by lion and bear. Rev. Bear holding shield.

53.	7 Ducats 1701	1000.00
54.	6 Ducats 1701	800.00
55.	5 Ducats 1701	600.00
56.	4 Ducats 1701 *	450.00

Two lions holding arms and cap. Rev. Legend and value in wreath.

57.	2 Ducats 1703, 19, 27, 71	150.00

Bear with or without shield. Rev. Cross.

58.	½ Ducat 1718, 81	250.00
59.	¼ Ducat 1707-81, ND *	125.00

Crowned arms. Rev. Legend in cartouche or wreath.

60.	4 Ducats 1734	600.00
61.	3 Ducats 1772	250.00
62.	2 Ducats 1679, 1788, 89 *	175.00
63.	1 Ducat 1679, 1725, 41, 81, 88, 89, ND *	100.00
64.	½ Ducat 1714, 17, 19	35.00

SWITZERLAND-BERNE (cont'd)

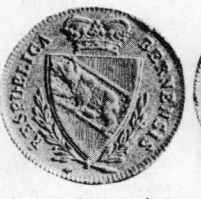

Crowned arms. Rev. Value and date in wreath, legend around.

65.	8 Ducats 1796	....	1000.00
66.	6 Ducats 1796	....	650.00
67.	4 Ducats 1796, 98, 1824	....	550.00
68.	2 Ducats 1796	...........................*	150.00
69.	1 Ducat 1793 (Rare), 94	...............*	50.00

Crowned arms. Rev. Legend in wreath.

70.	2 Duplones 1793-96	....	100.00
71.	1 Duplone 1793-96	...................*	60.00

Crowned arms. Rev. Warrior standing.

72.	6 Duplones or 12 Ducats 1794	....	2000.00
73.	4 Duplones or 8 Ducats 1797, 98	....	1700.00
74.	2 Duplones 1794, 96, 97, 98	.........*	175.00
75.	1 Duplone 1793, 97, 1819, 29	....	125.00
76.	½ Duplone 1797	....	75.00

Arms. Rev. Crowned monogram. Without the mark of value and not placed in circulation.

77.	(10 Francs) ND. (1800)	....	275.00

CHUR

A. Bishops of —

PETER II RASCHER, 1581-1601
Bust of St. Luke. Rev. Double eagle.

1.	7 Ducats ND	....	1500.00

JOHN V FLUG OF ASPERMONT, 1601-1627

Bust of St. Luke. Rev. Double eagle.

2.	7 Ducats 1613, 15, ND	................*	1000.00
3.	1 Goldgulden ND	....	200.00

Arms. Rev. Double eagle.

4.	2 Ducats ND	....	750.00

JOHN VI FLUG OF ASPERMONT, 1636-1661
Arms. Rev. Double eagle.

5.	1 Ducat 1636, 48, 49, 52	....	500.00

ULRIC VI, 1661-1692
Bust. Rev. Double eagle.

6.	6 Ducats 1664	....	1250.00

Arms. Rev. Double eagle.

7.	1 Ducat 1664, 91	....	500.00

ULRIC VII, 1692-1788
Bust. Rev. Double eagle.

8.	10 Ducats 1720	....	2000.00

Bust of St. Luke. Rev. Arms.

9.	1 Ducat 1697, 1713, 27	....	375.00

JOSEPH BENEDICT, 1728-1754
Bust of St. Luke. Rev. Arms.

10.	1 Ducat 1730	....	400.00

Bust. Rev. Arms.

11.	10 Ducats 1736, 49	....	1250.00
12.	7 Ducats 1749	....	750.00
13.	5 Ducats 1749	....	650.00
14.	1 Ducat 1749	....	175.00

JOSEPH ANTHONY, 1755-1777
Madonna. Rev. Arms.

15.	1 Ducat 1767	....	200.00

B. City of —

Bust of St. Luke. Rev. Double eagle.

16.	1 Goldgulden 1613, ND	....	300.00

St. Luke standing. Rev. Double eagle.

17.	1 Goldgulden 1618, 20, 22	....	200.00

Arms. Rev. Double eagle.

18.	1 Ducat 1634-47	....	1750.00

EINSIEDELN

Abbots of —

BEATUS KUTTEL, 1780-1808
Arms. Rev. Madonna of Einsiedeln.

1.	1 Ducat 1783	....	80.00

FISCHINGEN

Abbots of —

FRANCIS, 1688-1728

Arms. Rev. St. Ida with stag.

1.	2 Ducats 1726. Thick flan	..........*	300.00
2.	1 Ducat 1726	....	175.00

FRIBOURG

Eagle over fortress. Rev. Floriated cross.

SWITERLAND-FRIBOURG (cont'd)

1. 3 Ducats ND. (1600) 1500.00
2. 2 Ducats or 1 Pistole 1529 .... 1500.00
3. 1 Ducat or Goldgulden 1597, 98, 99, 1620 ..... * 325.00
4. ½ Ducat or Goldgulden 1610, ND 175.00

Eagle over fortress. Rev. St. Nicholas standing.

5. 1 Ducat or Goldgulden ND. (1600) 275.00

Eagle over fortress. Rev. Bust of St. Nicholas. The last three dates are rare.

6. 1 Ducat 1587, 91, 94, 97 .... 300.00

Eagle over fortress. Rev. Cross in quadrilobe.

7. 4 Ducats or 2 Pistoles 1622 .... 1500.00
8. 2 Ducats or 1 Pistole 1622, 35 .... * 500.00

GENEVA

Double eagle and arms. Rev. Sun.

1. 4 Ecus-Pistolets or Quadruple 1633-47 .... 400.00
2. 1 Ecu-Pistolet 1562-86. (Only the obv. is shown). . . * 80.00
3. 1 Large Pistole 1634-42 .... * 500.00

Double eagle. Rev. Legend in tablet.

4. 2 Ducats 1656-92 .... * 250.00
5. 1 Ducat 1644-56, 67 .... 125.00

Arms. Rev. Double eagle.

6. 1 Large Pistole 1659 .... 600.00
7. 1 Large Pistole of 40 Florins 1722, 23, 24. (Only the Rev. is shown.) .... * 100.00
8. 1 Small Pistole of 35 Florins 1772 .... * 100.00

Arms. Rev. Sun.

9. 1 Ecu d'or au Soleil ND. (1500-1600) 500.00
10. 3 Pistoles 1771 .... * 275.00
11. 1 Small Pistole of 35 Florins 1752-70. (Only the Rev. is shown.) .... * 60.00

Arms. Rev. Value.

12. 20 Francs 1848 .... 70.00
13. 10 Francs 1848 .... 65.00

GRAUBUNDEN

Three shields. Rev. Value.

1. 16 Francs 1813 .... 250.00

HALDENSTEIN

Barons of —

THOMAS I, 1609-1628
Bust. Rev. Double eagle.

1. 7 Ducats 1617 .... 1250.00
2. 4 Ducats 1617 .... 600.00
3. 2 Ducats 1617 .... 500.00

Ruler kneeling before seated Christ. Rev. Double eagle.

4. 1 Goldgulden ND 150.00

Ruler kneeling before standing Christ. Rev. Double eagle.

5. 1 Goldgulden 1618, ND 200.00

JULIUS OTTO I, 1628-1666
Ruler standing. Rev. Double eagle.

6. 1 Ducat 1638, 42, 48, 49 .... 500.00

THOMAS II, (1667)

7. 1 Ducat 1667 .... 1000.00

GUBERT, (1733)
Bust. Rev. Arms.

8. 6 Ducats 1733 .... 2000.00
9. 1 Ducat 1733 .... 700.00

THOMAS III, (1767)
Bust. Rev. Eagle.

10. 1 Ducat 1767 .... 500.00

HELVETIAN REPUBLIC

Warrior standing. Rev. Value.

1. 32 Francs 1800 ....* 150.00
2. 16 Francs 1800 .... 100.00

LAUSANNE

Bishops of —

AYMON DE MONTFAUCON, 1491-1517
Bust. Rev. Arms.

1. 1 Ducat ND 500.00

LUCERNE

Eagle over arms. Rev. Bust of St. Leodegar.

1. 4 Ducats ND. (1600) 1000.00
2. 2 Ducats 1603 .... 1000.00

Arms. Rev. St. Leodegar standing.

3. 10 Ducats 1698 .... 2500.00
4. 5 Ducats 1698 .... 500.00
5. 4 Ducats 1698 .... 400.00

Value in cartouche. Rev. St. Leodegar and St. Maurice standing.

6. 1 Ducat ND. (1695-1700) 250.00

Arms. Rev. St. Leodegar and the city church.

7. 2 Ducats 1675 .... 500.00

Warrior seated. Rev. St. Leodegar standing.

8. 5 Ducats 1695 .... 2000.00
9. 2 Ducats 1695 .... 500.00

Value in cartouche. Rev. St. Leodegar seated.

10. 10 Ducats 1714 .... 1000.00
11. 6 Ducats 1714 .... 700.00
12. 5 Ducats 1714 .... 500.00
13. 4 Ducats 1714 .... 500.00

Value in cartouche. Rev. St. Leodegar standing. The 1725 date is rare.

14. 3 Ducats 1714 .... 375.00
15. 2 Ducats 1714 ....* 175.00
16. 1 Ducat 1715, 25 .... 150.00

Arms supported by wild men. Rev. Value.

17. 5 Ducats 1741 .... 500.00
18. 4 Ducats 1741 .... 300.00
19. 3 Ducats 1741 .... 250.00
20. 2 Ducats 1741 ....* 175.00
21. 1 Ducat 1741 ....* 75.00

Arms. Rev. Value in wreath.

22. 24 Munzgulden 1794, 96 ....* 300.00
23. 12 Munzgulden 1794, 96 .... 100.00

Arms. Rev. Warrior seated at shield.

24. 20 Francs 1807 .... 200.00
25. 10 Francs 1804 ....* 85.00

MESOCCO

Marcheses of —

JOHN JACOB TRIVULZIO, 1487-1518
Arms with three crosses. Rev. Cross.

1. 1 Scudo d'oro ND 400.00

Arms with Lily of France. Rev. Cross.

2. 1 Scudo d'oro ND 1000.00

Arms with three shields. Rev. Cross.

3. 1 Scudo d'oro ND 1200.00

Madonna. Rev. Orb.

4. 1 Zecchino or Florin ND 1200.00

MURI

Abbots of —

PLACIDUS ZURLAUBEN, 1684-1723
Bust. Rev. View of the Abbey.

1. 5 Ducats 1720 .... 650.00

Bust. Rev. Arms of Zurlauben.

2. 1 Ducat 1720 .... 125.00

NEUCHATEL

Counts of —

HENRY I, 1575-1595

Bust. Rev. Arms. Known only in the Museum of Neuchatel.

1. 1 Ecu Pistolet .... **Unique**

HENRY II, 1595-1663

Bust. Rev. Arms. The 1 Pistole is known only in the Museums of Vienna and Neuchatel.

2. 2 Pistoles 1603 .... 1000.00
3. 1 Pistole 1618 .... **Rare**

MARIE OF NEMOURS, 1694-1707

Bust. Rev. Arms.

4. 4 Pistoles 1694. Neuchatel Museum .... **Unique**
5. 2 Pistoles 1694 .... 750.00

Cross of four M's, "16" in center. Rev. Arms.

6. Gold 16 Kreuzers or 1 Ducat 1694 .... 250.00

(For the 1 Pistole of 1713, see under Germany-Prussia.)

OBWALDEN (UNTERWALDEN)

Arms. Rev. St. Nicholas Von Flue standing.

1. 8 Ducats 1728 .... 1250.00

Legend. Rev. Double Eagle and Cantonal arms.

2. 1 Ducat 1726 .... 450.00

Legend. Rev. St. Nicholas Von Flue standing.

3. 1 Ducat 1726 .... 175.00

Legend. Rev. St. Nicholas Von Flue kneeling to right or left.

4. 5 Ducats 1732 .... 800.00
5. 1 Ducat 1725, 30, 43, 87 ....*...... 75.00
6. 1 Ducat 1787. Restruck in 1887 .... 30.00

Arms. Rev. St. Nicholas Von Flue kneeling.

7. 1 Ducat 1774 .... 125.00

RHEINAU

Abbots of —

GEROLD ZURLAUBEN, 1695-1735

Two shields. Rev. View of the Abbey.

1. 1 Ducat 1710 .... 175.00

Bust. Rev. Arms.

2. 2 Ducats 1723 .... 250.00

Arms. Rev. St. Fintan standing.

3. 2 Ducats 1723 ....*...... 200.00
4. 1 Ducat 1723 .... 125.00

ST. GALLEN

A. City of —

Bear. Rev. Double eagle.

1. 4 Ducats 1620. Square. Museum of St. Gallen .... **Unique**
2. 3 Ducats 1618, 19. Museum of St. Gallen .... **Unique**
3. 2 Ducats 1621 ....*...... 300.00

B. Abbots of —

BEDA ANGEHRN, 1765-1796

Arms. Rev. St. Gallus on throne.

4. 1 Ducat 1773, 74 .... 175.00

Arms. Rev. Bear.

5. 1 Ducat 1781 .... 150.00

SCHAFFHAUSEN

Ram in city gate. Rev. Double eagle.

1. 20 Ducats 1656 .... 2500.00
2. 3 Ducats 1632 .... 1500.00
3. 1 Florin 1622 .... 150.00

SWITZERLAND-SCHAFFHAUSEN (cont'd)

Ram to left in shield. Rev. Double eagle.

4. 1 Ducat 1633, 57, ND 100.00

Arms. Rev. Single head eagle.

5. ½ Ducat ND (1650) 100.00
6. ¼ Ducat ND (1650) 100.00

SCHWYZ

Double eagle over Cantonal arms. Rev. Floriated cross. Struck at Bellinzona, 1510-20.

1. 1 Scudo d'oro ND 1000.00

St. Martin and beggar. Rev. Madonna.

2. 1 Ducat 1653, ND 200.00

Legend and date. Rev. Lion holding shield.

3. 1 Ducat 1781, 88, 90 ND 125.00

Lion and shield. Rev. Legend.

4. 1 Ducat 1844 .... 150.00

SOLOTHURN

Eagle over arms. Rev. Bust of St. Ursus.

1. 3 Ducats ND (1550-60) 1500.00

Arms. Rev. St. Ursus standing in enclosure.

2. 1 Ducat 1630 .... 500.00
3. ½ Ducat 1630 ....*...... 200.00

Double eagle and arms. Rev. St. Ursus standing.

4. 1 Ducat ND (1620-30) .... Rare

Arms. Rev. St. Ursus standing.

5. 1 Ducat 1768 .... 250.00
6. 2 Duplones 1796, 97, 98 .... 175.00
7. 1 Duplone 1787, 96, 97, 98 ....*...... 125.00
8. ½ Duplone 1787, 96 ....*...... 100.00
9. ¼ Duplone 1789, 96 .... 60.00

Crowned oval shield. Rev. St. Ursus standing.

10. 16 Franken 1813 .... 250.00
11. 8 Franken 1813 ....*...... 300.00

URI

Floriated cross over Cantonal arms. Rev. St. Martin on horse-back and beggar.

1. 1 Pistole ND. Small size. (1600-1700) ....*...... 150.00
2. 1 Pistole 1613. Large size 300.00

Value and arms. Rev. St. Martin standing and beggar.

3. 1 Ducat 1701 .... 200.00

Arms. Rev. St. Martin on horseback and beggar.

4. 1 Ducat 1720, 36 .... 100.00

URI, SCHWYZ AND UNTERWALDEN

Three shields, double eagle and keys. Rev. Floriated cross. Struck at Bellinzona, 1503-50.

1. 1 Scudo d'oro ND 800.00

Same Obv. as above. Rev. St. Martin and beggar.

2. 1 Ducat ND. Bellinzona Mint 800.00

Three Cantonal shields and double eagle. Rev. Floriated cross. Struck at Altdorf, 1550-1600.

3. 1 Gold Krone ND 800.00

SWITZERLAND (cont'd)

URI AND UNTERWALDEN

Two Cantonal shields and double eagle. Rev. Floriated cross. Struck at Bellinzona, 1503-50.

1. 1 Scudo d'oro ND 800.00

WALLIS AND SION

Bishops of —

HILDEBRAND OF RIEDMATTEN, 1565-1604
Floriated cross. Rev. Bust of St. Theodoule over arms.

1. 1 Ducat ND 375.00

ADRIEN III OF RIEDMATTEN, 1640-1646
Arms of Riedmatten. Rev. Eagle and arms of Wallis.

2. 1 Ducat ND 400.00

ZUG

Arms and "1/6". Rev. Double eagle.

1. Gold 1/6 Assis or ¼ Ducat ND (1600-1700) 100.00

Double eagle and arms. Rev. Bust of St. Oswald.

2. 1 Florin 1615 .... 1000.00

Arms. Rev. Legend.

3. 1½ Ducats 1692 .... 1000.00

Arms. Rev. Value.

4. ½ Ducat 1692 .... 125.00

ZURICH

Arms in trilobe. Rev. Shield.

1. Goldgulden 1526, 27 .... 600.00

Two lions with three shields. Rev. Circle of nine shields around Cantonal arms.

2. 10 Ducats 1559 ....*...... 1500.00
3. 9 Ducats 1559 .... 1250.00
4. 8 Ducats 1559 .... 1000.00

Arms on double eagle. Rev. Floriated cross.

5. 1 Gold Krone 1631, ND 400.00
6. ½ Gold Krone ND (1560, 61) 125.00

Eagle and arms. Rev. Charlemagne on throne.

7. 1 Florin ND (1600) 600.00

Legend in wreath. Rev. Charlemagne on throne.

8. 2 Ducats ND (1600) 600.00
9. 1 Ducat ND (1600) ....*...... 150.00

Charlemagne on throne. Rev. Saints Regula and Felix standing.

10. 1 Ducat ND (1600) 200.00

Eagle and arms. Rev. Charlemagne standing.

11. 1 Ducat ND (1600) ....*...... 250.00
12. ½ Ducat ND (1600) 250.00

Lion with shield. Rev. Double eagle.

13. 4 Ducats 1624, 29 ....*...... 600.00
14. 2 Ducats 1624, 29 .... 400.00

Warrior standing. Rev. Legend in wreath.

15. ½ Ducat 1639 ....*...... 125.00
16. ¼ Ducat 1639 .... 125.00

Two lions and shield. Rev. Double eagle.

17. 4 Ducats 1640, 41 .... **600.00**
18. 2 Ducats 1641 .... * **300.00**

Legend in wreath. Rev. Two lions and shield.

19. 1 Ducat 1641-50 .... **100.00**

Legend in wreath. Rev. Lion and arms.

20. 4 Ducats 1666 .... **600.00**
21. 1 Ducat 1645, 61, 80, 97, ND .... * **100.00**
22. ½ Ducat 1641-51, 60-70 .... **25.00**
23. ¼ Ducat 1645-49 .... **15.00**

Two lions and two shields. Rev. Legend.

24. 15 Ducats 1649 .... **1250.00**
25. 8 Ducats 1646 .... **800.00**
26. 6 Ducats 1647 .... **600.00**

Legend in wreath. Rev. Arms.

27. 1 Ducat 1651 .... **100.00**

Arms. Rev. Date in wreath.

28. ½ Ducat 1654-62 .... **25.00**
29. ¼ Ducat 1654-66 .... **15.00**

Lion and shield. Rev. View of the city.

30. 10 Ducats ND (1600-1700) **1250.00**
31. 5 Ducats 1720, 33, 39, 40 .... * **650.00**

Two lions and arms. Rev. View of the city.

32. 10 Ducats 1724, 25 .... **1250.00**

Lion and arms. Rev. Date or legend in wreath.

33. ½ Ducat 1671-1767, 76 .... * **15.00**
34. ¼ Ducat 1671-1767 .... **12.50**

Two lions and shield. Rev. Legend in wreath.

35. 2 Ducats 1708-76 .... **125.00**

Lion and arms. Rev. Legend in wreath.

36. 2 Ducats 1673 .... **250.00**
37. 1 Ducat 1705-75, 1810 .... * **40.00**

Bust of Zwingli to left. Rev. Bible on table. On the Reformation.

38. 2 Ducats 1719 .... **125.00**

Bust of Zwingli to left. Rev. Legend. On the Reformation.

39. 1 Ducat 1719 .... **35.00**

Bust of Zwingli to right. Rev. Legend. On the Reformation.

40. 1 Ducat 1819 .... **25.00**

VATICAN CITY (ROME)

Popes of —

A. Coinage struck at Rome

POPULAR GOVERNMENT, 1305
St. John. Rev. Arms.

1. 1 Florin ND 1000.00

JOHN XXII, 1316-1334
INNOCENT VI, 1352-1362
URBAN V, 1362-1370
CLEMENT VII, 1378-1394

(See under France-Avignon).

THE ROMAN SENATE, 1350-1439

Senator kneeling before St. Peter. Rev. Christ.

2. 1 Ducat ND 40.00

ALEXANDER V, 1409-1410
JOHN XXIII, 1410-1415
MARTIN V, 1421-1428

(See under Vatican-Bologna).

EUGENE IV, 1431-1447

St. Peter. Rev. Arms.

3. 1 Ducat ND 50.00

NICHOLAS V, 1447-1455
St. Peter and St. Paul. Rev. Crossed keys.

4. 3 Ducats ND 2500.00

Pope seated. Rev. Keys.

5. 1 Ducat ND 1000.00

St. Peter. Rev. Arms.

6. 1 Ducat ND 50.00

CALIXTUS III, 1455-1458

St. Peter in ship. Rev. Arms.

7. 1 Ducat ND 100.00

St. Peter standing. Rev. Arms.

8. 1 Ducat ND .... 100..00

St. Peter and St. Paul. Rev. Arms.

9. 1 Ducat ND 100.00

PIUS II, 1458-1464
St. Peter and St. Paul. Rev. Ship at sea.

10. 2 Ducats ND 2000.00

Ship at sea. Rev. Arms.

11. 1 Ducat ND 500.00

St. Peter. Rev. Arms.

12. 1 Ducat ND 50.00

PAUL II, 1464-1471
Christ and St. Peter. Rev. Eight apostles.

13. 4 Ducats 1464, 65 .... 2000.00

Christ and St. Peter. Rev. Arms.

14. 1 Ducat 1464 .... 300.00

Pope kneeling before St. Peter. Rev. Arms.

15. 2 Ducats ND .... * 400.00
15a. 1 Ducat 1464, ND 100.00

Pope kneeling before Christ. Rev. Arms.

16. 1 Ducat ND 100.00

St. Peter. Rev. Arms.

17. 2 Ducats ND 600.00
18. 1 Ducat ND 75.00

Two apostles. Rev. Arms.

19. 1 Ducat ND 75.00

St. Veronica. Rev. Arms.

20. 1 Ducat ND 150.00

SIXTUS IV, 1471-1484
Christ and St. Peter in landscape. Rev. Apostles in ship.

21. 10 Ducats 1475 .... 5000.00

Christ and St. Peter. Rev. Arms.

22. 2 Ducats ND 1000.00

St. Peter in ship. Rev. Arms.

23. 1 Ducat 1475, ND 75.00

Pope kneeling before Christ. Rev. Arms.

24. 1 Ducat ND 300.00

Two apostles. Rev. Arms.

25. 1 Ducat ND 75.00

INNOCENT VIII, 1484-1492

St. Peter in ship. Rev. Arms.

26. 1 Ducat ND 60.00

Two apostles. Rev. Arms.

27. 1 Ducat ND 100.00

ALEXANDER VI BORGIA, 1492-1503
Bust. Rev. Arms.

28. 3 Ducats 1495, 1500 .... 3000.00

St. Peter in ship. Rev. Arms.

29. 5 Ducats ND 3000.00
30. 2 Ducats ND ....*...... 150.00
31. 1 Ducat ND 100.00

Two apostles. Rev. Legend.

32. 1 Ducat ND 500.00

PIUS III, 1503
St. Peter in ship. Rev. Arms.

33. 1 Ducat ND 2000.00

JULIUS II, 1503-1513
Bust. Rev. Pastoral scene.

34. 4 Ducats ND 3000.00

Bust. Rev. St. Peter seated.

35. 3 Ducats ND 2500.00

Bust. Rev. Two apostles in ship.

36. 2 Ducats ND 300.00

Bust. Rev. Two apostles kissing.

37. 2 Ducats ND 1500.00

Bust. Rev. St. Peter in ship.

38. 2 Ducats ND 1000.00

Two apostles in ship. Rev. Arms.

39. 2 Ducats ND 125.00
40. 1 Ducat ND ....*...... 40.00

St. Peter in ship. Rev. Arms.

41. 2 Ducats ND 125.00
42. 1 Ducat ND 75.00

LEO X, 1513-1521

Bust. Rev. The three Magi.

43. 2½ Ducats ND ....*...... 600.00
44. 2   Ducats ND 1000.00

Two apostles in ship. Rev. Arms.

45. 2 Ducats ND 100.00
46. 1 Ducat ND ....*...... 40.00

Two apostles standing. Rev. Arms.

47. 1 Ducat ND 75.00

St. Peter in ship. Rev. Arms.

48. 1 Ducat ND 40.00

SEDE VACANTE, 1521

St. Peter in ship. Rev. Arms.

VATICAN CITY (ROME) (cont'd)

49. 1 Ducat ND 150.00

ADRIAN VI, 1522-1523

St. Peter in ship. Rev. Arms.

50. 2 Ducats ND ....*...... 300.00
51. 1 Ducat ND 175.00

CLEMENT VII, 1523-1534

Birth of Christ. Rev. Pope opening the Holy Door.

52. 5 Zecchini 1525 .... 3000.00

Bust. Rev. Angel and St. Peter.

53. 2 Ducats ND 2500.00

Bust. Rev. Christ standing.

54. 2 Ducats ND 2000.00

Pope and Emperor Charles V standing. Rev. Two apostles.

55. 2 Ducats ND 2500.00

Two apostles. Rev. Arms.

56. 3 Ducats ND 2000.00

Two apostles in ship. Rev. Arms.

57. 2 Ducats ND 400.00

St. Peter. Rev. Arms.

58. 2 Ducats ND 125.00

St. Peter in ship. Rev. Arms.

59. 2 Ducats ND ....*...... 100.00
60. 1 Ducat ND 50.00

St. Peter seated. Rev. Arms.

61. 2 Ducats ND 400.00

PAUL III, 1534-1549

Bust. Rev. St. Peter in ship.

62. 2 Ducats ND 500.00

St. Paul in ship. Rev. Arms.

63. 1 Ducat ND 75.00

St. Peter in ship. Rev. Arms.

64. 1 Ducat ND 75.00

St. Paul standing. Rev. Arms. There are several varieties of the standing figure.

65. 1 Scudo d'oro ND 40.00

JULIUS III, 1550-1555

Bust. Rev. St. Peter in ship.

66. 1 Ducat 1551 .... 500.00

St. Peter. Rev. Arms.

67. 1 Scudo d'oro ND 500.00

Arms. Rev. The Holy Door.

68. 1 Scudo d'oro 1550 .... 850.00

Bust of Christ. Rev. Arms.

69. 1 Scudo d'oro 1551, 52, ND 85.00

SEDE VACANTE, 1555

St. Peter. Rev. Arms.

70. 1 Scudo d'oro 1555 .... 500.00

PAUL IV, 1555-1559

St. Paul. Rev. Arms.

71. 1 Scudo d'oro ND 500.00

St. Peter. Rev. Arms.

72. 1 Scudo d'oro ND 500.00

SEDE VACANTE, 1559

St. Peter. Rev. Arms.

73. 1 Scudo d'oro 1559 .... 100.00

PIUS IV, 1559-1565

(See under Vatican-Bologna).

ST. PIUS V, 1566-1572

Bust. Rev. St. Peter in ship.

74. 2 Ducats 1566 .... 3000.00
75. 1 Ducat ND 1000.00

St. Peter kneeling before Christ. Rev. Arms.

76. 4 Scudi d'oro ND 3000.00

GREGORY XIII, 1572-1585

Bust. Rev. The Holy Door.

77. 1 Scudo d'oro 1575 .... 2000.00

Bust. Rev. Charity standing.

78. 1 Scudo d'oro 1576 .... 500.00

VATICAN CITY (ROME) (cont'd)

Bust. Rev. Christ and two apostles in ship.

79. 1 Doppia 1578 .... **2000.00**

Bust. Rev. St. Peter.

80. 1 Scudo d'oro 1581 .... **500.00**

Bust. Rev. Madonna seated.

81. 1 Scudo d'oro ND **500.00**

Bust. Rev. St. Paul.

82. 1 Scudo d'oro ND **400.00**

Arms. Rev. The Holy Door.

83. 1 Scudo d'oro 1575 .... **600.00**

St. Peter in ship. Rev. Arms.

84. 1 Scudo d'oro 1575, 76 .... **400.00**

Bust of Christ. Rev. Arms.

85. 1 Scudo d'oro 1577-82, ND **75.00**

SIXTUS V, 1585-1590

Bust of Christ. Rev. Arms.

86. 1 Scudo d'oro 1585, 87, 88 .... **250.00**

St. Peter. Rev. Arms.

87. 1 Scudo d'oro 1585 .... **250.00**

SEDE VACANTE, 1590

St. Peter and angel. Rev. Arms.

88. 4 Scudi d'oro 1590 .... **2000.00**

Roma seated. Rev. Arms.

89. 1 Scudo d'oro 1590 .... **500.00**

Bust of Christ. Rev. Arms.

90. 1 Scudo d'oro 1590 .... **500.00**

URBAN VII, 1590
GREGORY XIV, 1590-1591

(See under Vatican-Bologna).

SEDE VACANTE, 1591

David with harp. Rev. Arms.

91. 4 Scudi d'oro 1591 .... **2000.00**

INNOCENT IX, 1591-1592

(See under Vatican-Bologna).

CLEMENT VIII, 1592-1605

Bust. Rev. Justice standing.

92. 4 Scudi d'oro 1598 .... **2000.00**

Bust. Rev. The Church seated.

93. 4 Scudi d'oro ND **2000.00**

Bust. Rev. The Lateran Church.

94. 1 Scudo d'oro ND **1000.00**

Arms. Rev. The Church seated.

95. 1 Scudo d'oro ND **600.00**

Pope kneeling. Rev. Arms.

96. 1 Scudo d'oro ND **600.00**

Arms. Rev. Dove.

97. 1 Scudo d'oro ND **600.00**

SEDE VACANTE, 1605

The Church seated. Rev. Arms.

98. 4 Scudi d'oro 1605 .... **3000.00**
99. 1 Scudo d'oro 1605 .... **1000.00**

PAUL V, 1605-1621

Bust. Rev. St. Paul seated.

100. 4 Scudi d'oro 1606, 07 .... **500.00**

Bust. Rev. St. Paul standing.

101. 4 Scudi d'oro 1609 .... **500.00**
102. 1 Scudo d'oro 1617 ....*...... **75.00**

Bust of St. Paul. Rev. Arms.

103. 4 Scudi d'oro 1608, 09 .... **500.00**
104. 1 Scudo d'oro 1607, 15 ....*...... **75.00**

Busts of St. Peter and St. Paul. Rev. Arms.

105. 1 Scudo d'oro 1609 .... **100.00**

St. Paul seated. Rev. Arms.

106. 4 Scudi d'oro 1617 .... 500.00
107. 1 Scudo d'oro 1606, 11 ....* 75.00

GREGORY XV, 1621-1623
Bust. Rev. Madonna standing.

108. 1 Scudo d'oro 1622 .... 75.00

Bust. Rev. Church of St. Mary the Major.

109. 1 Scudo d'oro 1622 .... 100.00

Madonna standing. Rev. Arms.

110. 4 Scudi d'oro ND ....* 600.00
111. 2 Scudi d'oro ND 100.00

St. Paul standing. Rev. Arms.

112. 2 Scudi d'oro ND 100.00

SEDE VACANTE, 1623
Christ standing. Rev. Arms.

113. 4 Scudi d'oro 1623 .... 1000.00

URBAN VIII, 1623-1644

Bust. Rev. The Holy Door.

114. 1 Scudo d'oro 1625 .... 75.00

Bust. Rev. Madonna standing.

115. 4 Scudi d'oro 1634 .... 700.00
116. 1 Scudo d'oro 1627-36, ND ....* 60.00

Bust. Rev. St. Michael standing.

117. 4 Scudi d'oro 1634 .... 700.00
118. 1 Scudo d'oro 1629, 36 .... 75.00

Bust. Rev. Bust of Christ.

119. 1 Scudo d'oro 1630 .... 100.00

Madonna standing. Rev. Arms.

120. 2 Scudi d'oro 1624 .... 400.00
121. 1 Scudo d'oro 1642, 43, ND 100.00

Busts of St. Peter and St. Paul. Rev. Arms.

122. 2 Scudi d'oro 1624 .... 400.00

Arms. Rev. The Holy Door.

123. 1 Scudo d'oro 1625 .... 100.00

Bust of St. Paul. Rev. Arms.

124. 1 Scudo d'oro 1627 .... 100.00

St. Michael standing. Rev. Arms.

125. 1 Scudo d'oro 1642, 43, ND 100.00

INNOCENT X, 1644-1655
Bust. Rev. Arms.

126. 4 Scudi d'oro 1647 .... 1000.00

Bust. Rev. The Holy Door.

127. 4 Scudi d'oro 1650 .... 1000.00

Bust of St. Peter. Rev. Arms.

128. 2 Scudi d'oro 1652 .... 500.00
129. 1 Scudo d'oro 1644, 52 ....* 150.00

Madonna standing. Rev. Arms.

130. 1 Scudo d'oro 1645, 52 .... 150.00

Arms. Rev. The Holy Door.

131. 2 Scudi d'oro 1651 .... 500.00

SEDE VACANTE, 1655

Arms. Rev. Dove.

132. 4 Scudi d'oro 1655 .... 700.00
133. 2 Scudi d'oro 1655 ....* 300.00

ALEXANDER VII, 1655-1667

Arms. Rev. Money chest.

134. 4 Scudi d'oro ND 1000.00

Arms. Rev. Legend.

135. 2 Scudi d'oro ND ....* 600.00
136. 1 Scudo d'oro ND 150.00

SEDE VACANTE, 1667
Arms. Rev. Dove.

1 Scudo d'oro 1667 .... 200.00

VATICAN CITY (ROME) (cont'd)

CLEMENT IX, 1667-1669

Madonna. Rev. Arms.

138.	4 Scudi d'oro ND	.....................*	750.00
139.	2 Scudi d'oro ND	....	250.00
140.	1 Scudo d'oro ND	....	100.00

SEDE VACANTE, 1669

Arms. Rev. Dove.

141.	4 Scudi d'oro 1669	....	700.00
142.	2 Scudi d'oro 1669	....	350.00
143.	1 Scudo d'oro 1669	....	200.00

CLEMENT X, 1669-1676

Bust. Rev. St. Peter

144.	2 Scudi d'oro 1670	....	750.00

St. Venantius. Rev. Arms.

145.	2 Scudi d'oro ND	....	500.00

Bust. Rev. King David.

146.	4 Scudi d'oro 1673	....	750.00

Arms. Rev. The Holy Door.

147.	1 Scudo d'oro 1675	....	200.00

Arms. Rev. King David.

148.	4 Scudi d'oro ND	....	750.00

St. Peter and St. Paul. Rev. Arms.

149.	2 Scudi d'oro ND	....	300.00

St. Peter. Rev. Arms.

150.	1 Scudo d'oro ND	....	150.00

Madonna. Rev. Arms.

151.	1 Scudo d'oro ND	....	150.00

INNOCENT XI, 1676-1689

Bust. Rev. Madonna and four saints.

152.	4 Scudi d'oro 1676, 77	....	700.00

Bust. Rev. Holy figure among clouds.

153.	4 Scudi d'oro 1678	....	700.00

Bust. Rev. Legend.

154.	4 Scudi d'oro 1681, 82, 85	....	500.00

Religion seated. Rev. Arms.

155.	2 Scudi d'oro 1678	....	300.00

Arms. Rev. Legend.

156.	4 Scudi d'oro 1687	....	450.00
157.	2 Scudi d'oro 1677-87	....	200.00
158.	1 Scudo d'oro 1684, ND	...................*	100.00

Madonna. Rev. Arms.

159.	1 Scudo d'oro ND	....	100.00

Bust of Madonna. Rev. Arms.

160.	1 Scudo d'oro ND	....	100.00

Bust of St. Peter. Rev. Arms.

161.	1 Scudo d'oro ND	....	100.00

SEDE VACANTE, 1689

Arms. Rev. Dove.

162.	4 Scudi d'oro 1689	....	700.00

ALEXANDER VIII, 1689-1691

Bust. Rev. St. Peter and St. Paul.

163.	4 Scudi d'oro 1689	....	400.00

Bust. Rev. The Church standing.

164.	16 Scudi d'oro 1690	....	3000.00

Bust. Rev. Two oxen.

VATICAN CITY (ROME) (cont'd)

165. 4 Scudi d'oro 1690 .... **400.00**

Bust. Rev. St. Bruno.

166. 4 Scudi d'oro 1690 .... **400.00**

Bust. Rev. St. Magnus and St. Bruno.

167. 4 Scudi d'oro 1690 .... **400.00**

St. Bruno. Rev. Arms.

168. 2 Scudi d'oro 1689 .... **250.00**

St. Peter. Rev. Arms.

169. 1 Scudo d'oro 1689 .... **100.00**

Busts of St. Peter and St. Paul. Rev. Arms.

170. 1 Scudo d'oro 1690 .... **100.00**

Arms. Rev. Altar.

171. 2 Scudi d'oro 1690 .... **250.00**

SEDE VACANTE, 1691

Arms. Rev. Dove.

172. 2 Scudi d'oro 1691 .... **250.00**

INNOCENT XII, 1691-1700

Bust. Rev. Fountain.

173. 4 Scudi d'oro 1694 .... **400.00**

Bust. Rev. Noah's Ark.

173a. 2 Scudi d'oro 1697 .... **400.00**

Bust of St. Peter. Rev. Arms.

174. 1 Scudo d'oro 1691, 92 .... **100.00**
175. ½ Scudo d'oro 1694 .... **100.00**

St. Paul. Rev. Arms.

176. 2 Scudi d'oro 1692 .... **250.00**

Arms. Rev. Plant.

177. 1 Scudo d'oro 1694 .... **100.00**

Arms. Rev. The Holy Door.

178. 2 Scudi d'oro 1699 .... **250.00**
179. 1 Scudo d'oro 1700 .... **100.00**
180. ½ Scudo d'oro 1694 .... **100.00**

Arms. Rev. Corn ears in vessel.

181. 1 Scudo d'oro 1697 .... **100.00**

SEDE VACANTE, 1700
Arms. Rev. Dove.

182. 1 Scudo d'oro 1700 .... **250.00**

CLEMENT XI, 1700-1721

Bust. Rev. The Holy Door.

183. 2 Scudi d'oro 1700 .... **250.00**

Bust. Rev. Piety and Discord.

184. 4 Scudi d'oro 1706 .... **600.00**

Bust. Rev. Arms.

185. 1 Scudo d'oro 1710 .... **100.00**

Bust. Rev. Star over sea.

186. ½ Scudo d'oro 1716 .... **100.00**

Bust. Rev. Bust of St. Peter.

186a. ½ Scudo d'oro 1717 .... **100.00**

Bust. Rev. Legend.

187. 2 Scudi d'oro 1710, 14 .... **200.00**

VATICAN CITY (ROME) (cont'd)

Bust of St. Paul. Rev. Arms.

188.	2 Scudi d'oro 1702, 05	200.00
189.	1 Scudo d'oro 1702-09 ....*	50.00

Madonna. Rev. Arms.

190.	4 Scudi d'oro 1706	500.00

Arms and globe. Rev. Legend.

191.	2 Scudi d'oro 1706	250.00

Arms. Rev. Anchor.

192.	1 Scudo d'oro 1706	100.00

Charity standing. Rev. Arms.

193.	4 Scudi d'oro 1707	500.00

Arms. Rev. Three females.

194.	4 Scudi d'oro 1707	500.00

St. Francis kneeling. Rev. Arms.

195.	2 Scudi d'oro 1707	200.00

St. Francisca. Rev. Arms.

196.	2 Scudi d'oro 1709	200.00

Bust of St. Peter. Rev. Arms.

197.	½ Scudo d'oro 1709, 16, 17	30.00

Arms. Rev. Various legends.

198.	2 Scudi d'oro 1712	200.00
199.	1 Scudo d'oro 1711-18 ....*	40.00
200.	½ Scudo d'oro ND	30.00

Arms. Rev. Bow and arrow.

201.	1 Scudo d'oro 1716	100.00

Religion seated. Rev. Arms.

202.	1 Scudo d'oro 1718	50.00

Faith standing. Rev. Arms.

202a.	1 Scudo d'oro 1718	125.00

Arms. Rev. Olive tree.

203.	1 Scudo d'oro 1720	100.00

Three mountains. Rev. Star over sea.

204.	½ Scudo d'oro 1706	40.00

SEDE VACANTE, 1721
Arms. Rev. Dove.

205.	2 Scudi d'oro 1721	150.00
206.	1 Scudo d'oro 1721	100.00

INNOCENT XIII, 1721-1724

Bust. Rev. Eagle.

207.	1 Scudo d'oro 1724	100.00

Arms. Rev. Legend.

208.	1 Scudo d'oro 1722	75.00

Arms. Rev. Eagle.

209.	½ Scudo d'oro 1724	75.00

SEDE VACANTE, 1724
Arms. Rev. Dove.

210.	1 Scudo d'oro 1724	250.00

BENEDICT XIII, 1724-1730

Arms. Rev. The Holy Door.

211.	2 Scudi d'oro 1725	400.00
212.	1 Scudo d'oro 1725 ....*	100.00

The Church seated. Rev. Rose and value.

213.	1 Zecchino 1729	50.00

SEDE VACANTE, 1730
Arms. Rev. Dove.

214. 2 Scudi d'oro 1730 .... 500.00

The Church seated. Rev. Arms on cross and value.

215. 1 Zecchino 1730 .... 100.00

CLEMENT XII, 1730-1740

Bust. Rev. Various legends.

216. 1 Scudo d'oro 1735, 38, 39 .... 50.00

The Church seated. Rev. Arms.

217. 2 Zecchini 1731, 39 ....*...... 200.00
218. 1 Zecchino 1738, 39, ND 30.00
219. ½ Zecchino 1739 .... 25.00

Arms. Rev. Legend.

220. 1 Scudo d'oro 1734, 35 .... 40.00

Bust of St. Peter. Rev. Legend.

221. ¼ Zecchino ND 25.00

SEDE VACANTE, 1740
The Church seated. Rev. Arms.

222. 2 Zecchini 1740 .... 125.00
223. 1 Zecchino 1740 .... 75.00
224. ½ Zecchino 1740 .... 50.00

Bust of St. Peter. Rev. Legend.

225. ¼ Zecchino 1740 .... 25.00

BENEDICT XIV, 1740-1758

The Church seated. Rev. Arms.

226. 2 Zecchini 1748 ....*...... 100.00
227. 1 Zecchino 1740-56, ND 30.00
228. ½ Zecchino 1740-55 .... 25.00

Bust of St. Peter. Rev. Legend.

229. ¼ Zecchino 1741, ND 15.00

Bust of St. Peter. Rev. Arms.

230. ¼ Zecchino 1751 .... 15.00

SEDE VACANTE, 1758
The Church seated. Rev. Arms.

231. 1 Zecchino 1758 .... 35.00

CLEMENT XIII, 1758-1769

The Church seated. Rev. Arms.

232. 2 Zecchini 1759, 66 ....*...... 100.00
233. 1 Zecchino 1758-69 .... 30.00
234. ½ Zecchino 1758, 67 .... 25.00

SEDE VACANTE, 1769
The Church seated. Rev. Arms.

235. 1 Zecchino 1769 .... 50.00

CLEMENT XIV, 1769-1774

The Church seated. Rev. Arms.

236. 1 Zecchino 1769-73 ....*...... 30.00
237. ½ Zecchino 1769 .... 25.00

SEDE VACANTE, 1774
The Church seated. Rev. Arms.

238. 1 Zecchino 1774 .... 65.00

PIUS VI, 1774-1799
The Church seated. Rev. Arms.

239. 1 Zecchino 1775-84 .... 27.50
240. ½ Zecchino 1796 .... 25.00

St. Peter seated. Rev. Lily.

241. 2 Doppia or 60 Paoli 1776, 77 ....*...... 65.00
242. 1 Doppia or 30 Paoli 1776-91 .... 40.00
243. ½ Doppia or 15 Paoli 1776-87 .... 25.00

PIUS VII, 1799-1823

St. Peter seated. Rev. Arms.

244. 1 Doppia 1800-23. R mm. ....*...... 27.50
245. 1 Doppia 1815-21. B mm. 32.50

SEDE VACANTE, 1823

St. Peter seated. Rev. Arms.

246. 1 Doppia 1823. R mm. 50.00
247. 1 Doppia 1823. B mm. ....*...... 50.00

VATICAN CITY (ROME) (cont'd)

LEO XII, 1823-1829

Bust. Rev. Faith standing.

248. 2 Zecchini 1828. R mm. **75.00**

Faith seated. Rev. Arms.

249. 2 Zecchini 1824, 25. R mm. **50.00**

St. Peter seated. Rev. Arms.

250. 1 Doppia 1823, 29. R mm. ....* **40.00**
251. 1 Doppia 1824. B mm. **45.00**

SEDE VACANTE, 1829

St. Peter seated. Rev. Arms.

252. 1 Doppia 1829. R mm. ....* **50.00**
253. 1 Doppia 1829. B mm. **50.00**

PIUS VIII, 1829-1830
Bust. Rev. St. Peter and St. Paul standing. Without the mark of value.
254. 20 Scudi 1830. B mm. **2500.00**

SEDE VACANTE, 1830

Arms. Rev. Dove.

255. 1 Doppia 1830. R mm. **75.00**

GREGORY XVI, 1831-1846

Bust. Rev. St. Peter and value.

256. 1 Doppia 1833, 34. R mm. ....* **50.00**
257. 1 Doppia 1834. B mm. **65.00**

Bust. Rev. St. Peter and St. Paul.

258. 5 Scudi 1834. R mm. **750.00**

Bust. Rev. Value.

259. 10 Scudi 1835-45. R mm. **75.00**
260. 10 Scudi 1835-45. B mm. **100.00**
261. 5 Scudi 1835-46. R mm. **35.00**
262. 5 Scudi 1835-43. B mm. **35.00**
263. 2½ Scudi 1835-45. R mm. **22.50**
264. 2½ Scudi 1835-46. B mm. ....* **22.50**

SEDE VACANTE, 1846

Arms. Rev. Dove.

265. 5 Scudi 1846. R mm. **60.00**

PIUS IX, 1846-1878

Bust. Rev. Value.

266. 10 Scudi 1850, 56. R mm. **100.00**
267. 5 Scudi 1846-54. R mm. **35.00**
268. 5 Scudi 1846. B mm. **40.00**
269. 2½ Scudi 1848-63. R mm. ....* ... **22.50**
270. 2½ Scudi 1854-59. B mm. **22.50**
271. 1 Scudo 1853-57. R mm. Small size **17.50**
272. 1 Scudo 1853, 54. B mm. Small size ....* ... **20.00**
273. 1 Scudo 1858-65. R mm. Large size **15.00**
274. 100 Lire 1866, 68, 69, 70 .... **200.00**
275. 50 Lire 1868, 70 .... **100.00**
276. 20 Lire 1866-70 ....* ... **25.00**
277. 10 Lire 1866, 67, 69 .... **25.00**
278. 5 Lire 1866, 67 ....* ... **35.00**

PIUS XI, 1922-1937

Bust. Rev. Christ standing.

279. 100 Lire 1929-35 ....* **40.00**
280. 100 Lire 1933 (1934). On the Holy Year and showing
     both dates **50.00**
281. 100 Lire 1936, 37. Size reduced **30.00**

321

PIUS XII, 1939-1958

Bust. Rev. Christ standing.

282. 100 Lire 1939, 40, 41 .... **25.00**

Bust. Rev. Charity seated with children.

283. 100 Lire 1942-49 .... **25.00**

Crowned bust. Rev. Opening of the Holy Door. On the Holy Year of 1950.

284. 100 Lire 1950 .... **25.00**

Bust. Rev. Charity standing.

285. 100 Lire 1951-56 .... **25.00**

B. Papal Coinage struck outside of Rome

These issues are distinguishable from those of the Rome Mint by differences of type, legend or arms.

ANCONA

SIXTUS IV, 1471-1484
St. Peter and St. Paul. Rev. Arms.

1. 1 Ducat ND **125.00**

INNOCENT VIII, 1484-1492
St. Peter in ship. Rev. Arms.

2. 1 Ducat ND **100.00**

Two saints. Rev. Arms.

3. 1 Ducat ND **100.00**

ALEXANDER VI BORGIA, 1492-1503
St. Peter. Rev. Arms.

4. 1 Ducat ND **125.00**

St. Peter in ship. Rev. Arms.

5. 1 Ducat ND **125.00**

St. Quiriacus. Rev. Knight on horse.

6. 1 Ducat ND **250.00**

JULIUS II, 1503-1513

St. Peter in ship. Rev. Arms.

7. 1 Ducat ND **200.00**

LEO X, 1513-1521

St. Quiriacus. Rev. Knight on horse.

8. 2 Ducats ND ....*...... **500.00**
9. 1 Ducat ND **125.00**

St. Peter and St. Paul. Rev. Arms.

10. 1 Ducat ND **200.00**

ADRIAN VI, 1522-1523
St. Quiriacus. Rev. Knight on horse.

11. 1 Ducat ND **200.00**

Two saints. Rev. Arms.

12. 1 Ducat ND **175.00**

CLEMENT VII, 1523-1534
St. Quiriacus. Rev. Knight on horse.

13. 1 Ducat ND **125.00**

Two saints. Rev. Arms.

14. 1 Ducat ND **100.00**

Arms. Rev. Cross.

15. 1 Scudo d'oro ND **200.00**

ANONYMOUS COINAGE, 1500-1600
St. Quiriacus. Rev. Knight on horse.

16. 2 Ducats ND **200.00**
17. 1 Ducat ND **75.00**

GREGORY XIII, 1572-1585
Bust. Rev. The Holy Door.

18. 1 Scudo d'oro 1575 .... **350.00**

Bust. Rev. Charity standing.

19. 1 Scudo d'oro ND **400.00**

Charity standing. Rev. Arms.

20. 1 Scudo d'oro ND **200.00**

VATICAN-ANCONA (cont'd)

SIXTUS V, 1585-1590
Arms. Rev. Legend.

21. 2 Scudi d'oro 1585 .... 500.00

Madonna. Rev. Arms.

22. 4 Scudi d'oro 1586 .... 1000.00

Arms. Rev. Cross.

23. 2 Scudi d'oro 1586 .... 400.00
24. 1 Scudo d'oro 1586 ....* 200.00

AVIGNON

(See under France-Cities).

BOLOGNA

ALEXANDER V, 1409-1410
Sun and shield. Rev. Uncertain.

1. 2 Zecchini ND 2500.00

St. Peter. Rev. Arms.

2. 1 Bolognino d'oro ND 200.00

JOHN XXIII, 1410-1415

St. Peter. Rev. Arms.

3. 1 Bolognino d'oro ND 125.00

MARTIN V, 1421-1428
St. Peter. Rev. Lion.

4. 1 Bolognino d'oro ND 100.00

St. Peter. Rev. Arms.

5. 1 Bolognino d'oro ND 100.00

ANONYMOUS COINAGE, 1350-1450

St. Peter. Rev. Lion.

6. 1 Bolognino d'oro ND 75.00

EUGENE IV, 1431-1447

St. Peter. Rev. Arms.

7. 1 Ducat ND 100.00

PIUS II, 1458-1464
St. Peter. Rev. Lion.

8. 1 Ducat ND 100.00

PAUL II, 1464-1471
St. Peter. Rev. Arms.

9. 1 Ducat ND 100.00

St. Peter. Rev. Lion.

10. 1 Ducat ND 100.00

SIXTUS IV, 1471-1484
St. Peter. Rev. Arms.

11. 1 Ducat ND 100.00

INNOCENT VIII, 1484-1492
St. Peter. Rev. Arms.

12. 1 Ducat ND 100.00

St. Peter. Rev. Lion.

13. 1 Ducat ND 100.00

ALEXANDER VI BORGIA, 1492-1503

St. Peter. Rev. Arms.

14. 1 Ducat ND 50.00

PIUS III, 1503
St. Peter. Rev. Arms.

15. 1 Ducat ND 1000.00

JULIUS II, 1503-1513
St. Peter. Rev. Arms.

16. 1 Ducat ND 40.00

Bust. Rev. St. Petronius seated.

17. 2 Scudi d'oro ND ....* 1000.00
18. 1 Scudo d'oro ND 500.00

LEO X, 1513-1521
Bust. Rev. St. Petronius seated.

19. 2 Ducats ND 1500.00

Bust. Rev. St. Peter.

20. 1 Ducat ND 1000.00

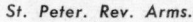

St. Peter. Rev. Arms.

VATICAN-BOLOGNA (cont'd)

21. 1 Ducat ND 40.00

St. Peter. Rev. Lion.

22. 1 Ducat ND 75.00

CLEMENT VII, 1523-1534

Bust of St. Petronius. Rev. Legend.

23. 10 Ducats 1529 .... 2500.00
24. 3 Ducats 1529 .... 1000.00

St. Peter. Rev. Lion.

25. 1 Ducat ND 40.00

Arms. Rev. Cross.

26. 1 Scudo d'oro ND ....* 30.00
27. ½ Scudo d'oro ND 40.00

PAUL III, 1534-1549

Arms. Rev. Cross.

28. 1 Scudo d'oro ND 100.00

JULIUS III, 1550-1555
Arms. Rev. Cross.

29. 1 Scudo d'oro ND 100.00
30. ½ Scudo d'oro ND 100.00

PAUL IV, 1555-1559

Arms. Rev. Cross.

31. 1 Scudo d'oro ND 65.00

PIUS IV, 1559-1565
Arms. Rev. Cross.

32. 1 Scudo d'oro ND 125.00

ST. PIUS V, 1565-1572

Arms. Rev. Cross.

---

33. 1 Scudo d'oro ND ....* 60.00
34. ½ Scudo d'oro ND 100.00

GREGORY XIII, 1572-1585
Arms. Rev. Cross.

35. 1 Scudo d'oro ND 60.00

SIXTUS V, 1585-1590

Arms. Rev. Cross.

36. 2 Scudi d'oro ND ....* 100.00
37. 1 Scudo d'oro ND 100.00

URBAN VII, 1590 (13 DAYS)

Arms. Rev. Cross.

38. 2 Scudi d'oro ND 1500.00

GREGORY XIV, 1590-1591

Arms. Rev. Cross.

39. 2 Scudi d'oro ND 250.00

INNOCENT IX, 1591-1592
Arms. Rev. Cross.

40. 2 Scudi d'oro ND 1500.00

CLEMENT VIII, 1592-1605
Arms. Rev. Cross.

41. 2 Scudi d'oro 1559, ND 500.00

ANONYMOUS COINAGE, 1500-1600
St. Peter. Rev. Lion.

42. 1 Bolognino d'oro ND 100.00

INNOCENT X, 1644-1655
Arms. Rev. Cross.

43. 4 Scudi d'oro 1651, 54 .... 600.00
44. 2 Scudi d'oro 1654 .... 250.00
45. 1 Scudo d'oro 1654 .... 100.00

ALEXANDER VII, 1655-1667

Arms. Rev. Cross.

46. 4 Scudi d'oro 1655-66 ....* 100.00
47. 2 Scudi d'oro 1655-66 .... 75.00
48. 1 Scudo d'oro 1655-66 .... 40.00

VATICAN-BOLOGNA (cont'd)

CLEMENT IX, 1667-1669
Arms. Rev. Cross.

49.	4 Scudi d'oro 1667	....	600.00
50.	2 Scudi d'oro 1667	....	300.00
51.	1 Scudo d'oro 1667	....	125.00

CLEMENT X, 1669-1676
Arms. Rev. Cross.

52.	8 Scudi d'oro 1671	....	2000.00
53.	4 Scudi d'oro 1673	....	600.00
54.	2 Scudi d'oro 1673	....	300.00
55.	1 Scudo d'oro 1671	....	100.00

CLEMENT XI, 1700-1721
Arms. Rev. Cross.

56.	2 Scudi d'oro 1713, 14, ND	....	500.00
57.	1 Scudo d'oro 1713	....	100.00

CLEMENT XII, 1730-1740
Arms. Rev. Cross.

58.	1 Scudo d'oro 1732, 36	....	100.00

Lion. Rev. Two shields.

59.	1 Zecchino 1737, 38	....	100.00

SEDE VACANTE, 1740
Lion. Rev. Two shields.

60.	1 Zecchino 1740	....	75.00

BENEDICT XIV, 1740-1758

Bust. Rev. Felsina standing.

61.	2 Zecchini 1741, 42	....	500.00
62.	1 Zecchino 1741, 42	........................*	150.00

Bust. Rev. Legend.

63.	10 Scudi d'oro 1756, 57	....	2000.00

Lion. Rev. Two shields.

64.	1 Zecchino 1746	....	100.00

Arms. Rev. Cross.

65.	1 Zecchino 1751	....	100.00

CLEMENT XIII, 1758-1769
Lion. Rev. Two shields.

66.	1 Zecchino 1758-69	....	60.00

CLEMENT XIV, 1769-1774

Lion. Rev. Two shields.

67.	1 Zecchino 1771	....	60.00

PIUS VI, 1774-1799

Lily. Rev. Two shields.

68.	4 Doppia 1786, 87	....	150.00
69.	2 Doppia 1778-96. (60 Paoli)	....	75.00
70.	1 Doppia 1778-92. (30 Paoli)	.............*	40.00
71.	½ Doppia 1778-91. (15 Paoli)	....	35.00

Lily. Rev. Arms.

72.	½ Doppia 1778	....	50.00

Bust. Rev. Temple.

73.	1 Zecchino 1782	....	75.00

St. Petronius over two shields. Rev. Arms.

74.	10 Zecchini 1786, 87	....	250.00
75.	5 Zecchini 1787	....	125.00
76.	2 Zecchini 1786, 87	....	40.00
77.	1 Zecchino 1778-87, ND	...................*	30.00
78.	½ Zecchino 1786	....	25.00
79.	100 Bolognini (Scudo d'oro) ND	....	125.00

(Later coinage of the Bologna Mint is of the same type as that of the Rome Mint and will be found under Vatican-Rome described with "B mm").

CAMERINO

PAUL III, 1534-1549

St. Paul. Rev. Arms.

1.	1 Scudo d'oro ND	....	400.00

FERRARA

PAUL V, 1605-1621

Bust. Rev. St. George and St. Maurelius.

1.	4 Scudi d'oro 1620	....	1500.00

VATICAN (cont'd)

FOLIGNO

PAUL II, 1464-1471

St. Peter kneeling before Christ. Rev. Arms.

1. 1 Zecchino ND 750.00

LEO X, 1513-1521
St. Peter and St. Paul. Rev. Lion.

2. 2 Scudi d'oro ND 600.00

St. Felician. Rev. Arms.

3. 1 Ducat ND 200.00

MACERATA

SIXTUS IV, 1471-1484
St. Peter. Rev. Arms.

1. 1 Ducat ND 150.00

INNOCENT VIII, 1484-1492

St. Peter in ship. Rev. Arms.

2. 1 Ducat ND 150.00

ADRIAN VI, 1522-1523
St. Peter in ship. Rev. Arms.

3. 1 Ducat ND 250.00

MODENA

LEO X, 1513-1521

Bust. Rev. St. Geminianus seated.

1. 1 Ducat ND 600.00

ADRIAN VI, 1522-1523
Bust. Rev. St. Geminianus seated.

2. 1 Ducat ND 800.00

CLEMENT VII, 1523-1534

Bust. St. Geminianus seated.

3. 1 Ducat ND 800.00

St. Geminianus seated. Rev. Arms.

4. 1 Ducat ND 250.00

PARMA

JULIUS II, 1503-1513
St. John and St. Hillary. Rev. Christ and Madonna.

1. 1 Ducat ND 1000.00

ADRIAN VI, 1522-1523
St. John and St. Hillary. Rev. Christ and Madonna.

2. 1 Zecchino ND 1000.00

CLEMENT VII, 1523-1534
Christ and Madonna. Rev. Arms.

3. 2 Ducats 1526 .... 1500.00

Madonna. Rev. Arms.

4. 1 Ducat ND 1000.00

PAUL III, 1534-1549

Pallas seated. Rev. Arms.

5. 1 Scudo d'oro ND 80.00

Arms. Rev. Cross.

6. ½ Scudo d'oro ND 250.00

PERUGIA

LEO X, 1513-1521
Arms. Rev. Griffin.

1. 1 Zecchino ND 500.00

St. Herculanus. Rev. Griffin.

2. 1 Zecchino ND 500.00

PAUL III, 1534-1549

Arms. Rev. Griffin and shield.

3. 1 Scudo d'oro ND 200.00

326

VATICAN-PERUGIA (cont'd)

Arms. Rev. Griffin in square.

4. 1 Scudo d'oro ND 250.00

JULIUS III, 1550-1555
Arms. Rev. Cross.

5. 1 Scudo d'oro ND 250.00

PIACENZA

ADRIAN VI, 1522-1523
Bust. Rev. Legend.

1. 1 Doppia ND 1000.00

Bust. Rev. Keys.

2. 1 Zecchino ND 500.00

CLEMENT VII, 1523-1534

Bust. Rev. St. Anthony on horse.

3. 1 Zecchino ND 1000.00

PAUL III, 1534-1549

Arms. Rev. Cross.

4. 1 Scudo d'oro ND ....*...... 60.00
5. ½ Scudo d'oro ND 100.00

RAVENNA

LEO X, 1513-1521

St. Appolinaris. Rev. Arms.

1. 1 Zecchino ND 700.00

SPOLETO

PAUL II, 1464-1471

St. Peter. Rev. Arms.

1. 1 Ducat ND 500.00

WALLACHIA

Voivods of —

MICHAEL THE BRAVE, 1600-1601
Bust with furred hat. Rev. Legend.

1. 10 Ducats 1600 .... 1250.00
2. 5 Ducats 1600 .... 750.00

CONSTANTINE BRENCOVAN, 1688-1714
Bust with furred hat. Rev. Arms. On the 25th year of reign.

3. 6 Ducats 1713 .... 750.00

YUGOSLAVIA

A. Kings of —

ALEXANDER I, 1921-1934

Head. Rev. Value and date.

1. 20 Dinars 1925 .... 30.00

Conjoined heads of the King and Queen. Rev. Eagle.

2. 4 Ducats 1931, 32 .... 90.00

Head. Rev. Eagle.

3. 1 Ducat 1931, 32, 33 .... 15.00

B. Cities of —

RAGUSA (DUBROVNIK)

St. Blasius standing. Rev. Christ amid stars.

4. 1 Gold Perper or 2 Doppia 1618, 83 .... 500.00

LAIBACH (LJUBLIANA)

Bishops of —

THOMAS GRONN, 1599-1630
Two shields. Rev. Legend.

5. 3 Ducats 1599 .... 300.00

Part III

....

AFRICA AND THE ORIENT

Africa, Asia Minor, Asia, Australia and the Islands of the Mediterranean,
Indian and Pacific Oceans.

AFGHANISTAN	HAWAII	PHILIPPINE ISLANDS
ANNAM	HEJAZ	RHODES
ARAB-ASIAN EMPIRES	INDIA	SAUDI ARABIA
AUSTRALIA	JAPAN	SIAM
BURMA	JERUSALEM	SOUTH AFRICA
CAMBODIA	KOREA	SYRIA
CEYLON	MALAYA	TANGIER
CHINA	MALTA	TIBET
CYPRUS	MOROCCO	TRANQUEBAR
EGYPT	MOZAMBIQUE	TUNIS
ETHIOPIA	NEPAL	TURKESTAN, CHINESE
GERMAN EAST AFRICA	NETHERLANDS EAST INDIES	TURKEY
GERMAN NEW GUINEA	PERSIA	ZANZIBAR

AFGHANISTAN

Shahs of —

Seated Goddess. Rev. Legend. Struck during the period 1192-1300.

1. 1 Stater ND 75.00

Arab legend on each side. Struck during the period 1725-1747 and with dates from about 1138-1160 A.H.

2. 2 Mohurs 150.00
3. 1 Mohur 65.00
4. ⅓ Mohur 30.00
5. ¼ Mohur 25.00

AHMED SHAH, 1747-1773
Arab legend on each side.

6. 1 Mohur 1160-86 A.H. (1747-72 A.D.) 50.00

TAIMUR SHAH, 1773-1793

Arab legend on each side.

7. 1 Mohur 1195-1209 A.H. (1780-94 A.D.) 50.00

ZAMAN SHAH, 1793-1801

Arab legend on each side. Struck by Dost Mohammed in the name of Zaman in 1835.

8. 3 Mohurs 1251 A.H. (1835 A.D.) 350.00

MOHAMMED SHAH, 1801-1829

Arab legend on each side.

9. 2 Mohurs 1217 A.H. (1802 A.D.) ....* 200.00
10. 1 Mohur 1217 A.H. (1802 A.D.) 75.00
11. 1 Dinar 1219 A.H. (1804 A.D.) 75.00

SHUJA SHAH, 1801 AND 1803-1809

Arab legend on each side.

12. 1 Mohur 1223 A.H. (1808 A.D.) 60.00

SHER ALI, 1863-1878

Arab legend on each side.

13. 1 Mohur 1285-88 A.H. (1868-71 A.D.) ....* 60.00
14. 1 Tilla 1283 A.H. (1866 A.D.) 40.00

ABDUR RAHMAN, 1880-1901

Arab legend on each side.

15. 1 Tilla 1298 A.H. (1880 A.D.) 40.00

Throne room. Rev. Toughra over crossed quivers.

16. 1 Dinar 1314 A.H. (1896 A.D.) 125.00

HABIBULLAH, 1901-1919

Throne room. Rev. Toughra over crossed quivers.

17. 1 Dinar 1319, 20 A.H. (1901, 02 A.D.) 100.00

AMANULLAH, 1919-1929
(The Afghanistan calendar was changed in 1920, when by Royal Decree, the corresponding A.H. year of 1338, was declared to be A.H. 1298).

Throne room in star. Rev. Legend in wreath.

18. 2 Amani 1298 A.H. (1920 A.D.) 90.00
19. 1 Amani 1337 A.H. (1919 A.D.). Crossed guns below throne. 60.00
20. 1 Amani 1337 A.H. (1919 A.D.). Star below throne. * 60.00

Throne room in star. Rev. Toughra.

21. 5 Amani 1299 A.H. (1921 A.D.) ....* 350.00
22. 2 Amani 1299-1302 A.H. (1921-24 A.D.) 75.00
23. 1 Amani 1299 A.H. (1921 A.D.) 50.00
24. ½ Amani 1299 A.H. (1921 A.D.) ....* 35.00

Large plain throne room. Rev. Toughra.

25. 2½ Amani 1306 A.H. (1928 A.D.) 350.00
26. 1   Amani 1304-06 A.H. (1926-28 A.D.) ....* 50.00
27. ½ Amani 1304-06 A.H. (1926-28 A.D.) 35.00

HABIBULLAH GHAZI, 1929

(The name assumed by the Brigand Bacha-i-Saquao who held Kabul for nine months in 1929 but was captured and executed by Mohammed Nadir).

Throne room in star. Rev. Legend in wreath.

28. 6 Rupees 1347 A.H. (1929 A.D.) 150.00

MOHAMMED NADIR, 1929-1933
Large throne room. Rev. Toughra.

29. 1 Amani 1347-50 A.H. (1929-32 A.D.) 125.00

ANNAM

Emperors of —

MING MANG, 1820-1841

Chinese legend on each side. Rectangular bars.

1.	100 Ounces (1833)	**Rare**
2.	50 Ounces (1837, 38)	**Rare**
3.	40 Ounces (1840), ND	**Rare**
4.	30 Ounces (1840)	**Rare**
5.	10 Ounces (1837)	1500.00
6.	5 Ounces (1837)	1000.00
7.	1 Ounce ND	200.00
8.	$5/10$ Ounce ND ....*	150.00
9.	$4/10$ Ounce ND	100.00
10.	$3/10$ Ounce ND	75.00
11.	$2/10$ Ounce ND	75.00
12.	$1/10$ Ounce ND	65.00

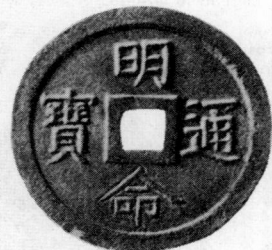

Four Chinese characters on each side around square central hole.

13. ½ Piastre ND 200.00

Four Chinese characters around radiant sun. Rev. Dragon.

14. 1 Piastre (1834) 350.00
15. ½ Piastre (1834) ....* 200.00

Four Chinese characters around radiant sun. Rev. Heavenly bodies.

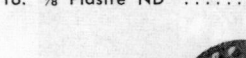

16. ⅛ Piastre ND 75.00

Two vertical Chinese characters. Rev. Eight precious symbols.

17. ⅛ Piastre ND 75.00

Two vertical Chinese characters. Rev. Five precious symbols.

18. ⅛ Piastre ND 75.00

Two vertical Chinese characters. Rev. The Three Abundances.

19. ¼ Piastre ND 200.00

THIEU TRI, 1841-1847

Chinese legend on each side. Rectangular bars.

20.	100 Ounces ND	**Rare**
21.	50 Ounces ND	**Rare**
22.	10 Ounces ND	1500.00
23.	1 Ounce ND ....*	200.00
24.	$5/10$ Ounce ND	150.00
25.	$4/10$ Ounce ND	125.00
26.	$3/10$ Ounce ND	125.00
27.	$2/10$ Ounce ND	100.00
28.	$1/10$ Ounce ND	100.00

Sun between two dragons. Rev. Four Chinese characters. With square central hole.

29. $7/10$ Ounce ND ....* 300.00
30. $7/20$ Ounce ND 175.00

Heavenly bodies flanked by four vertical characters. Rev. Long legend in form of a quatrain. With square central hole.

31. $5/10$ Ounce ND 300.00
32. $5/20$ Ounce ND 200.00

ANNAM (cont'd)

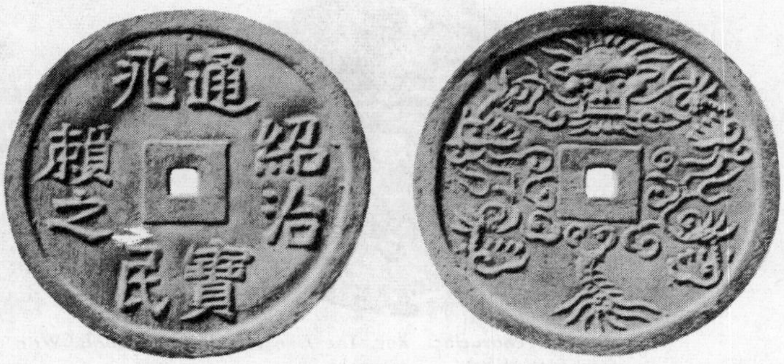

Eight Chinese characters. Rev. Facing dragon head. With square central hole.

33. 5/10 Ounce ND 200.00
34. 5/20 Ounce ND 150.00

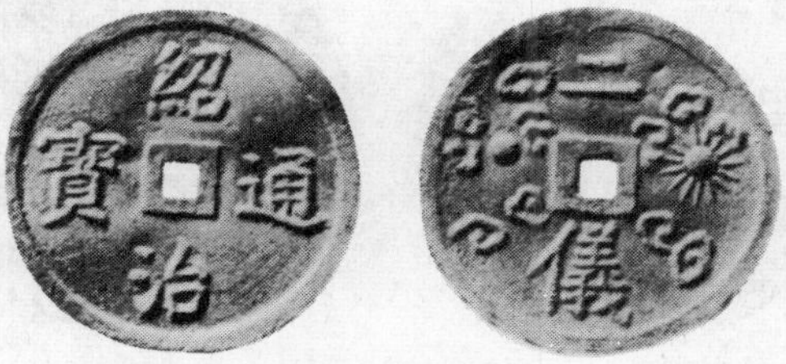

Four Chinese characters. Rev. Sun and moon between two vertical characters. With square central hole.

35. 1/4 Piastre ND 125.00

Four Chinese characters on each side around square central hole.

36. 1/2 Piastre ND 200.00

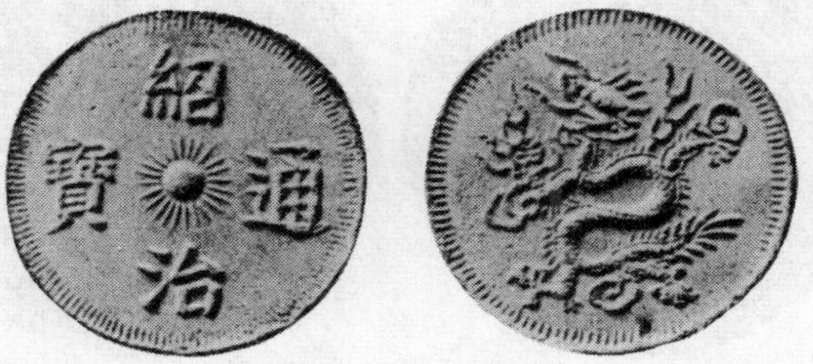

Four Chinese characters around radiant sun. Rev. Dragon.

37. 1 Piastre ND 300.00
38. 1/2 Piastre ND 150.00

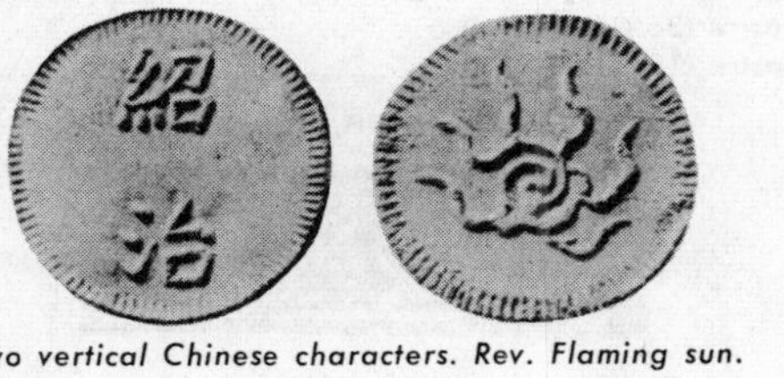

Two vertical Chinese characters. Rev. Flaming sun.

39. 1/8 Piastre ND 100.00

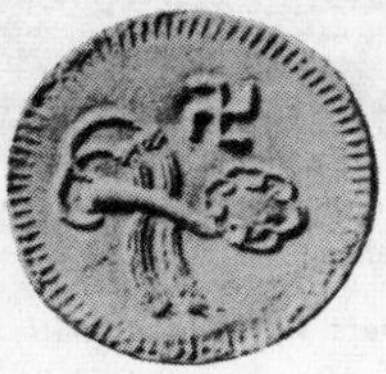

Same Obv. Rev. Sceptre.

40. 1/8 Piastre ND 100.00

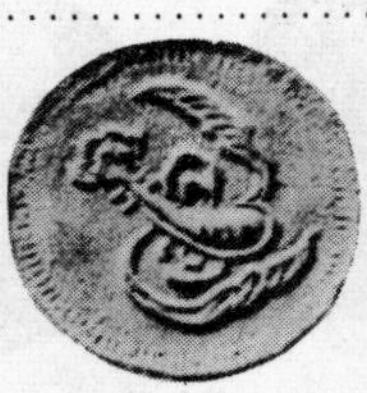

Same Obv. Rev. Guitar.

41. 1/8 Piastre ND 100.00

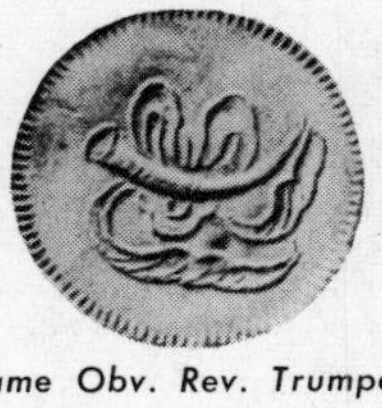

Same Obv. Rev. Trumpet.

42. 1/8 Piastre ND 100.00

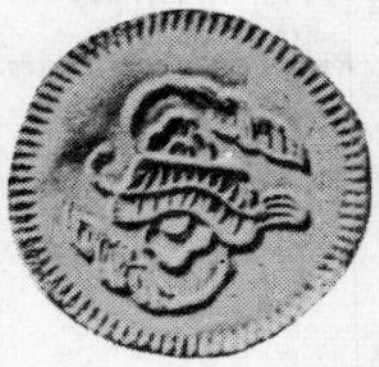

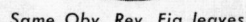

Same Obv. Rev. Fig leaves.

43. 1/8 Piastre ND 100.00

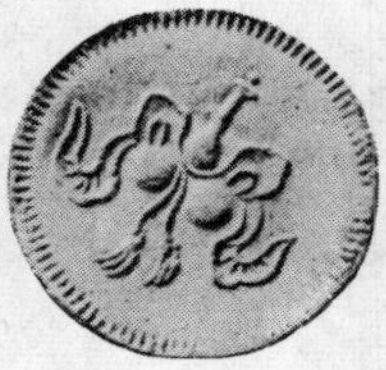

Same Obv. Rev. Gourde.

44. 1/8 Piastre ND 100.00

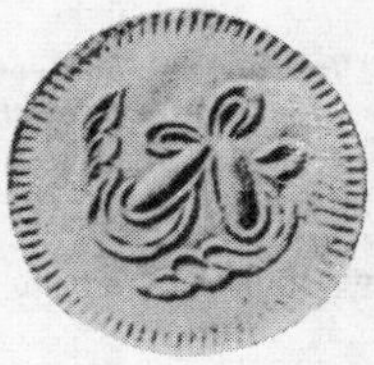

Same Obv. Rev. Castanets.

45. 1/8 Piastre ND 100.00

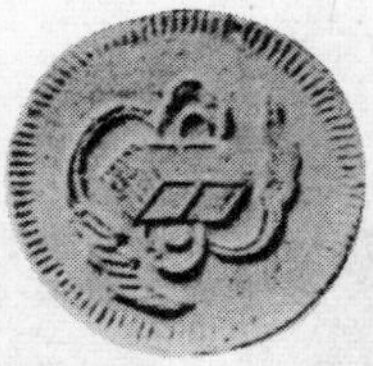

Same Obv. Rev. Tablets.

46. 1/8 Piastre ND 100.00

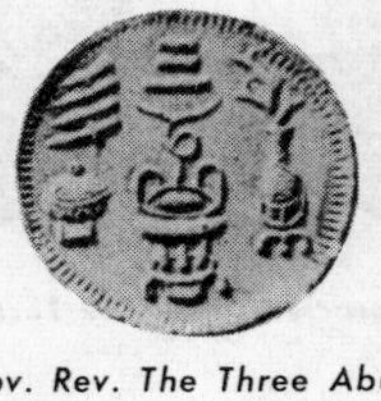

Same Obv. Rev. The Three Abundances.

47. 1/8 Piastre ND 100.00

TU DUC, 1847-1883

Four Chinese characters. Rev. Five Chinese characters. Rectangular bars.

48.	10 Ounces ND	1500.00
49.	5 Ounces ND	1000.00
50.	1 Ounce ND	200.00
51.	5/10 Ounce ND	125.00
52.	4/10 Ounce ND	* 75.00
53.	3/10 Ounce ND	* 65.00
54.	2/10 Ounce ND	* 65.00
55.	1/10 Ounce ND	* 50.00

Sun between two dragons. Rev. Four characters. With square central hole.

56.	7/10 Ounce ND	300.00

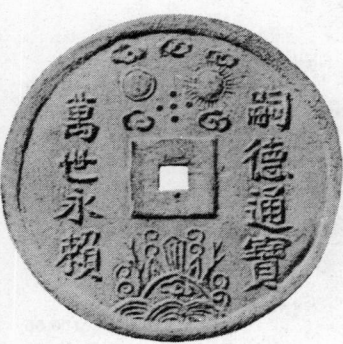

Heavenly bodies flanked by four vertical characters. Rev. Long legend in form of a quatrain. With square central hole.

57.	1 Ounce ND	400.00
58.	5/10 Ounce ND	* 300.00

Eight Chinese characters. Rev. Facing dragon head. With square central hole.

59.	5/10 Ounce ND	200.00

Legend on each side. With square central hole.

60.	½ Piastre ND	150.00
61.	¼ Piastre ND	85.00

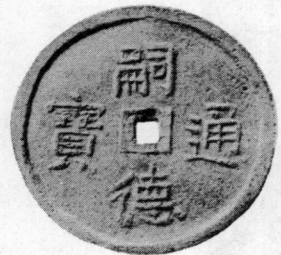

Four Chinese characters. Rev. The Three Longevities. With square central hole.

62.	½ Piastre ND	150.00

Four Chinese characters. Rev. The Four Perfections. With square central hole.

63.	½ Piastre ND. (The Rev. is shown)	200.00

Four Chinese characters. Rev. The Five Happiness symbols. With square central hole.

64.	¾ Piastre ND. (The Rev. is shown)	200.00

Four Chinese characters around radiant sun. Rev. Dragon.

65.	1 Piastre ND	* 350.00
66.	½ Piastre ND	200.00

Four characters around sun with blunt rays. Rev. Dragon coiled around similar sun.

67.	1½ Piastres (37½ Grams) ND	* 500.00
68.	1 Piastre (26 Grams) ND	350.00
69.	¾ Piastre (19 Grams) ND	250.00

DONG KHANH, 1885-1889

Five Chinese characters on each side.

70.	1 Ounce ND. Rectangular Bar	400.00

Four Chinese characters. Rev. Blank. With square central hole.

71.	1/16 Piastre ND	50.00

Four Chinese characters. Rev. Sun, moon and two constellations. With square central hole.

72.	¼ Piastre ND	250.00

ANNAM (cont'd)

THANH THAI, 1889-1905

Four Chinese characters. Rev. Five Chinese characters.

73. 1 Ounce ND. Rectangular bar **250.00**

Heavenly bodies flanked by four vertical characters. Rev. Long legend in form of a quatrain. With square central hole.

74. 1 Ounce ND **400.00**

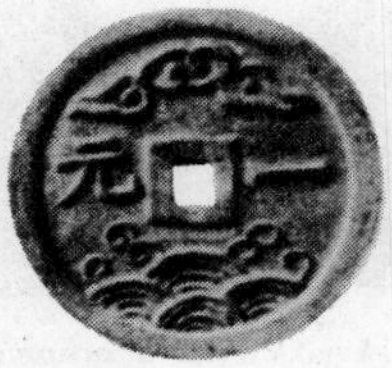

Four Chinese characters. Rev. Clouds and symbols for cosmic evolution. With square central hole.

75. ⅛ Piastre ND. (The Rev. is shown) **150.00**

Four Chinese characters around radiant sun. Rev. Dragon.

76. ⅓ Piastre (10½ Grams). ND **150.00**

Four Chinese characters. Rev. Sun, moon and characters. With square central hole.

77. ¼ Piastre ND **150.00**

Four Chinese characters. Rev. The Three Longevities. With square central hole.

78. ⅓ Piastre ND **150.00**

Four Chinese characters around radiant sun. Rev. The Four Perfections around radiant sun.

79. ½ Piastre ND **300.00**

ARAB-ASIAN EMPIRES

Caliphs, Sultans and Khans of —

A. ANONYMOUS CALIPHS
(Earliest Issues of North Africa and Spain)

Cross potent. Rev. Legend.

1. ⅓ Solidus ND (630-720 A.D.) **100.00**

Star. Rev. Legend.

2. ⅓ Solidus ND (630-720 A.D.) **100.00**

Legend on each side.

3. ⅓ Solidus ND (630-720 A.D.) **100.00**

Cross potent. Rev. Star.

4. ⅓ Solidus ND (630-720 A.D.) **100.00**

B. THE OMAYYAD CALIPHS OF DAMASCUS, 660-750 A.D.
(Successors to the first four Caliphs after Mohammed)

Arab legend on each side. With dates from about 38-132 A.H.

5.	1 Dinar ....*		35.00
6.	½ Dinar		30.00
7.	⅓ Dinar ....*		25.00
8.	¼ Dinar		25.00

C. THE ABBASID CALIPHS OF BAGHDAD, 750-1517 A.D.
(This coinage was superseded by that of the Ottoman Sultans of Turkey).

Arab legend on each side. With dates from about 133-923 A.H.

9.	3	Dinars	150.00
10.	2	Dinars	75.00
11.	1½	Dinars	65.00
12.	1	Dinar ....*	25.00
13.	½	Dinar	20.00
14.	¼	Dinar	17.50

Bull. Rev. Horseman.

15. 1 Dinar .... **Unique**

D. THE ABBASID GOVERNORS OF EGYPT, 637-968 A.D.
(Including the lesser Dynasties of the Tulunuds, 868-1905, and the Ikhshidis, 935-969).

Arab legend on each side. With dates from about 15-356 A.H.

16. 1 Dinar **25.00**

E. THE FATIMITE CALIPHS OF EGYPT, 969-1173 A.D.

Arab legend on each side. With dates from about 357-570 A.H.

17.	1 Dinar ....*		25.00
18.	¾ Dinar		25.00
19.	½ Dinar		20.00
20.	¼ Dinar		17.50
21.	⅙ Dinar		17.50

F. THE AYUBITE SULTANS OF EGYPT, 1173-1250 A.D.

Arab legend on each side. With dates from about 570-650 A.H.

22.	2 Dinars		75.00
23.	1 Dinar ....*		40.00

ARAB-ASIAN EMPIRES (cont'd)

G. THE MAMELUKE SULTANS OF EGYPT, 1250-1517 A.D.

Arab legend on each side. With dates from about 650-923 A.H.

24.	2 Dinars	....	75.00
25.	1 Dinar	...................................*......	25.00

H. THE OMAYYAD CALIPHS OF CORDOVA, 756-1024 A.D.
(Northwest Africa and Spain)

Arab legend on each side. With dates from about 138-415 A.H.

26.	1 Dinar	....*......	30.00
27.	⅓ Dinar	....	20.00

I. THE ALMORAVIDE AMIRS OF SPAIN, 1056-1147 A.D.
(Northwest Africa and Spain)

Arab legend on each side. With dates from about 448-541 A.H.

28.	1 Dinar	....*......	30.00
29.	½ Dinar	....	20.00
30.	¼ Dinar	....	15.00

J. THE ALMOHADE CALIPHS OF SPAIN, 1130-1269 A.D.
(Northwest Africa and Spain)

Arab legend within square on each side. With or without dates from about 524-666 A.H.

31.	1 Dinar	....*......	40.00
32.	½ Dinar	....	30.00
33.	¼ Dinar	....	20.00

K. THE SELJUK SULTANS OF WESTERN ASIA, 1040-1308 A.D.
(Dynasties in Persia, Syria and Asia Minor)
Arab legend on each side. With or without dates from about 431-708 A.H.

34.	1 Dinar	....	30.00

L. THE MONGOL KHANS OF ASIA, 1251-1700 A.D.
Native legend on each side. With or without dates from about 750-1113 A.H.

35.	1 Dinar	....	30.00

M. THE MONGOL KHANS OF KHOKAND AND BOKHARA, 1700-1875 A.D.

Native legend on each side. With dates from about 1113-1296 A.H.

36.	1 Tilla	....	50.00

AUSTRALIA

A. Early Issues of —
ADELAIDE ASSAY OFFICE

Crown and date. Rev. Value in beaded circle within two linear circles.

1.	1 Pound 1852	....	100.00

Crown and date. Rev. Value in ornamental circle. The 5 Pound piece was not placed in circulation and no originals are known. The seven known pieces are re-strikes from the original dies.

2.	5 Pounds 1852	....	Rare
3.	1 Pound 1852	...............................*......	85.00

SOUTH AUSTRALIA GOLD INGOTS

Ingots of irregular shape stamped with a crown over SA and with other stamps denoting weight and fineness. Rev. Blank.

4.	Gold Ingot ND (1852)	....	1500.00

PORT PHILIP COINAGE

Kangaroo and date in circle. Rev. Large value in circle.

5.	2 Ounces 1853, 54	.........................*......	2000.00
6.	1 Ounce 1853	....	1250.00
7.	½ Ounce 1853	....	750.00
8.	¼ Ounce 1853	.........................*......	750.00

B. British Sovereigns of —
VICTORIA, 1837-1901

Young head. Rev. "Sidney Mint One Sovereign" or "Half."

9.	1 Sovereign 1855-70	.........................*......	25.00
10.	½ Sovereign 1856-66	....	17.50

AUSTRALIA (cont'd)

(The remaining coins of Victoria and all those of the following rulers are of the same types as English gold coins, but with the distinguishing Australian mintmarks as indicated).
Young head. Rev. Arms, mintmark below.

11.	1 Pound 1871-80. S mm.	30.00
12.	1 Pound 1886. M mm.	40.00
13.	½ Pound 1879-86. S mm.	20.00

Young head with mintmark below. Rev. Arms.

14.	1 Pound 1880-87. S mm.	20.00
15.	1 Pound 1881-86. M mm.	20.00
16.	½ Pound 1884-86. M mm.	12.50

Young head with mintmark below. Rev. St. George.

17.	1 Pound 1871-87. S mm.	20.00
18.	1 Pound 1874-87. M mm.	20.00

Jubilee head. Rev. St. George with mintmark on ground below horse.

19.	5 Pounds 1887. S mm.	1000.00
20.	2 Pounds 1887. S mm.	350.00
21.	1 Pound 1887-93. S mm.	17.50
22.	1 Pound 1887-93. M mm.	17.50
23.	½ Pound 1887-93. M mm.	12.50

Veiled head. Rev. Similar to above.

24.	1 Pound 1893-1901. S mm.	17.50
25.	1 Pound 1893-1901. M mm.	17.50
26.	1 Pound 1899-1901. P mm.	22.50
27.	½ Pound 1893-1901. M mm.	15.00
28.	½ Pound 1893. S mm.	20.00
29.	½ Pound 1900, 01. P mm.	15.00

EDWARD VII, 1901-1911
Head. Rev. St. George with mintmark on ground below horse.

30.	5 Pounds 1902. S mm.	1000.00
31.	2 Pounds 1902. S mm.	650.00
32.	1 Pound 1902-09. S mm.	17.50
33.	1 Pound 1902-10. M mm.	17.50
34.	1 Pound 1902-10. P mm.	17.50
35.	½ Pound 1902. S mm.	25.00
36.	½ Pound 1908. M mm.	15.00

GEORGE V, 1910-1936
Head. Rev. St. George with mintmark on ground below horse.

37.	1 Pound 1911-18. S mm.	20.00
38.	1 Pound 1911-26. M mm.	17.50
39.	1 Pound 1911-31. P mm.	17.50
40.	½ Pound 1911-18. S mm.	12.50
41.	½ Pound 1915. M mm.	12.50

BURMA

Kings of —
MINGDUN MENG, 1852-1878

Burmese type lion. Rev. Legend in wreath.

1.	4 Rupees ND ....*	50.00
2.	2 Rupees ND ....*	35.00
3.	1 Rupee ND	25.00

Peacock. Rev. Legend in wreath.

4.	2 Rupees ND ....*	40.00
5.	1 Rupee ND	30.00

CAMBODIA

The bird Hamsa. Rev. Legend.

1.	1 Fuang ND (1846)	100.00

Head of King Norodom I. Rev. Arms. Souvenir gold coins struck from dies used for silver coins.

2.	2 Francs 1860 ....*	200.00
3.	1 Franc 1860	100.00
4.	50 Centimes 1860	75.00

CEYLON

Ruler standing. Rev. Ruler seated. Crude style. Struck during the period 840-1295 A.D.

1.	1 Stater ND ....*	125.00
2.	½ Stater ND	60.00
3.	¼ Stater ND	40.00
4.	⅛ Stater ND	30.00

Ruler kneeling. Rev. Legend. Crude style.

5.	1 Mas ND (840-1295 A.D.)	25.00

Ruler standing. Rev. Legend. Crude style.

6.	1 Mas ND (840-1295 A.D.)	25.00

"C" (For Colombo) and "VOC" monogram (Dutch East India Company) counterstamped on continental Dutch gold coins.

7.	2 Ducats 1691	Unique

Standing god. Rev. Granular surface.

8.	1 Pagoda ND (1760-94)	30.00

CHINA

A. Emperors of —
KUANG HSU, 1875-1908

Large dragon. Rev. Legend. The coins with reeded edge were reportedly not struck officially.

CHINA (cont'd)

1. 1 Tael 1906, 07. Plain edge 375.00
2. 1 Tael 1906, 07. Reeded edge 300.00

B. Republic of —

Head of President Yuan Shi Kai. Rev. Dragon with Chinese
legend reading "Empire of China".

3. 10 Dollars 1916 .... 250.00

Head of President Yuan Shi Kai. Rev. Legend and wreath.

4. 20 Dollars 1919 ....*...... 175.00
5. 10 Dollars 1919 .... 90.00

C. Republican Provinces of —

SHANTUNG

Dragon and Phoenix. Rev. Legend.

6. 20 Dollars 1926 .... 600.00
7. 10 Dollars 1926 ....*...... 500.00

YUNNAN

Five vertical characters flanked on each side by five dots. Rev. Blank.

8. 10 Dollars ND (1917) 75.00
9. 5 Dollars ND (1917) 75.00

Facing head of General Tang Chi Yao. Rev. Crossed flags.

10. 10 Dollars 1919. Numeral "1" below flags ....*..... 75.00
11. 10 Dollars 1919. Without numeral 125.00
12. 5 Dollars 1919. Numeral "2" below flags. ....*..... 50.00

Four characters around central dot. Rev. One character within grain wreath.

13. 10 Dollars ND (1925) ....*...... 175.00
14. 5 Dollars ND (1925) 125.00

CYPRUS

Kings of —

JOHN I, 1184-1185
King standing. Rev. Christ seated.

1. 1 Bezant ND 250.00

HUGH I, 1205-1218

King standing. Rev. Christ seated.

2. 1 Bezant ND 150.00

HENRY I, 1218-1253
King standing. Rev. Christ seated.

3. 1 Bezant ND 150.00

HENRY II, 1285-1324
King standing. Rev. Christ seated.

4. 1 Bezant ND 150.00

EGYPT

A. French Occupation of —

Toughra and accession date 1203 in Arabic (1789 A.D.). Rev.
Arab legend and regnal year 13 or Arabic letter B (for
Bonaparte). Struck during the rule of Selim III following
Napoleon's invasion of Egypt.

1. 1 Sequin. Size 21 millimetres ....*...... 30.00
2. ½ Sequin. Size 19 millimetres ....*...... 125.00
3. ¼ Sequin. Size 17 millimetres 25.00

B. Turkish Sultans of —
(Earlier coins were of the same types as those of Turkey).

ABDUL MEJID, 1839-1861

Toughra and value in plain field. Rev. Legend and date. All
coins bear the accession date 1255 in Arabic numerals in
addition to other Arabic numerals for the regnal year, which
indicate the precise date of coinage.

4. 100 Piastres ....*...... 40.00
5. 50 Piastres 22.50
6. 25 Piastres 20.00
7. 10 Piastres 17.50
8. 5 Piastres 15.00

ABDUL AZIZ, 1861-1876

Same type as above. All coins bear the accession date 1277 in
Arabic numerals in addition to other Arabic numerals for the
regnal year, which indicate the precise date of coinage.

EGYPT (cont'd)

9.	500 Piastres	....	300.00
10.	100 Piastres	....................*	35.00
11.	50 Piastres	....	22.50
12.	25 Piastres	....	15.00
13.	10 Piastres	....	10.00
14.	5 Piastres	....	7.50

ABDUL HAMID, 1876-1909

Same type as above. All coins bear the accession date 1293 in Arabic numerals in addition to other Arabic numerals for the regnal year, which indicate the precise date of coinage.

15.	500 Piastres	....................*	300.00
16.	100 Piastres	....	35.00
17.	50 Piastres	....	22.50
18.	10 Piastres	....	10.00
19.	5 Piastres	....	7.50

Toughra in lobed floral circle, value below. Rev. Legend and date. On larger flan than the preceding 100 Piastre pieces.

20. 100 Piastres. Year 12 (1888) 75.00

C. Independent Sultans of —

HUSEIN KAMIL, 1915-1917

Arab legend. Rev. Value and date in English.

21. 100 Piastres 1916 .... 60.00

D. Kings of —

FUAD, 1917-1936

Civilian bust to right. Rev. Legend.

22.	500 Piastres 1922	....	200.00
23.	100 Piastres 1922	....................*	40.00
24.	50 Piastres 1923-29	....	25.00
25.	20 Piastres 1923-29	....	20.00

Military bust to left. Rev. Legend.

26.	500 Piastres 1929-32	...................*	200.00
27.	100 Piastres 1930		45.00
28.	50 Piastres 1929, 30		25.00
29.	20 Piastres 1929, 30		20.00

FAROUK, 1937-1952

Military bust. Rev. Legend.

30.	500 Piastres 1938		275.00
31.	100 Piastres 1938		50.00
32.	50 Piastres 1938	.................*	30.00
33.	20 Piastres 1938		25.00

E. Republic of —

Ancient chariot and small Arabic date 1952. Rev. Legend and dates 1955 and 1374 in Arabic. On the Flight of Farouk and the formation of the Republic in 1952. This issue is without the mark of value.

34.	(500 Piastres) 1955	....	325.00
35.	(100 Piastres) 1955	...................*	75.00

ETHIOPIA

A. Axumite Kings of —

ENDYBIS, ABOUT 300 A.D.

Helmeted bust on each side.

1. ½ Aureus ND 750.00

AFILAS, ABOUT 300 A.D.

Crowned bust. Rev. Helmeted bust.

2. ½ Aureus ND 600.00

Helmeted bust. Rev. Legend.

3. ¹/₁₀ Aureus ND .... Rare

(Type:—The coins of the following kings of Axum are all of the same type and show a crowned bust on the obverse, and a helmeted bust on the reverse.)

OUSANAS I, ABOUT 350 A.D.

4. ⅓ Solidus ND 600.00

ETHIOPIA (cont'd)

WAZEBA, ABOUT 375 A.D.

5. ⅓ Solidus ND .... Rare

EZANAS AND/OR EZANA, ABOUT 400 A.D.

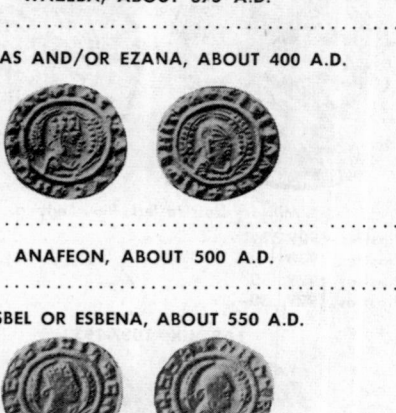

6. ⅓ Solidus ND 600.00

ANAFEON, ABOUT 500 A.D.

7. ⅓ Solidus ND 600.00

ESBEL OR ESBENA, ABOUT 550 A.D.

8. ⅓ Solidus ND 500.00

CALEB, ABOUT 575 A.D.

9. ⅓ Solidus ND 500.00

NEZANA, ABOUT 600 A.D.

10. ⅓ Solidus ND 750.00

OUSANAS II, ABOUT 600 A.D.

11. ⅓ Solidus ND .... Rare

OUSAS, ABOUT 600 A.D.

12. ⅓ Solidus ND 600.00

ALALMIRYIS, ABOUT 650 A.D.

13. ⅓ Solidus ND .... Rare

ELLA GABAZ, ABOUT 700 A.D.

14. ⅓ Sodius ND 750.00

JOEL, ABOUT 700 A.D.

15. ⅓ Solidus ND 750.00

ISRAEL, ABOUT 750 A.D.

16. ⅓ Solidus ND 600.00

JATHLIA, ABOUT 750 A.D.

17. ⅓ Solidus ND 750.00

GERSEM, ABOUT 850 A.D.

18. ⅓ Solidus ND 750.00

B. Modern Emperors of —

MENELIK II, 1889-1913

Crowned bust. Rev. Lion of Judah. Posthumously struck in 1916.

19. 1 Wark ND ....*...... 75.00
20. ½ Wark ND 50.00
21. ¼ Wark ND 40.00
22. ⅛ Wark ND 35.00

EMPRESS ZAUDITU, 1916-1930

Crowned bust. Rev. Lion of Judah.

23. 4 Warks ND. Size 31 millimetres 500.00
24. 2 Warks ND. Size 25 millimetres ....*...... 350.00
25. 1 Wark ND. Size 20 millimetres 200.00

HAILE SELASSIE, 1930-1936 AND 1941-

Head. Rev. St. George slaying dragon.

26. 1 Wark 1931 .... 200.00
27. ½ Wark 1931 .... 125.00

GERMAN EAST AFRICA

Elephant. Rev. Eagle.

1. 15 Rupees 1916 .... 60.00

GERMAN NEW GUINEA

Bird of Paradise. Rev. Value.

1. 20 Marks 1895 .... 300.00
2. 10 Marks 1895 .... 300.00

HAWAII

Head of King Kalakua. Rev. Arms. Souvenir gold and platinum coins struck from dies used for silver coins.

1. ½ Dollar 1884. Gold .... Rare
2. ½ Dollar 1884. Platinum .... Rare
3. ¼ Dollar 1884. Gold .... Rare
4. ¼ Dollar 1884. Platinum .... Rare
5. ⅛ Dollar 1883. Gold .... Rare
6. ⅛ Dollar 1883. Platinum .... Rare

(The two coins following were privately struck in England by Reginald Huth).

Head of Queen Liliuocalania to right. Rev. Map of the islands.

7. 20 Dollars 1893 .... Rare

Head of Queen Liliuocalania to left. Rev. Crown over value and date.

8. 20 Dollars 1893 .... Rare

HEJAZ

Kings of —
HUSEIN IBN ALI, 1916-1924

Arab legend in panels on each side.

1. 1 Dinar 1923 .... 40.00

INDIA

A. British Sovereigns of —
WILLIAM IV, 1830-1837

Head. Rev. Lion and palm tree. Issued by the East India Company.

1. 2 Mohurs 1835 ....* 200.00
2. 1 Mohur 1835 .... 65.00

VICTORIA, 1837-1901

Head. Rev. Lion and palm tree. Issued by the East India Company.

3. 1 Mohur 1841 .... 60.00

Thin face with title of Queen. Rev. Value.

4. 1 Mohur 1862-70 ....* 40.00
5. 10 Rupees 1862-70 .... 30.00
6. 5 Rupees 1862-70 ....* 25.00

Plump face with title of Queen. Rev. Value.

7. 1 Mohur 1870 ....* 50.00
8. 10 Rupees 1870 .... 35.00
9. 5 Rupees 1870 .... 30.00

Thin face with title of Empress. Rev. Value.

10. 1 Mohur 1877-89 .... 40.00

Plump face with title of Empress. Rev. Value.

11. 10 Rupees 1879 .... 35.00
12. 5 Rupees 1879 .... 30.00

GEORGE V, 1910-1936

Head. Rev. Value.

13. 15 Rupees 1918 .... 50.00

Head. Rev. St. George. This is the same type as the English Pound but with the distinguishing Indian mint mark "I" on ground below horse.

14. 1 Pound 1918 .... 50.00

B. Private Tola Coinage of —

Gold coins issued by various Indian banking houses during the present generation. There are many varieties and the pieces may be round, square, diamond shaped, or scalloped. The Tola weighs a little more than 11.50 Grams and is thus similar to the Mohur. Tola coinage is undated.

15. 10 Tola piece 500.00
16. 5 Tola piece 350.00
17. 1 Tola piece 50.00
18. ½ Tola piece 40.00
19. ¼ Tola piece 35.00

C. Native States of —

AGRA

Indian legend on each side. Oblong shape.

1. 1 Mohur. About 1550-1600 .... 200.00

AJMIR AND DELHI

Goddess seated. Rev. Legend.

1. 1 Stater. About 1010-1160 .... 75.00

ARCOT

Indian legend on each side. Coinage of the East India Company in the name of Alamgir II of Hindustan. With dates from about 1172-1214 A.H. (1758-99).

1. 1 Mohur 50.00
2. ½ Mohur ....* 30.00
3. ¼ Mohur 25.00

INDIA (cont'd)

ASSAM

Indian legend on each side. Octagonal shaped coins struck during the period 1540-1820.

1.	1 Mohur ....*	75.00
2.	½ Mohur	40.00
3.	¼ Mohur	30.00
4.	⅛ Mohur	20.00
5.	1/16 Mohur	15.00
6.	1/32 Mohur	15.00

AWADH

Kings of —

GHAZI-ED-DIN-HAIDAR, 1819-1827

Legend. Rev. Two fish crowned, supported by tigers.

1. 1 Mohur 1234-1243 A.H. 75.00

MOHAMMED ALI SHAH, 1837-1842

Legend. Rev. Two females standing and supporting crown.

2. 1 Mohur 1253-1258 A.H. 75.00

AMJAD ALI SHAH, 1842-1847

Legend. Rev. Umbrella over crown over fish.

3. 1 Mohur 1258-1262 A.H. 85.00
4. ½ Mohur 1258-1262 A.H. ....* 50.00

WAJID ALI SHAH, 1847-1856

Legend. Rev. Arms supported by mermaids holding clubs and banners.

5. 1 Mohur 1263-1272 A.H. ....* 75.00
6. ½ Mohur 1263-1272 A.H. ....* 50.00
7. ¼ Mohur 1263-1272 A.H. 40.00
8. ⅛ Mohur 1263-1272 A.H. 35.00

BAHAWALPUR

Bust of Rajah Sadik Mohammed V. Rev. Arms.

1. 1 Mohur 1343 A.H. (1925) 125.00

BAJRANGGARH

Indian legend on each side. Struck under Jai Singh.

1. 1 Mohur (1798-1818). Octagonal 125.00

BARODA

Bust of the Gaikwar Sayaji Rao III (1875-1902). Rev. Legend. With dates from about 1940-1953 Samvat (1883-1896 A.D.).

1. 1 Mohur ....* 200.00
2. ⅓ Mohur 100.00
3. ⅙ Mohur ....* 65.00

BENARES

Indian legend on each side. Coinage of the East India Company in the name of Shah Alam of Hindustan. With dates from about 1212-1235 A.H. (1797-1819).

1. 1 Mohur 60.00

BENGAL

Indian legend on each side. Royal coinage struck during the period 1302-1518.

1. 1 Mohur 40.00

Indian legend on each side. Coinage of the East India Company struck during the period 1750-1820.

2. 2 Mohurs 175.00
3. 1 Mohur 40.00
4. ¼ Mohur 30.00

340

BHARTPUR

Indian legend on each side. Rajah coinage struck during the period 1805-1823.

1. 1 Mohur **50.00**

Crude head of Queen Victoria. Rev. Legend.

2. 1 Mohur ND. (About 1860) **125.00**

BHOPAL

Indian legend on each side. Coinage of the Begums.

1. 1 Mohur (1840-1850) **60.00**

BIKANIR

Bust of the Maharajah Sri Ganga Singhji. Rev. Legend.

1. 1 Mohur 1994 Samvat (1937) ....*...... **100.00**
2. ½ Mohur 1994 Samvat (1937) **75.00**

BOMBAY

Arms of the English East India Company. Rev. "Bombay" and date.

1. 1 Mohur 1765 .... **250.00**
2. ½ Mohur 1765 .... **175.00**
3. ¼ Mohur 1765 .... **150.00**

Indian legend on each side. Coinage of the East India Company in the name of Shah Alam of Hindustan.

4. 1 Mohur 1182 A.H. (1768) **60.00**

Indian legend. Rev. English name, date and value.

5. 15 Rupees (1 Mohur) 1770 .... **300.00**

BUNDI

Indian legend on each side. Maharajah coinage struck during the period 1800-35.

1. 1 Mohur **60.00**

CALCUTTA

Indian legend on each side with a large C on Rev. Coinage of the East India Company in the name of Shah Alam of Hindustan.

1. 1 Mohur 1216 A.H. (1801) **125.00**

CHOLAS

Ruler standing on each side. Crude tribal coinage struck during the period 1000-1300.

1. 1 Stater **75.00**

COCHIN

Crude symbols on each side. Struck during the period 1740-80.

1. 1 Fanam **10.00**

COROMANDEL COAST

Symbols on each side. Struck during the period 1700-1800.

1. 1 Fanam **10.00**

CUTCH-BHUJ

MAHARAJAH PRAGMALJI II, 1860-1875

Arabic legend with Christian date in Arabic numerals. Rev. Indian legend with Samvat date.

1. 100 Kori 1866 ....* 125.00
2.   50 Kori 1873, 74 .... 75.00
3. `25 Kori 1862-70 .... 60.00

CUTCH-BIHAR

Legend in square. Rev. Legend. Struck under Rajah Narendra Narayana, 1847-1863.

1. 1 Mohur 100.00

Arms supported by lion and elephant. Rev. Legend. Struck under Rajah Jitandra Narayana, 1912-1922.

2. 1 Mohur. Years 402, 404 (1912, 14) 200.00

DAHALA

Goddess seated. Rev. Legend. Coinage of Governors struck during the period 1000-1100.

1. 1 Stater 75.00

DELHI

Sultans of —

MOHAMMED I, 1193-1206

Indian legend within square on each side. With dates from about 589-602 A.H.

1. 1 Tanka. Large flan. Ghazni mint 200.00

Ruler on horse within circle. Rev. Legend.

2. 1 Tanka .... Unique

Crude figure of Lakshmi seated. Rev. Legend.

3. ½ Tanka 60.00

SHAMSUDIN ILTUTMISH, 1210-1235

Ruler on horse. Rev. Legend.

4. ½ Tanka ND .... Rare

ALADDIN MASUD, 1242-1246

Indian legend within square on each side. With dates from about 639-644 A.H.

5. 1 Mohur 200.00

NASREDIN MAHMUD I, 1246-1266

Indian legend within circle on each side. With dates from about 644-664 A.H.

6. 1 Mohur 60.00

Indian legend within square on each side.

7. 1 Mohur 75.00

GHIYASU-EDIN BALBAN, 1266-1287

Indian legend within circle on each side. With dates from about 664-686 A.H.

8. 1 Mohur 50.00

FIRUZ II, 1290-1296

Indian legend on each side. With dates from about 689-695 A.H.

9. 1 Mohur 50.00

ALADDIN MOHAMMED, 1296-1316

Indian legend on each side. With dates from about 695-715 A.H.

10. 1 Mohur. Round ....* 50.00
11. 1 Mohur. Square 75.00

SHIHABU-EDIN UMAR, 1316

Indian legend on each side.

12. 1 Mohur 715 A.H. 100.00

QUETBU-EDIN MUBARAK, 1316-1320

Indian legend on each side. With dates from about 716-720 A.H.

13. 1 Mohur. Round 50.00
14. 1 Mohur. Square ....* 75.00
15. ⅓ Mohur. Square 40.00

NASREDIN KHUSRU, 1320

Indian legend on each side.

16. 1 Mohur 720 A.H. 100.00

GHIYASU-EDIN TUGHLUK, 1320-1325

Indian legend on each side. With dates from about 720-725 A.H.

17. 1 Mohur 50.00

INDIA-DELHI (cont'd)

MOHAMMED III, 1325-1351

Indian legend on each side. With dates from about 725-752 A.H.

18.	1½ Mohurs	100.00
19.	1 Mohur ....*......	40.00
20.	½ Mohur ....*......	30.00

FIRUZ III, 1351-1388

Indian legend on each side. With dates from about 752-790 A.H.

21.	1 Mohur	50.00

FATH KHAN, 1351-1388
(Son of Firuz III)
Indian legend on each side.

22.	1 Mohur	50.00

TUGHLUK II, 1388-1389
Indian legend on each side. With dates from about 790-791 A.H.

23.	1 Mohur	125.00

FIRUZ ZAFAR, 1389
Indian legend on each side.

24.	1 Mohur 791 A.H.	100.00

ABU BAKRE, 1389-1390
Indian legend on each side. With dates from about 791-793 A.H.

25.	1 Mohur	75.00

MOHAMMED IV, 1390-1393
Indian legend on each side. With dates from about 792-795 A.H.

26.	1 Mohur	65.00

MAHMUD II, 1393-1413
Indian legend on each side. With dates from about 795-815 A.H.

27.	1 Mohur	50.00

NUSRAT SHAH, 1395-1399
Indian legend on each side. With dates from about 779-802 A.H.

28.	1 Mohur	60.00

MUBARAK II, 1421-1434
Indian legend on each side. With dates from about 824-837 A.H.

29.	1 Mohur	50.00

MOHAMMED V, 1434-1445
Indian legend on each side. With dates from about 837-849 A.H.

30.	1 Mohur	50.00

SHER, 1538-1545
Indian legend on each side. With dates from about 945-952 A.H.

31.	1 Mohur	200.00

ISLAM, 1545-1552
Indian legend on each side. With dates from about 952-960 A.H.

32.	1 Mohur	200.00

MOHAMMED ADIL, 1552-1556

Indian legend on each side. With dates from about 960-964 A.H.

33.	1 Mohur	250.00

DIU

Portuguese Kings of —
JOHN V, 1706-1750

St. Thomas standing. Rev. Crowned arms. Crude style.

1.	5 Xerafins 1719	200.00

JOSEPH I, 1750-1777

Crowned arms. Rev. Cross of St. Thomas. Crude style.

2.	10 Xerafins. Usually poorly dated	250.00

EAST INDIA COMPANY

(For other issues of the Company, see under British sovereigns of India. In addition, the Company struck native type coins at the mints of Arcot, Benares, Bengal, Bombay, Calcutta, Madras, Murshidabad and Surat, which see).

Arms supported by lions; English legend. Rev. Native legend.

1.	1 Mohur ND (1820)	40.00

Lion with crown on plain ground; English legend. Rev. Native legend.

2.	½ Mohur ND (1820)	30.00
3.	¼ Mohur ND (1820) ....*......	22.50

Lion standing on shield; English legend. Rev. Native legend.

4.	⅓ Mohur ND (1820)	25.00

GOA

A. Chiefs of —
Lion, sun and moon. Rev. Legend. Struck during the period 1185-1215.

1.	1 Pagoda ND	75.00

B. Portuguese Kings of —
MANUEL I, 1495-1521

MEA under crown. Rev. Globe.

2.	½ Esphera ND	200.00

JOHN III, 1521-1557

St. Thomas seated. Rev. Arms.

3. 1 Pardau San Tome ND 500.00

ALFONSO VI, 1656-1683

St. Thomas standing. Rev. Arms.

4. 1 Pardau San Tome ND 500.00

PETER, PRINCE REGENT, 1667-1683

St. Thomas standing. Rev. Arms.

5. 1 San Tome 1677, 80 .... 250.00

Arms. Rev. Cross of Jerusalem.

6. 1 Xerafin ND 50.00

JOHN V, 1706-1750
St. Thomas standing. Rev. Arms.

7. 1 San Tome 1719 .... 150.00

Arms. Rev. Cross of St. Thomas.

8. 12 Xerafins 1732 ....* 500.00
9. 10 Xerafins 1737 .... 500.00

Arms. Rev. Cross of Jerusalem.

10. 1 Xerafin 1715, 16, 18, 21 .... 100.00

JOSEPH I, 1750-1777

Arms. Rev. Cross of St. Thomas.

11. 12 Xerafins 1755-77 ....* 100.00
12.   8 Xerafins 1766, 71 .... 150.00
13.   4 Xerafins 1769, 77 .... 125.00
14.   2 Xerafins 1766, 68, 72, 74 .... 100.00

MARY I, 1777-1816

Arms. Rev. Cross of St. Thomas

15. 12 Xerafins 1781-1806 .... 100.00
16.   8 Xerafins 1787 .... 500.00
17.   4 Xerafins 1803 .... 500.00

JOHN, PRINCE REGENT, 1799-1816
Arms. Rev. Cross of St. Thomas.

18. 12 Xerafins 1808-15 .... 100.00

JOHN VI, 1816-1826
Arms. Rev. Cross of St. Thomas.

19. 12 Xerafins 1819, 25 .... 150.00

MARY II, 1834-1853

Arms. Rev. Cross of St. Thomas.

20. 12 Xerafins 1840, 41 .... 200.00

GUJARAT

Indian Legend on each side. Sultanate coinage struck during the period 1450-1560.

1. 1 Mohur ....* 50.00
2. ½ Mohur 40.00

GWALIOR

Turbaned bust of the Rajah Madho III, 1886-1925. Rev. Arms.

1. ⅓ Mohur 1959 Samvat (1902) 125.00

HINDUSTAN

Mogul Emperors of —
HUMAYUN, 1530-1554

Indian legend on each side. With dates from about 937-960 A.H.

1. ¹⁄₁₀ Mohur 25.00
2. ¹⁄₂₀ Mohur 20.00

AKBAR, 1556-1605
(Coinage with dates from about 963-1014 A.H.)

Indian legend on each side.

3. 100 Mohurs ....Unknown
4.   50 Mohurs ....Unknown
5.   20 Mohurs. Round ....Unknown
6.   20 Mohurs. Square ....Unknown
7.   5 Mohurs 1500.00
8.   2 Mohurs. Round ....Unknown
9.   2 Mohurs. Square ....Unknown
10.   1 Mohur. Round ....* 50.00
11.   1 Mohur. Square ....* 65.00
12.   1 Mohur. Oblong with scalloped corners ....* 250.00
12a.   ½ Mohur. Lozenge shaped 150.00
13.   ½ Mohur. Square 40.00

14.	¼ Mohur. Round	....	40.00
15.	¼ Mohur. Square	....	40.00
16.	¹⁄₁₀ Mohur	....	20.00
17.	¹⁄₂₀ Mohur	....	17.50

Indian legend within square on each side.

18. 1 Mohur 75.00

Indian legend within octagon on each side.

19. 1 Mohur 100.00

Hawk standing. Rev. Legend.

20. 1 Mohur 350.00

Duck standing. Rev. Legend.

21. 1 Mohur 350.00

Male and female figures standing, the male holding bow and arrows. Rev. Legend.

22. ½ Mohur 300.00

JAHANGIR, 1605-1627
(Coinage with dates from about 1014-1037 A.H.)

Turbaned bust with or without fruit or goblet in front of face. Rev. Lion to right or left under radiate sun.

23. 1 Mohur 350.00

King seated cross-legged. Rev. Legend.

24. ¼ Mohur 200.00

Small figure seated cross-legged. Rev. Lion under radiate sun.

25. 1 Mohur 500.00

Large figure seated cross-legged. Rev. Radiate sun in square within panelled legend.

26. 1 Mohur 500.00

Sign of the Zodiac as noted. Rev. Legend. The famous Zodiac Mohurs.

27.	1 Mohur. Twins (Gemini)	....	350.00
28.	1 Mohur. Goat (Capricorn)	....	350.00
29.	1 Mohur. Scales (Libra)	....	350.00
30.	1 Mohur. Bull (Taurus)	....	350.00
31.	1 Mohur. Crab (Cancer)	....	400.00
32.	1 Mohur. Female (Virgo)	....	350.00
33.	1 Mohur. Ram (Aries)	....	400.00
34.	1 Mohur. Lion (Leo)	....	500.00
35.	1 Mohur. Scorpion (Scorpio)	....	400.00
36.	1 Mohur. Archer (Sagittarius)	....	400.00
37.	1 Mohur. Water carrier (Aquarius)	....	500.00
38.	1 Mohur. Fish (Pisces)	....	400.00

Indian legend on each side.

39.	5 Mohurs	....	1500.00
40.	1 Mohur. Round	...........................*	50.00
41.	1 Mohur. Square	..........................*	75.00

SHAH-JAHAN, 1628-1658
(Coinage with dates from about 1037-1068 A.H.)
Indian legend on each side.

42.	1 Mohur. Round	....	50.00
43.	1 Mohur. Square	....	75.00

Indian legend within square on each side.

44.	200 Mohurs	.................................Unknown
45.	1 Mohur	..................................*	50.00

345

Indian legend within lozenge or diamond on each side.

46. 1 Mohur 50.00

Indian legend within circle on each side.

47. 1 Mohur 60.00

MURAD BAKHSH, 1658

Indian legend within square on each side.

48. 1 Mohur 1068 A.H. 125.00

AURANGZIB, 1659-1707
(Coinage with dates from about 1069-1118 A.H.)

Indian legend on each side.

49. 100 Mohurs .... Unknown
50. 1 Mohur 50.00
51. ¼ Mohur .... * 30.00

Indian legend within square on each side.

52. 1 Mohur 60.00

AZAM SHAH, 1707
Indian legend on each side.

53. 1 Mohur 1118, 19 A.H. 125.00

KAM BAKHSH, 1708
Indian legend on each side.

54. 1 Mohur 1120 A.H. 150.00

BAHADUR, 1702-1712

Indian legend on each side. With dates from about 1119-1124 A.H.

55. 1 Mohur. Usual size 50.00
56. 1 Mohur. Broad type .... * 125.00

JAHANDAR, 1712
Indian legend on each side.

57. 1 Mohur 1124 A.H. 75.00

FARRUKH-SIYAR, 1713-1719

Indian legend on each side. With dates from about 1124-1131 A.H.

58. 1 Mohur 50.00
59. ¼ Mohur .... * 25.00
60. ⅛ Mohur .... * 20.00

RAFIYAD DARAJAT, 1719
Indian legend on each side.

61. 1 Mohur 1131 A.H. 75.00

SHAH JAHAN II, 1719
Indian legend on each side.

62. 1 Mohur 1131 A.H. 75.00

NIKU-SIYAR, 1719
Indian legend on each side.

63. 1 Mohur 1131 A.H. or year 1 .... 75.00

IBRAHIM, 1720
Indian legend on each side.

64. 1 Mohur 1132 A.H. 100.00

MOHAMMED SHAH, 1719-1748
Indian legend on each side. With dates from about 1131-1161 A.H.

65. 1 Mohur 50.00
66. ¼ Mohur .... * 25.00

AHMED SHAH, 1748-1754
Indian legend on each side. With dates from about 1161-1167 A.H.

67. 1 Mohur 50.00
68. 1/64 Mohur. Rev. Blank 12.50

ALAMGIR II, 1754-1759
Indian legend on each side. With dates from about 1167-1173 A.H.

69. 1 Mohur 50.00
70. ¼ Mohur 25.00

Indian legend within square on each side.

71. 1 Mohur 60.00

SHAH JAHAN III, 1759-1760
Indian legend on each side.

72. 1 Mohur 1173, 74 A.H. 60.00

SHAH ALAM, 1759-1806

Indian legend on each side. With dates from about 1173-1221 A.H.

73. 1 Mohur. Usual size .... * 50.00
74. 1 Mohur. Broad type 125.00
75. 1/16 Mohur 25.00

Indian legend within circle on each side, the whole within a floral wreath formed by roses, thistles and shamrocks.

76. 1 Mohur 150.00

BIDAR BAKHT, PRETENDER, 1788
Indian legend on each side.

77. 1 Mohur 1202, 03 A.H. 75.00

HYDERABAD

Arabic legend on each side. Coinage of the Nizams, struck during the period 1700-1902, and with dates from about 1114-1320 A.H.

1.	1 Mohur	.........................*	40.00
2.	½ Mohur	....	30.00
3.	¼ Mohur	....	20.00
4.	⅛ Mohur	....	12.50
5.	¹⁄₁₆ Mohur	....	10.00

Persian type minaret or mosque. Rev. Legend. Struck under the Nizam Mir Mahbub, 1868-1911.

6.	1 Mohur 1321-29 A.H. (1903-11)	...............*	60.00
7.	½ Mohur 1321-29 A.H. (1903-11)	....	40.00
8.	¼ Mohur 1321-29 A.H. (1903-11)	....	30.00
9.	⅛ Mohur 1321-29 A.H. (1903-11)	....	25.00

Type similar to above but struck under the Nizam Mir Usman, 1911-1957.

10.	1 Mohur 1330-66 A.H. (1911-47)	....	75.00
11.	½ Mohur 1330-66 A.H. (1911-47)	....	50.00
12.	¼ Mohur 1330-66 A.H. (1911-47)	....	35.00
13.	⅛ Mohur 1330-66 A.H. (1911-47)	....	30.00

IKARI

Goddess seated. Rev. Legend. Coinage of Governors struck during the period 1500-1700.

1.	1 Pagoda ND	....	50.00

JAIPUR

Arab legend on each side. Maharajah coinage struck during the period 1800-1924.

1.	1 Mohur	....	50.00

JAISALMIR

Arab legend on each side. Rajah coinage struck during the period 1840-1870.

1.	1 Mohur	....	75.00

JAUNPUR

Indian legend on each side. Royal coinage struck during the period 1400-1500.

1.	1 Mohur	....	75.00

JEJAKABHUKTI

Goddess seated. Rev. Legend. Coinage of Governors struck during the period 1000-1300.

1.	1 Stater	....	75.00

JIND

Indian legend on each side. Rajah coinage struck during the period 1840-1865.

1.	1 Mohur	....	60.00

JODHPUR

Indian legend. Rev. Arab legend. Rajah coinage struck during the period 1860-1912.

1.	1 Mohur	....	60.00

JUNAGARH

Indian legend on each side. Struck under Rajah Bahadur Khan II.

1.	1 Kori 1309 A.H. (1891)	..................*	150.00
2.	½ Kori 1309 A.H. (1891)	....	100.00

KALINGA

Recumbent bull. Rev. Date. Coinage of Governors struck during the period 1050-1150.

1.	1 Fanam	....	20.00

The Monkey god Hanuman. Rev. Blank.

2.	1 Fanam (1050-1150)	....	20.00

KALPI

Native legend on each side. Shah coinage struck during the period 1500-1600.

1.	1 Mohur. Square	....	100.00

KALYANI

Temple. Rev. Blank. Coinage of Governors struck during the period 1100-1200.

1.	1 Pagoda	....	50.00

The Monkey god Hanuman. Rev. Blank.

2.	1 Pagoda (1100-1200)	....	50.00

KANAUJ

King standing. Rev. Goddess. Royal coinage struck during the period 600-900.

1. 1 Stater 40.00

KASHMIR

King standing. Rev. Goddess seated. Royal coinage struck during the period 700-800.

1. 1 Stater 75.00

Indian legend on each side.

2. 1 Mohur (1450-1550) 40.00

KISHANGARH

Arab legend on each side. Maharajah coinage struck during the period 1800-79.

1. 1 Mohur 60.00

KOTAH

Indian legend on each side. Rajah coinage struck during the period 1800-1900.

1. 1 Mohur 75.00
2. ½ Mohur 50.00

KULBARGA

Indian legend on each side. Bahmani coinage struck during the period 1400-1500.

1. 1 Mohur 60.00

MADRAS

Arab legend on each side. Coinage of the East India Company struck during the period 1750-1820.

1. 1 Mohur 40.00
2. ½ Mohur 30.00
3. ⅓ Mohur 20.00

Vishnu seated. Rev. Star.

4. 1 Pagoda (1750) 30.00

Vishnu standing. Rev. Star.

5. 1 Pagoda (1750) 25.00

Vishnu standing. Rev. Grains.

6. 1 Pagoda (1750) 20.00

Three gods standing. Rev. Grains.

7. 1 Pagoda (1750) 25.00

Four armed god. Rev. Grains.

8. 1 Pagoda (1750) 25.00

Siva and Parvati seated. Rev. Grains.

9. 1 Pagoda (1750) 25.00

Pagoda amid stars. Rev. Vishnu and English legend.

10. 2 Pagodas (1810) 40.00
11. 1 Pagoda (1810) 30.00

MAHAKOSALA

Rampant lion. Rev. Legend. Coinage of Governors struck during the period 1100-1200.

1. 1 Stater 75.00

MALWA

Indian legend on each side. Royal coinage struck during the period 1400-1600.

1. 1 Mohur. Round 40.00
2. 1 Mohur. Square ....*...... 50.00
3. 1 Mohur. Octagonal ....*...... 75.00

MANIPUR

Indian legend on each side. Rajah coinage struck during the period 1760-1780.

1. 1 Mohur. Square 75.00
2. ½ Mohur. Square 50.00
3. ¼ Mohur. Square 30.00

MASULIPATAN

Three gods standing. Rev. Grains.

1. 1 Pagoda (1750) 15.00

MEWAR-UDAIPUR

Indian legend on each side. Maharaja coinage struck during the period 1825-1915.

1. 1 Mohur 75.00

Legend in two lines. Rev. Five characters in lobed circle.

2. 1 Mohur (1825-1915) 75.00

MOGUL EMPIRE

(See under Hindustan)

MURSHIDABAD

Native legend on each side, with oblique or straight milling or with plain edge. Coinage of the East India Company in the name of Shah Alam of Hindustan. With dates from about 1182-1204 A.H. (1768-1832).

1.	1 Mohur	...........................*	50.00
2.	½ Mohur	....	30.00
3.	¼ Mohur	....	25.00
4.	⅛ Mohur	...........................*	20.00
5.	1/16 Mohur	....	15.00

MYSORE

Sultans of —

RANADHIRA WODEYAR, 1638-1659
Vishnu seated. Rev. Legend.

1.	1 Fanam ND	....	12.50

HAIDAR ALI, 1761-1782

Siva and Parvati seated. Rev. Initial on grains.

2.	1 Pagoda ND	....	25.00

Half-length figure of Vishnu. Rev. Initial on grains.

3.	½ Pagoda ND	....	50.00

TIPOO, 1782-1799
(Coinage with dates from about 1197-1213 A.H.)
Arab legend on each side.

4.	1 Mohur	....	75.00
5.	½ Mohur	....	60.00
6.	1 Pagoda	....	20.00

Initial. Rev. Legend.

7.	1 Pagoda	...........................*	25.00
8.	1 Fanam	....	10.00

KRISHNA WODEYAR, 1799-1868
(Coinage with dates from about 1214-1285 A.H.)

Siva and Parvati seated. Rev. Legend.

9.	1 Pagoda ND	....	20.00

Arab legend on each side.

10.	1 Mohur	...........................*	60.00
11.	½ Mohur	....	35.00
12.	1 Pagoda	...........................*	20.00

NAWANAGAR

Bi-lingual legend on each side. Rajah coinage struck during the period 1300-1400.

1.	½ Mohur	....	30.00

Legend. Rev. Track-like device. Struck under Vibahji II, 1852-1895.

2.	1 Kori	....	125.00

NEGAPATNAM

Crude four armed god. Rev. Grains.

1.	1 Pagoda (1660-1780)	....	50.00

Vishnu standing. Rev. Grains.

2.	1 Pagoda (1660-1780)	....	25.00

Crude human figure. Rev. Legend and "OC" (East India Company).

3.	3 Fanams (1690-95)	....	75.00
4.	1 Fanam (1690-95)	....	25.00

ORISSA

Elephant. Rev. Scroll. Coinage of Governors struck during the period 1200-1400.

1.	1 Pagoda	....	75.00

Crude figure. Rev. Legend.

2.	1 Pagoda	....	40.00
3.	½ Pagoda	....	25.00

PATIALA

Native legend on each side. Rajah coinage struck during the period 1840-1900.

1.	1 Mohur	....	50.00

PONDICHERRY

(French Colony)
Crown and stars. Rev. Fleur-de-lis.

1.	1 Pagoda (1715-74)	....	60.00

Goddess. Rev. Symbol amid grains.

2.	1 Pagoda (1715-74)	....	25.00

Two goddesses. Rev. Symbol amid grains.

3.	1 Pagoda (1715-74)	....	25.00

Vishnu between two figures. Rev. Grains.

4. 1 Pagoda (1715-74) 25.00

PULICAT

(Dutch settlement on the Coromandel Coast)

Crude four armed god. Rev. Legend.

1. 1 Pagoda (1646-1781) ....•........ Unique

Crude symbol. Rev. Grains.

2. 1 Fanam (1646-1781) 25.00

PUNJAB

Native legend on each side. Sikh coinage struck during the period 1750-1875.

1. 1 Mohur 75.00

RADHANPUR

Crude head of Queen Victoria. Rev. Legend.

1. 1 Mohur (1860) 175.00

RAJKOT

Radiant sun. Rev. Tridents and crescent.

1. 1 Mohur 1945 .... 250.00

SOUTH INDIA

Crude floral devices. Rev. Blank. Struck during the period 600-1000.

1. 1 Tanka 20.00

SURAT

Indian legend on each side. Coinage of the East India Company in the name of Shah Alam of Hindustan. This issue was struck in 1825.

1. 1 Mohur ....*...... 40.00
2. ½ Mohur 50.00
3. ¼ Mohur 25.00
4. 1/16 Mohur 17.50

Very small crowned head amid legend. Rev. Legend with date 1802 on small oval panel.

5. ¼ Mohur 1802 .... 125.00

TELLICHERRY

Native legend on each side.

1. 1 Pagoda (1806) 35.00

Native legend on each side with date on reverse.

2. ⅕ Rupee 1809 .... 75.00

TIPERAH

Native legend on each side. Rajah coinage struck during the period 1700-1800.

1. 1 Mohur 50.00

TONK

Native legend on each side. Rajah coinage struck during the period 1800-1900.

1. 2 Mohurs ....*...... 200.00
2. 1 Mohur 50.00

TRAVANCORE

Pellets and lines on each side.

1. 1 Fanam (1700-1880) 10.00

Pellets. Rev. Symbol.

2. 1 Fanam (1700-1880) 10.00

Crescent. Rev. Symbol.

3. 1 Fanam (1700-1880) 10.00

Symbol. Rev. Dots.

4. 1 Fanam (1700-1880) 10.00

Dagger. Rev. Heart.

5. 1 Fanam (1700-1880) 15.00

Bust of the Maharaja Sri Rama Varma, 1881-1924. Rev. Arms supported by elephants.

6. 1 Sovereign 1881 ....* 250.00
7. ½ Sovereign 1881 .... 350.00

Shell. Rev. Legend.

8. 2 Pagodas (1881-1924) 125.00
9. 1 Pagoda (1881-1924) ....* 75.00
10. ½ Pagoda (1881-1924) 50.00
11. ¼ Pagoda (1881-1924) 35.00

Shell. Rev. "R.V." and "1877" in wreath, "Travancore" above.

12. 2 Pagodas 1877 .... 200.00
13. 1 Pagoda 1877 .... 125.00

Native legend. Rev. Blank. Struck on smaller and thicker flans than preceding issues.

14. 2 Pagodas (1881-1924) ....* 100.00
15. 1 Pagoda (1881-1924) 65.00
16. ½ Pagoda (1881-1924) 40.00
17. ¼ Pagoda (1881-1924) 30.00

TUTICORIN

Crude symbols on each side.

1. 1 Fanam (1675-1760) 15.00

UJAIN

Native legend on each side. Rajah coinage struck during the period 1750-1800.

1. 1 Mohur 125.00

VENGI

Boar and umbrella. Rev. Blank. Coinage of Governors struck during the period 1000-1100.

1. 1 Pagoda 50.00

VIJAYANAGAR

God and Goddess seated. Rev. Legend. Royal coinage struck during the period 1400-1600.

1. 1 Pagoda ....* 30.00
2. ½ Pagoda 20.00

Deity seated. Rev. Legend.

3. 1 Pagoda 30.00

Eagle and elephants. Rev. Legend.

4. 1 Pagoda 50.00
5. ½ Pagoda ....* 40.00

Vishnu standing. Rev. Legend.

6. 1 Pagoda ....* 30.00
7. ½ Pagoda 20.00

JAPAN

Emperors of —

A. Odd-Shaped Pieces of the Old Coinage

Oval shaped pieces averaging about 150 x 100 millimetres and characterized by seals punched into the metal and by legends applied with ink. The dates given are approximate.

OBANS OR 10 TAEL PIECES

1. Tensho Oban 1591. Diamond shaped seals 1500.00
2. Tensho Naga Oban 1591. Round seals 2000.00
3. Keicho Oban 1601 .... 1000.00
4. Genroku Oban 1695 .... 1000.00
5. Kyoho Oban 1725 .... 300.00
6. Tempo Oban 1838 .... 500.00
7. Manen Oban 1860 (Size 132 x 80) 300.00

Type similar to above but averaging about 90 x 50 millimetres and without the ink legends.

GORYOBAN OR 5 TAEL PIECES

8. Tempo Goryoban 1837 .... 150.00

JAPAN (cont'd)

Type similar to above but averaging about 70 x 40 millimetres.

KOBANS OR 1 TAEL PIECES

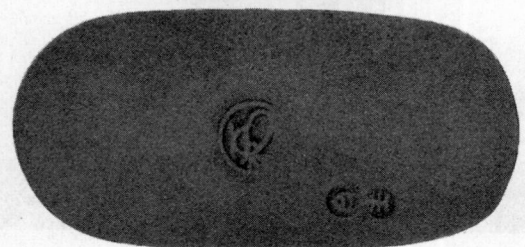

9.	Keicho Koban 1601	60.00
10.	Genroku Koban 1695	150.00
11.	Hoei Koban 1710	75.00
12.	Kyoho Koban 1716 ....*	50.00
13.	Genbun Koban 1736	35.00
14.	Bunsei Koban 1819	40.00
15.	Tempo Koban 1837	30.00
16.	Ansei Koban 1859	50.00
17.	Manen Koban 1860 (Size 35 x 20)	25.00

Rectangular pieces averaging about 23 x 15 millimetres and bearing legends and floral designs.

NI-BU OR 2 BU PIECES

18.	Shinbun 2 Bu 1818 ....*	20.00
19.	Sobun 2 Bu 1828	20.00
20.	Ansei 2 Bu 1856	12.50
21.	Manen 2 Bu 1860 ....*	7.50
22.	Kaheishi 2 Bu 1868	7.50

Type similar to above but averaging about 18 x 10 millimetres.

ICHI-BU OR 1 BU PIECES

23.	Taiko 1 Bu 1591 ....*	150.00
24.	Keicho 1 Bu 1601	30.00
25.	Genroku 1 Bu 1695	20.00
26.	Hoei 1 Bu 1710	20.00
27.	Kyoho 1 Bu 1716	25.00
28.	Genbun 1 Bu 1736	20.00
29.	Bunsei 1 Bu 1819	20.00
30.	Tempo 1 Bu 1837	20.00
31.	Ansei 1 Bu 1859	20.00
32.	Manen 1 Bu 1860. (Size reduced)	20.00

Type similar to above but averaging 13 x 8 millimetres.

NI-SHU OR 2 SHU PIECES

33.	Genroku 2 Shu 1695	15.00
34.	Tempo 2 Shu 1832	7.50
35.	Manen 2 Shu 1860	7.50

Type similar to above but averaging 10 millimetres square.

IS-SHU OR 1 SHU PIECE

36.	Bunsei 1 Shu 1824	10.00

B. Round Pieces of the Old Coinage

Five characters around circle on each side. Size about 20 millimetres.

37.	Taiko Gold coin 1591	300.00

Four characters around square central hole on each side.

38.	Eiraku Gold coin 1593 ....*	75.00
39.	Kanei Gold coin 1626	100.00

Legend and ornaments on each side. Issued by Koshu Province about 1850.

40.	1 Bu. Size 13 millimetres	20.00
41.	2 Shu. Size 11 millimetres	10.00
42.	1 Shu. Size 10 millimetres	7.50
43.	½ Shu. Size 8 millimetres	25.00
44.	½ Shu. Size 6 millimetres square	20.00

C. The Modern Coinage of Japan

MUTSUHITO, 1867-1912
(The Meiji Era)

Dragon. Rev. Wreath over crossed banners.

45.	20 Yen. Years 3-13 (1870-80)	200.00
46.	10 Yen. Years 4-13 (1871-80)	75.00
47.	5 Yen. Years 3-30 (1870-97) ....* ...	35.00
48.	2 Yen. Years 3-13 (1870-80)	30.00

Japanese character. Rev. Wreath over crossed banners.

49.	1 Yen. Years 4-13 (1871-80)	17.50

Radiant sun. Rev. Value in wreath. Reduced size coins struck after revaluation of the gold yen in 1897.

50.	20 Yen. Years 30-45 (1897-1912)	60.00
51.	10 Yen. Years 30-43 (1897-1910) ....* ...	35.00
52.	5 Yen. Years 30-45 (1897-1912)	22.50

YOSHIHITO, 1912-1926
(The Taisho Era)

Radiant sun. Rev. Value in wreath.

53.	20 Yen. Years 1-9 (1912-20) ....*	60.00
54.	5 Yen. Years 1, 2 (1912, 13)	25.00

HIROHITO, 1926-
(The Showa Era)
Radiant sun. Rev. Value in wreath.

55.	20 Yen. Years 5-7 (1930-32)	75.00
56.	5 Yen. Year 5 (1930)	40.00

```
*              2 · 3 · 47 *
*              3 · 47 I
H             20 · 00 *
B             16 · 59 *
E              1861
          02 · 22 · 83
```

Thank you

```
#              0 · 00
          02 · 22 · 83
```

Thank you

```
*              0 · 40 *
*              0 · 40 I
*              0 · 40 I
E              1862
          02 · 22 · 83
```

Thank you

```
#              0 · 00
          02 · 22 · 83
```

Thank you

```
*              1 · 19 *
*              1 · 19 I
*              0 · 06 *
*              1 · 25 I
H             10 · 00 *
G              8 · 75 *
E              1863
          02 · 22 · 83
```

Dios
Patria
Ubertad

Centavos 25
Gramos

JERUSALEM

(Including the Principality of Antioch and the Counties of Edessa and Tripoli).

Crusader Kings of —

BALDWIN I AND II, 1100-1131

Pseudo-Cufic legend on each side.

1. 1 Saracenic Bezant ND 40.00

BOHEMOND I AND II, 1098-1130

Pseudo-Cufic legend on each side, with the letter B on obverse and T on reverse. (Bohemond and Tancred)

2. 1 Saracenic Bezant ND 40.00

CONRAD AND CONRADIN, 1243-1268

Genuine Cufic legend on each side spelling out both the Christian date and phrases relating to Christianity.

3. 1 Bezant 1250-1259 .... 75.00

KOREA

Dragon. Rev. Value.

1. 20 Won 1906, 08, 09, 10 .... 750.00
2. 10 Won 1906, 09 ....*...... 350.00
3. 5 Won 1908, 09 .... 300.00

MALAYA

Native legend on each side. Sultanate coinage struck during the period 1720-60.

1. 1 Mas ND. Octagonal 20.00

MALTA

(The Knights of St. John of Jerusalem at Malta. For earlier coins of the Knights, see under Rhodes).

Grand Masters of —

PHILIPPE VILLIERS, 1521-1534

Ruler kneeling before St. John. Rev. Christ standing.

1. 1 Zecchino ND 350.00

Bust. Rev. Arms.

2. 1 Zecchino ND 1250.00

PETER DEL PONTE, 1534-1535
Ruler kneeling before St. John. Rev. Christ standing.

3. 1 Zecchino ND .... Unique

JOHN DE HOMEDES, 1536-1553
Ruler kneeling before St. John. Rev. Christ standing.

4. 1 Zecchino ND 250.00

JOHN DE LA VALLETTE, 1557-1568
Ruler kneeling before St. John. Rev. Christ standing.

5. 1 Zecchino ND 60.00

PETER DEL MONTE, 1568-1572

Ruler kneeling before St. John. Rev. Christ standing.

6. 1 Zecchino ND 50.00

JOHN DE LA CASSIERE, 1572-1581
Ruler kneeling before St. John. Rev. Christ standing.

7. 1 Zecchino ND 50.00

HUGH DE VERDALA, 1581-1595
Ruler kneeling before St. John. Rev. Christ standing.

8. 1 Zecchino ND 50.00

MARTIN GARZES, 1595-1601
Ruler kneeling before St. John. Rev. Christ standing.

9. 1 Zecchino ND 50.00

ALOFIUS DE WIGNACOURT, 1601-1622
Ruler kneeling before St. John. Rev. Christ standing.

10. 1 Zecchino ND 50.00

ANTHONY DE PAULE, 1623-1636
Ruler kneeling before St. John. Rev. Christ standing.

11. 1 Zecchino ND 250.00

JOHN PAUL LASCARIS, 1636-1657
Ruler kneeling before St. John. Rev. Christ standing.

12. 1 Zecchino ND 250.00

GREGORY CARAFFA, 1680-1690

Ruler kneeling before St. John. Rev. Arms.

13. 1 Zecchino ND 250.00

MALTA (cont'd)

ADRIEN DE WIGNACOURT, 1690-1697

Ruler kneeling before St. John. Rev. Arms.

14. 4 Zecchini 1695 ....*	500.00
15. 1 Zecchino 1691-96	100.00

RAYMON PERELLOS, 1697-1720

Bust. Rev. Arms.

16. 4 Zecchini 1717, 18, 19 .... 300.00

Ruler kneeling before St. John. Rev. Arms.

17. 10 Zecchini 1699	2000.00
18. 4 Zecchini 1699, 1705	350.00
19. 1 Zecchino 1699, 1717, ND ....*	100.00

St. Michael. Rev. Arms.

20. 2 Zecchini ND 300.00

MARCANTONIO ZONDADARI, 1720-1722
Bust. Rev. Legend.

21. 4 Zecchini 1721 .... 600.00

Bust. Rev. Arms.

22. 4 Zecchini 1722 .... 600.00

Ruler kneeling before St. John. Rev. Arms.

23. 1 Zecchino 1722 .... 125.00

ANTHONY DE VILHENA, 1722-1736

Bust. Rev. Arms.

24. 12 Zecchini 1725	1500.00
25. 10 Zecchini 1722	1000.00
26. 4 Zecchini 1722-28	300.00
27. 2 Zecchini 1723-28 ....*	200.00

Ruler kneeling before St. John. Rev. Arms.

28. 1 Zecchino 1723, 24, 25, 28 .... 75.00

EMANUEL PINTO, 1741-1773

Bust. Rev. Arms.

29. 4 Zecchini 1742, ND	200.00
30. 2 Zecchini 1742, ND ....*	125.00
31. 1 Zecchino 1742, ND ....*	50.00

Bust to right or left. Rev. Arms on cross.

32. 20 Scudi 1764, 65, 70, 72 .... 90.00

St. John standing. Rev. Two shields.

33. 20 Scudi 1764 .... 125.00

St. John standing. Rev. Arms.

34. 10 Scudi 1756, 61, 62, 63	50.00
35. 5 Scudi 1756 ....*	40.00

FRANCIS XIMINES, 1773-1775

Bust in circle. Rev. Two shields.

36. 20 Scudi 1773	175.00
37. 10 Scudi 1773 ....*	75.00

MALTA (cont'd)

Bust not in circle. Rev. Two shields.

38. 10 Scudi 1774 .... **60.00**

Bust not in circle. Rev. Arms on cross.

39. 20 Scudi 1774 .... **125.00**
40. 10 Scudi 1774 ....* **60.00**

EMANUEL DE ROHAN, 1775-1797

Bust. Rev. Two shields.

41. 20 Scudi 1778, 81, 82 .... **90.00**
42. 10 Scudi 1778, 82 ....* **50.00**
43. 5 Scudi 1779 ....* **50.00**

FERDINAND DE HOMPESCH, 1797-1799

St. John standing. Rev. Arms on double eagle. Although dated 1778, this coin is attributed to Hompesch.

44. 20 Scudi 1778 .... **750.00**

THE SIEGE OF MALTA, 1798-1800

Oblong gold Ingot struck by General Vaubois, French defender of the island, during the blockade by the British. Rampant lion. Rev. Value. Size 25 x 20 Millimetres.

45. 17 Scudi, 3 Tari, 5 Grani ND .... **Unique**

MOROCCO

Arab legend on each side. Sultanate coinage struck during the period 1600-1750. With dates from about 1009-1164 A.H.

1. 1 Dinar **30.00**
2. ½ Dinar **20.00**

Arab legend within star on each side. Struck during the period 1750-1860. With dates from about 1164-1277 A.H.

3. 1 Dinar **40.00**

Arab legend. Rev. "1201". Struck at Madrid.

4. 10 Mizquals 1201 A.H. (1786 A.D.) **250.00**

Six-pointed star. Rev. Value and date. Struck under French influence and the equivalent of the 20 Franc piece. This coin was not placed in circulation.

5. 4 Ryals 1297 A.H. (1879 A.D.) **600.00**

MOZAMBIQUE

Portuguese Kings of —
JOSEPH I, 1750-1777

Arms. Rev. Cross in quadrilobe.

1. 4000 Reis 1755 ....* **250.00**
2. 2000 Reis 1755 .... **200.00**
3. 1000 Reis 1755 .... **200.00**

MARY II, 1834-1853

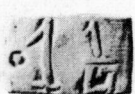

"M" in enclosure with various punches and stamps. Rev. Value.

4. 2½ Maticaes ND. Rectangular bar **100.00**
5. 1¼ Maticaes ND. Rectangular bar **75.00**

NEPAL

Kings of —

(The Nepalese Mohar is equal to about ½ of the Indian Mohur. Generally, the 2 and 1 Mohar pieces are of the same size and can be distinguished by different thickness and weight).

Square and legend. Rev. Circle and legend. Issued from about 1750-1880 and with Saka dates from about 1670-1802.

1. 4 Mohars **150.00**
2. 2 Mohars ....* **65.00**
3. 1 Mohar **40.00**

Legend and symbols on each side.

4. ½ Mohar ....* **30.00**
5. ¼ Mohar ....* **20.00**
6. ⅛ Mohar **12.50**
7. 1/16 Mohar **12.50**
8. 1/32 Mohar **12.50**
9. 1/64 Mohar **12.50**

NEPAL (cont'd)

PRITHVI, 1881-1911

Square between small and large circle. Rev. Circle within panelled legend. With Saka dates from 1803-1833 (1881-1911 A.D.). Up to Saka 1823 (1901 A.D.) the coinage is with plain edge. After Saka 1824 the coinage is with reeded edge and is of much finer workmanship.

10.	4 Mohars	.... *	125.00
11.	2 Mohars	....	75.00
12.	1 Mohar	....	40.00

Legend and symbols on each side.

13.	½ Mohar	....	30.00
14.	¼ Mohar	....	22.50
15.	⅛ Mohar	....	15.00
16.	1/16 Mohar	....	12.50
17.	1/32 Mohar	....	12.50
18.	1/64 Mohar	....	12.50

TRIBHUBANA, 1911-1954

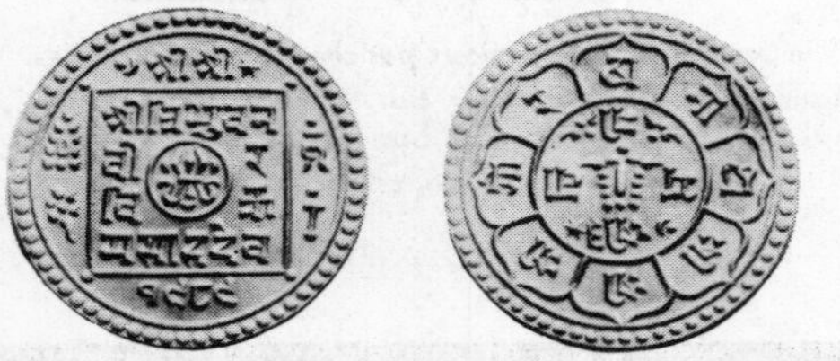

Type similar to above. With Samvat dates from 1969-1995 (1912-1938 A.D.).

19.	4 Mohars	....	150.00
20.	2 Mohars	.... *	100.00
21.	1 Mohar	....	50.00
22.	½ Mohar	....	30.00

NETHERLANDS EAST INDIES

A. Java Coinage

Symbol. Rev. Incuse square. Struck during the Hindu period, 896-1158. The largest piece weighs about 10 grams.

1.	96 Krisnalas ND	....	250.00
2.	24 Krisnalas ND	.... *	50.00
3.	12 Krisnalas ND	....	50.00
4.	6 Krisnalas ND	....	35.00

"B" (Batavia) counterstamped on Dutch ducats during the period 1686-1700.

5.	1 Ducat. Dates before 1700	....	200.00

Dutch lion in square counterstamped on Japanese gold Kobans of the Keicho era, 1596-1614.

6.	1 Koban ND	....	1000.00

"Java" (in Arabic) counterstamped on the obverse of Dutch ducats during the period 1753-1761.

7.	1 Ducat. Dates before 1761	....	100.00

Native legend with Christian date. Rev. Native legend. The "Rupee" (also known as mohur) coinage was struck from dies that were also used for silver coins. The issues from 1808-1816 were struck under foreign occupation; under the French from 1808-1811, and under the British from 1811-1816.

8.	2 Java Ducats 1746, 47, 48	....	350.00
9.	1 Java Ducat 1744, 45, 46	.... *	250.00
10.	2 Gold Rupees 1783	....	400.00
11.	1 Gold Rupee 1766-97	.... *	300.00
12.	½ Gold Rupee 1766-1807	.... *	150.00
13.	¼ Gold Rupee 1766	....	250.00
14.	1 Gold Rupee 1808-16	....	200.00
15.	½ Gold Rupee 1813-16	....	200.00

B. Sumatra Coinage

Native legend on each side. Struck under the Sultans of Atjeh during the period 1297-1760.

16.	1 Mas ND	....	15.00

C. Coinage under the Kingdom of the Netherlands

Knight standing. Rev. Legend in square tablet. This type was struck exclusively for use in the East Indies beginning in 1814. They were also used as trade coins among the Dutch banks. The type does not change from ruler to ruler.

17.	1 Ducat 1814-40. (William I). Utrecht Mint. Torch mm.	.....	20.00
18.	1 Ducat 1824-30. Brussels Mint. Palm branch mm.	....	40.00
19.	1 Ducat 1841. (William II)	....	30.00
20.	2 Ducats 1854, 67. (William III)	....	175.00
21.	1 Ducat 1849-85. (William III)	....	22.50
22.	1 Ducat 1894-1938. (Wilhelmina)	.... *	10.00

PERSIA (IRAN)

Shahs of —

ISMAIL I, 1502-1524

Arab legend on each side. With dates from about 907-930 A.H.

1.	1 Ashrafi	.... *	75.00
2.	¼ Ashrafi	....	50.00

TAHMASP I, 1524-1576
Arab legend on each side. With dates from about 930-984 A.H.

3.	1 Ashrafi	....	100.00

MOHAMMED KHUDABANDA, 1578-1587
Arab legend on each side. With dates from about 985-996 A.H.

4.	1½ Ashrafi	....	125.00

ABBAS I, 1587-1629
Arab legend on each side. With dates from about 996-1038 A.H.

5.	2 Ashrafis	....	125.00
6.	½ Ashrafi	....	35.00

PERSIA (IRAN) (cont'd)

HUSSEIN, 1694-1722
Arab legend on each side. With dates from about 1105-1135 A.H.
7   1 Ashrafi 50.00

TAHMASP II, 1722-1731

Arab legend on each side. With dates from about 1135-1144 A.H.
8.   1 Ashrafi 50.00

ASHRAF, 1725-1729
Arab legend on each side. With dates from about 1137-1142 A.H.
9.   1 Ashrafi 65.00

ABBAS III, 1731-1736
Arab legend on each side. With dates from about 1144-1148 A.H.
10.   1 Ashrafi 40.00

NADIR, 1736-1747

Arab legend on each side. With dates from about 1148-1158 A.H.
11.   1 Ashrafi .... * 40.00
12.   2 Mohurs 125.00
13.   1 Mohur .... * 50.00

RUKH, 1748-1750
Arab legend on each side. With dates from about 1161-1163 A.H.
14.   1 Mohur 75.00

KERIM KHAN, 1750-1779

Arab legend on each side. With dates from about 1163-1193 A.H.
15.   1 Mohur .... * 40.00
16.   ½ Mohur 30.00
17.   ¼ Mohur 25.00

Arab legend. Rev. Legend in star shaped pattern.
18.   1 Mohur 100.00

MOHAMMED HASAN KHAN, 1750-1759
Arab legend on each side. With dates from about 1163-1172 A.H.
19.   1 Mohur 50.00
20.   ¼ Mohur 35.00

ABUL FATH KHAN, 1779
Arab legend on each side.
21.   ¼ Mohur 1193 A.H. 125.00

SADIK KHAN, 1779-1782
Arab legend on each side. With dates from about 1193-1196 A.H.
22.   1 Mohur 50.00
23.   ¼ Mohur 30.00

ALI MURAD KHAN, 1779-1785
Arab legend on each side. With dates from about 1193-1199 A.H.
24.   1 Mohur 50.00
25.   ¼ Mohur 30.00

JAAFAR KHAN, 1785-1789
Arab legend on each side. With dates from about 1199-1203 A.H.
26.   1 Mohur 50.00

LUTFALI KHAN, 1789-1794
Arab legend on each side. With dates from about 1203-1209 A.H.
27.   ¼ Mohur 40.00

AKA MOHAMMED KHAN, 1794-1797

Arab legend. Rev. Embellished legend with date in panel.
28.   1 Toman 1209 A.H. (1794 A.D.) 150.00

FATH ALI, 1797-1834

Arab legend on each side. With dates from about 1212-1250 A.H.
29.   5 Tomans 175.00
30.   1 Toman .... * 35.00
31.   ½ Toman 25.00
32.   ⅔ Toman 25.00
33.   ⅓ Toman 15.00

Ruler on horse. Rev. Legend.
34.   2 Tomans 1239 A.H. (1823 A.D.) 300.00
35.   ⅔ Toman 1236 A.H. (1820 A.D.) 150.00

Ruler seated on throne. Rev. Legend in panel or star as indicated.
36.   ½ Toman 1249 A.H. (1833 A.D.). Panel 75.00
36a. ½ Toman 1249 A.H. (1833 A.D.). Star 100.00

MOHAMMED, 1834-1848

Lion. Rev. Legend in square.
37.   ½ Toman 1262 A.H. (1846 A.D.) 50.00

Arab legend on each side.
38.   ½ Toman 1250-1264 A.H. (1834-48 A.D.) 30.00

PERSIA (IRAN) (cont'd)

HASAN SALAR, REBEL, 1848-1850

Arab legend on each side.

39. ½ Toman 1265 A.H. (1848 A.D.) 75.00

NASREDIN, 1848-1896
(The coinage of this ruler is dated from 1265-1314 A.H.).

Arab legend on each side in either a circle, square or octogram.

40. 1 Toman ....* 30.00
41. ½ Toman 20.00
42. ¼ Toman 15.00

Toughra in wreath. Rev. Legend in wreath.

43. 2 Tomans 1281 A.H. (1864 A.D.) 200.00

Half-length uniformed bust facing. Rev. Legend.

44. 2 Tomans 1271 A.H. (1854 A.D.) 100.00
44a. 1 Toman 1273-91 A.H. (1856-74 A.D.) 50.00

Lion. Rev. Legend in wreath or circle.

45. 10 Tomans 175.00
46. 5 Tomans ....* 125.00
47. 2 Tomans 40.00
48. 1 Toman 25.00
49. ½ Toman 15.00
50. ⅕ Toman 10.00

Bust. Rev. Legend in wreath or circle.

---

51. 25 Tomans 750.00
52. 20 Tomans 350.00
53. 10 Tomans ....* 200.00
54. 5 Tomans 125.00
55. 2 Tomans ....* 50.00
56. 1 Toman 30.00
57. ½ Toman 20.00
58. ⅕ Toman 15.00

MUZAFFAREDIN, 1896-1907
(The coinage of this ruler is dated from 1314-1325 A.H.).

Uniformed bust with plumed hat. Rev. Legend in wreath.

59. 10 Tomans 350.00
60. 5 Tomans 200.00
61. 2 Tomans ....* 40.00
62. 1 Toman ....* 22.50
63. ½ Toman 17.50
64. ⅕ Toman 12.50

Same type as above but with Persian characters at each side of bust on Obv. On his birthday.

65. 2 Tomans 1322 A.H. (1904 A.D.) ....* 60.00
66. 1 Toman 1322 A.H. (1904 A.D.) 100.00

Lion. Rev. Legend in wreath.

67. 10 Tomans 300.00
68. 5 Tomans 150.00
69. 1 Toman ....* 20.00
70. ½ Toman 15.00
71. ⅕ Toman 10.00

MOHAMMED ALI, 1907-1909
Uniformed bust with plumed hat. Rev. Lion.

72. 5 Tomans 1324, 26 A.H. (1907, 09 A.D.) 350.00

Uniformed bust with plumed hat. Rev. Legend in wreath.

73. 2 Tomans 1326, 27 A.H. (1908, 09 A.D.) 150.00
74. 1 Toman 1326, 27 A.H. (1908, 09 A.D.) ....* 65.00
75. ½ Toman 1326 A.H. (1908 A.D.) ....* 40.00
76. ⅕ Toman 1326 A.H. (1908 A.D.) 30.00

Lion. Rev. Legend in wreath.

77. 1 Toman 1324 A.H. (1907 A.D.) 25.00
78. ½ Toman 1324 A.H. (1907 A.D.) 17.50

AHMED, 1909-1925
(The coinage of this ruler is dated from 1327-1344 A.H.).
Lion. Rev. Legend.

78a. 10 Tomans 275.00
79. 5 Tomans 100.00
80. 1 Toman 17.50
81. ½ Toman 12.50
82. ⅕ Toman 10.00

Bust with plumed hat. Rev. Legend.

PERSIA (IRAN) (cont'd)

83.	10 Tomans		250.00
84.	2 Tomans		35.00
85.	1 Toman	*	20.00
86.	½ Toman		15.00
87.	⅕ Toman		12.50

Bust with plumed hat. Rev. Lion. On the 10th year of reign.

88.	10 Tomans 1337 A.H. (1919 A.D.)		250.00
89.	5 Tomans 1337 A.H. (1919 A.D.)	*	150.00
90.	2 Tomans 1337 A.H. (1919 A.D.)		35.00
91.	1 Toman 1337 A.H. (1919 A.D.)		22.50

RIZA KHAN PAHLEVI, 1925-1941

(The Persian calendar was changed during this reign, causing 1304 A.H. to fall in 1926 A.D.)

Lion. Rev. Legend.

92.	5 Pahlevi 1305 A.H. (1927 A.D.)		35.00
93.	2 Pahlevi 1305 A.H. (1927 A.D.)		20.00
94.	1 Pahlevi 1305 A.H. (1927 A.D.)		15.00
95.	1 Toman 1305 A.H. (1927 A.D.)	*	25.00

Bust with plumed hat. Rev. Legend.

96.	5 Pahlevi 1306, 08 A.H. (1928, 30 A.D.)	*	40.00
97.	2 Pahlevi 1306, 08 A.H. (1928, 30 A.D.)	*	22.50
98.	1 Pahlevi 1306, 08 A.H. (1928, 30 A.D.)		17.50

Head left with military cap. Rev. Lion.

99.	1 Pahlevi 1310 A.H. (1932 A.D.)		75.00
100.	½ Pahlevi 1310-14 A.H. (1932-36 A.D.)		30.00

MOHAMMED RIZA PAHLEVI, 1942-

Lion. Rev. Legend.

101.	1 Pahlevi 1320-27 A.H. (1942-49 A.D.)		30.00
102.	½ Pahlevi 1322-27 A.H. (1944-49 A.D.)		20.00

Head. Rev. Lion. These coins appear in yellow gold with the designs struck in high relief, or in red gold with the designs struck in normal relief.

103.	1 Pahlevi 1330-34 A.H. (1952-55 A.D.)	*	35.00
104.	½ Pahlevi 1330-34 A.H. (1952-55 A.D.)	*	25.00
105.	¼ Pahlevi 1330-34 A.H. (1952-55 A.D.)		15.00

PHILIPPINE ISLANDS

Spanish Rulers of —

ISABELLA II, 1833-1868

Head. Rev. Arms.

1.	4 Pesos 1861-68	*	25.00
2.	2 Pesos 1861-68	*	17.50
3.	1 Peso 1861-68		15.00

ALFONSO XII, 1875-1886

Head. Rev. Arms.

4.	4 Pesos 1882		125.00

RHODES

(The Knights of St. John of Jerusalem at Rhodes)

Grand Masters of —

DIEUDONNE DE GOZON, 1346-1353

Ruler kneeling before St. John. Rev. Angel seated on Sepulcher of Christ.

1.	1 Zecchino ND		500.00

PIERRE DE CORNILLAN, 1354-1355

Ruler kneeling before St. John. Rev. Angel seated on Sepulcher of Christ.

2.	1 Zecchino ND		750.00

ANTOINE FLUVIAN, 1421-1437

Ruler kneeling before St. John. Rev. Christ standing.

3.	1 Zecchino ND		500.00

JACQUES DE MILLY, 1454-1461

Ruler kneeling before St. John. Rev. Christ standing.

4.	1 Zecchino ND		500.00

JEAN BAPTIST ORSINI, 1467-1476

Ruler kneeling before St. John. Rev. Christ standing.

5.	1 Zecchino ND		200.00

PIERRE D'AUBUSSON, 1476-1503

Ruler kneeling before St. John. Rev. Christ standing.

6.	1 Zecchino ND		150.00

EMERIC D'AMBOISE, 1503-1512

Arms. Rev. Lamb.

7.	2 Ducats ND	750.00
8.	1 Ducat ND .... *	750.00

Ruler kneeling before St. John. Rev. Christ standing.

9.	1 Zecchino ND	150.00

FABRIZIO DEL CARRETTO, 1513-1521
Bust with cap. Rev. Arms. (This may be a medal).

10.	10 Zecchini ND	Rare

Ruler kneeling before St. John. Rev. Christ standing.

11.	1 Zecchino ND	150.00

PHILIPPE VILLIERS
At Rhodes 1521-1522 and at Malta 1530-1534.

(For the coinage of this Grand Master and of his successors, see under Malta).

SAUDI ARABIA

Arab legend in circle on each side.

1.	1 Saudi Pound 1370 A.H. (1951)	25.00

Palm tree over crossed swords. Rev. Value and date.

2.	1 Saudi Pound 1377 A.H. (1957)	25.00

(Note: For the gold coins struck at the Philadelphia Mint, see under United States of America, following the 50 Dollar gold pieces).

SIAM

Kings of —

A. Gold Bullet Money of the Bangkok Dynasty

A roughly round shaped piece of gold, a portion of which dimples back on itself. The clear portion of the "Bullet" bears a mark which has been counterstamped on it and identifies it. The various marks used by the respective Kings are described below. These issues are without dates.

PRA NANG KLAO, 1824-1851
Palace mark (A crude gateway).

1.	1 Tical	175.00
2.	⅛ Tical	75.00
3.	1/16 Tical	50.00

Crude flower mark.

4.	⅛ Tical	75.00

Three leaves of the bale-fruit tree.

5.	⅛ Tical	75.00

MONGKUT, 1851-1868
Marks of the Chakra and the Siamese Crown.

6.	4 Ticals	250.00
7.	2 Ticals	175.00
8.	1 Tical	150.00
9.	½ Tical	75.00
10.	¼ Tical	50.00
11.	1½ Ticals. Elliptical shape	350.00

Waterpot mark.

12.	¼ Tical	50.00
13.	⅛ Tical	40.00
14.	1/16 Tical	35.00

B. Conventional or Standard Gold Coins
FIRST ISSUE OF MONGKUT (1863)

Crown between umbrellas with a few leaf scrolls in the field. Rev. Elephant in beaded circle within a chakra with narrow spokes.

15.	8 Ticals ND .... *	100.00
16.	4 Ticals ND .... *	60.00
17.	2 Ticals ND	40.00

SECOND ISSUE OF MONGKUT (1864)

Crown between umbrellas with flamboyant leaves in the field. Rev. Elephant in ornamental circle within a chakra with wide spokes. The coins of this issue are the same size as the corresponding silver coins of these values.

18.	2 Ticals ND .... *	1250.00
19.	1 Tical ND	500.00
20.	½ Tical ND	300.00
21.	¼ Tical ND	150.00
22.	⅛ Tical ND	100.00
23.	1/16 Tical ND	50.00

MISCELLANEOUS ISSUES OF MONGKUT
Large crown between flower sprays. Rev. Legend.

24.	2 Ticals ND	150.00

Chakra over crown flanked by waterpots. Rev. Blank.

25.	2 Ticals ND	150.00

CHULALONGKORN, 1868-1910

Bust. Rev. Crown and umbrellas.

26.	2 Ticals ND	50.00

SOUTH AFRICA

A. Presidents of —

Head of Thomas Francois Burgers. Rev. Arms.

1. 1 Pound 1874 .... **500.00**

Head of Krueger. Rev. Arms.

2. 1 Pound 1892-1900 ....*...... 25.00
3. ½ Pound 1892-97 .... 17.50

ZAR in script letters. Rev. EEN POND. The so-called Veld Pound struck at Pilgrims Rest.

4. 1 Pound 1902 .... **100.00**

B. British Sovereigns of —

GEORGE V, 1910-1936

Head. Rev. St. George. This is the same type as the English Pound but with the distinguishing South African mint mark SA on ground below horse.

5. 1 Pound 1923-32 .... 22.50
6. ½ Pound 1923-26 .... 15.00

GEORGE VI, 1937-1952

Head. Rev. Springbok.

7. 1 Pound 1952. Proof 35.00
8. ½ Pound 1952. Proof 25.00

ELIZABETH II, 1952-

Head. Rev. Springbok.

9. 1 Pound 1953-58. Proof **30.00**
10. ½ Pound 1953-58. Proof **20.00**

SYRIA

Eagle. Rev. Legend in rectangular panel.

1. 1 Pound 1950 .... **30.00**
2. ½ Pound 1950 .... **15.00**

TANGIER

Hercules standing. Rev. Legend, weight and fineness. A private bank issue of Tangier.

1. 1 Hercules ND (1954) **80.00**

TIBET

Tibetan style lion. Rev. Legend.

1. 20 Srangs (1917-20) **200.00**

Tibetan style lion. Rev. Pagoda.

2. 20 Srangs (1929) **250.00**

TRANQUEBAR

Danish Kings of —

CHRISTIAN VII, 1766-1808

Monogram. Rev. The God Swami.

1. 1 Pagoda ND **100.00**

TUNIS

A. Beys of —

MOHAMMED, 1854-1858 AND SADIK, 1859-1882

Three line Arab legend in open wreath. Rev. Arab date and value.

TUNIS (cont'd)

1. 100 Piastres 1272-81 A.H. (1855-64) ....*..... 150.00
2.   80 Piastres 1272 A.H. (1855) 150.00
3.   50 Piastres 1272-84 A.H. (1855-67) 100.00
4.   40 Piastres 1272 A.H. (1855) 100.00
5.   25 Piastres 1274-98 A.H. (1857-81) 50.00
6.   20 Piastres 1272 A.H. (1855) 50.00
7.   10 Piastres 1272-88 A.H. (1855-71) 30.00
8.   5 Piastres 1281-89 A.H. (1864-72) 20.00

B. French Protectorate of —

New type legend in closed wreath. Rev. Arab date and value.

9. 25 Piastres 1300 A.H. (1882) 85.00

French value. Rev. Arab value and date. Two denominations appear on this coin, the old Tunisian value of 25 Piastres and the new French equivalent of 15 Francs.

10. 15 Francs-25 Piastres 1304-07 A.H. (1886-89). No mm 75.00
11. 15 Francs-25 Piastres 1308, 09 A.H. (1890, 91). A mm..*.. 100.00

Arab legend in wreath. Rev. French name, value and date.
Very small amounts were coined of the 20 Franc pieces of 1894-96, 1902, 05-28 and of the 10 Franc pieces from 1892-1928.

12. 20 Francs 1891-1928 ....*...... 22.50
13. 10 Francs 1891-1928 .... 17.50

Arab legend in vertical panel. Rev. Value and date in circle.

14. 100 Francs 1930-37 .... 60.00

Arab legend in vertical panel. Rev. Large date. Without the mark of value, although the coins have the same specifications as the preceding issues. Only about 30 pieces were struck in each year.

15. (100 Francs) 1938-55 .... 125.00

TURKESTAN, CHINESE

Native legend on each side. Struck during the period 1865-1877 by the rebel, Yakub Beg. With dates from about 1283-1294 A.H.

1. 1 Tilla 75.00

Four Chinese characters in circle. Rev. Dragon, and in English, "Sungarei ... 2 Mace".

2. 2 Mace (1906) ....   Rare

Dragon. Rev. Four Chinese characters in circle.

3. 2 Mace (1907) ....*...... 175.00
4. 1 Mace (1907) 150.00

TURKEY

A. Ottoman Sultans of —

MOHAMMED II, 1451, TO MUSTAFA IV, 1808

Arab legend on each side. This general type was used by the Sultans from 1451 to 1808; with dates from about 943-1223 A.H.

1. 1 Sequin ....*...... 20.00
2. ½ Sequin 12.50
3. ¼ Sequin 10.00

AHMED III, 1703, TO MAHMUD II, 1839

Toughra as main motif. Rev. Arab legend. This general type was used by the Sultans from 1703 to 1839; with dates from about 1116-1254 A.H.

4.   6 Sequins 250.00
5.   5 Sequins 100.00
6.   4 Sequins 200.00
7.   3 Sequins 65.00
8.   2 Sequins 40.00
9.   1½ Sequins 40.00
10. 1 Sequin ....*...... 20.00
11. ½ Sequin 12.50
12. ¼ Sequin 10.00

ABDUL MEJID, 1839-1861
Same type as above.

13. 1 Sequin 1255-59 A.H. (1839-43) 25.00
14. ½ Sequin 1255-59 A.H. (1839-43) 15.00
15. ¼ Sequin 1255-59 A.H. (1839-43) 12.50

TURKEY (cont'd)

Toughra and regnal date. Rev. Legend and accession date. All coins bear the accession date 1255 in Arabic numerals, in addition to other numerals for the regnal year, which indicate the precise date of coinage.

16.	500	Piastres	200.00
17.	250	Piastres .... *	100.00
18.	100	Piastres	35.00
19.	50	Piastres	20.00
20.	25	Piastres	15.00
21.	10	Piastres	10.00
22.	5	Piastres	7.50

ABDUL AZIZ, 1861-1876

Same type as above but with the accession date 1277.

23.	500	Piastres	135.00
24.	250	Piastres	70.00
25.	100	Piastres .... *	22.50
26.	50	Piastres	17.50
27.	25	Piastres	12.50
28.	10	Piastres	7.50

MURAD V, 1876

Toughra and regnal year 1. Rev. Legend and accession date 1293.

29.	100	Piastres	150.00
30.	25	Piastres	60.00

ABDUL HAMID II, 1876-1909
Standard Gold Coins

Same type as above and with the same accession date, 1293.

31.	500	Piastres	125.00
32.	250	Piastres	60.00
33.	100	Piastres	20.00
34.	50	Piastres	15.00
35.	25	Piastres	10.00

De Luxe Gold Coins

Toughra. Rev. Legend. Ornamental wreath on each side. With accession date 1293. Although very large and quite thin, these coins are of standard weight.

36.	500	Piastres	225.00
37.	250	Piastres .... *	150.00
38.	100	Piastres	65.00
39.	50	Piastres	50.00
40.	25	Piastres	35.00

MOHAMMED V, 1909-1918
Standard Gold Coins

Same type as previous issues but with the accession date 1327.

41.	500	Piastres .... *	125.00
42.	250	Piastres	60.00
43.	100	Piastres	20.00
44.	50	Piastres	15.00
45.	25	Piastres	10.00
46.	12½	Piastres	7.50

Type as above but with the name of a city added to the legend on coins with regnal dates 2 or 3. The following cities may be read in Arabic on the coins, which thus commemorate the Sultan's visit to that city:—Adrianople, Brousse, Kossova, Monastir, Salonica.

47.	500	Piastres	275.00
48.	250	Piastres	150.00
49.	100	Piastres	75.00
50.	50	Piastres	50.00
51.	25	Piastres	30.00
52.	12½	Piastres	20.00

De Luxe Gold Coins

Group of military weapons. Rev. Legend. With accession date 1327.

53.	500	Piastres .... *	175.00
54.	250	Piastres	100.00
55.	100	Piastres	40.00
56.	50	Piastres	30.00
57.	25	Piastres	20.00

MOHAMMED VI, 1918-1921
Standard Gold Coins

Same type as previous issues but with the accession date 1336.

58.	500	Piastres	150.00
59.	250	Piastres	75.00
60.	100	Piastres	25.00
61.	50	Piastres	17.50
62.	25	Piastres	10.00

De Luxe Gold Coins

Same general type as the previous issue of De Luxe Gold Coins but with the accession date 1336.

63.	500	Piastres	200.00
64.	250	Piastres	125.00
65.	100	Piastres	50.00
66.	50	Piastres	35.00
67.	25	Piastres	25.00

B. Republic of —

I. REGULAR ISSUES
Standard Gold Coins

Star, legend and Mohammedan year within crescent. Rev. Legend and corresponding Christian year (in Arabic numerals).

68.	500 Piastres 1926-28	.........................*	200.00
69.	250 Piastres 1926-28	....	125.00
70.	100 Piastres 1926-28	....	50.00
71.	50 Piastres 1926-28	....	35.00
72.	25 Piastres 1926-28	....	25.00

De Luxe Gold Coins

Sunburst and crescent. Rev. Date and wreath. As the de luxe coins of the Sultans, these pieces are highly decorative. They are very large and thin but of standard weight.

73.	500 Piastres 1927, 28	....	200.00
74.	250 Piastres 1927, 28	....	125.00
75.	100 Piastres 1927, 28	.........................*	60.00
76.	50 Piastres 1927, 28	....	40.00
77.	25 Piastres 1927, 28	....	30.00

II. SPECIAL ISSUES

The following coins do not bear the marks of value but are of the same sizes and weights as the previous issues.

PRESIDENT KEMAL ATATURK
Standard Gold Coins

Head and below "Ankara". Rev. Legend and date 1923, with two additional numerals below, which must be added to 1923 to determine the exact year of issue.

78.	500 Piastres 1943-55	....	200.00
79.	250 Piastres 1943-55	....	125.00
80.	100 Piastres 1943-58	.........................*	30.00
81.	50 Piastres 1943-55	....	30.00
82.	25 Piastres 1943-55	....	20.00

De Luxe Gold Coins

Head in circle of stars. Rev. Legend in circle of stars, date below.

83.	500 Piastres 1942-51	.........................*	300.00
84.	250 Piastres 1942-51	....	150.00
85.	100 Piastres 1942-51	....	60.00
86.	50 Piastres 1942-51	....	50.00
87.	25 Piastres 1942-51	....	30.00

PRESIDENT ISMET INONU
Standard Gold Coins

Head and below "Ankara". Rev. Legend and date 1923, with two additional numerals below, which must be added to 1923 to determine the exact year of issue.

88.	500 Piastres 1943-49	.........................*	125.00
89.	250 Piastres 1943-49	....	75.00
90.	100 Piastres 1943-49	....	40.00
91.	50 Piastres 1943-49	....	30.00
92.	25 Piastres 1943-49	....	20.00

De Luxe Gold Coins

Head in wreath. Rev. Legend and date.

93.	500 Piastres 1944-47	....	200.00
94.	250 Piastres 1944-47	....	125.00
95.	100 Piastres 1944-47	.........................*	50.00
96.	50 Piastres 1944-47	....	35.00
97.	25 Piastres 1944-47	....	25.00

ZANZIBAR

Arab legend. Rev. Arab legend and date, with value in Christian numerals.

1.	5 Rials 1299 A.H. (1881)	....	600.00
2.	2½ Rials 1299 A.H. (1881)	....	750.00

Appendix

THE PRINCIPAL GOLD COINS OF THE WORLD

Their weight, fineness, and original exchange value.

The tables below will show the relationship to each other in terms of U.S. gold dollars of the principal gold coins of the world.

The period of time used in arriving at the original exchange value is the so-called "Golden Age" of gold coinage—most of the 19th century and until the outbreak of World War I in 1914. It was during this period that a true international gold standard was in existence.

This standard came to an unofficial end in 1914 and to an official end in 1933, when following an outbreak of universal monetary failures, the world price of gold was raised to $35.00 per ounce.

During this stable period of about 100 years, the face value of U.S. gold coins was based on the legal value of $20.67183 per ounce of pure or fine gold. The original exchange values listed below are in terms of U.S. gold dollars based on U.S. gold coins struck during the period 1837-1933.

For those gold coins of the world struck before 1837 or after 1933, the values have been determined by judging the weight and fineness of the coins as though they had been struck during the period 1837-1933.

In consulting these tables it should be borne in mind that the fractions or multiples of a given gold coin are always in exact proportion as regards weight and value.

The original exchange values are approximate to the nearest cent—a fraction of ½ Cent or more has been carried to the next cent, and a lesser fraction to the preceding cent.

Some coinages that were struck over a century or more inevitably tend to show variations in weight, fineness or both and the figures given below for such coinages are for typical or average specimens of the coins in question.

Table I is confined to those coins of the same denomination and value but of different national origin which circulated in many countries over a long period of time, enjoying international acceptance.

Table II shows the principal gold coins of specific countries.

TABLE I

In this table especially (because the coinages extended over hundreds of years), the figures in the Gram and fineness columns are approximate and are for average, familiar specimens.

Name of Coin	Where Circulated and Ultimate Dates of Coinage	Weight of Coin in Grams	Purity or Fineness	Original Value in U.S. Gold Dollars
THE DINAR	**Africa and Asia, 660-1902**			
3 Dinars		12.6000	.975	$ 7.80
2 Dinars		8.4000	.975	5.20
1 Dinar		4.2000	.975	2.60
½ Dinar		2.1000	.975	1.30
¼ Dinar		1.0500	.975	.65
THE DUCAT	**All Europe, 1280-1938**			
100 Ducats		350.0000	.986	229.00
50 Ducats		175.0000	.986	114.50
20 Ducats		70.0000	.986	45.80
10 Ducats		35.0000	.986	22.90
5 Ducats		17.5000	.986	11.45
4 Ducats		14.0000	.986	9.16
3 Ducats		10.5000	.986	6.87
2 Ducats		7.0000	.986	4.58
1 Ducat		3.5000	.986	2.29
½ Ducat		1.7500	.986	1.15
¼ Ducat		.8750	.986	.58
⅛ Ducat		.4375	.986	.29
1/16 Ducat		.2188	.986	.15
1/32 Ducat		.1094	.986	.08

Name of Coin	Where Circulated and Ultimate Dates of Coinage	Weight of Coin in Grams	Purity or Fineness	Original Value in U.S. Gold Dollars
THE ESCUDO	**Spain and Spanish-America, 1598-1873**			
8 Escudos		27.0000	.875	$16.00
4 Escudos		13.5000	.875	8.00
2 Escudos		6.7500	.875	4.00
1 Escudo		3.3750	.875	2.00
½ Escudo		1.6875	.875	1.00
THE FLORIN	**All Europe, 1200-1896** Similar to the Ducat.			
THE GOLDGULDEN	Same as the Florin			
THE MOHUR	**Asia, 1200-1947**			
	See Table II, under India			
THE POUND	**British Empire, 1817-1957**			
	See Table II, under Great Britain			
THE SEQUIN	**Ottoman Empire, 1451-1839**			
	See Table II, under Turkey			

TABLE II

Country and Denomination	Period of Coinage	Weight of Coin in Grams	Purity or Fineness	Original Value in U.S. Gold Dollars
AFGHANISTAN				
5 Amani	1921	22.7500	.900	$13.50
2 Amani	1921-1924	9.1000	.900	5.40
1 Amani	1919-1932	4.5500	.900	2.70
½ Amani	1921-1928	2.2750	.900	1.35
ALBANIA				
100 Francs	1926-1938	32.2580	.900	19.29
50 Francs	1938	16.1290	.900	9.65
20 Francs	1926-1938	6.4516	.900	3.86
10 Francs	1927	3.2258	.900	1.93
ARGENTINA				
5 Pesos	1881-1896	8.0645	.900	4.82
2½ Pesos	1881-1884	4.0322	.900	2.41
AUSTRIA				
1 Souverain d'or or Sovrano	1781-1800	11.0600	.919	6.86
½ Souverain d'or or Sovrano	1781-1800	5.5300	.919	3.43
1 Sovrano	1820-1856	11.3320	.900	6.86
½ Sovrano	1820-1856	5.6660	.900	3.43
1 Krone	1858-1866	11.1110	.900	6.66
½ Krone	1858-1866	5.5550	.900	3.33
8 Florins-20 Francs	1870-1892	6.4516	.900	3.86
4 Florins-10 Francs	1870-1892	3.2258	.900	1.93
100 Corona	1908-1915	33.8753	.900	20.26
20 Corona	1892-1916	6.7750	.900	4.05
10 Corona	1892-1912	3.3375	.900	2.03
100 Schillings	1926-1938	23.5240	.900	14.12
25 Schillings	1926-1938	5.8810	.900	3.53
BELGIUM				
100 Francs	1853-1912	32.2580	.900	19.29
40 Francs	1834-1841	12.9032	.900	7.72
25 Francs	1847-1850	8.0645	.900	4.82
20 Francs	1835-1914	6.4516	.900	3.86
10 Francs	1849-1912	3.2258	.900	1.93
BOLIVIA				
35 Grams Pure Gold	1952	38.9000	.900	23.30
14 Grams Pure Gold	1952	15.5600	.900	9.31
7 Grams Pure Gold	1952	7.7800	.900	4.65
3½ Grams Pure Gold	1952	3.8900	.900	2.33
BRAZIL				
20,000 Reis	1724-1727	53.6000	.916⅔	32.77
10,000 Reis	1724-1727	26.8000	.916⅔	16.38
4,000 Reis	1703-1727	10.7200	.916⅔	6.54
2,000 Reis	1703-1727	5.3600	.916⅔	3.27
1,000 Reis	1708-1727	2.6800	.916⅔	1.64
400 Reis	1725-1730	1.0720	.916⅔	.65

(The above six coins were struck under the national system and bear the cross of Jerusalem. The following three coins were struck under the colonial system and bear a plain cross, except for the dates from 1823 to 1833 of the 4,000 Reis piece, which show the Brazilian emperor.)

4,000 Reis	1695-1833	8.2000	.916⅔	4.93
2,000 Reis	1695-1793	4.1000	.916⅔	2.47
1,000 Reis	1696-1787	2.0500	.916⅔	1.24
12,800 Reis	1727-1733	28.6000	.916⅔	17.47
6,400 Reis	1727-1833	14.3000	.916⅔	8.74
3,200 Reis	1727-1786	7.1500	.916⅔	4.37
1,600 Reis	1727-1784	3.5750	.916⅔	2.19
800 Reis	1727-1786	1.7875	.916⅔	1.10
400 Reis	1730-1734	0.8938	.916⅔	.55
20,000 Reis	1849-1922	17.9296	.916⅔	10.93
10,000 Reis	1849-1922	8.9648	.916⅔	5.46
5,000 Reis	1854-1859	4.4824	.916⅔	2.73
BULGARIA				
100 Leva	1894-1912	32.2580	.900	19.29
20 Leva	1894-1912	6.4516	.900	3.86
10 Leva	1894	3.2258	.900	1.93
BURMA				
4 Rupees	1852-1878	2.8000	.900	1.70
2 Rupees	1852-1878	1.4000	.900	.85
1 Rupee	1852-1878	.7000	.900	.43
CANADA				
10 Dollars	1912-1914	16.7185	.900	10.00
5 Dollars	1912-1914	8.3592	.900	5.00
CHILE				
10 Pesos	1853-1890	15.2000	.900	9.15
5 Pesos	1858-1873	7.6000	.900	4.58
2 Pesos	1857-1875	3.0400	.900	1.84
1 Peso	1860-1873	1.5200	.900	.92
20 Pesos	1896-1917	11.9500	.916⅔	7.30
10 Pesos	1895-1901	5.9900	.916⅔	3.65
5 Pesos	1895-1900	2.9900	.916⅔	1.83
100 Pesos	1926-1955	20.3397	.900	12.20
50 Pesos	1926	10.1698	.900	6.10
20 Pesos	1926	4.0680	.900	2.44
CHINA				
20 Dollars-Republic	1919	14.8000	.900	9.00
10 Dollars-Republic	1916-1919	7.4000	.900	4.50
10 Dollars-Yunnan	1919	9.0000	.900	5.40
5 Dollars-Yunnan	1919	4.5000	.900	2.70
COLOMBIA				
20 Pesos	1859-1877	32.2580	.900	19.29
10 Pesos	1856-1877	16.1290	.900	9.65
5 Pesos	1856-1885	8.0645	.900	4.82
2 Pesos	1856-1876	3.2258	.900	1.93
1 Peso	1856-1878	1.6129	.900	.96
10 Pesos	1919-1924	15.9761	.916⅔	9.73
5 Pesos	1913-1930	7.9881	.916⅔	4.87
2½ Pesos	1913-1928	3.9940	.916⅔	2.43
COSTA RICA				
10 Pesos	1870-1876	14.3000	.875	8.60
5 Pesos	1867-1875	7.1500	.875	4.30
2 Pesos	1866-1876	2.8600	.875	1.72
1 Peso	1864-1872	1.4300	.875	.86
20 Colones	1897-1900	15.5600	.900	9.31
10 Colones	1897-1900	7.7800	.900	4.65
5 Colones	1899-1900	3.8900	.900	2.33
2 Colones	1897-1928	1.5560	.900	.93
CUBA				
20 Pesos	1915-1916	33.4370	.900	20.00
10 Pesos	1915-1916	16.7185	.900	10.00
5 Pesos	1915-1916	8.3592	.900	5.00
4 Pesos	1915-1916	6.6872	.900	4.00
2 Pesos	1915-1916	3.3436	.900	2.00
1 Peso	1915-1916	1.6718	.900	1.00
DANISH WEST INDIES				
10 Daler-50 Francs	1904	16.1290	.900	9.65
4 Daler-20 Francs	1904-1905	6.4516	.900	3.86
DANZIG				
25 Gulden	1923-1930	7.9881	.916⅔	4.87
DENMARK				
2 Christian d'or	1826-1870	13.3000	.903	8.00
1 Christian d'or	1775-1869	6.6500	.903	4.00
20 Kroner	1873-1931	8.9606	.900	5.36
10 Kroner	1873-1917	4.4803	.900	2.68
DOMINICAN REPUBLIC				
30 Pesos	1955	29.5000	.900	17.85
ECUADOR				
10 Sucres	1899-1900	8.1360	.900	4.87
1 Condor	1928	8.3592	.900	5.00
EGYPT				
500 Piastres	1861-1938	42.5000	.875	24.70
100 Piastres	1839-1938	8.5000	.875	4.94
50 Piastres	1839-1938	4.2500	.875	2.47
20 Piastres	1923-1938	1.7000	.875	.99
10 Piastres	1839-1909	.8500	.875	.49
5 Piastres	1839-1909	.4250	.875	.25

Country and Denomination	Period of Coinage	Weight of Coin in Grams	Purity or Fineness	Original Value in U.S. Gold Dollars
ETHIOPIA				
1 Wark	1931	About 7.0000	.900	4.10
½ Wark	1931	About 3.5000	.900	2.05
FINLAND				
20 Markkaa	1878-1913	6.4516	.900	3.86
10 Markkaa	1878-1913	3.2258	.900	1.93
200 Markkaa	1926	8.4210	.900	5.10
100 Markkaa	1926	4.2105	.900	2.55
FRANCE (Until 1803, the figures are an average of familiar pieces)				
1 Ecu d'or	1266-1641	3.4000	.963	2.25
1 Chaise d'or	1285-1422	4.7000	1.000	3.15
1 Royal d'or	1285-1461	4.2000	1.000	2.81
1 Lion d'or	1328-1350	4.9000	1.000	3.28
1 Pavillion d'or	1328-1350	5.1000	1.000	3.42
1 Ange d'or	1328-1350	7.2500	1.000	4.86
1 Franc a Cheval	1350-1461	3.8900	1.000	2.61
1 Mouton d'or	1350-1422	4.7000	1.000	3.15
1 Franc a Pied	1350-1380	3.8200	1.000	2.56
1 Salut d'or	1380-1461	3.8900	1.000	2.61
1 Heaume d'or	1380-1422	5.1000	.916⅔	3.12
1 Henry d'or	1550-1559	3.6000	.958	2.28
2 Louis d'or	1640-1792	13.40-17.20	.916⅔	8.10-10.40
1 Louis d'or	1640-1793	6.70- 8.60	.916⅔	4.05- 5.20
½ Louis d'or	1640-1784	3.35- 4.30	.916⅔	2.03- 2.65
100 Francs	1855-1913	32.2580	.900	19.29
50 Francs	1855-1904	16.1290	.900	9.65
40 Francs	1803-1839	12.9039	.900	7.72
20 Francs	1803-1914	6.4516	.900	3.86
10 Francs	1854-1914	3.2258	.900	1.93
5 Francs	1854-1889	1.6129	.900	.96
100 Francs	1929-1936	6.5500	.900	3.94
GERMAN EAST AFRICA				
15 Rupees	1916	7.5000	.900	4.48
GERMAN NEW GUINEA				
20 Marks	1895	7.9650	.900	4.76
10 Marks	1895	3.9825	.900	2.38
GERMANY				
20 Marks	1871-1915	7.9650	.900	4.76
10 Marks	1872-1914	3.9825	.900	2.38
5 Marks	1877-1878	1.9913	.900	1.19
10 Taler	1742-1857	13.3000	.900	7.96
5 Taler	1699-1856	6.6500	.900	3.98
2½ Taler	1699-1855	3.3200	.900	1.99
1 Carolin	1726-1782	9.7000	.770	4.90
½ Carolin	1726-1737	4.8500	.770	2.45
¼ Carolin	1726-1736	2.4250	.770	1.23
10 Gulden	1819-1842	6.8500	.904	4.16
5 Gulden	1819-1835	3.4250	.904	2.08
1 Krone	1857-1870	11.1110	.900	6.66
½ Krone	1857-1869	5.5550	.900	3.33
1 Pistole	Same as the 5 Taler piece above			
1 Frederick d'or (or other name)	Same as the 5 Taler piece above			
GREAT BRITAIN (Until 1663, the figures are an average of familiar pieces)				
1 Noble	1327-1483	8.0000	.975	5.30
1 Angel	1422-1625	5.0000	.958	3.20
1 Ryal	1485-1625	13.0000	.958	8.25
1 Sovereign	1485-1625	12.0000	.958	7.65
1 George Noble	1509-1547	4.5000	.916⅔	2.75
3 Pounds (Triple Unite)	1642-1644	27.0000	.916⅔	16.50
20 Shillings (1 Unite or Laurel)	1603-1663	9.0000	.916⅔	5.50
2 Crowns or 10 Shillings	1603-1663	4.5000	.916⅔	2.75
1 Crown or 5 Shillings	1509-1663	2.2500	.916⅔	1.38
½ Crown or 2½ Shillings	1509-1625	1.1250	.916⅔	.69
5 Guineas	1668-1777	41.7500	.916⅔	25.50
2 Guineas	1664-1777	16.7000	.916⅔	10.20
1 Guinea	1663-1813	8.3500	.916⅔	5.10
½ Guinea	1669-1813	4.1750	.916⅔	2.55
⅓ Guinea	1797-1813	2.7834	.916⅔	1.70
¼ Guinea	1718-1762	2.0875	.916⅔	1.28
5 Pounds	1820-1953	39.9403	.916⅔	24.33
2 Pounds	1820-1953	15.9761	.916⅔	9.73
1 Pound	1817-1957	7.9881	.916⅔	4.87
½ Pound	1817-1953	3.9940	.916⅔	2.43
GREECE				
100 Drachmae	1876	32.2580	.900	19.29
50 Drachmae	1876	16.1290	.900	9.65
40 Drachmae	1852	12.9039	.900	7.72
20 Drachmae	1833-1884	6.4516	.900	3.86
10 Drachmae	1876	3.2258	.900	1.93
5 Drachmae	1876	1.6129	.900	.96
GUATEMALA				
20 Pesos	1869-1878	32.2580	.900	19.29
16 Pesos	1863-1869	25.8078	.900	15.44
10 Pesos	1869	16.1290	.900	9.65
8 Pesos	1864	12.9039	.900	7.72
5 Pesos	1869-1878	8.0645	.900	4.82
4 Pesos	1861-1869	6.4516	.900	3.86
2 Pesos	1859	3.2258	.900	1.93
1 Peso	1859-1860	1.6129	.900	.96
4 Reales (½ Peso)	1859-1864	.8065	.900	.48
20 Quetzals	1926	33.4370	.900	20.00
10 Quetzals	1926	16.7185	.900	10.00
5 Quetzals	1926	8.3592	.900	5.00
HEJAZ				
1 Dinar	1923	7.2166	.916⅔	4.39
HUNGARY				
8 Florins-20 Francs	1870-1892	6.4516	.900	3.86
4 Florins-10 Francs	1870-1892	3.2258	.900	1.93
100 Korona	1907-1908	33.8753	.900	20.26
20 Korona	1892-1916	6.7750	.900	4.05
10 Korona	1892-1915	3.3375	.900	2.03
INDIA				
200 Mohurs (sic!)	1628-1658	2332.0000	.916⅔+	1,416.00
100 Mohurs (sic!)	1556-1707	1166.0000	.916⅔+	708.00
5 Mohurs	1556-1627	58.3000	.916⅔+	35.40
2 Mohurs	1556-1835	23.3200	.916⅔	14.16
1 Mohur	1200-1947	11.6600	.916⅔	7.08
½ Mohur	1200-1947	5.8300	.916⅔	3.54
¼ Mohur	1200-1947	2.9150	.916⅔	1.77
⅛ Mohur	1200-1947	1.4575	.916⅔	.89
1/16 Mohur	1500-1820	.7288	.916⅔	.45
1/32 Mohur	1500-1820	.3644	.916⅔	.23
10 Rupees (⅔ Mohur)	1862-1879	7.7740	.916⅔	4.72
5 Rupees (⅓ Mohur)	1820-1879	3.8870	.916⅔	2.36
15 Rupees	1918	7.9881	.916⅔	4.87
1 Pagoda (crude style)	1200-1868	3.0000	.800	1.60
(The following for Cutch-Bhuj)				
100 Kori	1866	18.7000	.916⅔	11.35
50 Kori	1873-1874	9.3500	.916⅔	5.68
25 Kori	1862-1870	4.6750	.916⅔	2.84
(The following for Madras; modern style coinage)				
2 Pagodas	(1810)	5.8500	.916⅔	3.56
1 Pagoda	(1810)	2.9250	.916⅔	1.78
(The following for Travancore)				
2 Pagodas	1877-1924	5.1000	.916⅔	3.12
1 Pagoda	1877-1924	2.5500	.916⅔	1.56
½ Pagoda	1881-1924	1.2750	.916⅔	.78
¼ Pagoda	1881-1924	.6375	.916⅔	.39
ITALY				
100 Lire	1832-1927	32.2580	.900	19.29
80 Lire	1821-1831	25.8078	.900	15.44
50 Lire	1832-1927	16.1290	.900	9.65
40 Lire	1806-1848	12.9039	.900	7.72
20 Lire	1800-1927	6.4516	.900	3.86
10 Lire	1832-1927	3.2258	.900	1.93

Country and Denomination	Period of Coinage	Weight of Coin in Grams	Purity or Fineness	Original Value in U.S. Gold Dollars
5 Lire	1863-1865	1.6129	.900	.96
100 Lire	1931-1936	8.7990	.900	5.25
50 Lire	1931-1936	4.3995	.900	2.63

(The following for Florence:

80 Florins = 10 Zecchini = 200 Paoli = 133⅓ Lire)

80 Florins	1827-1828	32.6180	1.000	21.66
1 Ruspone (3 Zecchini)	1719-1859	10.4610	1.000	6.93
1 Zecchino	1712-1853	3.4870	1.000	2.31

(The following for Naples: 30 Ducati = 10 Ducats = 10 Oncie)

6 Ducati	1749-1785	8.8200	.875	5.12
4 Ducati	1749-1782	5.8800	.875	3.42
2 Ducati	1749-1772	2.9400	.875	1.71
30 Ducati	1818-1856	37.8670	.996	25.00
15 Ducati	1818-1856	18.9330	.996	12.50
6 Ducati	1826-1856	7.5730	.996	5.00
3 Ducati	1818-1856	3.7860	.996	2.50

(For the following, please see Table I)

1 Doppia	1280-1815	Equal to 2 Ducats		
1 Florin	1250-1500	Equal to 1 Ducat		
1 Scudo d'oro	1300-1750	Equal to 1 Ducat		
1 Zecchino	1500-1800	Equal to 1 Ducat		
1 Genovino	1200-1415	Equal to 1 Ducat		

JAPAN

20 Yen	1870-1880	33.3332	.900	19.94
10 Yen	1871-1880	16.6666	.900	9.97
5 Yen	1870-1897	8.3333	.900	4.98
2 Yen	1870-1880	3.3333	.900	1.96
1 Yen	1871-1880	1.6666	.900	.98
20 Yen	1897-1932	16.6666	.900	9.97
10 Yen	1897-1910	8.3333	.900	4.98
5 Yen	1897-1930	4.1666	.900	2.49

KOREA

20 Won	1906-1910	16.6666	.900	9.97
10 Won	1906-1909	8.3333	.900	4.98
5 Won	1908-1909	4.1666	.900	2.49

LIECHTENSTEIN

20 Kronen	1898-1900	6.7750	.900	4.05
10 Kronen	1898-1900	3.3375	.900	2.03
100 Franken	1952	32.2580	.900	19.29
20 Franken	1930-1946	6.4516	.900	3.86
10 Franken	1930-1946	3.2258	.900	1.93
50 Franken	1956	11.2900	.900	6.84
25 Franken	1956	5.6450	.900	3.42

LUXEMBOURG

20 Francs	1953	6.4516	.900	3.86

MALTA

20 Scudi	1764-1778	16.0000	.840	9.00
10 Scudi	1756-1782	8.0000	.840	4.50
5 Scudi	1756-1779	4.0000	.840	2.25

MEXICO

20 Pesos	1870-1905	33.8400	.875	19.72
10 Pesos	1870-1905	16.9200	.875	9.86
5 Pesos	1870-1905	8.4600	.875	4.93
2½ Pesos	1870-1905	4.2300	.875	2.47
1 Peso	1870-1905	1.6900	.875	.99
50 Pesos	1921-1947	41.6666	.900	24.90
20 Pesos	1916-1921	16.6666	.900	9.97
10 Pesos	1906-1920	8.3333	.900	4.98
5 Pesos	1906-1955	4.1666	.900	2.49
2½ Pesos	1918-1945	2.0833	.900	1.25
2 Pesos	1919-1945	1.6666	.900	1.00

MONACO

100 Francs	1882-1904	32.2580	.900	19.29
40 Francs	1838	12.9039	.900	7.72
20 Francs	1838-1892	6.4516	.900	3.86

MONTENEGRO

100 Perpera	1910	32.2580	.900	19.29
20 Perpera	1910	6.4516	.900	3.86
10 Perpera	1910	3.2258	.900	1.93

MOROCCO

4 Ryals	1879	6.4516	.900	3.86

NEPAL

4 Mohars	1750-1938	23.0500	.916⅔	14.00
2 Mohars	1750-1938	11.5250	.916⅔	7.00
1 Mohar	1750-1938	5.7625	.916⅔	3.50
½ Mohar	1750-1938	2.8813	.916⅔	1.75
¼ Mohar	1750-1911	1.4406	.916⅔	.88
⅛ Mohar	1750-1911	.7203	.916⅔	.44
1/16 Mohar	1750-1911	.3602	.916⅔	.22
1/32 Mohar	1750-1911	.1801	.916⅔	.11
1/64 Mohar	1750-1911	.0901	.916⅔	.06

NETHERLANDS

20 Guilders	1808-1810	13.6500	.916⅔	8.34
10 Guilders	1808-1810	6.8250	.916⅔	4.17
20 Guilders	1848-1853	13.4580	.900	8.04
10 Guilders	1818-1933	6.7290	.900	4.02
5 Guilders	1826-1912	3.3645	.900	2.01
14 Guilders	1749-1764	9.9300	.916⅔	6.10
7 Guilders	1749-1764	4.9650	.916⅔	3.05

NEWFOUNDLAND

2 Dollars	1865-1888	3.2828	.916⅔	2.00

NORWAY

20 Kronor	1874-1910	8.9606	.900	5.36
10 Kronor	1874-1910	4.4803	.900	2.68

PERSIA

1 Ashrafi	1500-1750	3.5000	.975	2.25
25 Tomans	1848-1896	71.9252	.900	43.00
20 Tomans	1848-1896	57.4880	.900	34.40
10 Tomans	1848-1925	28.7440	.900	17.20
5 Tomans	1848-1925	14.4372	.900	8.60
2 Tomans	1848-1925	5.7489	.900	3.44
1 Toman	1848-1927	2.8744	.900	1.72
½ Toman	1848-1925	1.4372	.900	.86
⅕ Toman	1848-1925	.5749	.900	.34
5 Pahlevi	1927-1930	9.5000	.900	5.66
2 Pahlevi	1927-1930	3.8000	.900	2.26
1 Pahlevi	1927-1930	1.9000	.900	1.13
1 Pahlevi	1932-1955	8.1000	.900	4.80
½ Pahlevi	1932-1955	4.0500	.900	2.40
¼ Pahlevi	1952-1955	2.0250	.900	1.20

PERU

20 Soles	1863	32.2580	.900	19.29
10 Soles	1863	16.1290	.900	9.65
5 Soles	1863	8.0645	.900	4.82
1 Libra	1898-1929	7.9881	.916⅔	4.87
½ Libra	1902-1913	3.9940	.916⅔	2.43
⅕ Libra	1906-1955	1.5976	.916⅔	.97
50 Soles	1930-1931	33.4370	.900	20.00
100 Soles	1950-1956	46.8071	.900	28.00
50 Soles	1950-1956	23.4035	.900	14.00
20 Soles	1950-1956	9.3614	.900	5.60
10 Soles	1956	4.6807	.900	2.80
5 Soles	1956	2.3404	.900	1.40

PHILIPPINE ISLANDS

4 Pesos	1861-1882	6.7600	.875	3.86
2 Pesos	1861-1868	3.3800	.875	1.93
1 Peso	1861-1868	1.6900	.875	.96

POLAND

50 Zloty	1817-1829	9.8000	.916⅔	6.04
25 Zloty	1817-1833	4.9000	.916⅔	3.02
20 Zloty-3 Roubles	1834-1840	3.4500	.980	2.26
20 Zloty	1925	6.4516	.900	3.86
10 Zloty	1925	3.2258	.900	1.93

PORTUGAL

4 Cruzados	1580-1652	14.0000	.986	9.15
2 Cruzados	1580-1647	7.0000	.986	4.58
1 Cruzado	1438-1647	3.5000	.986	2.29
4,000 Reis	1663-1722	10.7200	.916⅔	6.54
2,000 Reis	1663-1725	5.3600	.916⅔	3.27
1,000 Reis	1663-1821	2.6800	.916⅔	1.64
400 Reis	1717-1821	1.0720	.916⅔	.65
8 Escudos	1717-1732	28.6000	.916⅔	17.47
4 Escudos	1722-1835	14.3000	.916⅔	8.74

Country and Denomination	Period of Coinage	Weight of Coin in Grams	Purity or Fineness	Original Value in U.S. Gold Dollars
2 Escudos	1722-1831	7.1500	.916⅔	4.37
1 Escudo	1722-1821	3.5750	.916⅔	2.19
½ Escudo	1722-1821	1.7875	.916⅔	1.10
5,000 Reis	1836-1851	9.5600	.916⅔	5.92
2,500 Reis	1838-1853	4.7800	.916⅔	2.96
1,000 Reis	1851	2.3900	.916⅔	1.48
10,000 Reis	1878-1889	17.7300	.916⅔	10.81
5,000 Reis	1860-1889	8.8600	.916⅔	5.40
2,000 Reis	1856-1888	3.5400	.916⅔	2.16
1,000 Reis	1855-1879	1.7700	.916⅔	1.08

ROUMANIA

100 Lei	1906-1940	32.2580	.900	19.29
50 Lei	1906-1922	16.1290	.900	9.65
25 Lei	1906-1922	8.0645	.900	4.82
20 Lei	1867-1944	6.4516	.900	3.86
12½ Lei	1906	4.0323	.900	2.41

RUSSIA (From 1718 to 1825, Rouble gold coinage was of variable weight or fineness)

25 Roubles	1876	32.7000	.916⅔	19.90
10 Roubles	1836	13.0800	.916⅔	7.96
5 Roubles	1826-1885	6.5400	.916⅔	3.98
3 Roubles	1869-1885	3.9000	.916⅔	2.38
12 Roubles-Platinum	1930-1845	41.5000	1.000	9.52
6 Roubles-Platinum	1829-1845	20.7500	1.000	4.76
3 Roubles-Platinum	1828-1845	10.3750	1.000	2.38
10 Roubles	1886-1894	12.9039	.900	7.72
5 Roubles	1886-1894	6.4516	.900	3.86
15 Roubles	1897	12.9039	.900	7.72
7½ Roubles	1897	6.4516	.900	3.86
37½ Roubles	1902	32.2580	.900	19.29
25 Roubles	1896-1908	32.2580	.900	19.29
10 Roubles	1898-1923	8.6026	.900	5.15
5 Roubles	1897-1910	4.3013	.900	2.57

SALVADOR

20 Pesos	1892	32.2580	.900	19.29
10 Pesos	1892	16.1290	.900	9.65
5 Pesos	1892	8.0645	.900	4.82
2½ Pesos	1892	4.0323	.900	2.41
20 Colones	1925	15.5600	.900	9.31

SAN MARINO

20 Lire	1925	6.4516	.900	3.86
10 Lire	1925	3.2258	.900	1.93

SAUDI ARABIA

1 Saudi Pound	1951-1957	7.9881	.916⅔	4.87

SERBIA

20 Dinars	1879-1882	6.4516	.900	3.86
10 Dinars	1882	3.2258	.900	1.93

SIAM

8 Ticals	1851-1868	7.8400	.900	4.50
4 Ticals	1851-1868	3.9200	.900	2.25
2 Ticals	1851-1907	1.9600	.900	1.13

SPAIN

10 Doblas	1350-1369	34.9000	.986	22.84
5 Doblas	1454-1474	22.5000	.986	14.70
1 Dobla	1252-1474	4.5000	.986	2.94
½ Dobla	1454-1474	2.2500	.986	1.47
1 Excelente	1476-1516	Equal to 1 Ducat		
Escudo Coinage	1516-1833	See Table I with following exceptions regarding fineness.		
Escudo Coinage	1516-1772	—	.916⅔	—
Escudo Coinage	1773-1785	—	.900	—
Escudo Coinage	1786-1833	—	.875	—
320 Reales	1810-1823	27.0000	.875	15.54
160 Reales	1822	13.5000	.875	7.72
80 Reales	1809-1848	6.7500	.875	3.86
100 Reales or 10 Escudos	1850-1868	8.3500	.900	4.97
40 Reales or 4 Escudos	1861-1868	3.3400	.900	1.98
20 Reales or 2 Escudos	1861-1865	1.6700	.900	.99
100 Pesetas	1870-1897	32.2580	.900	19.29
25 Pesetas	1871-1885	8.0645	.900	4.82
20 Pesetas	1889-1904	6.4516	.900	3.86
10 Pesetas	1878	3.2258	.900	1.93

SWEDEN

1 Carolin or 10 Francs	1868-1872	3.2258	.900	1.93
20 Kronor	1873-1925	8.9606	.900	5.36
10 Kronor	1873-1901	4.4803	.900	2.68
5 Kronor	1881-1920	2.2401	.900	1.34

SWITZERLAND

20 Francs	1871-1947	6.4516	.900	3.86
10 Francs	1911-1922	3.2258	.900	1.93
100 Francs	1925	32.2580	.900	19.29
100 Francs	1934	25.9000	.900	15.50
100 Francs	1939	17.5000	.900	10.50
50 Francs	1955	11.2900	.900	6.84
25 Francs	1955	5.6450	.900	3.42
6 Duplones	1794	45.8400	.900	27.60
4 Duplones	1797-1798	30.5600	.900	18.40
2 Duplones	1793-1798	15.2800	.900	9.20
1 Duplone	1787-1829	7.6400	.900	4.60
½ Duplone	1787-1796	3.8200	.900	2.30
¼ Duplone	1789-1796	1.9100	.900	1.15
32 Franken	1800	15.2800	.900	9.20
16 Franken	1800-1813	7.6400	.900	4.60
8 Franken	1813	3.8200	.900	2.30
24 Munzgulden	1794-1796	15.2800	.900	9.20
12 Munzgulden	1794-1796	7.6400	.900	4.60
20 Francs (Geneva)	1848	7.6000	.750	3.86
10 Francs (Geneva)	1848	3.8000	.750	1.93

(Other denominations are similar to those of France, Germany or Italy)

SYRIA

1 Pound	1950	6.7500	.900	4.06
½ Pound	1950	3.3750	.900	2.03

TUNIS

100 Piastres	1855-1864	19.4920	.900	11.90
80 Piastres	1855	15.5936	.900	9.52
50 Piastres	1855-1867	9.7460	.900	5.95
40 Piastres	1855	7.7968	.900	4.76
25 Piastres	1857-1882	4.8730	.900	2.98
20 Piastres	1855	3.8984	.900	2.38
10 Piastres	1855-1871	1.9492	.900	1.19
5 Piastres	1864-1872	.9746	.900	.60
20 Francs	1891-1928	6.4516	.900	3.86
15 Francs	1886-1891	4.8387	.900	2.90
10 Francs	1891-1928	3.2258	.900	1.93
100 Francs	1930-1955	6.5500	.900	3.94

TURKEY

5 Sequins	1703-1839	15.0000	.800	8.00
4 Sequins	1703-1839	12.0000	.800	6.40
3 Sequins	1703-1839	9.0000	.800	4.80
2 Sequins	1703-1839	6.0000	.800	3.20
1 Sequin	1451-1839	3.0000	.800	1.60
½ Sequin	1451-1839	1.5000	.800	.80
¼ Sequin	1451-1839	.7500	.800	.40
500 Piastres	1839-1955	36.0829	.916⅔	21.98
250 Piastres	1839-1955	18.0414	.916⅔	10.99
100 Piastres	1839-1957	7.2166	.916⅔	4.40
50 Piastres	1839-1955	3.6083	.916⅔	2.20
25 Piastres	1839-1955	1.8041	.916⅔	1.10
12½ Piastres	1909-1918	.9021	.916⅔	.55
10 Piastres	1839-1876	.7216	.916⅔	.44
5 Piastres	1839-1861	.3608	.916⅔	.22

UNITED STATES

50 Dollars	1915	83.5920	.900	50.00
20 Dollars	1850-1933	33.4370	.900	20.00
10 Dollars	1795-1804	17.4957	.916⅔	10.68
10 Dollars	1838-1933	16.7185	.900	10.00
5 Dollars	1795-1833	8.7479	.916⅔	5.34
5 Dollars	1837-1929	8.3592	.900	5.00
4 Dollars	1879-1880	6.6872	.900	4.00
3 Dollars	1854-1889	5.0154	.900	3.00
2½ Dollars	1796-1833	4.3740	.916⅔	2.67
2½ Dollars	1837-1929	4.1796	.900	2.50
1 Dollar	1849-1889	1.6718	.900	1.00
4 Saudi Pounds	1945-1946	31.9522	.916⅔	19.48
1 Saudi Pound	1945-1946	7.9881	.916⅔	4.87

Country and Denomination	Period of Coinage	Weight of Coin in Grams	Purity or Fineness	Original Value in U.S. Gold Dollars
URUGUAY				
5 Pesos	1930	8.4800	.916⅔	5.20
VATICAN				
4 Doppia	1786-1787	21.8000	.900	13.04
2 Doppia	1776-1777	10.9000	.900	6.52
1 Doppia	1776-1834	5.4500	.900	3.26
½ Doppia	1776-1787	2.7250	.900	1.63
10 Scudi	1835-1856	17.3000	.900	10.36
5 Scudi	1835-1854	8.6500	.900	5.18
2½ Scudi	1835-1863	4.3250	.900	2.59
1 Scudo	1853-1865	1.7300	.900	1.04
100 Lire	1866-1870	32.2580	.900	19.29
50 Lire	1868-1870	16.1290	.900	9.65
20 Lire	1866-1870	6.4516	.900	3.86
10 Lire	1866-1869	3.2258	.900	1.93
5 Lire	1866-1867	1.6129	.900	.96
100 Lire	1929-1935	8.7990	.900	5.25
100 Lire	1936-1956	5.2000	.900	3.18

(Other denominations are the same as those of Italy)

Country and Denomination	Period of Coinage	Weight of Coin in Grams	Purity or Fineness	Original Value in U.S. Gold Dollars
VENEZUELA				
100 Bolivares	1875-1889	32.2580	.900	19.29
50 Bolivares	1875-1888	16.1290	.900	9.65
25 Bolivares	1875	8.0645	.900	4.82
20 Bolivares	1879-1912	6.4516	.900	3.86
10 Bolivares	1930	3.2258	.900	1.93
5 Bolivares	1875	1.6129	.900	.96
YUGOSLAVIA				
20 Dinars	1925	6.4516	.900	3.86
ZANZIBAR				
5 Rials	1881	8.3592	.900	5.00
2½ Rials	1881	4.1796	.900	2.50

WEIGHTS AND MEASURES

A. The purity or fineness of gold coins

The fineness of gold coins ranges from about .750 fine to 1000 fine or pure gold.

Chemically pure, unalloyed gold is considered to be 1000 fine or 24 karats. The term "Fine gold" as used in banking and government circles refers to gold of 1000 fineness.

24 Karats	=	1000	Fine
23 Karats	=	.958⅓	Fine
22 Karats	=	.916⅔	Fine
21 Karats	=	.875	Fine
20 Karats	=	.833⅓	Fine
18 Karats	=	.750	Fine
14 Karats	=	.583⅓	Fine

It will be noted that .900 fine gold (the standard of U.S. gold coins and of most other countries) would be about 21.6 Karats.

B. The weight of gold coins

The troy and metric systems are used in weighing gold coins or precious metals in general. The weight of gold coins is usually expressed in grams.

1	Troy Ounce	=	31.103½ Grams
1	Troy Ounce	=	480 Grains
1	Troy Ounce	=	20 Pennyweight
12	Troy Ounces	=	1 Troy Pound
32.15	Troy Ounces	=	1 Kilogram
1	Gram	=	15.432 Grains
1	Gram	=	0.643 Pennyweight
1,000	Grams	=	1 Kilogram
24	Grains	=	1 Pennyweight
5,760	Grains	=	1 Troy Pound
15,432	Grains	=	1 Kilogram
240	Pennyweight	=	1 Troy Pound
643.01	Pennyweight	=	1 Kilogram
1	Kilogram	=	2.68 Troy Pounds

Comparisons of Grains and Grams

Grains		Grams
1	=	.0648
10	=	.648
15.432	=	1
20	=	1.30
25	=	1.62
35	=	2.27
50	=	3.24
75	=	4.86
100	=	6.48
125	=	8.10
150	=	9.72
175	=	11.34
200	=	12.96
250	=	16.20
300	=	19.44
350	=	22.68
400	=	25.92
450	=	29.16
500	=	32.40
1000	=	64.80

Equivalents of the Troy and Avoirdupois systems

(The Troy Pound consists of 12 Ounces; the Avoirdupois Pound of 16 Ounces.)

Avoirdupois		Troy or Metric	
1	Ounce	=	437.50 Grains
1	Ounce	=	18.2291 Pennyweight
1	Ounce	=	28.3495 Grams
1	Ounce	=	0.9114 Ounce
1	Ounce	=	0.0625 Pound
1	Pound	=	7,000 Grains
1	Pound	=	291.666 Pennyweight
1	Pound	=	14.5833 Ounces
1	Pound	=	453.5926 Grams
35.2740	Ounces	=	1 Kilogram
2.2046	Pounds	=	1 Kilogram

C. Inches and Millimetres

The diameter or size of coins is usually expressed in millimetres. The table below shows the relationship between the millimetre scale and the more familiar inch scale.

Inches	Millimetres
¼	6.35
½	12.70
¾	19.05
1	25.40
1¼	31.75
1½	38.10
1¾	44.45
2	50.80

THE MOHAMMEDAN CALENDAR

This table shows the Christian or A.D. years of corresponding Mohammedan or A.H. years, and will enable one to ascertain at a glance the correct Christian year of those Afro-Asian coins which are dated according to the Mohammedan Calendar.

Year 1 A.H. of this Calendar began on July 16, 622 A.D. (A.H. is Anno Hegira, meaning in the year of Mohammed's flight from Mecca to Medina.)

A.H.	A.D.	A.H.	A.D.
1	622	600	1203
10	631	700	1300
20	640	800	1397
30	650	900	1494
40	660	1000	1591
50	670	1010	1601
60	679	1020	1611
70	689	1030	1620
80	699	1040	1630
90	708	1050	1640
100	718	1060	1650
200	815	1070	1659
300	912	1080	1669
400	1009	1090	1679
500	1106	1100	1688
		1110	1698

A. H.	A. D.						
1120	1708	1215	1800	1270	1853	1325	1907
1130	1717	1220	1805	1275	1858	1330	1911
1140	1727	1225	1810	1280	1863	1335	1916
1150	1737	1230	1814	1285	1868	1340	1921
1160	1747	1235	1819	1290	1873	1345	1926
1170	1756	1240	1824	1295	1878	1350	1931
1180	1766	1245	1829	1300	1882	1355	1936
1190	1776	1250	1834	1305	1887	1360	1941
1200	1785	1255	1839	1310	1892	1365	1946
1210	1795	1260	1844	1315	1897	1370	1950
		1265	1848	1320	1902	1375	1956

FOREIGN LANGUAGE NUMERALS

	1	2	3	4	5	6	7	8	9	0	10	100
CHRISTIAN												
ARABIC - TURKISH												
ARABIC - PERSIAN												
SIAMESE												
INDIAN												
CHINESE, JAPANESE, KOREAN, ANNAMESE												
ETHIOPIAN												

FOREIGN EXCHANGE RATES

This table has been prepared for use by overseas readers who might wish to know the equivalent in their own currency of the U.S. Dollar valuations in this book.

The rates quoted were in effect on the free New York City foreign exchange market as of noon on June 6, 1958 and were for immediate delivery of actual bank notes of the various countries listed against payment in U.S. dollars.

Country	Currency Unit	U.S. $10.00	U.S. $15.00	U.S. $20.00	U.S. $30.00	U.S. $50.00	U.S. $100.00	U.S. $250.00	U.S. $500.00
ARGENTINA	Pesos	420.00	660.00	840.00	1,260.00	2,100.00	4,200.00	10,500.00	21,000.00
AUSTRIA	Schillings	255.00	382.50	510.00	765.00	1,275.00	2,550.00	6,325.00	12,750.00
BELGIUM	Francs	490.00	735.00	980.00	1,470.00	2,450.00	4,900.00	12,250.00	24,500.00
BRAZIL	Cruzeiros	1,300.00	1,950.00	2,600.00	3,900.00	6,500.00	13,000.00	32,500.00	65,000.00
CANADA	Dollars	9.61	14.42	19.22	28.83	48.05	96.10	240.25	480.50
CHILE	Pesos	10,000.00	15,000.00	20,000.00	30,000.00	50,000.00	100,000.00	250,000.00	500,000.00
COLOMBIA	Pesos	77.00	115.50	154.00	231.00	385.00	770.00	1,925.00	3,850.00
COSTA RICA	Colones	66.60	100.00	133.00	200.00	333.00	666.00	1,665.00	3,330.00
CUBA	Pesos	10.10	15.15	20.20	30.30	50.50	101.00	252.50	505.00
DENMARK	Kroner	68.50	102.75	137.00	205.50	342.50	685.00	1,712.50	3,425.00
ECUADOR	Sucres	182.00	273.00	364.00	546.00	910.00	1,820.00	4,550.00	9,100.00
EGYPT	Pounds	5.30	7.95	10.60	15.90	26.50	53.00	132.50	265.00
FRANCE	Francs	4,460.00	6,690.00	8,920.00	13,380.00	22,300.00	44,600.00	111,500.00	223,000.00
GERMANY, WEST	Marks	41.60	62.40	83.20	124.80	208.00	416.00	1,040.00	2,080.00
GREAT BRITAIN	Pounds	3-11-0	5-6-6	7-2-0	10-13-0	17-15-0	35-10-0	88-15-0	177-10-0
GREECE	Drachmae	280.00	420.00	560.00	840.00	1,400.00	2,800.00	7,000.00	14,000.00
GUATEMALA	Quetzals	10.10	15.15	20.20	30.30	50.50	101.00	252.50	505.00
HAITI	Gourdes	50.00	75.00	100.00	150.00	250.00	500.00	1,250.00	2,500.00
HONDURAS	Lempiras	20.00	30.00	40.00	60.00	100.00	200.00	500.00	1,000.00
INDIA	Rupees	48.00	72.00	96.00	144.00	240.00	480.00	1,200.00	2,400.00
ITALY	Lire	6,170.00	9,255.00	12,340.00	18,510.00	30,850.00	61,700.00	154,250.00	308,500.00
LEBANON	Pounds	32.00	48.00	64.00	96.00	160.00	320.00	800.00	1,600.00
LUXEMBOURG	Francs	500.00	750.00	1,000.00	1,500.00	2,500.00	5,000.00	12,500.00	25,000.00
MEXICO	Pesos	124.00	186.00	248.00	372.00	620.00	1,240.00	3,100.00	6,200.00
MOROCCO	Francs	4,650.00	6,975.00	9,300.00	13,950.00	23,250.00	46,500.00	116,250.00	232,500.00
NETHERLANDS	Guilders	37.50	56.25	75.00	112.50	187.50	375.00	937.50	1,875.00
NEW ZEALAND	Pounds	3-17-0	5-15-6	7-14-0	11-11-0	19-5-0	38-10-0	96-5-0	192-10-0
NICARAGUA	Cordobas	80.00	120.00	160.00	240.00	400.00	800.00	2,000.00	4,000.00
NORWAY	Kronor	71.00	106.50	142.00	213.00	355.00	710.00	1,775.00	3,550.00
PAKISTAN	Rupees	71.00	106.50	142.00	213.00	355.00	710.00	1,775.00	3,550.00
PERSIA (IRAN)	Rials	770.00	1,155.00	1,540.00	2,310.00	3,850.00	7,700.00	19,250.00	38,500.00
PERU	Soles	220.00	330.00	440.00	660.00	1,100.00	2,200.00	5,500.00	11,000.00
PHILIPPINES	Pesos	31.25	46.88	62.50	93.75	156.25	312.50	781.25	1,562.50
PORTUGAL	Escudos	280.00	420.00	560.00	840.00	1,400.00	2,800.00	7,000.00	14,000.00
SALVADOR	Colones	25.00	37.50	50.00	75.00	125.00	250.00	625.00	1,250.00
SAUDI ARABIA	Riyals	50.00	75.00	100.00	150.00	250.00	500.00	1,250.00	2,500.00
SOUTH AFRICA	Pounds	3-12-0	5-8-0	7-4-0	10-16-0	18-0-0	36-0-0	90-0-0	180-0-0
SPAIN	Pesetas	540.00	810.00	1,080.00	1,620.00	2,700.00	5,400.00	13,500.00	27,000.00
SWEDEN	Kronor	51.80	77.70	103.60	155.40	259.00	518.00	1,295.00	2,590.00
SWITZERLAND	Francs	42.70	64.05	85.40	128.10	213.50	427.00	1,067.50	2,135.00
SYRIA	Pounds	33.30	50.00	66.60	99.90	166.50	333.00	832.50	1,665.00
TUNISIA	Francs	4,650.00	6,975.00	9,300.00	13,950.00	23,250.00	46,500.00	116,250.00	232,500.00
TURKEY	Pounds	145.00	217.50	290.00	435.00	725.00	1,450.00	3,625.00	7,250.00
URUGUAY	Pesos	60.50	90.75	121.00	181.50	302.50	605.00	1,512.50	3,025.00
VENEZUELA	Bolivares	33.30	50.00	66.60	99.90	166.50	333.00	832.50	1,665.00

ILLUSTRATIONS OF LARGE SIZE GOLD COINS

These illustrations are included here because some were too large to place within the format of the text, or because the types of others may already be illustrated in the text by smaller denominations.

The numbers refer to the corresponding coins in the text, to which please refer for full data pertaining to the illustrations.

PART I. AMERICA

ARGENTINA. 8 Escudos 1832. No. 2.

BRITISH COLUMBIA. 20 Dollars 1862. No. 1.

BRAZIL. 20,000 Reis 1726. No. 19.

CHILE. 8 Escudos 1833. No. 33.

BRAZIL. 12,800 Reis 1729. No. 35.

COLOMBIA. 8 Escudos 1766. No. 18.

BRAZIL. 20,000 Reis 1853. No. 95.

COLOMBIA. 8 Escudos 1834. No. 53.

COLOMBIA. 16 Pesos 1847. No. 60.

CUBA. 20 Pesos 1915. No. 1.

COLOMBIA. 20 Pesos 1869. No. 87.

ECUADOR. 8 Escudos 1843. No. 3.

COSTA RICA. 8 Escudos 1828. No. 1.

MEXICO. 8 Escudos 1745. No. 5.

COSTA RICA. 20 Pesos 1873. No. 19.

MEXICO. 8 Escudos 1748. No. 14.

PERU. 8 Escudos 1749. No. 10.

PERU. 8 Escudos 1853. No. 60.

PERU. 8 Escudos 1752. No. 14.

SALVADOR. 20 Pesos 1892. No. 1.

PERU. 8 Escudos 1794. No. 39.

UNITED STATES. 50 Dollars 1915. No. 105.

PART II. EUROPE

ALBANIA. 100 Francs 1938. No. 15.

AUSTRIA. 100 Corona 1914. No. 427.

BOHEMIA. 100 Ducats 1629. No. 40a.

BULGARIA. 100 Leva 1912. No. 5.

CZECHOSLOVAKIA. 10 Ducats 1936. No. 4.

FRANCE. 8 Louis d'or 1640. No. 155.

FRANCE. 100 Francs 1855. No. 304.

GREAT BRITAIN. 5 Guineas 1679. No. 145.

GREAT BRITAIN. 5 Guineas 1692. No. 163.

GREAT BRITAIN. 5 Guineas 1701. No. 172.

GREAT BRITAIN. 5 Guineas 1714. No. 179.

GREAT BRITAIN. 5 Guineas 1716. No. 187.

GREAT BRITAIN. 5 Guineas 1738. No. 194.

GREAT BRITAIN. 5 Pounds 1826. No. 229.

GREAT BRITAIN. 5 Pounds 1953. No. 265.

GREECE. 100 Drachmae 1876. No. 4.

HUNGARY. 100 Korona 1908. No. 88.

ITALY-VENICE. 50 Zecchini ND. No. 205.

ITALY. 100 Lire 1864. No. 6.

ITALY. 100 Lire 1883. No. 14.

ITALY. 100 Lire 1912. No. 21.

MONACO. 100 Francs 1884. No. 11.

ITALY. 100 Lire 1923. No. 25.

MONTENEGRO. 100 Perpera 1910. No. 1.

POLAND. 100 Ducats 1621. No. 4.

RUSSIA. 20 Roubles 1755. No. 85.

RUSSIA. 25 Roubles 1876. No. 119.

RUSSIA. Platinum 12 Roubles 1830. No. 116.

RUSSIA. 25 Roubles 1896. No. 127.

SPAIN. 10 Doblas ND. No. 3.

SPAIN. 10 Excelentes ND . No. 16.

SPAIN. 100 Pesetas 1897. No. 161.

SPAIN. 100 Escudos 1618. No. 42a.

SPAIN-ARAGON. 20 Ducats ND. No. 19.

380

EGYPT. 500 Piastres 1922. No. 22.

PERSIA. 25 Tomans 1301 A.H. No. 51.

EGYPT. 500 Piastres 1938. No. 30.

PERSIA. 10 Tomans 1334 A.H. No. 83.

JAPAN. 20 Yen 1871. No. 45.

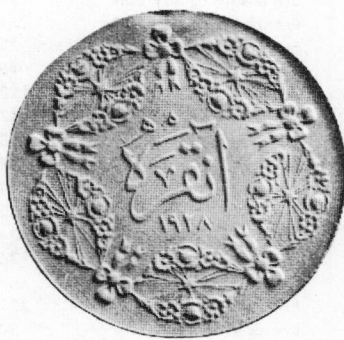

TURKEY. 250 Piastres 1927. No. 74.

PERSIA. 10 Tomans 1293 A.H. No. 45.

TURKEY. 500 Piastres 1947. No. 93.

GEOGRAPHICAL INDEX